Selected Landmark
Papers in
Concrete Materials
Research

Editors
R. Detwiler
K. Folliard
J. Olek
J.S. Popovics
L. Snell

American Concrete Institute®
Advancing concrete knowledge

SP-249

First printing, March 2008

DISCUSSION of individual contributions in this publication may be submitted in accordance with general requirements of the ACI Publication Policy to ACI headquarters at the address given below. Closing date for submission of discussion is September 2008. All discussion approved by the Technical Activities Committee along with closing remarks by the authors will be published in the January/February 2009 issue of either the *ACI Structural Journal* or the *ACI Materials Journal* depending on the subject emphasis of the individual contribution.

The Institute is not responsible for the statements or opinions expressed in its publications. Institute publications are not able to, nor intended to, supplant individual training, responsibility, or judgment of the user, or the supplier, of the information presented.

The contributions in this volume have been reviewed under Institute publication procedures by experts in the subject areas of the papers.

Printed in the United States of America

Editorial production: Lindsay K. Kennedy

Library of Congress catalog card number: 2008922022
ISBN-13: 978-0-87031-269-4

Preface to Selected Landmark Papers in Concrete Materials Research

In 2006, the ACI Publications Committee initiated an effort to identify technical papers that have significantly influenced the field of concrete and cement-based materials over the years. ACI Committee 120, History of Concrete joined in this effort soon thereafter. A subcommittee comprising members from both committees undertook the task of identifying these "landmark" papers. The subcommittee sought paper nominations from a pool of recognized experts in the field of concrete materials research. The experts were asked to list papers that had significantly influenced their research area, and an initial list of 25 nominations was obtained. From this list, the subcommittee then indentified the final 13 papers published in this volume by vote, after much deliberation. In the deliberation, issues such as quality of work, quality of writing, long-term relevance, and subsequent citation by others were considered. The subject matter of the selected landmark papers represents a broad range of topics, from the analysis of the chemical composition of portland cement to the development of fracture models of concrete in computational simulations. The subcommittee realizes that there are still many worthy papers that are not included in this volume; their exclusion reflects neither ignorance nor dismissal of the contributions by many other researchers from around the world.

In this volume, each landmark paper is preceded by a foreword written by an expert on the specific topic of the paper. Editorial in nature, these forewords serve to guide the reader through the content of the paper, to illuminate the significance of its contribution to the technical community and, in some cases, to reveal interesting historical context on the landmark work and its authors. The subcommittee sincerely thanks these invited experts—many of whom viewed their work as a labor of love—for their contributions to this volume. Without their insight, the true significance of the selected papers would not be fully realized.

The original objective of this effort was to increase awareness of the significance of concrete materials research as a whole and therefore raise the profile of the field. But what has also resulted is the creation of a collection of seminal papers, many of which continue to stand the test of time as vital and valid studies. This volume should take its place on the bookshelves of anyone interested in concrete materials research, and will serve as outstanding teaching material and inspiration for students in the field.

John S. Popovics, *The University of Illinois at Urbana-Champaign*

Table of Contents

A TRIBUTE TO

"Expansion of Concrete through Reaction between Cement and Aggregate"

by Thomas E. Stanton

Foreword by Michael Thomas

Thomas Elwood Stanton Jr. was born in Los Angeles in 1881. He graduated from Saint Vincent's College in 1899 and received a BSc in mining engineering from the University of California, Berkeley, CA, in 1904. After working for the City of Los Angeles, he joined the California Division of Highways in 1912 where he enjoyed a distinguished career until he retired in 1951. He was awarded ACI's Wason Medal for Materials Research in 1939 and ASCE's Norman Medal in 1943. In addition to his outstanding contributions to the understanding of concrete materials, of which the following paper is one of many, he organized the California State Employees' Association and the State Employees' Retirement System.

In December 1940, the American Society of Civil Engineers (ASCE) published a paper by Thomas Stanton that most would consider to be the first definitive work on what was then termed cement-aggregate reaction, but has since become known as alkali-aggregate (or alkali-silica) reaction. In fact, Stanton published an earlier paper[1] in the Engineering News Record in February of the same year reporting preliminary findings from his studies, which identified the alkalis as the constituent of the cement involved in the reaction and first proposed that a limit be placed on the cement alkalis (0.50% Na_2Oe) for certain localities. Stanton's paper in the ASCE Proceedings, however, presented full details of these studies,

---

1 Stanton, T.E., 1940, Engineering News Record, February 1, pp. 59-61.

which were initiated in response to the "failure" of a concrete pavement in 1938, just 1 or 2 years after construction. Other structures in Monterey County had shown similar types of distress in the form of map cracking (see Fig. 1 in Stanton's paper), one of which, the King City Bridge, particularly intrigued Stanton because it was the first case that really attracted the attention of a number of agencies whose investigations produced an equal number of speculative causes, which Stanton suggests were "in the category of interesting theories" leaving "an unsolved mystery."

The discoveries reported in Stanton's paper were not limited to the occurrence of a reaction between constituents of the cement and the aggregate, but included many phenomena that have since been "rediscovered" by numerous investigators many times over; the contributions Stanton made in this paper include the following:

- A test method, involving measuring the expansion of mortar bars stored over water in sealed containers, was developed to determine whether specific cement-aggregate combinations would produce deleterious expansion; Stanton modestly confessed this to be an accidental discovery. The test method formed the basis for the ASTM C227 Mortar-Bar Test, which still survives "on the books" at ASTM, although it is now well-established that the test fails to identify many slowly-reacting aggregate types. In a later paper published in 1943,[2] Stanton reported that the expansion could be accelerated by storing the mortar bars at higher temperatures (110 °F) or by immersing them in solutions of sodium hydroxide (at 70 or 110 °F). The latter approach is, of course, the precursor to the accelerated mortar bar test, which was rediscovered without reference to Stanton's work almost 50 years later. It is interesting to note that while Stanton says the approach has "definite possibilities," he also cautions against adopting these tests without first establishing a correlation with field experience, a step that often seems to be missing with some of the test procedures and associated test limits being proposed today!
- It was observed that only certain types of aggregate caused expansion, indicating the importance of aggregate mineralogy. However, such aggregates did not always cause expansion, implying that other conditions had to be met.
- The "other condition" was that alkalis from portland cement had to be present in sufficient quantity. Stanton concluded that the expansion was negligible when the cement alkalis were below 0.60% Na_2O. This formed the basis for the definition of low-alkali cement and the limit is still referred to in many specifications today, being an optional requirement in ASTM C150 for portland cement and a suggested measure for preventing expansion with reactive aggregates in the appendix of ASTM C33 for concrete aggregates. However, since this time, many researchers have shown that deleterious expansion can occur with low-alkali cement and that it is the total alkali content in the concrete that needs to be considered when controlling damaging reaction.
- Stanton reported that a chemical reaction between the alkali hydroxides and certain forms of hydrous silica, such as opaline silica, in the aggregate

---

[2] Stanton, T.E., 1943, *ASTM Proceedings*, Vol. 43, pp. 875-893.

produced an alkali-silica gel, which was often found at the base of popouts and exuding from cracks. Although he didn't provide a mechanism for the resulting expansion and cracking of concrete, he implied that this reaction may be the root cause.

- The greatest expansion in Stanton's tests were observed with a siliceous magnesian limestone. In an effort to explain this, Stanton conjectured that the reaction between magnesium carbonate and alkali hydroxide, the occurrence of which he confirmed by experimentation, may lead to expansion. Although, he didn't coin the term "dedolimitization," this is the first reference in the literature to an "alkali-carbonate reaction." Chemical equations and calculations of volume increase due to the formation of a hydrated sodium carbonate are given in the paper. Later Stanton reported[3] that it was opaline silica in the chert that was the cause of deleterious reaction with this rock.

- Early tests showed that a pozzolanic cement exhibited less expansion when combined with a reactive aggregate than might be predicted based on the alkali content of the cement. In follow-up tests, he demonstrated that 25% ground pumice (a pozzolan) eliminated deleterious expansion, whereas 25% ground quartz (Ottawa) sand did not, indicating that the beneficial action of the pozzolan extended beyond merely diluting the cement alkalis.

- Expansion tests with the siliceous magnesian limestone showed that expansion occurred when the aggregate was present in the amount of 1% (by mass of aggregate), that expansion was a maximum when 20% of the aggregate was present, and that there was little or no expansion when the reactive aggregate comprised 40% or more of the total aggregate. Although, Stanton did not coin the term himself, this phenomenon has become known as the "pessimum effect."

- Another serendipitous discovery was the role of the particle size of the reactive aggregate. Stanton theorized that expansion would increase as the surface area of the reactive aggregate increased. This proved to be correct to some extent as he observed the expansion to increase and reach a maximum when the siliceous magnesian limestone (used at a level of 5% of the total mass of aggregate) was crushed to pass the #30 sieve while being retained on the #80 sieve. However, he also observed that expansion was eliminated when the reactive aggregate was ground to pass the #80 sieve, showing that finely ground reactive silica does not lead to deleterious reaction. He surmised that this was due to either the reaction being so finely dispersed throughout the system that it did not produce sufficient expansive stresses or the reaction being largely complete before the concrete reached permanent set.

- Stanton also recognized that expansion due to the reaction may not always lead to failure of the concrete, but that the resultant cracking could promote attack of the concrete or embedded steel reinforcement due to seawater or other deleterious solutions.

Thus, in addition to discovering alkali-aggregate reaction, Stanton provided insight as to the probable mechanism, developed a test for evaluating specific

3   Stanton, T.E., 1944, Discussion appearing in the ACI Journal, *Proceedings* Vol. 40, pp. 573-580.

material combinations, suggested possible cures by limiting the cement alkalis or using a pozzolan, and made some interesting observations on the phenomenology of the reaction.

The impact of Stanton's findings cannot be overstated. Prior to his publication, aggregates were considered to be inert filler, but after it was clear that some aggregates were not suitable for use in concrete without special measures. Of course, Stanton's findings that cement alkalis could influence the durability of concrete caused great concern for the cement companies which were just coming to terms with the role of C_3A in determining sulfate resistance. Perhaps the most disturbing implication of Stanton's study was that concrete could "fail ... even if it is exposed to only normal curing and weathering conditions."

Stanton's discoveries spawned a multitude of research and the two decades that followed saw the publication of a number of seminal papers that are still required reading for today's students of alkali-aggregate reaction. Research continues in this area and later this year will see the staging of the 13th International Conference on Alkali-Aggregate Reaction (ICAAR) in Trondheim, Norway. The significance of Stanton's paper can be measured by the number of papers that will undoubtedly begin with reference to his findings of almost 70 years before. Perhaps of more immediate importance is that Stanton's work provided answers to agencies puzzled by the occurrence of mapcracking in their structures (for example, the Parker Dam) and allowed them to take measures to avoid problems in the construction of new facilities in the years that followed, an example of this being the use of pozzolans in the construction of the Davis Dam.

In summary, Stanton's paper represents a landmark in concrete technology because it embodies many of the principals of engineering, these being the correct identification of a problem, the elucidation of its mechanisms and the development of practical solutions to prevent its reoccurrence – all in one paper! Read it and you will be inspired!

Michael D. A. Thomas, *FACI, is a Professor in the Department of Civil Engineering at the University of New Brunswick. He is a member of ACI Committees 201, Durability of Concrete; 221, Aggregates; 232, Fly Ash and Natural Pozzolans in Concrete; 233, Ground Slag in Concrete; 236, Material Science of Concrete; 308, Curing Concrete; and 365, Service Life Prediction. He received the ACI Wason Medal for Materials Research in 1998 and the ACI Construction Practice Award in 2001.*

AMERICAN SOCIETY OF CIVIL ENGINEERS

Founded November 5, 1852

PAPERS

EXPANSION OF CONCRETE THROUGH REACTION BETWEEN CEMENT AND AGGREGATE

By Thomas E. Stanton,[1] M. Am. Soc. C. E.

Synopsis

Tests have demonstrated that excessive expansion of concrete may occur through chemical reactions between cements of relatively high alkali content and certain mineral constituents in some aggregates, such as certain types of shales, cherts, and impure limestones found along the coast of California between Monterey Bay on the north and Los Angeles County on the south. A new test procedure is described in this paper through which it is possible, in a comparatively short time, to develop the deleterious characteristics of cement-aggregate combinations similar to those reported in the California study. The procedure consists of curing the specimens in sealed containers at normal temperatures.

Introduction

Numerous tests conducted during recent years have established the value of low-heat cements in minimizing the shrinkage of concrete, and the value of the sulfate-resistant standard and puzzolanic-type cements in resisting attack by the sodium and magnesium sulfates and other deleterious constituents in alkali soils and sea water. Designers must now consider a third important factor in cement composition which may so affect the characteristics of a portland cement concrete as to produce excessive expansion and possible ultimate failure of a structure even if it is subjected to only normal curing and weathering conditions.

Given a properly designed cement-aggregate combination, such a condition can occur even when the cement is perfectly sound (in the generally accepted interpretation of the word) and of such a chemical composition as to be highly resistant to exterior attack by deleterious agents. This is fully and conclusively demonstrated through the tests described in this paper. A new test

Note.—Written comments are invited for immediate publication; to insure publication the last discussion should be submitted by **April 15, 1941.**

[1] Materials and Research Engr., State Div. of Highways, Sacramento, Calif.

procedure is also described without which it would probably have been impossible to make the laboratory tests.

Continual wetting or alternate wetting and drying of test specimens failed to develop (in any reasonable period of time, at least) any of the abnormal expansion characteristics experienced on many projects in certain districts of the state. It is now known that at least some of the field conditions of expansion can be duplicated in the laboratory when the specimens are cured in sealed containers, thereby retaining the original mixing water with few, if any, additions or subtractions through immersion or drying. It was not until this fact was discovered that invariable measurable expansion was obtained with certain cement-aggregate combinations, and that negligible, if any, expansion occurred with other combinations.

The complete documentary evidence sustaining the conclusions of the tests are presented for the first time in this paper, although a very brief preliminary report has been presented elsewhere.[2]

SALINAS VALLEY PAVEMENT FAILURE

Early in 1938, a section of concrete pavement north of the town of Bradley in the Salinas Valley, Monterey County, Calif., failed because of excessive expansion. An intensive field and laboratory investigation followed to determine the causes of the failure and to develop safeguards to prevent a recurrence of the condition in future work. The failed pavement was built in the fall, winter, and spring of 1936–1937. Most of it had passed through two winters when portions began to show distress in the spring of 1938. The distress became manifest in the form of excessive expansion which caused buckling at the expansion joints and a severe cracking throughout the length of certain slabs (Fig. 1(a)).

A coarse aggregate from a local commercial plant, located on a tributary to the Salinas River, was used throughout. The fine aggregate came from two sources, one the local deposit (herein referred to as Oro Fino), from which all of the coarse aggregate was secured, and the other (Coyote) imported from a commercially operated deposit near San Jose, Calif., in the San Francisco Bay area. The sands from these two deposits were used during alternate periods so that it was easy to identify the source of the fine aggregate in each section or day's run. A close inspection of all sections readily disclosed that excessive expansion had occurred only in those sections in which the local (Oro Fino) fine aggregate had been used, and it was obvious, therefore, that aggregates from this area contained at least one of the sources of trouble.

EARLIER FAILURES

The Bradley pavement failure culminated a series of concrete failures along the coast area from Monterey County in the north to the northern part of Los Angeles County in the south, throughout which aggregates of the same typical characteristics are encountered.

The first structure in which distress developed to such an extent as to attract attention was the King City Bridge (Fig. 1(e)) built in 1919–1920

---

[2] "Influence of Cement and Aggregate on Concrete Expansion," by Thomas E. Stanton, *Engineering News-Record*, February 1, 1940, p. 59.

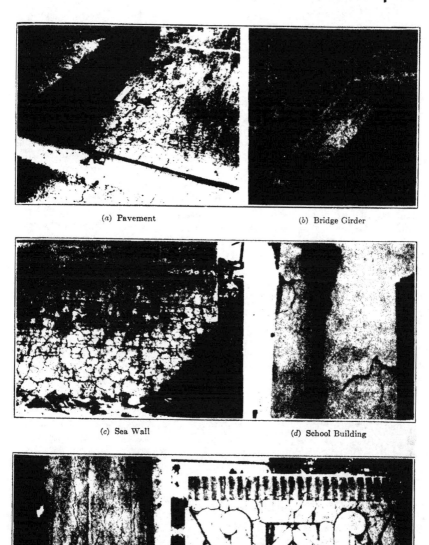

(a) Pavement   (b) Bridge Girder

(c) Sea Wall   (d) School Building

(e) Bridge Pier   (f) Bridge Pylon

FIG. 1.—TYPICAL CONCRETE FAILURES RESULTING FROM COMBINATIONS OF CERTAIN AGGREGATES AND HIGH-ALKALI CEMENTS

across the Salinas River at King City, Monterey County. This bridge consists of an all-concrete trestle approach to a series of concrete piers and steel trusses over the main channel of the river. The channel structure consists of steel trusses resting on concrete piers of two circular sections with battered sides connected by a 12-in. diaphragm wall.

The coarse aggregate was imported from an unquestioned source, but the fine aggregate was taken from the bed of the Salinas River, or a small tributary (Pine Creek) emptying into the river a short distance upstream from the bridge.

Within three years after construction, well-defined cracks were in evidence in the caps of the piers. Later, these cracks extended into the columns of the piers. By July, 1924, all of the pier caps were more or less affected.

The concrete in the pile and trestle construction has shown little, if any, distress, the severe distress being confined to the piers. Although it is possible that the cement was not of a uniform quality, so far as is known the two concretes differed only in the sands used. Pine Creek sand was used at first; then sand from pits in the stream bed of the Salinas River and later surface sand from the bed of the same river, deposited during the winter rains, was used.

The condition of the King City Bridge has been investigated by a number of agencies, including representatives of the Bureau of Public Roads, the Bureau of Standards, the Portland Cement Association, and the cement companies, as well as engineers and chemists of the California Division of Highways. In general, the number of opinions expressed equaled the number of reports made. The causes of failure advanced by the different investigators were the sand; unsound cement; excess water; extreme variations in temperature; faulty curing; faulty concrete design; variable coefficient of expansion between different parts (including reinforcing steel); electrolysis; overstressing or under design; and rusting of anchor bolts, reinforcing steel, iron pipes, washers, etc. All of the assumed causes, however, were purely speculative without any substantiating foundation and (in 1940) have remained in the category of interesting theories.

The King City Bridge has been enphasized because it was the first partial failure of a major structure to attract attention and because the definite cause of the difficulty has been an unsolved mystery. Subsequent to the King City Bridge trouble, several concrete trestles, built afterward in Monterey County, in which fine aggregate from the Salinas River or its tributaries had been used, developed serious distress (Fig. 1(b)).

Similar trouble had been noted in Ventura County where the concrete piers of the Southern Pacific Main Line Bridge over the Santa Clara River near Montalvo, built in 1914–1915, had developed map cracking similar to the Salinas Valley structures. On June 5, 1933, George W. Rear, M. Am. Soc. C. E., bridge engineer for the Southern Pacific Railroad Company, wrote that the piers showing distress had been built in 1914, using local sand from the bed of the stream, whereas imported sand had been used the following year in constructing the piers which were still in good condition after eighteen years.

Other pavement and structure failures were noted in Los Angeles, Ventura, Santa Barbara, San Luis Obispo, and Monterey counties, where the aggregate was all of the same general type, containing from 4% to 15% total of shale, cherty shale, and chert. A number of the more important failures were some sections of pavement and sea walls in Ventura and Santa Barbara counties (Fig. 1(c)).

Although the sulfates in sea water undoubtedly contributed to the serious deterioration of the sea walls, it was obvious that this deterioration was accelerated by the infiltration of sea water through cracks resulting from excessive expansion occasioned by other causes. The concrete walls of a school building in Santa Barbara, built in 1931, had cracked to such an extent by 1934 as to require at least partial reconstruction (Fig. 1(d)). All of the failures noted followed the same general pattern and were apparently due to the same underlying cause.

The solution of the problem was complicated by the fact that, although without exception cracking of the nature described was noted only when local fine aggregate had been used, there were numerous instances where the apparently same local aggregate performed in an entirely normal and satisfactory manner.

Immediately north of the pavement failure in Montery County is a section of pavement, constructed at least six years earlier, in which fine aggregate from the Salinas River was used, but which is still (1940) in excellent condition and shows no evidence of excessive expansion or cracking.

DEVELOPMENT OF TEST PROCEDURE

Upon conclusive evidence that the local sand used in the Bradley pavement, constructed in 1936–1937, had played an active part in the failure, a laboratory study was undertaken to determine, if possible, the cause or causes of the trouble and the reason for the inconsistencies that had been noted not only in the locality under immediate investigation, but likewise in all of the coast counties from Monterey to and including the northwesterly part of Los Angeles County.

The first step was to make up mortar and concrete bars of the local (Oro Fino) and the imported (Coyote) fine and coarse aggregates, and then subject some of these bars to continual wetting, some to continual dry exposure, under normal laboratory temperature and humidity conditions, and some to alternate wetting and drying. In one series, after initial curing for seven days, the specimens were dried for three days in an oven at 150° F and then soaked in water at 70° F for four days, the complete cycle taking one week. Another set was dried for two days in the oven at 150° F and soaked seven days in water at 160° F, the complete cycle requiring nine days.

Under none of these curing methods was any excessive expansion observable, even up to more than one year, regardless of the source or nature of the sand, except in the case of a coarse aggregate comprising 100% shale. In that case the expansion was obviously due to a physical expansion of the shale which, when present in large or concentrated quantities, had the effect, ultimately, of rupturing the concrete, but, when present in the normal percentages found in the aggregate under suspicion, had no measurable deleterious effects for the period under observation. In the case of the coarse aggregate with 100% shale, failure occurred on the fifty-first cycle of wetting and drying, at which time the expansion was 0.193%.

AN ACCIDENTAL DISCOVERY

In the meantime, however, upon removing the cover from a 2-in. by 4-in. mortar cylinder which had been cast and retained in a tin container for one year, the specimen was observed to be covered with blotches fringed with a

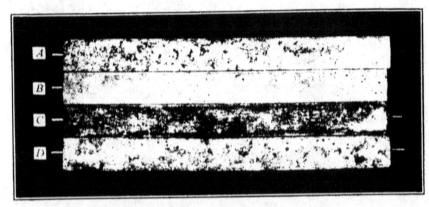

(a) Relative Length of 1-in. by 1-in. by 10-in. Mortar Bars (Mix 1 : 3)
Cured for Four Months Under Various Conditions

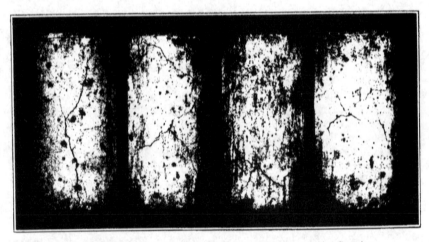

(b) Mortar Specimens (Mix 1 : 2) After Curing Seven Months in Sealed Containers

FIG. 2.—CONDITION OF LABORATORY SPECIMENS AFTER CURING IN AIR, WATER, AND SEALED CONTAINERS

white efflorescence (subsequently analyzed as sodium carbonate), and in a short time the entire specimen became covered with cracks similar to those shown in Fig. 2(b) and also to the crazing noted in the pavement and other structures in the area under investigation. A similar condition will be noted in the case of the mortar bars in Fig. 2(a). These specimens are identified, by letters, as follows:

Specimen (see Fig. 2(a))	Curing method	Expansion after four months, in millionths of an in. per in.
A	Sealed container	+7,310
B	Air	−1,350
C	Water	+ 40
D	Sealed container	+7,230

All bars contain the same quantity of high-alkali cement (1.14%) and a neutral aggregate to which was added 10% of the deleterious mineral No. 28039 (see Appendix I).

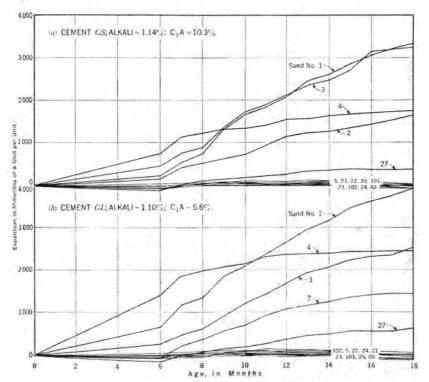

Fig. 3.—Expansion of Mortars on Certain California Sands and High-Alkali Cements of Relatively High and Low C₃A-Content

It was apparent that, when test specimens were kept in sealed containers, or at least protected from the atmosphere and any drying out, but at the same time prevented from any leaching of salts by constant immersion or alternate wetting and drying, a chemical reaction was going on which caused an excessive expansion of the mortar, with ultimate failure.

A series of tests was then started on 1-in. by 1-in. by 10-in. mortar bars cured in sealed containers, as well as in water, and measured for expansion at different ages. Experience with hundreds of specimens, subsequently fabricated, has invariably checked the results accidently noted in the case of the 2-in. by 4-in. mortar specimen. Bars fabricated with the same sands and the same cement have invariably followed the same expansion pattern.

The local Oro Fino fine aggregate (sand No. 4, Appendix II, and Fig. 3) used in the Monterey County job, in combination with the type of cement used in the work, always shows excessive expansion in a few months (considerable even at twenty-eight days); but the imported (Coyote) sand (No. 20) with the same cement has shown negligible expansion in periods exceeding eighteen months.

In Fig. 3, the specimens were of a 1 : 3 plastic mortar mix, and were cured in sealed containers. The C_3A-content (tricalcium aluminate) does not appear to be a factor in the expansion reactions. Later tests on specimens stored in the moist room, but protected from excess moisture, indicate the same expansion reaction as in sealed containers. However, for the sake of uniformity and convenience, all specimens, other than those constantly wet or dry, were cured in airtight cans.

CURING PROCEDURE

Immediately following fabrication, the test bars are cured twenty-four hours in the moist room under standard conditions. They are then removed from the molds, identified by marking with an indelible pencil, measured, and immediately placed in the containers.

The containers used are regular 6-in. by 12-in. tin cylinder molds with the joints soldered to prevent loss of moisture. The slip cover is probably sufficiently tight to seal the specimens without any other precautions, but if there is any doubt a strip of adhesive tape is wrapped around the joint.

Only enough free water (30 cc to 50 cc) is placed in the bottom of the container to insure keeping the air humid. The specimen rests on the $\frac{1}{2}$-in. monel metal gage point, and therefore the mortar of the bar is not in direct contact with the water.

Eighteen 1-in. by 1-in. by 10-in. specimens (a day's run) are usually stored in one container. The containers are stored under ordinary room temperature, no special effort being made to keep the temperature constant. The specimens are removed from time to time for measurement and then immediately returned to the containers for further curing and later tests. If rusted badly, the containers are replaced.

CEMENT

Other concrete structures in this area, in which the same type of local sand but a different cement had been used, developed no distress up to five or six years at least. This fact gave rise to the suspicion that the expansion resulted from a chemical reaction between certain ingredients in the aggregate and some ingredients in the cement. Alkali in the cement in the form of the sodium and potassium oxides was suspected and, as the cement used on the Bradley job contained approximately 1.14% total alkalis, the tests were repeated with another cement low in alkali (0.45%), with definite results, in that there was little, if any, expansion with the low-alkali cement in combination with the local (Oro Fino) sand which had shown so much expansion with the 1.14% alkali cement. The tests have been repeated many times, not only with the two aforementioned cements, but with other California cements of intermediate alkali content and sands from within and without the coast area.

The resultant expansion has almost invariably been proportional to the alkali content of the cement, whenever used in combination with aggregates containing minerals of the deleterious type found in the area under invesitgation. On the other hand, mortars containing commercial sands originating outside of this area, and containing negligible percentages of shale and chert, being essentially of quartz and feldspar fragments with some granitic and sandstone particles, have developed little, if any expansion, even with high alkali cements.

The data in Figs. 3 and 4 are offered in support of this observation, the mix in each case being a 1 : 3 plastic mortar, and the specimens all being cured in sealed containers. Note that cement HP is a puzzolanic type.

Tests on sands Nos. 2 and 4 made after those in Fig. 3 showed expansion as great as, if not greater than, sands Nos. 1 and 3. It would seem, therefore, that the tests in Fig. 3 were influenced either by lack of sufficient moisture to continue the reaction, or by a lower percentage of the deleterious ingredients than in later samples. In fact, these two conditions are probably the cause of some lack of consistency in the tests on other sands, as uniformity of sampling is exceedingly difficult where trouble-causing ingredients are present in such small quantities.

When sand No. 5, Fig. 3, failed to develop excessive expansion, a mineralogical study was made, and it was found that this sample of sand contained negligible percentages of shale, chert, and impure limestone. Therefore, the results are consistent with the nature of the material and confirm the conclusion previously reached regarding the probable source of the trouble.

Within the area under investigation, all of the aggregates from commercial sources, with one possible exception, contain appreciable percentages of shale and chert. All sands with small percentages, or entirely free, of shale and chert show little, if any, expansion up to one year, regardless of the cement used. All sands in the coast area relatively high in shale and chert, on the other hand, develop expansions in a few months roughly in proportion to the alkali content of the cement. In the latter case, negligible expansion is observed in the case of cements with less than 0.5% alkali and high expansion in the case of the 1.14% alkali cement, the other cements ranging in between roughly in proportion to the alkali content (see Fig. 4). Some inconsistencies are noted, but not of such magnitude that they cannot be accounted for by variations in the aggregate.

It is obvious, therefore, that in the presence of certain minerals an otherwise sound but high-alkali cement is a contributing factor to the excessive expansion and subsequent failure of a concrete structure. Under certain conditions this expansion may not be sufficient to disrupt the structure and may cease as soon as the reaction has been completed in any particular cement-

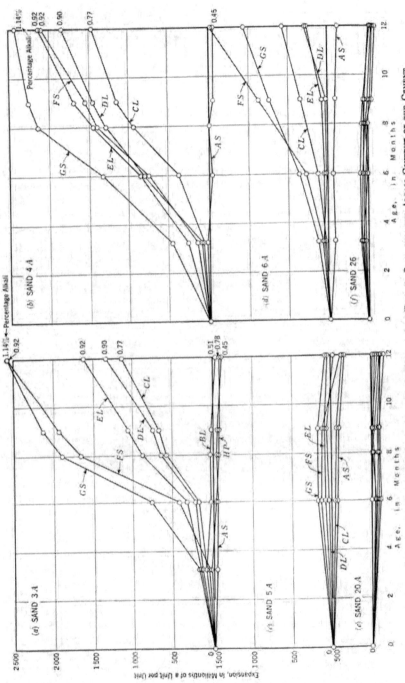

FIG. 4.—EXPANSION OF SAND-CEMENT MORTARS AS INFLUENCED BY THE TYPE OF SAND AND THE ALKALI CONTENT OF THE CEMENT

aggregate combination. In other cases, however, the initial cracking, although above normal but not excessive, may have very serious consequences when the structure is subsequently subjected to attack by sea or alkali waters which, seeping into the concrete mass through fine cracks formed from the primary cause, may take up the work of destruction through corrosion of reinforcing steel or attack on the vulnerable compounds of the cement itself.

AGGREGATES

The coast aggregates included in this study consist of mineral particles predominantly granitic in character with some quartz-feldspar, sandstone, impure limestone, shale, and chert. The granite, quartz-feldspar, and sandstone usually comprise more than 90% of the total; the impure limestone, shale, and chert comprise the remaining 5 to 10%. None of the adverse reactions have been traced to the first group. Some of the minerals in the second group, however, are definitely reactive under appropriate weathering conditions. The minerals in this latter group originate in the Upper Miocene sedimentary deposits. According to Ralph D. Reed,[3]

"The Upper Miocene in California was a period of widespread seas in which deposition of organic siliceous shale of the Monterey type took place * * *. Whatever conditions are necessary for the deposition of this material prevailed widely during the Upper Miocene from Lower California at least to the Northern Coast Range province and from the San Joaquin Valley area to the present shoreline of the Pacific Ocean."

Many of the types of shale and chert found in the Upper Miocene formations of California are different in several respects from the shale and chert of other geological periods commonly found in other parts of this state and the United States. It has been clearly demonstrated by geologists that the Monterey series of the Miocene, and particularly the Modelo formation, is unique in regard to petrological classification and mineralogical content. Although most of the Modelo formation consists largely of diatomaceous, tuffaceous, and other siliceous shales, many lenses and thin layers of calcareous shale ranging from a fraction of an inch in thickness to a number of feet are intermixed throughout the strata. It is common to find lime, opaline silica, or some chalcedonic silica as the cementing material in the shale. In many cases opaline silica and chalcedony are the main minerals in thin lenses and layers. The opaline silica greatly predominates over chalcedony, but these silicified bands, layers, and concretions have nevertheless been classified as chert by geologists and other authorities on the petrography of the Miocene formations.

The California cherts may be divided into two main classifications: (1) The deleterious cherts of the opaline types, which may or may not contain some chalcedony; and (2) the less questionable group of quartzose particles which includes the red and green varieties of chalcedonic silica such as radiolarian chert of the Franciscan formations, described and named by A. C. Lawson,[4] as well as jasper and the other varieties of chalcedony. The deleterious particles classified as chert contain opaline silica either in the main or as a

[3] "Geology of California," by Ralph D. Reed, 1933, p. 188.
[4] Geological Atlas, U. S. Geological Survey, San Francisco, Folio 193, 1914.

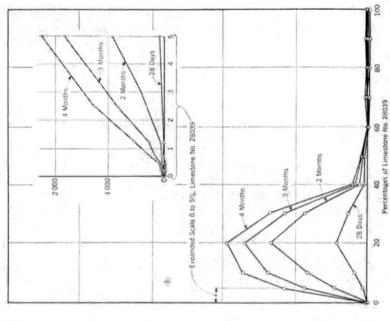

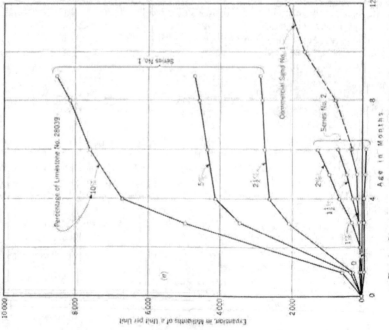

Fig. 5.—Comparative Expansion of Mortars Containing Sand No. 21, in Relation to Age and Percentage of Limestone No. 28039

cementing material throughout a shale particle. In the case of particles classified as cherty shale, some of the laminæ contain little or no opaline silica.

Throughout the coast area under investigation, the shale, chert, and impure limestone deposits range from types with negligible percentages of lime and magnesia to a high-lime magnesia shale which in this report is referred to as "siliceous magnesian limestone." This classification is consistent with that given by William Twenhoffel,[4] who states that:

> "The per cent of calcium carbonate or the double carbonate of calcium and magnesium in sedimentary rock ranges from nothing to approximately 100. If the per cent equals or exceeds 50, the rock may be termed a limestone. If the per cent is below 50 the rock should be assigned to some other group. There is, however, no sharp division between limestones and other sedimentary rocks; they grade without sharp break into the sandstones and shales, as well as nearly every other variety of rock."

Rocks covering a wide range from zero to a comparatively high percentage of lime and magnesia have been found in the coast area, and a sufficient number of these rocks have been included in the present study to cover the field fully.

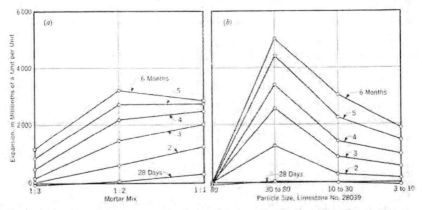

Fig. 6.—Comparative Expansion of Mortars Containing Sand No. 21, in Relation to Mortar Mix and Partial Size, the Percentage of Limestone No. 28039 Remaining Constant at 5%

An extensive study has been made in an effort to isolate the "bad actors" in the mineral content. Considerable success has attended this effort. Although it appears very probable that some form of hydrous silica plays a very active part, the greatest reaction in the tests described herein has been with material classified as a siliceous magnesian limestone (Nos. 28039 and 28039A in Table 4, Appendix I), of relatively high specific gravity, low absorption, high sodium sulfate resistance, and low rattler loss. This mineral is one of the most active causes of the trouble, even when present in percentages less than 1.00 (see Figs. 5 and 6). The high-alkali cement GS (Fig. 3) was used throughout. The same aggregate with the low-alkali cement developed no expansion. On the other hand, several of the shales and cherts which expanded moderately in

[4] "Treatise on Sedimentation," by William Twenhoffel, 1932, p. 238.

water showed negligible expansion in sealed containers, even with a high-alkali cement (see Table 1), as contrasted with the siliceous magnesian limestone (No. 28039), which developed no expansion when cured in water but high expansion in sealed containers. It has not been determined if the reaction in the

TABLE 1.—COMPARATIVE EXPANSION OF MORTARS OF SAND No. 21 WITH
10% OF DIFFERENT TYPES OF CRUSHED SHALE CHERT, AND
SILICEOUS MAGNESIAN LIMESTONE AND A
HIGH-ALKALI CEMENT

(In Millionths of a Unit per Unit)

Age	Mix[a]							
	1 : 3					1 : 2		
	No. 19374	No. 28037	No. 28038	No. 28039	No. 28042	No. 28044	No. 28045	No. 28046
28 days	+90	....	....	....	....	+55	+ 3	+ 25
2 months	....	....	....	....	....	+90	+42	+190
3 months	+238	+18	+47	+1,910	+62	+90	+370	+1,030
6 months	+1,220	− 5	+45	+4,140	+80	....	....	....
8 months	+2,065	− 3	+35	+5,175	+70	....	....	....
9 months	....	−38	− 3	+5,557	+72	....	....	....
1 year	....	−90	−37	+6,195	+50	....	....	....

[a] See Appendix I; all these specimens were cured in sealed containers.

case of this impure limestone is due entirely to some form of silica or in part to the magnesium carbonate. If it is due in any part to the magnesium carbonate, the probable chemical reactions in this respect are as follows:

The sodium oxide in the cement hydrates to form sodium hydroxide. The sodium hydroxide, in turn, probably reacts with at least some form of the magnesium carbonate in the siliceous magnesian limestone to form magnesium hydroxide and sodium carbonate; thus:

$$Mg\,CO_3 + 2\,Na\,OH \rightarrow Mg(OH)_2 + Na_2CO_3 \dots\dots\dots\dots (1)$$

The sodium carbonate ultimately crystallizes with seven to ten molecules of water, with an increase in volume, and thus causes expansion of considerable magnitude, resulting in stresses sufficient to rupture the concrete. The approximate volume change may be computed theoretically from Eq. 1, assuming the following specific gravities:

Description	Specific gravity
Magnesium carbonate in the rock................	3.037
Sodium hydroxide............................	2.130
Magnesian hydroxide	2.300
Sodium carbonate including 10 molecules of H_2O....	1.460

If the molecular weight of the reacting components and the end products are divided by the specific gravities, the following respective volumes are obtained:

$$\left. \begin{aligned} \text{Mg CO}_3 &= \frac{\text{Molecular weight}}{\text{Specific gravity}} = \frac{84.33}{3.037} = 27.7 \\ &+ \\ 2\,\text{Na OH} &= \frac{80.016}{2.13} = 37.6 \end{aligned} \right\} \text{65.3 (Combined volume of reacting components)}$$

reacts to form:

$$\left. \begin{aligned} \text{Mg(OH)}_2 &= \frac{58.336}{2.3} = 25.36 \\ &+ \\ \text{Na}_2\text{CO}_3,\ 10\ \text{H}_2\text{O} &= \frac{286.17}{1.46} = 196.00 \end{aligned} \right\} \text{221.36 (Combined volume of reaction products)}$$

or an increase in volume of 239%.

To check the accuracy of this assumption, tests were made to determine the action of sodium hydroxide upon various materials that might be present in the aggregate, such as magnesium carbonate, calcite, dolomite, etc., as well as on the siliceous magnesian limestone.

The method used was to subject the substance under observation to the action of a normal sodium hydroxide solution for seventy-two hours, excluding the possibility of contamination by atmospheric carbon dioxide. A portion of the clear liquid was titrated with normal hydrochloric acid using methyl orange as an indicator. A second volume equal to that used in the methyl orange titration was treated with barium chloride solution to precipitate the carbonates and then titrated with normal hydrochloric acid with phenolphthalein as the indicator. The difference between the volumes of acid used in these determinations was computed to sodium carbonate.

Treated in this manner a sample of:

(a) Standard calcite yielded only a trace of sodium carbonate as Na_2CO_3;

(b) Bakers calcium carbonate likewise yielded only a trace;

(c) Dolomite with 7.1% Mg O yielded 1.06% Na_2CO_3;

(d) Technical hydrated magnesium carbonate yielded 51.00% Na_2CO_3; and

(e) The siliceous magnesian limestone with 15.5% Mg O yielded 8.65% Na_2CO_3.

All material was crushed to pass an 80-mesh screen before test.

These results indicated that sodium hydroxide reacts with certain forms of magnesium carbonate, but not with carbonate of lime. It appears that some similar reaction occurs in the case of at least some of the hydrous silicates. Although some early expansion due to physical causes may be expected from some of the shales, and therefore the percentage of such shales should be held to a reasonable minimum (controlled by the sodium or magnesium sulfate test), nevertheless, when held to comparatively low limits, the expansive force may not be sufficient to cause rupture except in the nature of popouts when particles are close to the surface. This conclusion is confirmed by observation of numerous structures which, except for surface popouts, show no distress over a period of years even if the aggregate contains a relatively high percentage of many of the types of shale found in the area under investigation. With some cherts and shales, however, in addition to the siliceous magnesian limestone, a chemical reaction of a decidedly destructive nature always takes place in the presence of a high-alkali cement.

An astonishing development was the effect of a very small percentage of the high lime-magnesia rock. As will be seen by reference to Fig. 5(a), as low as 1.00% of this mineral caused considerable expansion in six months, the expansion in that period being almost identical with the expansion mortars of sand No. 1 in the same period of time, indicating that sand No. 1 contains not more than 1.00% of deleterious particles but that even this low percentage is objectionable.

The particle size of this mineral also has an important bearing on the result. It was thought that, by crushing the deleterious particles to pass 200-mesh completely, an accelerated reaction might be had. The reverse was the case, as specimens fabricated with −80-mesh particles developed no expansion in sealed containers, whereas the −30-mesh to +80-mesh particle specimens showed the greatest expansion (see Fig. 6(b)). Therefore, it appears that the reaction between the reactive ingredient in the aggregate and the alkali in the cement, when the aggregate is in a finely divided state, is either dissipated throughout the mass in such a way as to cause no high expansive forces or the reaction is largely over before the concrete attains permanent set. One theory is that the expansion is taken up in the interstices and by the gel, thus reducing the measurable manifestation of the reaction to negligible proportions.

MERRIMAN ALKALINITY AND FREE ALKALI TEST

The Merriman test[6] for alkalinity and free alkali was applied to the cements, but it was found that this test was not always consistent with the results. One cement, relatively low in the Merriman test, but with high alkali as determined by chemical analysis, developed high expansion; and its action, therefore, was consistent with the total alkali as determined from the chemical analysis rather than with the percentage of soluble alkali as determined by the Merriman test. Another cement with a high Merriman test, but low in alkali as determined by the chemical analysis, gave low expansion results. The reason for the discrepancy appears to be that the soluble portions of some cements go into solution much more slowly than others. The conclusion has been reached, therefore, that the Merriman test procedure, in its present form at least, is not suitable for a proper classification of cements in the order of the reactions encountered in the California tests.

EXTENT OF TESTS

Tests have been made on fine aggregate from all of the commercial sources within the region affected and from several sources outside of this area for comparison purposes; they have been made also on most of the commercial cements manufactured in California ranging in alkali content from less than 0.50% to approximately 1.14% (Table 5, Appendix III).

---

[6] Specifications for Cement, Board of Water Supply, City of New York.

As previously stated, negligible expansion developed with sands from outside the affected area. With one exception, all of the local sands showed high expansion in proportion to the alkali content of the cement. With the exception of the one sand, all of the samples contained from 5% to 10% of shale, chert, and the siliceous magnesian limestone. The sample of sand (sand No. 5) from the one deposit which failed to react was subsequently analyzed and found to contain only a very small percentage of the deleterious particles.

Numerous combinations have been made of aggregate from all commercial deposits and cement from most of the California mills. For check purposes, the study has been expanded to include, also, several cements from other parts of the United States.

Following a visit to the laboratory, when he was in California during the summer of 1939, the late Thaddeus Merriman, M. Am. Soc. C. E., who was much interested in the study, forwarded a sample of low-alkali cement (0.47%) from a Lehigh Valley plant (cement N in Table 5, Appendix III); and Ira Paul of the New York State Highway Department furnished a sample of 0.64% alkali cement from a New York plant (cement R). Through F. V. Reagel of the Missouri State Highway Department and W. E. Gibson, Assoc. M. Am. Soc. C. E., of Kansas, cements were secured similar to those used in pavements in Missouri and Kansas (cements M and O). These out-of-state cements have all been tested in combination with the Oro Fino and Coyote sands.

The expansion reactions have paralleled the reactions of the California brands. Cement M with a high-alkali content (0.83%) has developed excessive expansion with the Oro Fino sand (4,010 millionths of a unit per unit in fourteen months) and negligible expansion with the Coyote sand, whereas cements N, O, and R, comparatively low in alkali, have developed little if any expansion with either the Oro Fino or Coyote sands.

More than 3,000 1-in. by 1-in. by 10-in. mortar specimens of all combinations were fabricated and tested for expansion under different curing methods. The present status of knowledge of the subject was only arrived at through following numerous leads, some of which led into blind alleys and others of which were productive of results pointing the way and suggesting additional tests or lines of investigation.

Series I.—This series was started in May, 1938, and included only the two sands used on the Bradley job. Several coarse aggregates were used, including chert, shale, granite, and an altered dacite.

The cements in this first series were of the brand used in the Bradley job (a high-alkali cement) and in addition a low-alkali cement from another mill. The test specimens consisted of 2-in. by 2-in. by 11¼-in. bars of six-sack concrete, using 50% sand and 50% coarse aggregate, and the maximum size was ¾ in. One set of bars was cured in water, one set in air, and other sets alternately soaked and dried at air and water temperatures ranging from 70° F to 160° F. These tests produced no results of value, even up to one year, and at no time duplicated field experience with the local fine aggregate and job cement.

All specimens cured in water showed a slight expansion in the earlier period, but by 200 days all showed shrinkage from the peak length. At one year all specimens were shorter than the original length with the exception of the shale coarse aggregate specimens (ledge shale from Oro Fino Canyon), which showed a slight expansion (0.009%).

All specimens cured in air at laboratory temperature showed shrinkages ranging from 0.1% to 0.3%, but no cracking. In the alternately wet and dry group, there was shrinkage or negligible expansion with the exception of the coarse aggregate specimen of 100% shale which, by the fifty-first cycle, had expanded 0.193% and failed by cracking.

Series IA.—Shortly after Series I was started, supplementary specimens of the same size were placed under similar test, using aggregates from various spots in the Oro Fino deposit, and also from other commercial sources throughout the district between Monterey and Los Angeles counties. Again the results were negative.

Series II.—After Series I and IA had been under way approximately three months, the condition of the 2-in. by 4-in. mortar specimens cured in a sealed container was observed, and a new series was immediately started, the specimens in this series being fabricated in September and October, 1938. Because of the expense and labor involved in fabricating and measuring concrete specimens, and because it was apparent from an inspection of the mortar specimen cured in the sealed container that the fine aggregate was considerably more reactive, at early stages at least, than the coarse aggregate, Series II consisted of fine-aggregate mortar specimens only, and the specimens in all subsequent series, except one, were mortar specimens. At the start, six 1-in. by 1-in. by 10-in. 1 : 3 mortar bars were fabricated from each mix for curing under different conditions, and the results reported are the average of several specimens. As the 1 : 2 mortars were found much more reactive, all later specimens were fabricated from this mix.

Sands from fourteen sources were included in Series II—five from commercial sources throughout the affected area; seven from outside sources, free of shale and chert; and in addition a crushed diorite and a crushed quartz. With little information at that time relative to the most probable source of the trouble, and to ascertain if the situation could be corrected by the use of a low C_3A cement, two types of the brand of cement used on the Bradley job were included: (1) The job cement with 10.3% C_3A and 1.14% alkali, and (2) a modified cement from the same mill containing 5.6% C_3A and 1.10% alkali. To hold the amount of testing to a minimum, no other cements were included in Series II.

The mixes were put up in duplicate, one set with the high-alkali and comparatively high C_3A, and the other with the high-alkali and comparatively low C_3A cement. A uniform water-cement ratio (0.94) was used, the slump varying $1\frac{3}{4}$ in. to $2\frac{1}{8}$ in. with the natural sands, 1 in. to $1\frac{1}{4}$ in. for sands having rock chips in the coarser sizes, and $\frac{5}{8}$ in. to $1\frac{1}{2}$ in. for the crushed quartz and diorite. Some of the specimens were cured continuously in water, some in air, some alternately wet and dry, and some in sealed containers in the presence of a slight amount of free water.

As no material reaction was expected short of six months, the sealed containers were not opened or the specimens measured until six months had elapsed. The reaction was found to be so extensive by this time (Fig. 3) that in all subsequent series the measurements were started at earlier periods. After measuring, the specimens were returned to the sealed containers for further curing and measurement at subsequent test periods, usually monthly. At six months all of the sands from the shale-chert infected area, except one, showed considerable expansion. The exception was the sand which was subsequently found to be low in shale and chert.

All of the sands from outside the infected area, except one (all of which have a good construction history), showed either only a slight expansion or a shrinkage at six months. This relative condition has persisted throughout the entire test period to date. The expansion of the one exception (No. 27 in Fig. 3) was not especially high, but, as it was decidedly out of line with the others, a thorough study is being made (1940) to ascertain the cause.

Mortar cylinders (2 in. by 4 in.) for compression tests, fabricated from the same mixes as the bars and cured in water, developed equal strengths up to one year for the poor and the good sands. Later specimens cured in sealed containers showed a gradual falling off in strength with age whenever the infected sands were used.

Series III.—As soon as Series II was well under way and time permitted, a third series was started similar to Series II, but including a number of other California brands of cement ranging from low to high alkali. In addition to the bars 2-in. by 4-in. mortar cylinders were cast and cured in sealed containers for breaking at twenty-eight days, six months, and one, two, and five years.

As in the previous series, all bars cured continuously in water expanded slightly at first and then began to shrink. The first expansion measurements of the specimens cured in sealed containers were made at one hundred days. Even at that period, considerable expansion was noted in the case of the infected sands.

Series IV.—Having determined definitely from Series II and III that certain sands were reactive, the next step was to determine, if possible, which mineral ingredient or ingredients in the sands were the source of the trouble. Since all minerals except the shale and chert had been removed from suspicion by previous tests on selected sands, four suspected minerals were selected from the infected area, including a diatomaceous shale (No. 28037); a chert (No. 28038); and a calcareous shale (No. 28039), later classified as a siliceous magnesian limestone (Table 4, Appendix I). These shales and cherts were crushed to pass a No. 3 screen and were combined in various percentages with a neutral sand (No. 21) from the Russian River, north of San Francisco Bay.

This series was later expanded to include a serpentine found in the coast area, a calcareous shale (No. 19374) with approximately 6% Ca O but low magnesia, a siliceous chert (No. 19375), and two opaline cherty shales (Nos. 28045 and 28046). An opal and an opalized chert were likewise included to determine the effect of an opaline silica. Crushed limestone was used in other specimens.

The conclusion from this test was that the principal ingredient in the sand contributing to the abnormal volume change was the "siliceous magnesian limestone" and that probably the magnesia in the form of $Mg CO_3$ in this rock was one of the active reagents with the sodium hydroxide from the sodium oxide in the cement. However, excessive expansion was not confined to the specimens of No. 28039 but was likewise noted, although to a lesser degree, with the laminated calcareous shale No. 19374, and the opaline cherty shales Nos. 28045 and 28046 (Table 4, Appendix I).

The early tests in this series were made with 2.5%, 5%, and 10% additions to the Russian River sand. As evidence accumulated that excessive expansion occurred with even as low as $2\frac{1}{2}\%$ of No. 28039, the series was expanded to include specimens with lower percentages ranging down to as low as 0.10% (see Fig. 5(a)).

OTHER TESTS

Later test series have included observations to determine the effect of:

(1) Age of cement;

(2) Washing soluble salts out of the cement, treating the aggregate with this resultant liquor, and then testing for expansion;

(3) Admixtures such as pumicite, celite, ground Ottawa sand, calcium chloride, and Vinsol resin;

(4) Treating the sand with sodium hydroxide and dilute hydrochloric acid;

(5) Varying the quantity of cement, using 1 : 3, 1 : 2, and 1 : 1 mortar mixes; and

(6) Methods of accelerating reaction by heating so as to reduce the time of test.

Most of these later tests have not been conducted long enough to produce conclusive data of value. Apparently, however, the test cannot be accelerated by heat, by the autoclave, or by pulverizing the deleterious materials, but can be accelerated by using 1 : 2 mortar mixes instead of 1 : 3 and adding from 5% to 20% of the reactive minerals crushed and screened to the size range, a -30-mesh to $+80$-mesh size.

The addition of a puzzolanic material seems to be effective, as 25% pumicite substituted for an equivalent weight of high-alkali cement reduced the expansion to a negligible amount at early periods. Part of the reduction may have been due to the lower percentage of total alkali in the combined mix. Ground Ottawa sand, however, was much less reactive and calcium chloride had little effect (see Fig. 7). The reaction with the puzzolanic-type cement included in Series II (*HP* in Fig. 4) was likewise considerably less than with other standard cements of the same or less alkali content. Vinsol resin appears effective to a certain extent.

Treating the Oro Fino sand with water mixed with, and then leached from, a high-alkali cement, or with a solution of sodium hydroxide, apparently stops any subsequent reaction; but treating with a hydrochloric acid solution is ineffective. This would indicate that it may be some form of silicate rather than carbonate which causes the trouble.

CONCRETE TESTS

With the exception of Series I and IA, all of the tests described were made on mortar specimens. A later series consisted of 6-in. by 6-in. by 30-in. specimens of six-sack concrete, using different combinations of good and bad coarse and fine aggregates. Specimens of each mix were cured, sealed in water, and were kept continuously dry at laboratory humidity and temperature. This test has been in progress too short a time, however, to produce information of value.

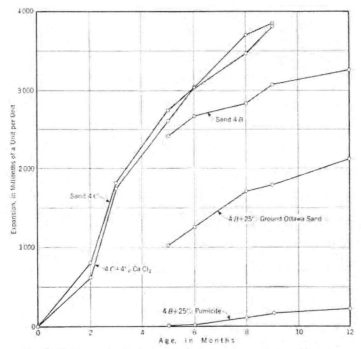

FIG. 7.—EFFECT OF VARIOUS ADMIXTURES ON THE EXPANSION OF A HIGH-ALKALI CEMENT AND REACTIVE SAND MORTAR (1 : 3 MIX)

SHALE AND CHERT POPOUTS

Although the laboratory investigations described herein conclusively demonstrate a very destructive chemical reaction between a high-alkali cement and some ingredient in the siliceous magnesian limestones, nevertheless one cannot overlook the fact that some chemical action is also taking place in the presence of some types of the low lime-magnesian shales and cherts, as evidenced by the data shown in Table 1, as well as by a study of the extensive popouts observed in numerous structures, including pavements, bridges, and buildings where shale or chert particles are invariably found at the base of the popouts, frequently accompanied by a soft viscous substance analyzed as a silica gel with some form of sodium silicate. Figs. 8(a) and 8(b) are views of large popouts from the basement of the old Times Building in Los Angeles. Fig. 8(a) is a part of a 5-in. popout showing at: (a) Sodium silicate gel; (b) an intermediate zone of partly altered shale; and (c) apparently unaltered rock. The chemical analyses of these samples, given in Table 2, were necessarily made on very small specimens and may therefore be inaccurate in some details.   Fig. 8(b) shows altered and unaltered parts of the mineral that caused the popout.

The aforementioned silica gel frequently has been observed exuding from cracks or pores in the face of concrete structures in which aggregates and ce-

TABLE 2.—CHEMICAL COMPOSITION OF ROCK AND GEL FOUND IN THE TWO TYPICAL POPOUTS SHOWN IN FIGS. 8(a) AND 8(b)

		Fig. 8(a)				Fig. 8(b)	
				Apparently Unaltered Rock			
Description	For-mula	Gel	Inter-mediate altered shale	Upper layer	Lower layer	Gel	Apparently unaltered rock
(1)	(2)	(3)	(4)	(5)	(6)	(7)	(8)
Moisture	....	12.63	8.92	3.12	3.23	9.69	3.38
Combined H_2O and organic matter	....	9.81	5.84	2.80	3.41	6.96	5.00
Iron	Fe_2O_3	2.40	1.92	3.83	3.83	3.19	2.55
Aluminum	Al_2O_3	4.38	5.84	1.09	6.37	4.61	4.69
Lime	CaO	2.90	2.36	0.92	2.50	2.62	1.36
Magnesia	MgO	0.58	0.72	0.54	1.09	0.85	0.79
Alkalis	Na_2O	12.93	9.62	2.04	4.90	12.77	5.00
Carbon dioxide	CO_2	....	2.50	0.71	1.43	3.93	1.79
Chlorides	Cl	....	0.72	0.40	0.24	0.48	0.16
Silica	SiO_2	53.86	60.16	83.30	71.22	53.40	74.00
Undetermined	....	0.51	1.40	1.25	1.78	1.50	1.28
Total	....	100.00	100.00	100.00	100.00	100.00	100.00

ments similar to those under investigation had been used.   This type of gel has also been found throughout the cores and pieces of concrete examined from all of the failed pavements and structures.   In some cases a number of aggregate particles had entirely altered to gel, so that it often swelled out above a freshly cut surface of a concrete specimen.   In many cases the reaction has only partly progressed into particles identified as siliceous shales or cherts of a type relatively free from lime and magnesium carbonates.   Although the gel has usually been found in a plastic state in fresh popouts, and in specimens cut from beyond the exposed surfaces of the concrete pavements and structures, it hardens readily and shrinks when dried on exposure to the air.

A detailed examination was made of approximately 200 popout and core specimens removed from the affected buildings, sea walls, bridges, and pavements over an area extending from Los Angeles on the south to the northern part of the Salinas Valley.   As defined by Allan H. Nicol, mineral technologist for the State Division of Highways, each popout particle had associated with it a considerable amount of optically isotropic material of very low index of refraction.   This material was identified as opaline silica with complex sodium silicates and was found to have indexes ranging from 1.41 to 1.54.   This substance, which was slightly plastic before drying, is hereafter referred to as "gel."   It was found that the index of refraction of the dried gel increased with the color.   The clear, glassy variety had indexes ranging from 1.41 to 1.47.

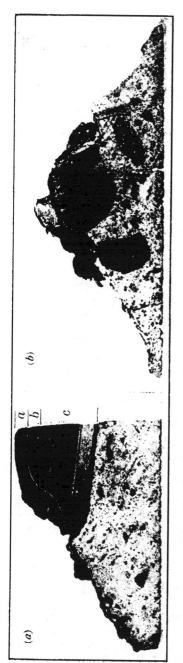

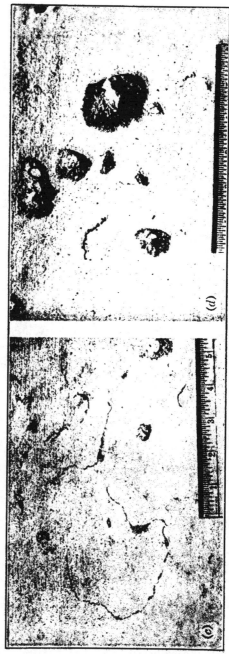

FIG. 8.—TYPICAL SHALE POPOUTS

The yellow and pale brown types showed values from 1.46 to 1.49, whereas with the brown to dark brown types the values ranged from 1.47 to 1.54.

Microchemical tests showed that the type of gel with a low refractive index was a nearly pure opaline silica, relatively free from sodium, magnesium, aluminum, calcium, and iron salts, whereas the yellow, amber, and brown varieties, which predominated in many specimens, contained increasing percentages of silicates and other compounds of these and other elements. The presence of these compounds, together with a variable content of adsorbed water, undoubtedly could account for the variable refractive indexes.

Most of this gel is fluorescent under ultraviolet light. A strong fluorescence was observed in the expansion bars and mortar cylinders which carried various percentages of No. 28039 (siliceous magnesian limestone; see Appendix I). These specimens had been subjected to the sealed curing test. The fluorescence in this case is due to gel derived from the particles of No. 28039 in the aggregate, as the rock in its original unaltered condition does not fluoresce.

The gel-like material associated with these specimens contains opaline silica, with varying amounts of sodium, magnesium, aluminum, calcium, and iron compounds. All of the gel examined on popouts, and in the cores and broken concrete from the various sources, shows similarity of optical properties and chemical composition.

Siliceous, calcareous, and cherty shales were the principal petrographic types associated with the popouts and the gels found in the concrete specimens. Chert was also commonly found, but it was impossible to determine how many of the completely altered particles may have been chert before the reaction.

The dark gel carrying the impurities was usually associated with a dark-colored, organic, siliceous shale or chert. The light-colored gel was normally found with light-colored shale or chert, usually cream, tan, or buff. These light-colored shales and cherts were generally more free from organic material and fossil remnants than their dark-colored equivalents.

It can be reasoned that this substance forms in the presence of moisture through the action of alkali in the cement or possibly in the rock on some form of silica in the rock, resulting in a gel-like end product consisting primarily of opaline silica, sodium silicates, and water. As a partial proof of this assumption, white deposits or incrustations containing more than 50% Na_2CO_3 have been found on the protected parts of structures where neither surface water nor ground water could come directly in contact with the concrete surface on which the deposit occurred. Presumably this sodium was in the form of sodium hydroxide in the concrete and was changed to sodium carbonate by carbon dioxide derived from the air.

Following this reasoning, mineralogy has well established the fact that hydrous forms of silica, such as opaline, are readily dissolved in either sodium or potassium hydroxide solutions, and also that these forms of silica are found in abundance throughout some of the Miocene formations in the area under discussion. All siliceous shales and cherts, therefore, are subject to question, in connection with the chemical reaction resulting in the gel substance. Extensive tests show that many types of shale and chert found in the gravel deposits are readily dissolved and disintegrated by soaking in a 10% solution of sodium hydroxide. In Fig. 9 the effects of soaking are shown for two materials—specimens cut from ledge rock, and ½-in. shale and chert particles from stream-bed gravel deposits.

Although these tests show only that the gel type of chemical action accompanying popouts and expansion failures can be approximately duplicated in the laboratory by the use of a sodium hydroxide (Na OH) solution, additional tests indicate that a similar action occurs when these types of aggregate are soaked in the mixing water from high-alkali cements. The chemical composi-

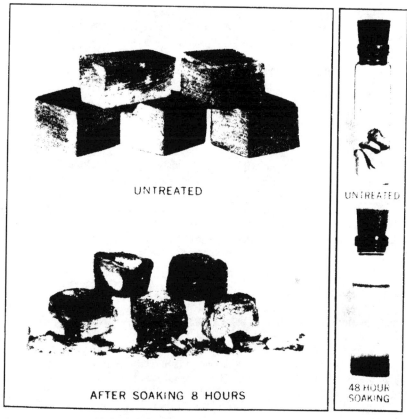

UNTREATED   UNTREATED

AFTER SOAKING 8 HOURS   48 HOUR SOAKING

(a) Specimens Cut from Ledge Rock   (b) Stream-Bed Gravel

Fig. 9.—Effect of a 10% Sodium Hydroxide Solution (at 70° F) on Some Types of Siliceous (Cherty) Shale and Chert from the California Miocene Formations

tion of water containing alkali, leached from a low-alkali (0.45%) and a high-alkali (1.14%) cement, is shown in Table 3, together with the change in each solution, after digesting for 120 hr at 200° F with Oro Fino sand containing about 9% of chert and shale particles. It is significant that the water from the high-alkali cement dissolved approximately ten times more silica during the treatment than the water from the low-alkali cement.

Figs. 8(c) and 8(d) show two typical popouts of the type accompanied by relatively large deposits of gel. It will be noted from Table 2 that these shale

TABLE 3.—Chemical Composition of Wash Waters from a Low-Alkali and a High-Alkali Cement and the Same Solutions After Digesting for 120 Hr at 200° F with Oro Fino Sand Containing About 9% of Shale and Chert Particles
(In Parts per Million)

Description	Cl	CO₂	H CO₃	OH	SO₃	Si O₂	Al₂O₃ (Fe₂O₃)	Ca O	Mg O	Na₂O[a]
WASH WATER FROM:										
Low-alkali cement	20	75	....	1,400	10	7	....	450	....	2,200
High-alkali cement	60	240	....	3,200	36	39	....	110	....	6,000
SOLUTIONS AFTER DIGESTING WITH SAND:[b]										
Low-alkali cement	4	250	....	870	23	590	42	....	....	1,800
High-alkali cement	50	660	....	2,800	45	6,100	....	....	....	5,600

[a] Alkalies (Na and K) reported as Na₂O.   [b] 3-mesh to 10-mesh sand particles.

particles have chemical compositions somewhat similar to No. 28042 (Table 4, Appendix I), particularly in regard to lime, magnesia, and alkali, although the shale in Figs. 8(a) and 8(b) is very much harder than that in Figs. 8(c) and 8(d), or the soft shale represented by No. 28042. Even if the gel type of reaction accompanies many popouts and other expansion failures observed in the field and also can be accounted for, at least theoretically, when a high-alkali cement is used, the volume change and the exact source of the stress causing the popouts and accompanying the reaction require further investigation.

CONCLUSION

The tests described herein justify the following conclusions:

1. Certain mineral constituents in concrete aggregates contribute to expansion of concrete and sometimes develop stresses of such magnitude as to cause failure.

2. Some shales expand excessively when saturated with water or when they are alternately wet and dry and, therefore, the percentage of such material should be kept to a practical minimum. This action, however, appears to be physical and of much less intensity than a chemical reaction with other minerals.

3. Excessive expansion, sufficient to rupture a concrete mass, may occur when certain minerals are present. The reaction in this case is chemical, and evidence indicates that it always takes place with the siliceous magnesian lime rocks found in the aggregates from the Upper Miocene sedimentary deposits of the state and frequently in the presence of some of the low-magnesia, low-lime shales and cherts.

4. The chemical reaction producing excessive expansion apparently occurs only when the portland cement component contains an appreciable percentage of alkali in the form of sodium and potassium oxides. It is of an intensity proportional to the percentage of such oxides, apparently being of such low order as to be negligible when the alkali content is less than 0.6%.

ACKNOWLEDGMENTS

The investigations and tests described in this paper were conducted as a research project of the California Division of Highways, of which State Highway Engineer Charles H. Purcell, Assoc. M. Am. Soc. C. E., is chief. The writer is indebted to the following members of his staff, all of whom have contributed valuable suggestions: Lester Meder, assistant physical testing engineer, for having first observed the accelerated expansion of specimens cured in sealed containers and for subsequent direction of the fabrication and measurement of test specimens and intelligent analysis of results; G. H. P. Lichthardt, chief chemist, for the direction of all chemical analyses and the development of the theory of the probable reactions; O. J. Porter, senior physical testing engineer and head of the Aggregate and Soils Department, and his assistant, Mr. Nicol, for their contribution to the geological and aggregate classification and discussion, identification of the mineral constituents, and suggestions as to probable reactions. In the field District Engineers L. H. Gibson, District V, San Luis Obispo, and S. V. Cortelyou, M. Am. Soc. C. E., District VII, Los Angeles, afforded wholehearted cooperation.

APPENDIX I

MINERAL IDENTIFICATION

The chemical analysis and physical properties of a few of the Miocene shales, cherts, and impure limestones, found in the coast area between Monterey and Los Angeles, Calif., are given in Table 4. Each sample is identified by a laboratory test number that identifies the following detailed description of each one:

No. 19374—Laminated Calcareous Shale:

Groundmass an impalpable mixture of clay, opaline silica, and sericite, carrying abundant fragments of quartz, orthoclase, chalcedony, and calcite, with some marcasite. Organic matter and fossil relics, including foraminifera and diatoms, are found occasionally as stringy accumulations parallel with the laminæ. The chalcedony occurs chiefly as fragmental grains, with an occasional veinlet. A few small clay lenses were observed without any appreciable embedded mineral grains of sufficient size to be identified. The laminations in this rock are quite high in clay and opaline silica, and carry the thickest layers of organic matter and fossils. This could explain the ease with which this material splits apart.

No. 19375—(Chalcedonic) Cherty Shale:

Predominant evidence of chalcedonic replacement of the shaly portions of this rock. The groundmass is predominantly chalcedony of the flamboyant type, with some areas not entirely replaced. Sizable fragments of recognizable minerals are lacking. Organic matter, low in content, occurs in layers that tend to parallel the bedding. The entire specimen is pierced throughout by chalcedony veinlets. Quartz and feldspar fragments are lacking. Opaline silica not observed in this material. Fossils absent.

TABLE 4.—CHEMICAL ANALYSIS AND PHYSICAL PROPERTIES OF SHALES,
CHERTS, AND LIMESTONES
(All Values Are Percentages)

No.	Description	Formula	LABORATORY TEST NOS.:			
			19374	19375	28037	28038
1	Moisture	....	0.75	0.22	3.88	2.14
2	Organic matter[a]	....	1.42	0.98	2.21	2.63
3	Iron	Fe_2O_3	3.38	2.64	2.59	2.59
4	Alumina	Al_2O_3	1.40	3.15	13.11	0.79
5	Lime	CaO	6.01	0.65	2.71	Trace
6	Magnesia	MgO	0.60	0.51	1.69	Trace
7	Alkali	Na_2O	0.58	0.78	2.11	1.43
8	Manganese	Mn_2O_3	0.01	0.03	0.36	....
9	Carbonates	CO_2	9.46	0.68	2.31	....
10	Undetermined		0.09	0.14	0.61	0.48
11	Silica	SiO_2	75.70	90.22	68.42	89.94
12	Totals	....	100.00	100.00	100.00	100.00
13	Average loss, Na_2SO_4 (percentages)	....	22.0	....	36.4	28.7
	Rattler Test:[b]					
14	100 revolutions	....	5.2	....	8.0	9.4
15	500 revolutions	....	23.0	....	31.2	34.6
	Specific Gravity:					
16	Le Chatlier	....	....	....	2.20	2.00
17	Saturated surface dry	....	1.82	....	1.80	1.89
	Absorption:					
18	Percentages	....	8.0	....	10.2	4.3

TABLE 4—(*Continued*)

No.	28039	28039A	28042	28045	28046	30704
1	0.42	0.92	3.92	4.74	5.09	3.8
2	4.15	0.58	3.12	Trace	2.19	8.3
3	0.83	0.99	3.24	3.19	3.52	1.1
4	0.27	1.22	12.40	5.09	3.90	3.5
5	26.24	30.85	1.80	5.18	3.58	0.4
6	15.55	8.75	1.33	0.52	0.52	Trace
7	0.20	0.53	4.21	2.09	1.87	....
8	0.02	....	....	....	....	....
9	33.92	37.03	0.44	2.50	2.30	....
10	0.58	0.39	0.84	0.44	0.66	1.6
11	17.82	18.74	68.70	76.25	76.37	85.1
12	100.00	100.00	100.00	100.00	100.00	100.00
13	2.8	....	72.7	56.3	48.2	....
14	4.8	....	11.2	10.2	....	....
15	20.0	....	41.8	36.0	....	....
16	2.62	....	2.50	2.28	2.16	....
17	2.43	....	1.90	1.94	1.94	....
18	1.7	....	7.1	8.4	7.7	....

[a] Combined water and organic matter.   [b] Los Angeles Rattler Test.

No. 28037—Diatomaceous Shale (Soft Siliceous Type):
Carries a few fragments of plagioclase and quartz. Groundmass consists chiefly of diatoms and other opaline material, together with clay, some mica (probably sericite), and a variable amount of organic matter. Groundmass is quite uniform.

No. 28038—Chert:
Opaline material, with some organic matter, and a few fine chalcedony fragments constitute the groundmass of this specimen. The groundmass is pierced throughout the entire length of the slide by a series of fine chalcedony veinlets that average about 0.15 mm in width. These veinlets

are all more or less parallel with each other and are apparently conformable with the bedding. They also parallel the heavy layers of organic matter. Abundant evidence of chalcedonic replacement throughout groundmass. "Canals" or veinlets are in portions partly opaline. No fossils or diatoms were noticed. Chalcedony of veinlets is of flamboyant type and carries minute opaque inclusions, possibly marcasite. Many canals or veinlets not entirely sealed from wall to wall by opaline cement, leaving innumerable fissures and openings.

No. 28039—Siliceous Magnesian Limestone:

A groundmass composed principally of chalcedony, opal, dolomite, and calcite. The dolomite occurs as rhombohedrons; calcite shows excellent twinning lamellæ; the chalcedony is flamboyant and shows aggregate polarization under *X* nicols. A few diatoms present in the groundmass, many showing replacement by calcite, dolomite, or chalcedony. Irregular patches of organic matter, concentrated near the chalcedony.

No. 28042—Soft Shale (Santa Margarita Formation):

Quartz and other mineral grains are very abundant in this material (over 25% of groundmass). Groundmass carries abundant organic matter and finely disseminated marcasite. No evidence of siliceous replacement. No diatoms or other micro-fossils observed. Cracks and fissures numerous. Cement of groundmass chiefly clay. No evidence of recrystallization—hence, material is probably quite soft and friable. Average size of grains approximately 0.039 mm. Consist principally of quartz, with some plagioclase and actinolite. Quartz has inclusions, possibly rutile. Organic matter strung out parallel to laminæ. This sample also carries a considerable amount of an anisotropic, pleochroic mineral (index greater than balsam) found in popouts.

No. 28045—Opaline Cherty Shale:

This rock shows strong similarity to No. 19374 and to No. 28046, under low-power magnification. It is of the same geological age as No. 19374 and No. 28046, as evidenced by the foraminifera and other fossils, which show partial chalcedonic replacement. The groundmass appears to be an intimate mixture of chiefly opaline silica with a small amount of diagenetic glauconite and clayey portions, with traces of organic matter. The latter is of fairly uniform distribution throughout the slide. Embedded in this groundmass are abundant coarse detrital grains of quartz, orthoclase, and plagioclase. Numerous feldspars appear partly glauconitized. Chalcedony is not very abundant in the groundmass, except as a replacement of the fossils. No free calcite or dolomite as fragments or veins was observed. This material differs from No. 19374 by a lower calcite-dolomite content, and by a higher amount of detrital quartz and feldspars, as well as a more uniform distribution of the organic matter.

No. 28046—Opaline Cherty Shale:

This rock is of the same geological age as No. 19374 and No. 28045 and strongly resembles them. The following differences, however, are noteworthy: In No. 28046 the detrital quartz and feldspar content is lower, and these grains are smaller; spherules of chalcedony are fairly abundant in the groundmass; glauconite and organic matter are more plentiful than in No. 28045 and occur in concentrated form parallel with the laminæ; although the groundmass is composed chiefly of opaline silica, it nevertheless appears partly pleochroic under high power and indicates the presence of intermixed diagenetic minerals (formed after deposition). No free dolomite or calcite was observed in this material, and what lime content is found on chemical analysis will be due in large part to the fossils and the detrital plagioclase grains. Due to concentration of organic matter and clay in definite layers, this rock is more laminated than No. 28045, and the evident lack of opaline replacement along these laminæ suggests the easy cleavability of this material.

No. 30704—(Dark) Opaline Chert:

Dark brown stringy accumulations of organic matter parallel the bedding, which is frequently distorted. An occasional quartz or orthoclase fragment is enclosed by opaline groundmass. Sample carries a few channels of brecciated material, cemented by opaline veinlets and clay. The quartz and orthoclase are the only recognizable anisotropic minerals observed in this material. Matrix predominantly opaline silica with some undistinguishable clay minerals. Material shows no evidence of chalcedonic replacements, and no fossils.

APPENDIX II

Sand Identification

Group I.—In this group rock fragments consist chiefly of granitic rock and sandstone with less than 15% quartzite, rhyolite, andesite, siltstone, and limestone, and from 4% to 15% shale and chert. The mineral grains consist chiefly of quartz and feldspar, with less than 10% of pyroxene, amphibole, mica, magnetite, hematite, limonite, serpentine, and calcite. Sands Nos. 1 to 6 in this group were secured from the following places:

Sand No.	Source
1	Santa Clara River at Saticoy, Ventura County
2	Sisquoc River at Sisquoc, Santa Barbara County
3	Piru Creek at Santa Clara River, Ventura County
4	Oro Fino, tributary to Salinas River, Monterey County
5	Bank adjacent to Salinas River at Atascadero, San Luis Obispo County
6	Salinas River at Templeton, San Luis Obispo County.

Group II.—Rock fragments in Group II consist chiefly of granitic rock and gneiss in Southern California, and of graywacke (sandstone) in Northern California, with less than 10% of basalt, andesite, quartzite, and jasper and usually less than 1% of shale and chert. Mineral grains in Group II are similar to Group I. Sands Nos. 20 to 24 in this group were found in:

Sand No.	Source
20	Coyote Creek, Santa Clara County
21	Russian River, Healdsburg, Sonoma County
22	Livermore Valley, Alameda County
23	Near Olympia, Santa Cruz County
24	Roscoe, San Fernando Valley, Los Angeles County
25	Irwindale, San Gabriel Valley, Los Angeles County
26	Monrovia, San Gabriel Valley, Los Angeles County
27	San Joaquin River at Friant, Fresno County

Group III.—The sands in Group III were made by crushing ledge rock to the desired gradation. Sands Nos. 101 and 102 in this group were found in:

Sand No.	Source
101	Crushed hornblende diorite, Logan, San Benito County
102	Crushed quartz, Jackson, Calaveras County.

APPENDIX III

CEMENT CLASSIFICATION

The cements used in the investigation were analyzed as shown in Table 5.

TABLE 5.—CEMENT ANALYSES

Cement identification	Oxide Analysis (percentages)							Compound Composition (percentages)				Merriman Alkali Test		Autoclave test (percentage expansion experiment)
	SiO_2	Fe_2O_3	Al_2O_3	Ca O	Mg O	SO_3	Alkali as Na_2O	C_4AF	C_3A	C_2S	C_3S	Alkalinity	Free alkali	
AS	22.76	2.00	4.02	66.04	1.80	1.54	0.45	6.1	7.2	62.3	17.9	3.3	1.0	0.05
BL	23.76	2.48	4.34	64.58	1.61	1.61	0.51	7.6	7.2	41.1	37.2	4.1	4.1	0.12
CL	20.42	5.68	5.92	62.86	1.57	1.74	0.77	17.3	5.8	52.5	17.6	3.6	2.5	0.09
DL	22.26	3.60	4.73	63.18	2.93	1.38	0.90	10.9	6.4	48.5	26.8	4.1	5.1	0.21
EL	21.57	3.52	4.49	62.44	4.08	1.50	0.92	10.6	6.1	50.8	23.3	3.8	3.7	0.25
FS	21.00	3.12	5.39	64.80	1.84	1.51	0.92	9.4	9.0	61.0	13.5	3.8	3.6	0.10
FL	23.34	3.96	4.28	64.32	1.09	0.87	0.50	12.1	4.6	49.5	28.8	3.5	2.6	0.05
FA	25.35	3.87	3.42	63.52	1.62	1.22	0.56	11.8	2.6	34.6	46.2	3.6	2.0	0.01
GS	21.48	2.72	5.64	64.50	1.72	1.71	1.14	8.2	10.3	54.1	20.3	5.1	6.3	0.09
GL	20.02	5.35	5.49	62.80	1.65	1.81	1.10	16.4	5.6	58.2	12.0	5.0	6.2	0.05
HS	21.14	2.48	6.43	64.16	2.23	1.78	0.69	7.5	12.8	49.5	23.0	3.3	1.5	0.18
HL	21.59	4.80	5.17	62.61	1.72	1.89	0.53	14.6	5.6	45.2	27.3	3.5	1.4	0.05
HP	31.10	2.40	6.77	53.30	1.86	1.57	0.78	Portland puzzolanic type						0.01
IS	22.56	2.40	5.52	65.33	1.48	1.49	0.44	7.3	10.6	50.1	26.7	3.2	2.1	0.17
M	21.30	2.90	5.70	63.44	2.78	1.97	0.83	8.8	10.3	49.4	23.4	4.2	4.4	0.12
N	22.34	3.78	4.78	63.32	3.44	1.51	0.47	11.5	6.3	46.1	29.3	3.1	1.6	0.10
O	21.65	3.55	5.65	63.35	1.45	1.85	0.51	10.8	9.0	46.0	27.0	3.7	3.9	0.01
R	22.37	4.00	4.35	64.65	1.36	1.45	0.64	12.2	4.8	54.5	22.8	3.8	2.7	0.01

In the identifying letters given in the first column, the first letter refers to the brand and the second letter to the type of cement, as follows:

S = Standard cement; in some cases the standard product contains less than 8% of C_3A and therefore might also be classified as a low or moderately low C_3A cement.

L = Cement having less than 8% C_3A and complying with American Association of State Highway Officials Specification M–60–38 as distinguished from the standard product of the same manufacturer with higher C_3A content.

A = Low-heat type "A."

P = Portland-puzzolan; insoluble, 15.44; all other cements less than 0.85% insoluble; cements M, N, O, and R are from mills outside California.

A TRIBUTE TO

"Calculation of the Compounds in Portland Cement"

by R.H. Bogue

Foreword by Paul Brown

Portland cements are primarily composed of compounds containing CaO, SiO_2, Al_2O_3, and Fe_2O_3. It is well recognized that the compounds formed from these oxides during cement production determine concrete properties. Bogue's publication is seminal in permitting the determination of the actual compounds present in a portland cement based on an oxide analysis.

Bogue's analyses relied on his appreciation of the results of prior studies and theoretical analyses that had been carried out during the 50 or so years prior to his publication. Various studies were initiated in the latter half of the 19th century to establish the nature of the compounds present in cements. Significant among these, in the 1880s, LeChatelier identified $2CaO.SiO_2$, $3CaO.Al_2O_3$ and $3CaO.2(Fe,Al)_2O_3$ in clinker phases by microsopical means. Also relying on optical microscopy, Tornebohm identified the major cementing phases and named them alite, belite, celite, and felite about the turn of the 20th century. These developments specific to clinker chemistry were accompanied by theoretical advances and development of new experimental techniques. Two events are notable with regard to characterization of cements. In 1878, Gibbs enunciated the phase rule and by doing so provided the basis for understanding aspects fundamental to heterogeneous equilibria between solids and liquids whose compositions may differ from each other. This provided the basis for understanding the events that occur when multicomponent oxide melts are crystallized. In 1913 and 1914, the Braggs established the technique of X-ray diffraction as a means to characterize crystalline solids. This permitted the determination of the crystalline solids present in cements as well as allowing an estimate of their proportions.

When the polished section of a polycrystalline, polyphase solid is viewed by microscopy, certain conclusions regarding the compositions of the solids present and their crystallization paths can be reached. Systematic variations in bulk composition can be used to establish the stability ranges for various compounds that may be present. If the compounds are minerals or synthetic analogs, indices of refraction can be used to estimate compositions. With regard to spatial distributions, compounds that crystallize first tend to be surrounded by those that crystallize at lower temperatures. For cement clinker, those phases that crystallize at lower temperatures are commonly called interstitial compounds. It is these phases that form a liquid at clinkering temperatures and it is from them that alite and belite form. Finally, rapid cooling can be used to quench in and observe compounds or polymorphs, such as $3CaO.SiO_2$, that would otherwise decompose with slow cooling. Grinding clinker to powder and carrying out X-ray diffraction allows detailed compositional analyses and permits effects of solid solution behavior to be assessed.

Bogue generalized these observations and reached the following conclusions:

(1) Only five oxides are present in clinker and these are CaO, SiO_2, Al_2O_3, Fe_2O_3, and MgO.

(2) All of the Fe_2O_3 present participates in the formation of $4CaO.Al_2O_3.Fe_2O_3$.

(3) MgO does not form any compounds and remains uncombined.

(4) Any Al_2O_3 that does not react to form $4CaO.Al_2O_3.Fe_2O_3$ reacts to form $3CaO.Al_2O_3$.

(5) Any CaO that is not consumed in the above reaction combines to form $2CaO.SiO_2$.

(6) Any CaO not used in the formation of $2CaO.SiO_2$, then reacts with it to form $3CaO.SiO_2$.

(7) Any CaO that remains after the $2CaO.SiO_2$ has reacted completely stays uncombined as free lime.

These observations were quantified by Bogue to calculate the proportions of cementing compounds as follows:

Deduct the proportion of free lime.

$C_4AF = 3.0Fe_2O_3$.
$C_3A = 2.7Al_2O_3 - 1.7Fe_2O_3$.
$C_2S = 8.6SiO_2 + 1.1Fe_2O_3 + 5.1Al_2O_3 - 3.1CaO$
$C_3S = 4.1CaO - 7.6SiO_2 - 1.4Fe_2O_3 - 6.7Al_2O_3$

When applied to cement, rather than clinker, the proportion of CaO is reduced by $0.7SO_3$ to account for the presence of calcium sulfate.

Bogue understood both cement chemistry and kiln chemistry well enough to appreciate the fact that the sequence of crystallization is actually the inverse of the sequence with which the aforementioned equations are solved in the calculation of the compounds present. In particular, the silicates form at a temperature where the aluminate and ferrite compounds are in the liquid state. The reaction between CaO and SiO_2 can locally produce C_2S, C_3S, and C_3S or C_3S only, depending on the local equilibria. Subsequently, the aluminate phase crystallizes and finally the ferrite phase. As Bogue points out in his book on cement chemistry [1], various subsequent refinements of the calculation of the phase proportions were carried out. It is now well understood that the Bogue calculation gives incorrect results. In particular, the Bogue calculation tends to underestimate the proportion of alite while overestimating that of belite. It is for this reason that the Bogue calculation of commonly cited as determining the "potential" phase composition of portland cement. There are two reasons for this. The first is that equilibria might not have been reached during clinker cooling. The second and more important reason is that the compositions of the major cement compounds depart from the ideal compositions [2]. Consequently, aluminum and iron oxide are present in the silicate phases and silica substitution occurs in the interstitial phases. Additionally, substitutions of alkalis, titania, magnesia, phosphate, and sulfate also occur.   Because the Bogue calculation involves the solution of four linear equations with four unknowns, it can be optimized by making various assumptions regarding the compositions of the phases that are produced as regards these substitutions.   Regardless of these substitutions, however, the Bogue calculation, which assumes cementing compounds to be C_3S, C_2S, C_3A, and C_4AF, is still widely relied on. Both the importance and the general acceptance of Bogue's calculation scheme are demonstrated by its inclusion in ASTM C150, "Standard Specification for Portland Cements." [3]

1.   R.H. Bogue, The Chemistry of Portland Cement, Reinhold, NY 1955.
2.   H.F.W. Taylor, Cement Chemistry, Thomas Telford, London, 1997.
3.   ASTM C150, Annual Book of ASTM Standards, Volume 4.01, 2007.

Paul Brown *is a Professor of materials science and engineering at Penn State University. He is a member of ACI Committees 201, Durability of Concrete; 236, Materials Science of Concrete; and 524, Plastering.*

Calculation of the Compounds in Portland Cement[1]

R. H. Bogue

PORTLAND CEMENT ASSOCIATION FELLOWSHIP, BUREAU OF STANDARDS, WASHINGTON, D. C.

SYSTEMS containing combinations of the components CaO, MgO, Al_2O_3, Fe_2O_3, and SiO_2 have been studied and reported by this and other laboratories (3, 5, 7, 8, 10, 11). It has been found that when these components are intimately mixed in proportions similar to those found in Portland cements, and burned to equilibrium, the following compounds are formed: $4CaO.Al_2O_3.Fe_2O_3$, $3CaO.Al_2O_3$, $2CaO.SiO_2$, $3CaO.SiO_2$, and MgO.

Note—In a former publication (6) it was reported that MgO enters into solid solution with $4CaO.Al_2O_3.Fe_2O_3$, the end member of the series being $4CaO.2MgO.Al_2O_3.Fe_2O_3$. Magnesia in excess of that required for the above combination was found to remain as uncombined MgO. More recent information obtained in this laboratory indicates that the amount of the solid solution was found to be much smaller than had previously been reported. Although there is no reasonable doubt that a large part of the magnesia remains uncombined, the exact nature and degree of the reaction by which the $4CaO.Al_2O_3.Fe_2O_3$ is changed in color and pleochroism in the presence of a small amount of magnesia has not been determined. This problem is under further investigation. At present the magnesia may be considered as remaining essentially uncombined, and the iron compound as existing essentially in the form of $4CaO.Al_2O_3.Fe_2O_3$.

[1] Received June 17, 1929. Publication approved by the Director of the National Bureau of Standards, U. S. Department of Commerce, Paper No. 21 of the Portland Cement Association Fellowship at the Bureau of Standards.

The bases for a calculation of the compounds present in Portland cement from chemical analyses are presented. Arithmetical and diagrammatical methods are given for such a calculation. The compounds considered are $4CaO.Al_2O_3.Fe_2O_3$, $3CaO.Al_2O_3$, $2CaO.SiO_2$, $3CaO.SiO_2$, uncombined MgO, uncombined CaO, and $CaSO_4$. Other components than those included in these compounds are not at present considered as their forms of combination are not known.

In addition to the five components listed above, commercial Portland cements contain small amounts of other materials in variable quantity. These may include soda, potash, titania, manganese oxides, phosphates, and perhaps still other materials. The total amount of these lesser components, however, probably does not often exceed 2 per cent.

The manner of combination of these lesser components is not known. It is possible that some of them, as perhaps the alkalies, may have a significant influence on the relative amounts of the major compounds that are formed, but since the manner of their combination is not yet known, the effects of their presence cannot now be evaluated. Consequently, it is not possible at present to consider those components in the calculation of cement constitution.

It is assumed that the compounds of Portland cement are essentially the same as those of the pure five-component system given above when the components are present in the proportions found in commercial cements. The general correctness of this assumption has been confirmed by information obtained from cooling curves (4), from microscopic examinations (1) and from x-ray diffraction photographs (1).

Manner of Reaction

The manner in which the components react determines the relative amounts of the resulting compounds. Information obtained at this laboratory leads to the following generalizations:

(1) The ferric oxide reacts with alumina and lime to form $4CaO.Al_2O_3.Fe_2O_3$. (See note.)
(2) The magnesia remains essentially in the form of uncombined MgO.
(3) The alumina remaining from combination as $4CaO.Al_2O_3.Fe_2O_3$ reacts with lime to form $3CaO.Al_2O_3$.
(4) The lime remaining from the above combinations reacts with the silica. The compound $2CaO.SiO_2$ is formed, and any CaO then uncombined reacts with the $2CaO.SiO_2$ to form $3CaO.SiO_2$. If CaO remains after converting all of the $2CaO.SiO_2$ to $3CaO.SiO_2$, it will be present as uncombined CaO.

The formation of the compounds as described assumes that a condition of equilibrium has been reached during the progress of the reactions in the kiln. A small amount of uncombined CaO may remain in the clinker, however, indicating (if the composition is such that the CaO would be completely combined at equilibrium) that the reactions are not altogether complete. This departure from complete combination is not usually of sufficient magnitude to produce a change in the nature of the compounds formed, but it does produce a change in the relative amounts of the compounds produced. For that reason it is important that free CaO in the cement be determined (9) and that the amount present be taken into consideration in the calculation of the constitution. If this is not done, an error of usually small but uncertain magnitude may be introduced.

The "insoluble residue" obtained in a cement analysis is composed of quartz, titania, and several other materials. The amount of the residue is usually very small, about 0.2 per cent. Because of the low quantity of this material and the variable and uncertain nature of its composition, it seems inexpedient to attempt to introduce a correction factor for it. In unusual cases where the amount of the residue is high, it may be desirable to analyze it to ascertain if an appreciable quantity of silica has remained as free quartz. If the residue is found to contain an appreciable amount of silica, then the silica content of the residue should be deducted from the total SiO_2 to obtain the value of the SiO_2 taking part in the reactions.

The "ignition loss" consists essentially of moisture and carbon dioxide that have been taken up by the cement following the burning operation. In calculating the constitution, this value is accordingly set down without further change.

By means of the information given above, the relative amounts of the compounds present in Portland cement or clinker may be calculated from the chemical analyses. It is essential in any case to consider the SO_3 content and calculate that to $CaSO_4$.

Accuracy of Computations

The accuracy of the computations depends on the correctness of both the postulations and the analytical values. The postulations as given represent the best available information, but are subject to revision and extension as has been pointed out. The general correctness of the analytical values will vary with the conditions of test and the personal factor. In any case it is not recommended that analyses be considered as accurate beyond the first decimal place.

An examination of the factors given below will show that errors of analysis often are magnified in the computations for compound composition. Thus a plus error (other values remaining fixed) of 0.2 per cent CaO or uncombined CaO (expressed as percentage of the cement) will increase the computed $3CaO.SiO_2$ about 0.8 per cent and decrease the computed $2CaO.SiO_2$ about 0.6 per cent. A plus error of 0.2 per cent Fe_2O_3 will increase the computed $4CaO.Al_2O_3.Fe_2O_3$ about 0.6 per cent, decrease the $3CaO.Al_2O_3$ about 0.3 per cent, decrease the $3CaO.SiO_2$ about 0.3 per cent, and increase the $2CaO.SiO_2$ about 0.2 per cent. A plus error of 0.2 per cent Al_2O_3 will increase the computed $3CaO.Al_2O_3$ about 0.5 per cent, decrease the $3CaO.SiO_2$ about 1.3 per cent, and increase the $2CaO.SiO_2$ about 1.0 per cent. A plus error of 0.2 per cent SiO_2 will decrease the computed $3CaO.SiO_2$ about 1.5 per cent and increase the $2CaO.SiO_2$, 1.3 per cent. For these reasons only analytical data that are believed to be reliable should be employed for the computation of compound composition, and an expression of the compounds $4CaO.Al_2O_3.Fe_2O_3$, $3CaO.Al_2O_3$, $3CaO.SiO_2$, and $2CaO.SiO_2$ should not be given to a closer approximation than the nearest whole number.

Method of Calculation

Each per cent of SO_3 enters into combination with 0.70 per cent CaO to form 1.70 per cent $CaSO_4$:

$$\frac{CaO}{SO_4} = \frac{56.07}{80.065} = 0.70 \text{ per cent CaO} \dots\dots\dots (c_1)$$

Each per cent of Fe_2O_3 enters into combination with 0.64 per cent Al_2O_3:

$$\frac{Al_2O_3}{Fe_2O_3} = \frac{101.92}{159.68} = 0.64 \text{ per cent } Al_2O_3 \dots\dots\dots (a_1)$$

and with 1.40 per cent CaO:

$$\frac{4CaO}{Fe_2O_3} = \frac{224.28}{159.68} = 1.40 \text{ per cent CaO} \dots\dots\dots (c_2)$$

to form 3.04 per cent $4CaO.Al_2O_3.Fe_2O_3$.

The total MgO is recorded as uncombined MgO.

The total Al_2O_3 minus (a_1) gives the Al_2O_3 (a_2) available for combination as $3CaO.Al_2O_3$. Each per cent of (a_2) will enter into combination with 1.65 per cent CaO to form 2.65 per cent $3CaO.Al_2O_3$:

$$\frac{3CaO}{Al_2O_3} = \frac{168.21}{101.92} = 1.65 \text{ per cent CaO} \dots\dots\dots (c_3)$$

The amount of CaO available for combination with SiO_2 is obtained by subtracting from the total CaO the sum of the uncombined CaO, the CaO (c_1) combined as $CaSO_4$, the CaO (c_2) combined as $4CaO.Al_2O_3.Fe_2O_3$, and the CaO (c_3) combined as $3CaO.Al_2O_3$:

$$\text{Total CaO} - (\text{uncombined CaO} + c_1 + c_2 + c_3) =$$
$$\text{CaO available to combine with } SiO_2 \dots\dots (c)$$

The total SiO_2 (s), unless corrected for silica in the "insoluble residue," is calculated first to combine with CaO to form $2CaO.SiO_2$. Each per cent of SiO_2 (s) will combine with CaO to form 2.87 per cent $2CaO.SiO_2$:

$$\frac{2CaO.SiO_2}{SiO_2} = \frac{172.20}{60.06} = 2.87 \text{ per cent } 2CaO.SiO_2$$

This first approximation to the value of $2CaO.SiO_2$ is subtracted from the SiO_2 (s) + CaO (c), which gives the CaO (c_4) available to combine with $2CaO.SiO_2$ to form $3CaO.SiO_2$. Each per cent of CaO (c_4) combines with $2CaO.SiO_2$ to form 4.07 per cent $3CaO.SiO_2$:

$$\frac{3CaO.SiO_2}{CaO} = \frac{228.27}{56.07} = 4.07 \text{ per cent } 3CaO.SiO_2$$

The $3CaO.SiO_2$ subtracted from the total SiO_2 (s) + CaO (c) gives the true amount of $2CaO.SiO_2$ present.

If the computed $3CaO.SiO_2$ is greater than $s + c$, no $2CaO.SiO_2$ is present. In that case each per cent of SiO_2 (s) combines with CaO to form 3.80 per cent $3CaO.SiO_2$:

$$\frac{3CaO.SiO_2}{SiO_2} = \frac{228.27}{60.06} = 3.80 \text{ per cent } 3CaO.SiO_2$$

This amount of $3CaO.SiO_2$ subtracted from SiO_2 (s) + CaO (c) gives the percentage of uncombined CaO. The above

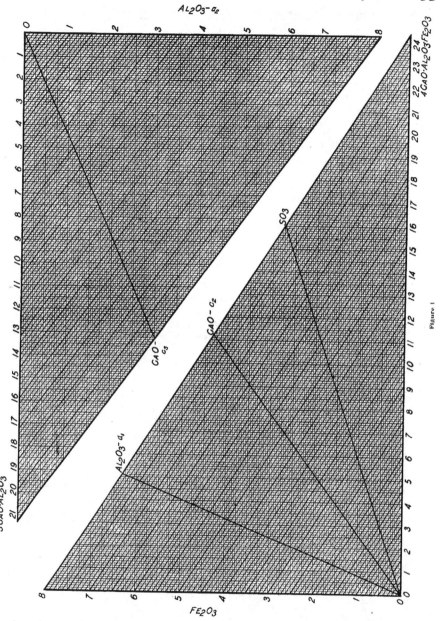

Figure 1

condition can obtain only when the lime is in excess of that which can go into combination at equilibrium, and the un-combined CaO has not been determined and deducted as previously described.

Application of the Method

A diagrammatic method for obtaining these relations has been found useful in computing the amounts of the compounds from chemical analyses. Such a method has not the precision

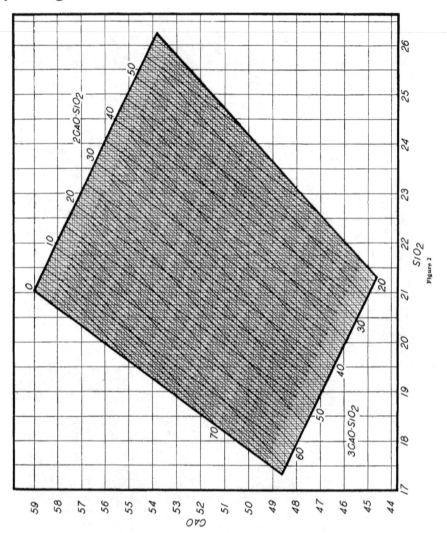

Figure 2

of the mathematical factors, but the values read are probably within the accuracy of the analytical procedures and the method has the advantage of speed and simplicity.

In Figures 1 and 2 the relations expressed in the factors given above are plotted in a convenient form. As an illustration of the use of the diagrams and the factors, an analysis of a commercial cement and the computation of compounds are presented. A chart (Table I) will be found an aid in the proper recording of the significant figures. The analytical data are given on the chart, together with the values as read from the diagrams. A few abbreviations appear on the chart:

C_4AF for $4CaO.Al_2O_3.Fe_2O_3$, C_3A for $3CaO.Al_2O_3$, C_2S for $3CaO.SiO_2$, and C_2S for $2CaO.SiO_2$.

The values for ignition loss, 1.1, and magnesia, 3.7, are transferred to the lower horizontal row, wherein are placed the compounds of the cement.

The value for free CaO, 0.3, is transferred to the "free CaO" column opposite CaO, and brought down to the lower row compounds.

The value for SO_3, 2.0, is transferred to the "SO_3 eq." column, and the CaO equivalent read from the lower diagram in Figure 1.

In this case only, both readings are taken from the horizontal axis. It is desired to find the CaO equivalent of 2.0 SO_3 in the formation of $CaSO_4$. The point 2.0 on the horizontal axis of the lower diagram in Figure 1 is followed upward on the vertical coördinate until it intercepts the radial line for SO_3. The diagonal coördinate is then followed until the radial line for CaO is intercepted. The vertical coördinate is again followed down from that point to the horizontal axis, and the value 1.4 obtained.

The value read, 1.4, is placed at c_1 and the sum of the two, 3.4, is placed at the bottom of the column under "$CaSO_4$." The value for Fe_2O_3, 3.4, is transferred to the "Fe_2O_3 eq." column and the Al_2O_3 and CaO equivalent to the Fe_2O_3 read from the lower diagram in Figure 1.

It is desired in this case to find the Al_2O_3 and CaO equivalents of 3.4 Fe_2O_3 in the formation of $4CaO.Al_2O_3.Fe_2O_3$. The point 3.4 on the vertical axis of the lower diagram in Figure 1 is followed on the diagonal coördinate until it intercepts the radial line for Al_2O_3. The vertical coördinate is then followed down from that point and the value 2.2 Al_2O_3 read off on the horizontal axis. The point 3.4 on the vertical axis is again followed on the diagonal coördinate until it intercepts the radial line for CaO. Again the vertical coördinate is followed downward and the value 4.8 CaO read off on the horizontal axis.

The values as read are placed in the column at their proper places: the Al_2O_3, 2.2, at a_1; and the CaO, 4.8, at c_2. The three figures in the column are now added to give the $4CaO.Al_2O_3.Fe_2O_3$. This value to the nearest whole number is placed at the base of the column. The amount also may be read directly from the diagram if desired.

Table I—Chart Used for Recording Significant Data in Computation of Compounds

COMPONENTS	ANALYSIS	FREE CaO	SO_2 EQ.	Fe_2O_3 EQ.	Al_2O_3 EQ.	c AND s	C_2S
CaO	62.8	0.3	c_1 1.4	c_2 4.8	c_3 3.8	c 52.5	
MgO	3.7						
Al_2O_3	4.5			a_1 2.2	a_2 2.3		
Fe_2O_3	3.4			3.4			
SiO_2	22.3					s 22.3	
SO_3	2.0		2.0				
Loss	1.1						
Insoluble	0.1						
Free CaO	0.3						
Ignition loss	Free MgO	Free CaO					
	1.1	3.7	0.3	3.4	10	6	44	31
				$CaSO_4$	C_4AF	C_3A	C_3S	C_2S

The value a_1, 2.2, is subtracted from Al_2O_3, 4.5, to give a_2, 2.3, the Al_2O_3 available to combine as $3CaO.Al_2O_3$, which is placed in the "Al_2O_3 eq." column at a_2. The CaO equivalent of this, 3.8, is read from the upper diagram of Figure 1 and placed at c_3. The two values are added to give the $3CaO.-Al_2O_3$ and that figure to the nearest whole number brought to the foot of the column. This value also may be read directly if desired.

The CaO, c, available for combination with the silica is now found by subtracting from the total CaO the free CaO, c_1, c_2, and c_3: $62.8 - (0.3 + 1.4 + 4.8 + 3.8) = 52.5$ which is set down at c. The total SiO_2, 22.3 (unless corrected for the quartz in the insoluble residue) is set down at s.

The computed tricalcium silicate and dicalcium silicate are now read directly from the diagram (2) in Figure 2. The point is found which is the intersection of the vertical coördinate representing SiO_2 (s) and the horizontal coördinate representing the CaO (c) available for combination with the silica. The $3CaO.SiO_2$ corresponding to this point, 44 per cent, is read to the nearest whole number on the diagonal coördinate that is parallel to the lower right base line, as indicated. The $2CaO.SiO_2$, 31 per cent, is read on the diagonal coördinate that is parallel to the upper left base line, as indicated. These values are set down in the lower row of compounds under C_3S and C_2S, respectively.

In the event that the point represented by the intersection of the coördinates for CaO and SiO_2 lies to the left of the diagram, there is present an excess of lime above that required

to convert all of the $2CaO.SiO_2$ to $3CaO.SiO_2$. In that case there is some uncombined CaO present and no dicalcium silicate. The tricalcium silicate content is found by reading that value at the point where the SiO_2 coördinate intersects the upper left boundary of the figure. The lime required for that compound is then read off on the CaO (horizontal) coördinate and the remaining lime is uncombined. For example, consider that $c = 59.0$ and $s = 20.5$. The SiO_2 coördinate cuts the upper boundary at a point represented by about 78 per cent $3CaO.SiO_2$. The CaO required is read to be 57.5 per cent. The free CaO is then 1.5 per cent. Such a value should be recorded in the "free CaO" column opposite SiO_2 and brought to the lower row of compounds.

The upper right boundary curve as drawn represents the compositions at which the sum of the two calcium silicates is 80 per cent. The remaining material includes all other compounds—as $3CaO.Al_2O_3$, $4CaO.Al_2O_3.Fe_2O_3$, MgO, alkalies, $CaSO_4$ if present, and any other constituents. The lower left boundary curve as drawn represents the compositions at which the sum of the two silicates is 65 per cent, the remaining 35 per cent being the other compounds as above. It is probable that most commercial cements fall within these limits, but the diagram may be extended up to the line representing 100 per cent $2CaO.SiO_2$ plus $3CaO.SiO_2$, and down as far as desired. The upper left boundary is the line for zero $2CaO.SiO_2$ and the lower right boundary is cut at 20 per cent $3CaO.SiO_2$ since Portland cements will scarcely be found with less than that amount of the tribasic silicate. If desired, however, the diagram may be extended to the lower right to zero $3CaO.SiO_2$.

The data necessary to construct the diagrams in Figure 1 are obtainable from the factors previously given. The following locations of the external angles of the diagram in Figure 2 will define the position of that figure.

	LEFT	TOP	RIGHT	BOTTOM
CaO	48.64	58.95	53.81	44.70
SiO_2	17.36	21.05	26.19	21.30

The diagrams must be prepared with the highest precision and should be drawn to such a scale that estimates may properly be made to 1 per cent.

There now appear on the bottom row of the chart the values for all of the compounds which we are able at present to calculate from the chemical analysis of a cement.

The use of factors in the calculation gives values differing but slightly from those obtained by the use of the diagrams. This is brought out in Table II, in which are shown the values obtained by factors and by the diagrams from the composition represented by the analysis given. In this case, in order to demonstrate the difference, the values are expressed to the first decimal place.

Table II—Comparison of Computations by Factors and by Diagram

COMPONENTS	ANALYSIS	COMPOUNDS	BY FACTORS	BY DIAGRAM
	Per cent		Per cent	Per cent
CaO	62.8	$3CaO.SiO_2$	44.4	44.4
MgO	3.7	$2CaO.SiO_2$	30.5	30.6
Al_2O_3	4.5	$3CaO.Al_2O_3$	6.1	6.1
Fe_2O_3	3.4	$4CaO.Al_2O_3.Fe_2O_3$	10.3	10.4
SiO_2	22.3	Free MgO	3.7	3.7
SO_3	2.0	Free CaO	0.3	0.3
Ignition loss	1.1	$CaSO_4$	3.4	3.4
Insoluble[a]	0.1	Ignition loss	1.1	1.1
Free CaO[a]	0.3			
Total	99.8		99.8	100.0

[a] Not included in total.

Literature Cited

(1) Brownmiller, Paper in preparation.
(2) Grün and Kunze, *Zement*, **17**, 1166 (1928); *Concrete*, **34**, 115 (1929), used a diagram of similar coördinates.
(3) Hansen, *J. Am. Chem. Soc.*, **50**, 2155 (1928).

(4) Hansen, Paper in preparation.
(5) Hansen and Bogue, *J. Am. Chem. Soc.*, **48**, 1261 (1928).
(6) Hansen and Brownmiller, *Am. J. Sci.*, **15**, 225 (1928).
(7) Hansen, Brownmiller, and Bogue, *J. Am. Chem. Soc.*, **50**, 396 (1928).
(8) Hansen, Dyckerhoff, Ashton, and Bogue, *J. Phys. Chem.*, **31**, 607 (1927).
(9) Lerch and Bogue, IND. ENG. CHEM., **18**, 739 (1926).
(10) Rankin and Merwin, *Am. J. Sci.*, **45**, 301 (1918).
(11) Rankin and Wright, *Ibid.*, **39**, 1 (1915).

A TRIBUTE TO

"Expression and Analysis of Pore Fluids from Hardened Cement Pastes and Mortars"

by R.S. Barneyback Jr. and S. Diamond

Foreword by Kevin J. Folliard

The definition of a landmark paper can not be found in a dictionary, encyclopedia, or Wikipedia, for that matter. But a paper that advances the state of the art, builds upon previous research accomplishments, is cited in many subsequent publications, and whose key products or techniques are used by researchers for decades certainly would satisfy the definition of landmark. Such is the case for the following paper by Barneyback and Diamond (1981), whose research described in the paper built upon the pioneering work of Longuet et al. (1973) and led to the development of an improved apparatus for expressing pore solution from hardened pastes or mortars. The apparatus and techniques described by Barneyback and Diamond have since been used by a variety of researchers to extract and analyze pore solution for studies on topics ranging from cement hydration to alkali-silica reaction to corrosion of reinforcing steel. As a testament to the effect of this paper on researchers and practitioners, well over 100 technical papers have cited this specific paper. This foreword briefly describes some key aspects of this paper and discusses its effect since its publication in 1981.

This paper describes the development of an apparatus for expressing pore solution from hardened paste or mortar and describes appropriate methods for analyzing the expressed pore solution. As highlighted by the authors, the apparatus, referred to in the paper as a "pore fluid expression device" and typically referred to today simply as a "pore press," was designed and constructed based on previous work by Longuet at al. (1973), but with significant modifications and improvements to allow it to be used for testing mortars (and concretes), as opposed to just cement pastes. The device described by Barneyback and Diamond was able to operate at pressures up to 550 MPa (80,000 psi), as opposed to the device developed by Longuet et al, which was only able to operate at pressures up to 350 MPa (~ 50,000 psi). The device described by Barneyback and Diamond and illustrated in Figure 1 of their paper was used extensively at Purdue University in the years leading to the publication of this landmark paper and was a key tool used by Barneyback in his highly-regarded PhD research on alkali-silica reaction (1981).

The design and construction of a device to safely extract pore solution from hardened pastes, mortars, and concretes is by no means trivial. As described in the paper, the device is constructed using heat-treated alloys and the fabrication method employs a shrink fitting technique that allows the outer cylinder to be tightly bonded to the inner cylinder, essentially precompressing the inner cylinder. As the authors vividly point out, this design, coupled with other key design and construction features, prevents catastrophic failure of the device, which could otherwise be a major safety concern. In addition to the innovative design of the body of the apparatus, the authors incorporated other key innovations into the device to allow the pore solution to be drawn from the specimen under load, down through a drain ring and channel, and out through a tube to an awaiting syringe. The authors provide important details in the paper on what type specimens should be tested in the apparatus and how the load should be applied (and removed) to extract the desired volume of pore solution. Lastly, the authors describe how the extracted pore solution should be analyzed to determine the types and amounts of dissolved ions.

This paper focuses primarily on the pore solution extraction device, including its design, construction, and use, and also provides key information on how to accurately measure the composition of the pore solution. It is a well-written, detailed paper that has been read and cited by many, and most importantly, the apparatus described in the paper (or similar types of devices) has been used extensively.

So one question that may come to mind is – Why would one want to know the composition of pore solution in portland cement-based systems? As Barneyback and Diamond clearly point out, the hydration of portland cement takes place through direct interactions with pore solution, with hydration before setting occurring between cement compounds and a continuous liquid phase, and hydration after setting occurring between cement compounds and a discontinuous pore solution. The authors note the relative ease of extracting pore solution from fresh pastes (or mortars or concretes), as the pore solution can easily be extracted by filtration (with or without a vacuum). The real challenge is extracting the pore solution from a hardened matrix, which is the challenge that is overcome with the pore press developed by Barneyback and Diamond. With this apparatus, researchers can and have evaluated pore solution in mature concrete and related its composition to several key aspects of concrete behavior, especially with regard to durability issues. A few examples are provided next for conciseness as a more exhaustive review of work based on pore solution extraction and analysis is beyond the scope of this foreword.

Alkali-silica reaction (ASR) is a common form of concrete distress and one that is much better understood today because of mechanistic studies that have employed pore solution extraction and analysis techniques. Various studies on ASR have evaluated pore solution composition to gain insight into the role of supplementary cementing materials (Shehata et al., 1999; Thomas and Shehata, 2004) and lithium compounds (Diamond, 1999; Diamond and Ong, 1992; Bérubé et al., 2004) in suppressing ASR, and the potential release of alkalies from aggregates (Constantiner and Diamond, 2003). Research on corrosion of reinforcement steel, another phenomena greatly affected by pore solution composition, has also benefited from research performed using pore solution extraction and analysis. The pioneering work of Page and Vennesland (1983) showed the strong effect of silica fume in reducing both pore solution alkalinity and chloride-binding capacity, which has direct relevance to the corrosion process.

In summary, this landmark paper by Barneyback and Diamond has had a significant effect on cement and concrete research over the past 25 years or so. A number of researchers have since used the pore solution extraction and analysis techniques described in this paper for studies focusing on topics ranging from cement hydration to alkali-silica reaction to corrosion of reinforcing steel. It is likely that researchers will continue using these techniques in the future to further advance our understanding of portland cement concrete.

References

Barneyback, R.S., "Alkali-Silica Reactions in Portland Cement Concrete, Ph.D. Thesis, School of Civil Engineering, Purdue University, 1981.

Bérubé, M.A., Tremblay, C., Fournier, B., Thomas, M.D.A. & Stokes, D.B., "Influence of Lithium-based Products Proposed for Counteracting Alkali-Silica Reactivity on the Chemistry of Pore Solution and Cement Hydrates," *Cement and Concrete Research*, Volume 34, Issue 9, 2004, pp. 1645-1660.

Constantiner, D. and Diamond, S., "Alkali release from feldspars into pore solutions," *Cement and Concrete Research*, Volume 33, Issue 4, 2003, pp. 549-554.

Diamond, S., "Unique response of $LiNO_3$ as an alkali silica reaction-preventive admixture, *Cement and Concrete Research*, Volume 29, Issue 8, 1999, pp. 1271-1275.

Diamond, S. and Ong, S., "The mechanisms of lithium effects on ASR," *Proceedings of the 9th International Conference on Alkali–Aggregate Reaction*, Concrete Society of U.K., (London), 1992, p. 269.

Longuet, P., Burglen, L., and Zelwer, A., "The liquid phase of hydrated cement," Rev. Mater. Constr. (in French) , No. 676, 1973, pp. 35-41.

Page, C.L. and Vennesland, "Pore solution composition and chloride binding capacity of silica-fume cement pastes," Materials and Structures, Volume 16, Number 1, 1983, pp. 19-25.

Shehata, M., Thomas, M.D.A. and Bleszynski, "The effect of fly composition on the chemistry of pore solution." *Cement and Concrete Research*, Volume 29, Issue 12, 1999, pp. 1915-1920.

Thomas, M.D.A. and Shehata, M.S., "Use of blended cements to control expansion of concrete due to alkali-silica reaction." Supplementary Paper Proceedings of the 8th CANMET/ACI International Conference on Fly Ash, Silica Fume, Slag and Natural Pozzolans in Concrete, Las Vegas, 2004.

Kevin J. Folliard, *FACI, is an Associate Professor and the Austin Industries Endowed Teaching Fellow in the Department of Civil, Architectural, and Environmental Engineering at the University of Texas at Austin. He received his PhD in civil engineering from the University of California at Berkeley in 1995. He is Secretary of ACI Committee 201, Durability, a Member of the Publications Committee, and a Member of ACI 318-Subcommittee A. He received the ACI Young Member Award for Professional Achievement in 2002. His research interests include concrete durability, especially alkali-silica reaction.*

CEMENT and CONCRETE RESEARCH. Vol. 11, pp. 279-285, 1981. Printed in the USA
0008-8846/81/020279-07$02.00/0 Copyright (c) 1981 Pergamon Press, Ltd.

EXPRESSION AND ANALYSIS OF PORE FLUIDS FROM HARDENED CEMENT PASTES AND MORTARS

R. S. Barneyback, Jr.[1] and Sidney Diamond
School of Civil Engineering
Purdue University
West Lafayette, IN 47907 USA

(Communicated by D.M. Roy)
(Received Nov. 21; in final form Dec. 29, 1980)

ABSTRACT

A device is described that has been used for several years for expression of pore solution from hardened portland cement pastes and mortars. Particulars with respect to the design, fabrication, and operation of such equipment are given, and methods for the analysis of the resulting small volumes of pore solutions are briefly discussed. It is believed that the compositions of the pore solutions obtained are representative of that of the bulk of the pore solution within the paste or mortar from which the solutions have been obtained.

本文介紹一儀器可用以自已硬化之混凝土及砂漿中壓取纖孔液。於有關儀器之設計、製造及使用均作一概略之敘述。本文並簡介就已壓取之微量纖孔液如何作一分析。作者推論壓取之纖孔液可視同為混凝土及砂漿內所含纖孔液之代表。

Introduction

The hydration of portland cement may be looked on as a process involving a sequence of chemical reactions between the solid cement components and a fluid. The fluid involved is initially the mix water, and is a continuous

[1] Present Address: School of Engineering, Calif. State Univ. Fresno, CA 93740 USA

phase in which the cement (and aggregate) is suspended. Shortly after mixing the water is converted to a rather complex alkali- and sulfate bearing solution. On setting, the continuous fluid is converted to a discontinuous (although interconnected) pore solution. Further hydration takes place by continued reaction of the cement components with this pore solution. The extent of reaction usually accomplished before set is actually quite modest, only a few percent or so of the total hydration possible. Thus the preponderance of cement hydration involves reaction with pore solution rather than with continuous phase solution or with mix water.

Studies of the composition of the continuous phase solution prior to setting are relatively easy to carry out, since the solution may be obtained by simple filtration or filtration assisted by vacuum or modest pressure application. After setting, and particularly after extensive subsequent hydration, somewhat more radical procedures are required to recover pore solution for analysis. Only a very few groups have thus far constructed apparatus to accomplish this. These laboratories have been primarily concerned with chemical durability problems rather than with cement hydration studies. Steel corrosion in concrete and alkali-aggregate reactions both involve long-term chemical reactions involving the pore solution, and pore solution compositional changes over long-term periods are of great significance in studying these processes. The results of such studies have not been widely publicized and are generally not familiar to workers not concerned with durability problems.

Our interest has been to develop equipment and procedures by which pore solutions may be expressed from cement pastes and from mortars ranging in age from a few minutes after mixing to several years after setting. The objective has been to provide fundamental information on changes in pore solution composition over time. Such information can be applied both to studies of cement hydration and to studies of the reactions involved in alkali-aggregate attack, steel corrosion, and similar problems. The purpose of this report is to describe the specific apparatus and procedures developed in sufficient detail that others may profit from our experience. The results of the various research investigations to which this apparatus has been applied will be published separately.

General Description of the Apparatus and Procedures Employed

The apparatus developed employs an operating pressure of the order of 550 MPa (about 80,000 psi) applied to a roughly 250 g. specimen of hardened cement paste or mortar over a period of several minutes in order to completely fracture and remold the specimen and at the same time express and recover a reasonable amount of pore solution for analysis. The diameter of the bore in which the specimens are placed is just over 2 inches (5.3 cm) and we have found it convenient to standardize on specimens cast into standard 4-oz. size pharmaceutical plastic ointment jars. These fit loosely into the bore of the device. Paste or mortar can be conveniently cast into such jars, sealed, and stored at the desired temperature until just prior to the actual expression of the pore solution.

The yield of pore solution depends on whether cement paste or mortar is involved, on the water:cement ratio, on the extent of hydration that has taken place, and on other factors. Much of our experience has been with mortars, typically of sand:cement ratio 2.0 and water:cement ratio 0.5. Such mortars yield typically 10 ml or thereabouts of expressed pore solution shortly after set, but long-term yields are progressively reduced and may be only 1 or 2 ml. Yields from cement pastes are larger because of the greater volume of pore solution present, and pastes of quite low water:cement ratios can be studied conveniently even after long periods of hydration.

It is possible to manipulate the small volumes of pore solution recovered by only slight modification of normal chemical laboratory technique, although of course care and skill are required. Our chemical analyses are carried out on appropriately diluted aliquots of the pore solution by the usual atomic absorption, flame emission, and titrimetric methods.

Normally we are interested in following changes in pore solution composition over time. To do this we cast a relatively large number of specimens from a single mix batch, seal each individually in its container, and store the samples together in a constant temperature environment. At designated intervals there-after, individual plastic jar containers are removed from storage, broken apart to liberate the cast specimen, and immediately subjected to the expression process. The expressed pore solutions are likely to be relatively unstable, and are analyzed as rapidly as possible after expression, usually within the next day.

<u>Apparatus for Expression of Pore Fluid</u>

The apparatus in use in this laboratory was designed after a similar device reported by Longuet et al. (1). It differs from the latter in that since it was desired to express pore fluid from mortars as well as from pastes, a higher operating pressure was provided for. The present device is designed to operate at a pressure of 550 MPa (80,000 psi), significantly higher than the 350 MPa operating pressure of the quipment of Longuet et al. SAE 4340 alloy steel, recommended for use in high stress service where fatigue resistance is important, was selected for fabrication of the die. It was specified that all components of the apparatus made from this alloy be heat treated to attain a potential yield stress of 1.31 GPa (190 ksi), and a potential ultimate tensile stress of 1.45 GPa (210 ksi).

An isometric half-section of the device is shown as Fig. 1. All of the steel parts shown except the support cylinder at the base are of the heat-treated SAE 4340 alloy mentioned above; the support cylinder is mild steel. The die body is designed as a jacketed cylinder. In fabricating this part of the apparatus the outer and inner cylinders were machined separately, with the inner cylinder slightly oversize. In assembly the outer cylinder was heated so as to expand its diameter, and the cool inner cylinder was inserted into position. On cooling, the outer cylinder contracts, providing a tight "skrink fit" and precompressing the inner cylinder. This precompression is an integral feature of the design.

After initial assembly of the die body, the bore of the inner cylinder was honed to precise size and the top and bottom surfaces of the die body and the top surface of the platen were ground to surface planeness of ± 0.0005 in. on any six inch diameter. These surfaces and the piston shaft and face were then hard chrome plated to improve chemical and abrasion resistance.

A necessary feature of the design is the provision of a drain ring scribed into the top of the platen that serves to collect and transmit the expressed fluid to a fluid drain channel drilled upward from the bottom surface of the platen. This drain channel was tapered with a standard taper pin reamer of sufficient size to allow insertion of a short length of heavy

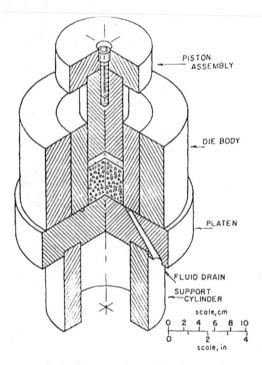

PISTON
ASSEMBLY

DIE BODY

PLATEN

FLUID DRAIN

SUPPORT
CYLINDER

scale,cm

0 2 4 6 8 10

0   2   4
scale, in

Fig. 1.   Isometric half-section of pore fluid expression device.

plastic tubing approximately one-third of the way up the channel. This tubing
is inserted with sufficient pressure to form an air-tight seal. In operation,
the plastic tip of a disposable plastic syringe of standard design is inserted
into this plastic tubing, and the expressed pore fluid is delivered into this
syringe. The other non-metallic portion of the apparatus is an approximately
6 mm-thick Teflon seal turned from bar stock that is inserted between the top
of the specimen and the bottom surface of the piston. This seal deforms and
degrades with repeated use, and is replaced periodically as needed.

The assembly described above has been used satisfactorily for several
hundred expressions without mishap. However, the reader is cautioned that, as
with all high pressure apparatus a potential hazard exists should the die burst
under load. Even with careful design and the use of adequate safety factors
defects in materials, errors in machining, faulty heat treatment of alloys, or
improper operation may contribute to unexpected failure of the device. A careful
reading of Bridgman's classic treatment (2) on the "special sorts of rupture
peculiar to high pressures" is highly recommended. The following paragraph
summarizes the more salient points of Bridgman's remarks.

Simple elastic theory suggests that rupture will initiate at the inner
surface when the maximum shearing stress capacity (Coulomb-Tresca failure
criterion) is exceeded. This was not confirmed by Bridgman's many tests. He
found that cylinders designed according to these criteria could withstand signi-

ficantly higher pressures than anticipated, assuming no materials defects. Rupture of cylinders made from ordinary steel invariably initiated at the outside surface and traveled inward. The rupture may progress along an approximately equiangular spiral through the entire thickness of the wall, or it may, on approaching the inner surface, branch along two planes of shear at nearly 90° to each other so that a triangular prism is detached at the inside. This may be projected with great violence through the open crack and outward into the room.

We therefore earnestly suggest that attempts to design and fabricate equipment similar to that described here be undertaken only if the design can be rigorously checked by a competent engineering designer familiar with this class of problem, and only if correct heat treatment of the high strength steel and a high standard of machining, fabrication, and assembly can be assured. The authors specifically disclaim any liability for any consequences even if these conditions are met.

Operation of the Apparatus

Prior to each use of the apparatus a thin coating of film-bonding grade fluorocarbon is sprayed from a pressure can so as to cover the bore of the die body, the mating surfaces of the die body and platen, and the shaft of the piston with a continuous film of fluorocarbon. The die body is then assembled on the center of the platen, the specimen is removed from its container and dropped into the bore, and the Teflon seal and piston inserted. A short length of heavy plastic tubing is inserted into the tapered drain channel as previously described, and a plastic disposable syringe, without needle, is fitted into the open end of the tubing. The piston is then loaded at a rate equivalent to a compressive stress increase of about 2.8 MPa/s (about 400 psi/s) until the maximum 550 MPa stress is attained. The rate of loading is not critical but a relatively slow rate such as is scheduled here appears to result in a greater yield of pore fluid. As the loading increased, expressed gas and pore fluid collects in the syringe. It is helpful to withdraw the plunger of the syringe a short distance so as to put a slight negative pressure on the pore fluid drainage system. It is also helpful to temporarily disconnect the syringe and vent the accumulated gas from it several times during each cycle. The load is maintained at the maximum stress level for a few minutes. If the desired amount of pore fluid has not been collected on this first cycle, the pressure is reduced to about 350 MPa to allow some elastic rebound to occur. On increasing the pressure back to the maximum level additional pore fluid can be withdrawn into the syringe. Several such cycles may be employed as needed, but it is seldom possible to materially increase fluid recovery by reloading more than three or four times.

After the final unloading of the pressure the syringe is removed from the plastic delivery tube, any gas trapped within the syringe is expelled, and the cap is replaced over the needle port of the syringe. The capped syringe then serves as an appropriate storage chamber until chemical analysis can be commenced.

It is necessary to disassemble the apparatus, recover the remolded specimen, and clean all surfaces immediately after recovery of the expressed fluid. The die body is disassembled from the platen and the platen surface and its drain system are flushed with absolute ethanol and wiped clean with soft facial tissue at least twice, and until no residue remains. The piston cap is removed from the piston, and pressure is applied to the top of the

piston, which then serves as a plunger to eject the remolded specimen from
the bore into the central opening of the support cylinder. The apparatus is
again disassembled and the specimen recovered and sealed in a plastic bag
for storage or further analysis. The piston and die are cleaned using absolute ethanol and facial tissue until all residual material is removed, and
finally all surfaces are resprayed with a fresh coating of fluorocarbon.

Fluid can be expressed readily from fresh cement paste or mortar before
set using the same apparatus, and of course recovery is much greater.
Occasionally the fluid recovered just before or just after set is cloudy or
becomes cloudy as solids are actively precipitating within it. If desired,
these solids (which constitute only an insignificant portion of the mass of
the recovered solution) can be filtered off prior to analysis.

Analytical Procedures

The pore solutions recovered after set are highly alkaline (pH usually
far in excess of 13 and sometimes approaching 14) and to a first approximation
are concentrated solutions of alkali hydroxides with only modest contents of
other components. Analytical procedures must be developed in the light of
this, and in the light of the fact that only a few ml. of solution will
generally be available for all of the analyses desired.

One necessity is accurate handling and dispensing of small volumes of
the solution for dilution purposes. In our laboratory aliquots are delivered
using a Hamilton gas-tight syringe equipped with a teflon positive displacement piston. This syringe has a calibrated capacity of 500 µl and a least
reading of 10 µl, and seems well adapted to the purpose. Appropriate dilutions
are prepared for determinations of Na, K, and Li by flame photometry, and for
Si, Al, Fe, Mg, and Ca by atomic absorption spectrometry, using standard
methods. Sulfate is determined indirectly by $BaSO_4$ precipitation in a solution
containing excess $BaCl_2$, with the residual Ba being determined by atomic absorption spectrometry.

Efforts to determine pH directly using micro pH glass electrodes were
abandoned when it became apparent that the electrode glass was not sufficiently stable to resist attack by these highly alkaline pore solutions, even
though manufacturer's literature suggests that they may be used over the
entire pH range 0-14. We determine OH ion concentration by direct titration
against standard HCl.

Details of the analytical procedures employed will be provided in the
Ph. D. thesis of the first-named author (3).

Adjustment of Solution Concentrations to Permit Comparison at Constant Water Content

For many purposes, the actual concentrations of the dissolved ionic
species is the only information desired from investigations of pore solution
concentrations. However, when secondary reactions such as those involved in
alkali aggregate attack are under consideration, information may be desired
on the rate at which the ionic species react, that is, move from solution to
be incorporated into solid reaction products. The desired information is the
net movement of dissolved species out of (or in some cases, into) the pore
solutions. Reflection will confirm that raw concentration data in hydrating
cement systems does not directly provide such information, since concentration
changes reflect changes in solvent present as well as changes in solute present

The solvent, that is, the water, is progressively depleted by continuing cement hydration, being progressively bound up in solid hydration product. In order to monitor changes in the amount of solute in the pore solution free of this effect, one must adjust the analytically-determined concentration by a factor that reflects the ongoing changes in free water content. To do this, we recover the remolded specimen from which the pore solution has been expressed and determine its non-evaporable water content, that is, the bound water retained between 105° C and the ignited condition at 1050° C. From this we calculate a factor that represents the proportion of the original mix water that has not been bound into the hydrated cement solid, and adjust the analytical concentration of solute by dividing it by this factor. The adjusted concentration so obtained is that which would be present had the bound water been replaced by an equal mass of additional water; thus the "standard" amount of solvent on which comparisons are based is the initial water content of the mix. Comparison of a series of such adjusted concentrations over time provides a direct reflection of solute movement in or out of the pore solution, independent of the solvent-depleting effect of progressive cement hydration. Such adjusted concentrations are always more dilute than the actual concentrations occurring in the pore solution within the paste or mortar. The differences may be significant.

Discussion

The method of pore solution expression and analysis outlined here has been in use at Purdue University for a number of years, and has provided insight and useful information in connection with a variety of problems. The procedures, while somewhat tedious, are effective, reasonably trouble-free, and provide reproducible results.

Objections have been raised that there is no certainty that the expressed pore solution is fully representative of all of the fluid present within the paste or mortar, and indeed it is possible that there exist layers of fluid of concentration different from the bulk solution next to (and influenced by) the solid surfaces of the hydrated cement products. Nevertheless we feel that the insight gained from analysis of the bulk pore solutions expressed in this manner is extremely valuable, and see no reason to suppose that the solution expressed from the specimens would not be representative of the bulk pore solution as it exists prior to expression.

Acknowledgements

The program of research in which the development of the apparatus and procedures described here was accomplished was supported by the U.S. National Science Foundation (Grants No. ENG74-21495 and ENG77-09166) and by the U. S. Department of Energy (Grant No. EM-78-S-02-5207). The support of these agencies is gratefully acknowledged. We appreciate the assistance of E. C. Ting in the structural design of the apparatus, and the continuous assistance and advice provided by W. L. Dolch.

References

1. P. Longuet, L. Burglen, and A. Zelwer, "The Liquid Phase of Hydrated Cement," (in French) Rev. Mater. Constr. No. 676 35-41 (1973).

2. P. C. Bridgman, "The Physics of High Pressure," G. Bell, London, Chapter IV, pp 78-97 (1949).

3. R. S. Barneyback, Jr., "Alkali Silica Reactions in Portland Cement Concrete," Ph. D. Thesis, School of Civil Engineering, Purdue University (1981).

A TRIBUTE TO

"Hydrated Calcium Silicates, Part 1: Compound Formation at Ordinary Temperatures"

by H.F.W. Taylor

Foreword by Sidney Diamond

This article is of landmark significance for two distinct reasons. The work presented not only provided a major turning point in understanding the nature of cement hydration, but it also was pivotal in permanently diverting the professional interest of H.F.W. Taylor to the field of cement chemistry, and away from the crystallography of complex biological molecules (including DNA), which had occupied his attention during his early professional career. Biological crystallography's loss was cement chemistry's gain. A few years later (while still in his early thirties) Taylor was awarded a full professorship at the University of Aberdeen and went on to become the undisputed international leader in cement chemistry until his untimely death in 2002. His monograph entitled "Cement Chemistry" has been by far the most influential and widely-read book in the field, and has been translated into a number of languages. His steady flow of original research contributions over the years and his guidance of younger researchers exerted unique influence among cement chemists around the world.

To appreciate the context within which this landmark paper was written, it is necessary understand the existing state of knowledge of cement hydration as of 1950. It was appreciated that the main crystalline compound in portland cement, tricalcium silicate (C_3S or alite) and dicalcium silicate (C_2S or belite) were jointly responsible for the strength developed during the hardening of conventional concrete. These compounds were known to develop strength as the result of their reactions with mixture water, which generated a gel-like hydrated calcium silicate product. However, the nature of this hydration product was very poorly understood. The minor products of cement hydration (calcium hydroxide and the hydrated calcium aluminate compounds) were crystalline and could be studied by crystallographic means, but these were seen to be peripheral to strength development compared with the hydration product produced by C_3S and C_2S.

It was evident in 1950 that this gel-like product was composed of calcium, silica, and water, but its almost completely amorphous character prevented any progress in understanding its internal structure. Indeed, it was not clear whether it was a true thermodynamic phase of an organized internal structure, or simply a random gel-like substance of no fixed character or property. It should be appreciated that at that time chemists and others attempting to understand and model the internal structures of materials had to rely almost entirely on X-ray crystallography, which was Taylor's original field of expertise. But the X-ray response of the product in hydrating cement was so weak and indefinite that it offered no real handle on which to base structural analysis.

Another difficulty was that this calcium silicate hydration product did not appear to have a consistent chemical composition, but varied considerably in the proportions of calcium and silica. Indeed, there was considerable doubt as to whether it was indeed a single substance or a mixture of several different substances of different compositions.

As suggested in the extensive review of prior literature given in the paper itself, research seemed to be stymied at that point, and it appeared that the nature of the hydrated calcium silicate gel formed in concrete would remain a mystery. Taylor wrote, "It appeared impossible to make any progress with further problems such as the degrees of hydration and structures of the compounds, until the phase equilibria and x-ray data had been established with greater precision." But how was this to be accomplished?

Taylor decided to study not the badly organized gel found in concrete itself, but rather analogous calcium silicate hydrates prepared at room temperature in the laboratory, by hydrating C_3S in excess water or by reacting other substances containing calcium and silica in solution. These reacting substances included calcium hydroxide reacting with silica gel, and calcium nitrate reacting with sodium silicate.

In the results of more than 100 experimental trials, Taylor found that, regardless of the starting materials, method of preparation, and proportions used, a single thermodynamic substance was generated in all cases. This product, which he designated calcium silicate hydrate (I) had a definite and consistent X-ray diffraction pattern, despite the fact that its composition varied over a considerable range. The X-ray diffraction pattern, which consisted of approximately 15 X-ray peaks, was sufficiently detailed that Taylor was able to sketch out the likely main features of the internal structure. He suggested that it was a layer structure with the individual layers well organized, but with the organization in the third direction, that is, the direction of stacking of the layers, very poorly organized. Taylor noted that these features of calcium silicate hydrate (I) somewhat resembled those of the clay mineral structures. Subsequent work by Taylor and others showed that this calcium silicate hydrate (I) was in fact related to, and apparently a disordered form of, the naturally-occurring mineral tobermorite. Indeed, for a time the actual cement hydration product gel produced in concrete was called tobermorite gel by many researchers. It was later considered that the layers in the cement hydration product gel might also have features related to a slightly different natural mineral called jennite, and that the layers might be partly bent and crumpled.

Technicalities aside, the landmark character of this paper rests on several features:

(1) The finding that indeed an equilibrium phase is produced by hydrating C_3S or by equivalent chemical reaction between any calcium and silica-bearing reactive materials. Thus, the product produced by hydration of C_3S (and C_2S) in concrete (which is now generally called C-S-H gel) must also be a form of this thermodynamically identifiable substance. This feature is central to current research by various workers (including Taylor's long-term colleague Professor Fred Glasser) in which the hydration of portland cement is accurately modeled on a purely thermodynamic basis;

(2) The clear evidence that despite the variation in composition, the product is a single phase with composition that can vary only within well-defined limits, and

(3) The first clear indication of the likely internal structure of that phase.

In summary, the conclusions reached in this paper and in other related early findings of Professor Taylor rescued the field of cement chemistry from nearly-complete confusion as to the nature of the main cement hydration product. Much of the progress in understanding (and influencing) the chemistry of cement hydration over the past almost 60 years has stemmed directly or indirectly from these findings.

Sidney Diamond, *FACI, is Professor Emeritus of Engineering Materials in the School of Civil Engineering, Purdue University. He has contributed extensively to research in cement chemistry and concrete durability over the last 50 years.*

726. *Hydrated Calcium Silicates. Part I. Compound Formation at Ordinary Temperatures.*

By H. F. W. TAYLOR.

Hydrous calcium silicates prepared at room temperature appear amorphous, but X-ray photographs show that compounds are formed having a considerable degree of crystalline character. Essentially the same product, calcium silicate hydrate (I), can be obtained by the action of water on tricalcium silicate, by double decomposition of calcium nitrate and sodium silicate, or by reaction of calcium hydroxide solution with silica gel, although crystallisation is more marked in the first case. The composition of this phase varies between approximately $CaO,SiO_2,aq.$ and $3CaO,2SiO_2,aq.$ without significant change in X-ray pattern. The phase relationships between solid and solution have been investigated and are sufficiently reproducible to suggest that the results represent a fair approximation to equilibrium conditions. A second phase, calcium silicate hydrate (II), with a composition in the neighbourhood of $2CaO,SiO_2,aq.$ and an X-ray pattern differing only slightly from the above, has been obtained by decomposition of tricalcium silicate and probably exists in equilibrium with calcium hydroxide solutions containing over 1.13 g./l. of CaO. A tentative interpretation of the X-ray data of calcium silicate hydrate (I) suggests a layer structure, possibly showing some similarities to the clay minerals.

THE system $CaO-SiO_2-H_2O$ is of considerable interest in pure and applied chemistry, and in geochemistry, if for no other reason than the abundance and accessibility of the materials involved. In particular, calcium silicates are the principal constituents of Portland cement and are the compounds chiefly responsible for the setting and hardening actions on mixing with water. Knowledge of the hydrated system is therefore essential to the understanding of these processes.

Earlier Investigations.—The study of the system at ordinary temperatures is made difficult by the indefinite nature of the substances involved, and although numerous investigations have been carried out, considerable doubt remains regarding the results. Previous studies have recently been reviewed by Steinour (*Chem. Reviews*, 1947, **40**, 391), and it is apparent that much of the recorded work is open to serious criticism and that very large discrepancies exist between the results of even the most recent investigations. Thus, Bessey (" Symposium on the Chemistry of Cements," Stockholm, 1938, p. 178), obtained evidence from phase-equilibrium data for the formation of two distinct phases, having compositions $CaO,SiO_2,aq.$—$3CaO,2SiO_2,aq.$ and $2CaO,SiO_2,aq.$ The latter was found to exist in equilibrium with saturated calcium hydroxide at 17°. Beitlich (*J. Amer. Chem. Soc.*, 1938, **60**, 1832), however, considered that only a single phase existed in equilibrium with aqueous solutions in this region and that its composition varied between $4CaO,5SiO_2,aq.$ and $2CaO,SiO_2,aq.$ Cirilli (*Ric. sci.*, 1939, **10**, 1042), on the basis of X-ray powder data, also rejected Bessey's view that $2CaO,SiO_2,aq.$ existed as a distinct phase but considered the limits of composition of the other phase to be $CaO,SiO_2,aq.$ and $3CaO,2SiO_2,aq.$ Roller and Ervin (*J. Amer. Chem. Soc.*, 1940, **62**, 461) reached a similar conclusion but believed, as did Beitlich and also Flint and Wells (*J. Res. Nat. Bur. Stand.*, 1934, **12**, 751), that a further phase, poorer in lime than $CaO,SiO_2,aq.$, could also be formed at room temperature.

Bessey, who alone among the previous investigators studied materials prepared by essentially different methods, considered that reproducibility in the phase data could be obtained. On the other hand, Steinour, while pointing out the possibilities of experimental errors in some of the investigations, also suggested tentatively that the differing lime : silica molar ratios of solid phases, supposedly in equilibrium with solutions of the same concentration, might be due to differences in their colloidal properties.

Degree of Crystalline Character.—Hydrated calcium silicates prepared at room temperature normally appear completely amorphous or gel-like under the microscope. A few optical investigations, discussed by Steinour (*loc. cit.*), indicated the formation of needles instead of or as well as the gel, but the conditions necessary for this are not clear and attempts by various workers to reproduce certain of these preparations have been unsuccessful. More recently, electron-microscope studies by Radczewski, Muller, and Eitel (*Naturwiss.*, 1939, **27**, 807), Sliepcevich, Gildart, and Katz (*Ind. Eng. Chem.*, 1943, **35**, 1178), and McMurdie (unpublished work quoted by Bogue, " The Chemistry of Portland Cement," Reinhold, 1947) have given indications that the gel itself may have a degree of crystalline character although, as Bogue points out, the results so far obtained by this method are inconclusive. More definite evidence of crystallinity has arisen from the X-ray powder studies by Chassevent (*Compt. rend.*, 1934, **199**, 673), Brandenberger (*Schweiz. Archiv*, 1937, **3**, 239), Forsen (" Symposium on the Chemistry of Cements," Stockholm, 1938, 389), Cirilli (*loc. cit.*), Stratling (*Zement*, 1940, **29**, 427, 441, 455, 475), McMurdie and Flint (*J. Res. Nat. Bur. Stand.*, 1943, **31**, 225), and Brocard (*Ann. Inst. Tec. Bat. Trav. Pub.*, 1948, No. 1, 1). While nearly all the patterns obtained show a general similarity, all, as will be shown, are incomplete and some include spacings due to other substances. No attempts to interpret the data have been recorded.

The Present Investigation.—This was undertaken because it appeared impossible to make any progress with further problems, such as the degrees of hydration and structures of the compounds, until the phase equilibria and *X*-ray data had been established with greater precision. A systematic study of hydrated calcium silicates prepared at room temperature by various methods was therefore carried out. This has made possible more conclusive identification of the compounds and knowledge of their limits of composition, and has yielded some indications regarding their structures.

Preparation of Hydrated Calcium Silicates.—Samples for phase equilibrium and *X*-ray investigation were prepared by decomposition of anhydrous tricalcium silicate, by reaction of calcium hydroxide solution with silica gel, and by double decomposition of calcium nitrate with sodium silicate. The products were white powders which appeared amorphous under the polarising microscope except for traces of calcium carbonate and, in the case of samples C6 and C7 (below), of calcium hydroxide. Analytical data are given in Table I. Following Roller and Ervin (*loc. cit.*), it was assumed that the carbon dioxide was present as calcium carbonate and the values given for % CaO and CaO/SiO_2 in Table I and elsewhere in this paper exclude CaO present in this form. In the case of samples made by double decomposition the small amounts of Na_2O present as impurity are included in the values given for CaO, since investigations by Kalousek (*J. Res. Nat. Bur. Stand.*, 1944, **32**, 285) suggest that some replacement of lime in hydrated calcium silicates by soda can take place. The correction is in any case of little significance.

TABLE I.

Method of preparation.	Sample.	CaO, % (corr.).	SiO_2, %.	H_2O, %.	$CaCO_3$, %.	CaO/SiO_2 (corr.).
Tricalcium silicate and water	A1 *	39·8	30·5	22·2	7·5	1·40
	A2	40·5	30·8	23·9	4·8	1·41
	A3	45·9	30·0	23·4	0·66	1·64
	A4	47·6	26·9	23·8	1·7	1·90
	A5	45·1	24·8	29·5	0·59	1·94
Calcium hydroxide and silica gel	B1	32·9	38·2	26·0	2·9	0·92
Calcium nitrate and sodium silicate	C1	27·2	42·9	28·4	1·5	0·68
	C2	26·0	29·6	41·6	2·8	0·94
	C3	34·9	37·8	25·8	1·5	0·99
	C4	37·1	32·2	27·3	3·3	1·24
	C5	42·1	27·8	28·7	1·4	1·62
	C6	37·5	22·3	36·7	3·5	1·80
	C7	42·7	19·3	36·2	1·8	23·7

* Contained a trace of unchanged tricalcium silicate.
Na_2O was determined separately in two cases : C5, 0·33% and C7, 0·31%.

Investigation of Phase Equilibria.—Equilbria between the solid phases and aqueous solutions were investigated by shaking weighed amounts of the above preparations with water or calcium hydroxide solutions. In other experiments silica gel was shaken directly with calcium hydroxide solutions. From the initial and final concentrations of calcium hydroxide and silica in solution, the final lime : silica molar ratio of the solid phase was calculated in each case. The results of these experiments, expressed by plotting the lime : silica molar ratios of the solids against concentrations of lime in solution, are given in Fig. 1. Concentrations of silica in solution are given in Fig. 2.

Attainment of Equilibrium.—The existence of equilibrium in these experiments was demonstrated by the following tests : (i) Out of over 100 separate experiments all but a few gave results in fairly good agreement with each other, as shown in Fig. 1. In the few cases (not shown in Fig. 1) in which divergent results were obtained, repetition of the experiment with a longer period of shaking nearly always gave results in agreement with the remainder. (ii) Consistent results were obtained by the use of eleven different samples prepared by three distinct methods. (iii) Satisfactory agreement was obtained between experimental points obtained by the decalcification of lime-rich samples, such as C7, and points obtained by addition of lime to silica gel or lime-poor materials such as C3. (iv) In many cases pairs of points very near together in Fig. 1 represent the results of experiments which differed only in the period of shaking.

Fig. 1.

Equilibria between hydrous calcium silicates and solution.

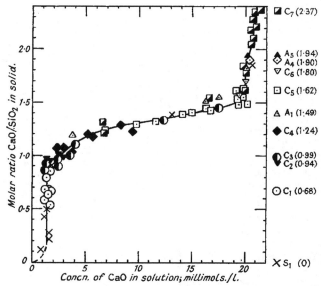

On right of figure : *key to samples used, showing initial values of* CaO/SiO₂.

Fig. 2.

Silica concentrations in solution.

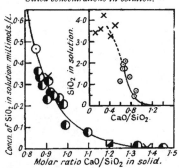

The symbols have the same significance as in Fig. 1. Inset : extension of figure on reduced scale.

Time needed to reach equilibrium. This was found to vary between a few days and several months, according to the nature of the initial material and the change in concentration of the solution which was involved. Small adjustments in the composition of the solid took place rapidly but large changes were often very slow. Different preparations varied markedly in this respect, the silica gel sample (S1) taking up 1·38 mols. of lime in 26 days, whereas with the hydrated calcium silicate preparation C3, continuous shaking for 68 and 80 days respectively was needed to obtain the points having CaO/SiO₂ values of 1·45 and 1·33.

Results of Phase-equilibrium Experiments.—It is probable from the above considerations that, in the case of solid phases having CaO/SiO$_2$ below about 1·5, the curve drawn in Fig. 1 approximates closely to equilibrium conditions. In the case of solids having CaO/SiO$_2$ greater than 1·5 it appears likely, for reasons discussed later, that only those points obtained by the use of samples A4 and A5, prepared from tricalcium silicate, represent true equilibrium. The true equilibrium curve cannot however differ greatly in this region from that shown in Fig. 1 since the concentration of lime in solution cannot exceed the solubility of calcium hydroxide. Owing mainly to the influence of particle size it is difficult to decide upon the value for this quantity which is most appropriate to the present case. Bassett (*J.*, 1934, 1270) obtained the value 0·0213M. for coarse particles at 18°, rising to 0·0236M. for very fine particles. The former value alone refers to a thermodynamically stable and reproducible condition, and is possibly to be preferred.

X-Ray Investigation.—Powder photographs were taken of all the samples listed in Table I and of 24 solids recovered from the phase-equilibrium experiments. In the latter, the moist solids were placed in cells having walls of mica : this prevented attack by atmospheric carbon dioxide or deposition of calcium hydroxide by evaporation of the solution, and avoided the danger of altering the composition of the solid by complete removal of the solution.

Preparations from tricalcium silicate, CaO/SiO$_2$ *below* 1·65. The X-ray pattern of sample A2 is given in Table II. Patterns identical with this were given by samples A1 and A3 with additional very weak lines, attributed to calcium carbonate, at 1·92 and 1·86 A. in the case of sample A1. The lines were broader than those given by normally crystalline substances under comparable experimental conditions and, as compared with zinc oxide, exposures of about ten times as long were needed to produce photographs of comparable intensity. The spacings were, however, sharp enough to allow measurement without difficulty to the degree of accuracy given in the table.

TABLE II.

Sample A2, obs.		Sample B1, obs.		Calculated.	
Spacing, A.	Intensity.*	Spacing, A.	Intensity.*	Spacing, A.	Indices.
10·0	s	11·5	s, d	—	—
5·3	vvw	5·3	w	—	—
3·03	vs	3·03	vs	3·02	110
2·80	ms	2·80	m	2·80	200
2·40	w	2·4	vw, d		
2·14	vw }	2·1	w, d	—	—
2·04	w }				
1·81	ms	1·80	ms	1·80	020
1·66	mw	1·66	mw	1·66	310
1·52	vw	1·52	vw	1·51	220
1·40	w	1·40	w	1·40	400
1·23	vvw	1·23	vvw	—	—
1·18	vvw	1·17	vvw	1·175	130
1·11	vw	1·11	vw	1·105	420
1·075	vvw	1·070	vvw	1·070	510

* vs = very strong ; s = strong ; ms = moderately strong ; m = moderate ; mw = moderately weak ; w = weak ; vw = very weak ; d = diffuse.

Some early preparations made from tricalcium silicate contained traces of unchanged starting material. This could easily be recognised in the X-ray photographs not only by the positions of its stronger lines but also by the fact that, on account of the greater size of the crystalline particles, these lines had a much rougher appearance than the remainder.

Preparations made from silica gel or by double decomposition. The X-ray pattern of a sample (B1), made from silica gel, is also given in Table II. It was almost identical with that of sample A2, but several of the lines were more diffuse than the remainder, and the longest observed spacing was increased from 10·0 to 11·5 A. Patterns very similar to this were given by the samples prepared by double decomposition, and by solids recovered from phase-equilibrium experiments in which these had been used, provided that the lime : silica ratio of the sample when subjected to X-ray analysis lay between about 0·5 and 1·65. Slight variations were observed in the patterns of these samples. The longest spacing appeared to vary between about 11·0 and 12·5 A., and the 5·3 A. spacing varied in intensity from very, very weak to moderate. The reasons for these variations were not discovered ; they did not appear to be related to differences in lime : silica ratio. In a very few cases of samples isolated from phase-equilibrium experiments additional very weak lines were observed. One sample having

$CaO/SiO_2 = 1·05$ showed lines at $8·25$ and at $3·55$ A., and two others having $CaO/SiO_2 = 0·99$ and $1·17$ showed one at $3·69$ A. The rare occurrence of these lines suggests the possibility that they may have been due to some unidentified impurity.

Silica-rich solids. When the lime/silica ratio fell below $0·4$—$0·5$, the X-ray patterns became indistinct. Samples having $CaO/SiO_2 = 0·27$ and $0·21$ showed only the strongest spacing of $3·03$ A., together with a weak diffuse band of about the same or rather greater spacing, while one having $CaO/SiO_2 = 0·11$ showed only the band.

Lime-rich solids. Samples A4 and A5, prepared from tricalcium silicate, had $CaO/SiO_2 = 1·90$ and $1·94$, respectively, and gave identical X-ray patterns (Table III) which differed slightly from those of the samples of lower lime : silica ratio. The most easily recognisable differences were the increased intensity of the $2·80$ A. line relative to that of $3·05$ A. and the presence of a relatively strong line of $1·55$ A. in place of that of $1·66$ A.

TABLE III.

Spacing, A.	Intensity.	Spacing, A.	Intensity.	Spacing, A.	Intensity.
10·0	s	2·00	m	1·225	vw
3·05	s	1·80	ms	1·165	vw
2·80	s	1·71	vvw	1·1	vvw/d
2·40	w	1·61	vvw	1·045	vvw
2·20	vw	1·55	w	1·025	vvw
2·10	vw	1·39	vw	1·000	vvw

Attempts to prepare a product identical with these by other methods were not successful. Samples C6 and C7, obtained by double decomposition and having $CaO/SiO_2 = 1·80$ and $2·37$, respectively, gave X-ray photographs showing the spacings observed for lower lime : silica ratios together with those of calcium hydroxide. A similar result was obtained when sample C5 ($CaO/SiO_2 = 1·62$) was treated with saturated calcium hydroxide. The periods of shaking before filtration lay between 7 and 14 days in these experiments; it is possible that more prolonged treatment would have yielded different results.

DISCUSSION.

Reproducibility of Phase Data.—The results given in Fig. 1 show that, although reproducibility is probably not of the order to be expected in the case of fully crystalline substances, it is sufficiently good to suggest that a close approximation to true equilibrium can be attained. This view was held by Bessey (*loc. cit.*) and by Roller and Ervin (*loc. cit.*) and is in accordance with the considerable degree of crystalline character shown by the powder photographs. It is therefore probable that the wider discrepancies, at least, among the earlier data, are due, not to the differing particle sizes or other colloidal properties, but to experimental errors. Of the 15 investigations discussed by Steinour (*loc. cit.*), four, those of Jolibois and Chassevent (*Compt. rend.*, 1929, **188**, 452), Beitlich (*loc. cit.*), Tavasci (*Ann. Chim. appl.*, 1938, **23**, 413), and Nacken and Mosebach (*Z. anorg. Chem.*, 1935, **223**, 161) gave results in particularly bad agreement with each other and with all the remainder. In the last two investigations the data were obtained from experiments in which tricalcium silicate was shaken with water, and Steinour (*loc. cit.*) has suggested that equilibrium may not have been obtained. This view receives support from the difficulties encountered in the present investigation both of ensuring complete decomposition of this compound and of demonstrating its absence in the product except by X-ray photographs, which were not used by the above workers. Beitlich used a silica gel containing 20% of water; experiments in the present investigation showed a silica gel as dry as this to react extremely slowly, and it seems probable, as Roller and Ervin (*loc. cit.*) have suggested, that here also equilibrium was not obtained. The reason for the anomalous results of Chassevent is not clear.

X-Ray Data.—(i) *Lime/silica ratios* $1·0$—$1·5$. Comparison of the spacings given in Table II with those of calcium carbonate, calcium hydroxide, and silica (Hanawalt, Rinn, and Frevel, *Ind. Eng. Chem. Anal.*, 1938, **10**, 457; A.S.T.M. index) shows that they cannot be accounted for by the presence of any or all of these substances. The strongest spacing observed is almost identical with that of calcium carbonate, but the strong calcium carbonate doublet $1·92$ and $1·86$ A. was only seen in a sample (A1) which contained 7·5% of calcium carbonate and was then so much weaker than the $3·05$ A. spacing that the latter could not possibly have been due in more than a small degree to carbonate. The spacings are therefore those of a hydrated silicate, calcium silicate hydrate (I). The number and definition of the spacings shows that this phase has a considerable degree of crystalline character. The phase-equilibrium data (Fig. 1) indicate a maximum lime : silica molar ratio of about 1·5 and a minimum value which is less rather than greater than 1·0.

Comparison of the X-ray data of calcium silicate hydrate (I) with those of previous investigators shows good agreement with the results of Brandenberger (*loc. cit.*) and especially of Stratling (*loc. cit.*), although a greater number of spacings has been recorded than by either of these investigators. On the other hand, Chassevent's data (*loc. cit.*) appear to be compatible with a mixture of calcium silicate hydrate (I) and calcium carbonate. Cirilli's data (*loc. cit.*) and especially those of Brocard (*loc. cit.*) are in less satisfactory agreement with the remainder and it has not been found possible to account for this. Unpublished data by Bessey (private communication) agree closely with the results of the present investigation. The longest spacing of 10—12·5 A. has not previously been reported and, as will be shown, it is probable that its occurrence and characteristics afford an important clue to the structure of the compound.

The preparation studied by McMurdie and Flint (*loc. cit.*) was made by the prolonged (10-year) action of water on β-dicalcium silicate and had the composition $3CaO,2SiO_2,1·5H_2O$. The dissimilarity of its X-ray pattern to those of samples made and examined in much shorter periods of time may possibly indicate a very slow ageing process. Flint, McMurdie, and Wells (*J. Res. Nat. Bur. Stand.*, 1938, **21**, 617), who described the preparation of this sample, also carried out a similar experiment using tricalcium silicate as starting material and state that X-ray photographs showed the product to be crystalline, but do not quote any data.

The independence of the powder diagram of calcium silicate hydrate (I) with regard to lime : silica ratio indicates that lime in excess of about 1·0 mol. is held in some manner sufficiently random not to influence the diffraction pattern. Certain workers, notably Bessey (*loc. cit.*) and Cirilli (*Ric. sci.*, 1939, **10**, 459), have considered that solid solution occurs between $CaO,SiO_2,aq.$ and $3CaO,2SiO_2,aq.$ If this is so, the solution must be of such a kind, as was envisaged by Lafuma (*Rev. mat. Const. Trav. pub.*, 1931, **1**, 45), as would not affect the X-ray spacings or intensities. The data are, however, equally consistent with the possibly not widely differing view that the excess lime is held by adsorption.

The differences between the powder patterns of the products obtained from tricalcium silicate and the remainder are of a kind which indicates differing degrees of crystallisation rather than distinct compounds. This, together with the phase-equilibrium results, supports Bessey's view (*loc. cit.*) that the same compound is obtained by the three different methods of preparation. The most nearly crystalline product is obtained by the decomposition of tricalcium silicate ; this may be because formation of the hydrate occurs more slowly than in the other methods, or because the mechanism of the reaction is of a different character.

A fourth method of preparation, which may be possible at room temperatures but has so far been effected only under hydrothermal conditions, consists in the hydrolysis of sodium calcium silicates. Thilo (250th Anniv. Lecture, German Acad. Sci., Berlin, 1950) obtained a product of composition CaH_2SiO_4 by treatment of $CaNa_2SiO_4$ with water at 180°. X-Ray examination, by the author, of a sample kindly supplied by Professor Thilo gave a powder photograph identical with that of sample B1 of calcium silicate hydrate (I).

Solids of low lime/silica ratio. The existence of additional compounds, poorer in lime than calcium silicate hydrate (I), has been assumed by several investigators, formulæ $CaO,2SiO_2,aq.$, $3CaO,4SiO_2,aq.$, and $4CaO,5SiO_2,aq.$ having been suggested (Steinour, *loc. cit.*). The X-ray data obtained in the present investigation do not provide any positive support for this view since a sample having CaO/SiO_2 as low as 0·41 showed all the spacing of calcium silicate hydrate (I) down to 1·66 A. and no others. It is possible that a compound poorer in lime may exist which is so similar to calcium silicate hydrate (I) as to have been indistinguishable from it by this means, but the simplest explanation of the observed data is that products having CaO/SiO_2 below about 1·0 consist of calcium silicate hydrate (I) mixed with gelatinous silica. Roller and Ervin (*loc. cit.*) based their evidence for the existence of $3CaO,4SiO_2,aq.$ mainly on the presence of a break in their phase-equilibrium curve; this could not be confirmed in the present investigation, although the results do not entirely exclude the possibility of its existence. Flint and Wells (*loc. cit.*) based their conclusions on a study of the liquid phase in which they assumed all the silica to be present in the form of simple ions. It seems equally probable, however, that the variation in silica concentration (Fig. 2) corresponding to a constant calcium hydroxide concentration of about 0·0014M. is due, as Baylis (*J. Physical Chem.*, 1928, **32**, 1236) and Krasil'nikov and Kiselev (*J. Physical Chem. U.S.S.R.*, 1944, **18**, 527) have supposed, to the presence of varying amounts of silica in colloidal form. If this interpretation is correct, the concentration of silica in true solution at the invariant point is most probably that found in equilibrium with a solid having CaO/SiO_2 approaching unity, *i.e.*, in the order of 0·00025M.

Solids of high lime : silica ratio.   The X-ray powder data given in Table III for the products obtained from tricalcium silicate and having $CaO/SiO_2 \approx 2$ strongly resemble those found for lower lime : silica ratios and, like the latter, do not contain any spacings which can be due wholly to calcium carbonate or hydroxide.   In order to ascertain the minimum amount of calcium hydroxide detectable in admixture with the hydrated silicate, mixtures of calcium silicate hydrate (I) with calcium hydroxide were prepared in the dry state. X-Ray powder photographs of these preparations showed that the strongest spacing of calcium hydroxide could just be distinguished when $0\cdot 1$ mol. of $Ca(OH)_2$ per mol. of SiO_2 was present, while a very strong calcium hydroxide pattern was observed if $0\cdot 3$ or more mols. were present.   The data given in Table III therefore indicate the existence of a compound, calcium silicate hydrate (II), which has a composition approximating to $2CaO,SiO_2,aq.$, and a structure probably very similar to, although distinct from, that of calcium silicate hydrate (I).   The existence of such a compound was first suggested by Bessey (*loc. cit.*) on the basis of the observation, confirmed in the present investigation, that the phase-equilibrium curve (Fig. 1) rises sharply from $CaO/SiO_2 = 1\cdot 5$ to $2\cdot 0$ at a concentration appreciably below the solubility of calcium hydroxide. The present results show, however, that even when calcium silicate hydrate (II) has not been formed and free calcium hydroxide is present, the concentration of the latter may be depressed. The reason for this is not clear; since the materials used had been prepared by double decomposition it may have been due to the presence of traces of alkali in the solution.

The failure of several attempts by the present author to prepare calcium silicate hydrate (II) may account for Cirilli's observation (*Ric. sci.*, 1939, **10**, 1042) that a preparation having $CaO/SiO_2 = 1\cdot 67$ showed in its X-ray pattern a considerable proportion of calcium hydroxide. On the other hand, Forsen (*loc. cit.*), in general agreement with the present results, quoted powder data for a solid of composition $2CaO,SiO_2,4H_2O$, prepared from tricalcium silicate, which do not appear to show the presence of any calcium hydroxide but which could be interpreted as indicating either calcium silicate hydrate (I) or (II), mixed probably with some calcium carbonate.

Since the aqueous treatment used to produce the calcium silicate hydrate (II) samples in the present investigation was prolonged (5 months in the case of A5), it appears probable that this phase exists in equilibrium with calcium hydroxide solutions more concentrated than about $0\cdot 020$M. and that the mixtures of calcium silicate hydrate (I) with excess of calcium hydroxide represent an unstable though somewhat persistent condition.   It is, however, also possible that calcium silicate hydrate (II) is a metastable product peculiar to the decomposition of tricalcium silicate.

It has not yet been established whether any formation of solid solutions with phase (I) or other variation in composition of calcium silicate hydrate (II) is possible.   There is, however, some evidence that its maximum value of CaO/SiO_2 cannot greatly exceed $2\cdot 0$ and that it certainly lies well below $3\cdot 0$.   Numerous optical investigations, quoted by Steinour (*loc. cit.*) have shown that, whereas β-dicalcium silicate hydrates in a limited amount of water with the formation of barely enough calcium hydroxide to saturate the solution, yet tricalcium silicate yields under these conditions a hydrated silicate together with a considerable quantity of solid calcium hydroxide.   Attempts to determine the latter quantitatively have proved difficult, but values between $0\cdot 6$ and $1\cdot 0$ mol. of hydroxide per mol. of tricalcium silicate have usually been obtained (Steinour, *loc. cit.*).   This suggests that the maximum lime : silica ratio of the hydrated product lies between $2\cdot 0$ and $2\cdot 4$.

The behaviour of β-dicalcium silicate in the above experiments strongly supports the view that a hydrated dicalcium silicate can be formed at room temperature.   It cannot easily be accounted for if, as has sometimes been supposed, the hydrated compound does not have a lime : silica molar ratio exceeding $1\cdot 5$.

A Tentative Interpretation of the X-*Ray Data of Calcium Silicate Hydrate* (I).—Although the present data do not permit of any complete interpretation, certain facts appear significant. The spacings given in Table I can be divided into those which are in all cases relatively sharp, and of consistent spacing and intensity, and those which vary in one or more of these respects. All those of the first category can be accounted for on the assumption that they are the $hk0$ spacings of a c-face centred unit cell having a and b axes of $5\cdot 60$ and $3\cdot 60$ A., respectively, the angle between these axes being $90°$; moreover, all the $hk0$ spacings possible for such a cell, *i.e.*, those for which $(h + k)$ is even, are actually observed down to the shortest ones visible. Although the agreement may be fortuitous, it is sufficiently striking to suggest that the true unit cell spacings at least bear some simple relation to those postulated.

The facts that the remaining spacings are few in number, and sometimes more diffuse than the above, and that the longest observed spacing in particular can vary independently of the remainder, are reminiscent of the behaviour of the clay minerals (Hofmann, Endell, and Wilm, *Z. Krist.*, 1933, **86**, 340; Nagelschmidt, *ibid.*, 1936, **93**, 481), and could possibly admit of a somewhat similar explanation. It seems possible that calcium silicate hydrate (I) has a layer structure in which the individual layers, in the plane of the a and b axes, are relatively well crystallised, while the distances between them represented by the 10—12·5 A. spacing are less rigidly defined. Such a structure might also account for the ability of the lattice to accommodate varying amounts of lime without fundamental change. The postulated a and b axes, however, differ from those found in the clay minerals, and it is probable that on account of its greater ionic radius, calcium is unable to replace the magnesium or aluminium of the latter, without bringing about a considerable change in the structure of the silicate layer. Comparison of the postulated spacings with the unit cell of calcium hydroxide (hexagonal; $a = 3\cdot584$, $c = 4\cdot896$ A.; Bunn, Clark, and Clifford, *Proc. Roy. Soc.*, 1935, A, **151**, 141) suggests that distorted calcium hydroxide layers may be present in calcium silicate hydrate (I). The data are, however, inadequate for a definite conclusion.

Further investigations on the rôle of the water in calcium silicate hydrates, and on the influence of temperature on the phase equilibria, are in progress.

Experimental.

Considerable care must always be taken in the preparation and subsequent handling of hydrated calcium silicates to minimise contamination by atmospheric carbon dioxide. This can be achieved by suitable design of apparatus. The use of glass vessels has been found undesirable whenever prolonged treatment with aqueous solutions is required (Bessey, *loc. cit.*; Thorvaldson, *loc. cit.*, p. 218), and metal or other inert vessels are to be preferred.

Preparative Methods.—(i) *Decomposition of anhydrous tricalcium silicate.* 2—5-G. portions of tricalcium silicate (90% passed through a 170-mesh sieve) were shaken at 17° for 3—5 weeks with 250 ml. of carbon dioxide-free water in stainless-steel vessels of 350-ml. capacity, having caps lined with polyvinyl chloride. By use of a rubber bung fitted with a pipette and a soda-lime tube, 100 ml. of the solution were then removed and filtered, and portions titrated with acid. 100 Ml. of carbon dioxide-free water were added to replace the solution removed, and shaking was resumed. This procedure was repeated at 3—14-day intervals until the total amount of lime removed or in solution indicated that the lime : silica ratio of the solid had fallen to the desired value. A total period of shaking of at least 6 weeks was found necessary to effect complete decomposition of the tricalcium silicate as shown by subsequent *X*-ray analysis and behaviour in phase-equilibrium experiments. The solid was then filtered off by means of a Buchner funnel suitably fitted with a cover and inlet tube reaching into the reaction vessel to prevent atmospheric contamination, and washed with 50% acetone followed by pure acetone, ether, and finally carbon dioxide-free air until all the ether had been removed. The final concentration of calcium hydroxide in the solution was determined.

(ii) *Reaction of calcium hydroxide solution with silica gel.* The silica gel (S1) was supplied by The British Drug Houses Ltd., and had the following composition : SiO_2, 23·69; ignition loss, 75·80; Na_2O, 0·27; K_2O, 0·07; CaO + MgO, nil; Fe_2O_3, 0·01; Al_2O_3, 0·14; TiO_2, 0·015%. The same apparatus as above being used, 1·21 g. were shaken with 250 ml. of calcium hydroxide solution of initial concentration 1·245 g./l. (of CaO) for 45 days. The product was isolated as above.

(iii) *Double decomposition of calcium nitrate with sodium silicate.* Klasse and Kuhl (*Zement*, 1928, **17**, 2, 49) and Bessey (*loc. cit.*) showed that, provided sufficient calcium nitrate was added, the lime : silica ratio of the precipitate was dependent on the ratio of Na_2O to SiO_2 in the sodium silicate solution. 0·05—0·1 Mol. of the above silica gel was therefore dissolved in amounts of N- or 2N-sodium hydroxide indicated by Klasse and Kuhl's data and treated with 0·2—0·4 mol. of calcium nitrate. The lime : silica ratios of the products were usually in approximate agreement with those obtained by Klasse and Kuhl although anomalous results were sometimes obtained for reasons which have not been fully investigated.

The apparatus consisted of a 1-l. bolt-head flask fitted with tap-funnel, mercury-seal stirrer, inlet tube for carbon dioxide-free air and outlet tube reaching to the bottom of the flask which led to a Buchner funnel fitted with an air-tight cover. The silica gel (S1) was first placed in the flask and carbon dioxide-free air drawn through the apparatus for 30 minutes. Suction was discontinued, and the sodium hydroxide added from the tap-funnel, followed by a little carbon dioxide-free water to wash the latter. The silica gel was dissolved by stirring, aided if necessary by gentle warming. The flask was then cooled to room temperature, and the calcium nitrate, dissolved in 200 ml. of carbon dioxide-free water, was added. Stirring was continued for one hour, and the solid was then filtered off by reapplying suction to the Buchner flask. The precipitate was washed on the filter with 4—5 l. of calcium hydroxide solution which had itself been filtered directly into the tap-funnel to remove any carbonate present ; this quantity was found sufficient to remove nitrate and all but a trace of sodium ions. The concentration of the washing solution varied from 0·1 g./l. (of CaO) in the case of precipitates of low lime : silica ratio to 1·10 g./l. when the predicted molar ratio was 1·5 or above. Washing was completed with 50% acetone, pure acetone, and carbon dioxide-free air, and the product was removed from the funnel and a portion analysed. The remainder was shaken for 7—14 days with calcium hydroxide solution of a concentration with which Bessey's data (*loc. cit.*) showed it to be in equilibrium, the same apparatus and method of isolation being used as for methods (i) and (ii). This treatment was carried out because the precipitate had been formed in a solution containing excess of calcium nitrate and sodium hydroxide. In view of the sensitivity of the composition of the solid to that of the solution it seemed advisable to bring it approximately into equilibrium with a pure calcium hydroxide solution before it was used in subsequent experiments.

Carbon dioxide was determined in the above preparations by Jones's method (*J. Soc. Chem. Ind.*, 1940, **51**, 29).

Investigation of Phase Equilibria.—100—300-Mg. portions of the initial solids were shaken continuously with 25 ml. of water or calcium hydroxide solutions in vessels of 40-ml. capacity at 17—20°. Some of the vessels were of brass, plated internally with silver, and others of polystyrene, the caps being lined in each case with polyvinyl chloride. No variations in the results could be traced to changes in the type of vessel or in temperature within the limits stated. After shaking, the solid was filtered off by using an apparatus designed to suck the liquid out of the vessel through a No. 4 sintered-glass filter into a receiving vessel, an inlet tube for carbon dioxide-free air being provided. Lime in the filtrate was determined by titration of 10-ml. portions with 0·1N-hydrochloric acid, a methyl-red–methylene-blue indicator being used. Silica, where significant, was determined colorimetrically as ammonium silicomolybdate on 1—10-ml. portions by means of a Hilger " Spekker " photoelectric colorimeter which was calibrated by using sodium silicate solutions of known concentration.

X-Ray Apparatus.—Copper-$K\alpha$ radiation was obtained, either sealed high vacuum or gas X-ray tubes being used with a nickel filter in contact with the film. Some photographs were taken by means of a 9-cm. powder camera, but the backgrounds were heavy in relation to the more diffuse lines, and much better results were obtained with 6-cm. cameras designed for single-crystal work, the specimen being mounted either on a glass fibre or in a mica cell. This had walls 0·0005 in. thick and 0·01 in. apart. It gave particularly clear backgrounds in the 3—10 A. region since no amorphous matter was present, and the characteristic spots and Laue streaks due to the mica could easily be distinguished, but was unsuitable for the investigation of spacings (using copper radiation) shorter than about 1·6 A. In all cases, exposures of 24—48 hours were necessary to bring out the weaker lines.

Spacings were usually determined by direct measurement on the film, and intensities estimated visually. In a few cases this was supplemented by using a Hilger non-recording microphotometer.

I am much indebted to Professor J. D. Bernal, F.R.S., Dr. J. W. Jeffery, and Mr. R. W. Nurse (of the Building Research Station, Watford, Herts.), for their interest, encouragement, and advice. Part of the experimental work was carried out at the Building Research Station, and I am indebted to the Director of Building Research for making this possible. My thanks are also due to Miss A. Goddard and Mr. F. M. MacConnell, of the Building Research Station, for assistance with experimental work and for analyses respectively. The work was carried out as part of an extra-mural contract for the Building Research Board and my thanks are due to the Director of Building Research for permission to publish this paper.

BIRKBECK COLLEGE RESEARCH LABORATORY,
21 TORRINGTON SQUARE, LONDON, W.C.1.   [*Received, August 11th,* 1950.]

A TRIBUTE TO
"Proportioning Concrete Mixtures"
by D.A. Abrams

Foreword by V.M. Malhotra

In 1980, the writer [1] had made the following concluding statement in a paper entitled, "Superplasticizers: Their Effect on Fresh and Hardened Concrete":

> There have been very few major developments in concrete technology in recent years. The concept of air entrainment in the 1940s was one—it revolutionized concrete technology in North America. It is believed that development of superplasticizers is another major breakthrough which will have a very significant effect on the production and use of concrete for years to come.

When the above statement was made, it was in reference to new products for the enhancement of concrete properties with regard to its durability and placement in a fundamental way. Duff A. Abrams' [2] landmark report, published in the 1920s and entitled, "Proportioning of Concrete Mixtures," was more than a breakthrough. Based on voluminous empirical data, it established the very basis of modern concrete technology. From the terminology used in the title of the paper, Proportioning of Concrete Mixtures, to the major principle of w/c-strength relationship enunciated in the paper, have stood the test of time.

Most of the books and technical papers, when citing Abrams' classic paper, refer generally to the w/c-strength relationship, that is: "The strength of concrete mixture (note the use of the word mixture not mix) depends on the quality of the mixing water in the batch, expressed as a ratio to the volume of cement, so long as the concrete is workable, and the aggregates are clean and structurally sound." Granted, the above principle is the cornerstone of modern concrete technology, however, one should not ignore a number of other important issues addressed in Abrams' paper. These will be discussed later.

From the 1920s to the 1960s, there were no significant challenges to the Abrams' so-called law of w/c-strength relationship. In 1961, Gilkey, [3] in another outstanding and well researched paper, brought to attention some of the limitations of the w/c-strength relationship. Based on his research dealing with the aggregates of different types and varying in size from pure fines to coarse aggregate with a maximum size of

1.5 in. (38 mm), he proposed that the Abrams' w/c-strength relationship needs to be modified as follows:

"For a given cement and acceptable aggregates, the strength that may be developed by a workable, properly placed mixture of cement, aggregate and water (under the same mixing, curing, and testing conditions) is influenced by the:

   (a) ratio of cement to mixing water
   (b) ratio of cement to aggregates
   (c) grading, surface texture, shape, strength and stiffness of aggregate particles
   (d) maximum size of aggregates"

Gilkey's suggested modifications were, indeed, applauded by the concrete research community, and were a significant contribution to the advancement of concrete technology. However, in the writer's opinion, Gilkey was unnecessarily harsh in his criticism of the limitations of Abrams' w/c-strength relationship pronouncement. Gilkey's suggested modifications only become significant when one departs significantly from the use of usual ¾ in. (19 mm) maximum size aggregate, or when one is dealing with mortars. Neville [a] correctly points out, and this writer agrees, that the factors (b) to (d) suggested by Gilkey are of lesser importance than factor (a). It is important to point out that concrete dams comprising concrete with the size of aggregates of more than 1½ in. (40 mm) are being phased out because of excessive wear and tear on the concrete mixers. The advent of ready mixed concrete and the use of large capacity pumps for transporting concrete, limits the use of maximum size aggregate to ¾ in. (19 mm) worldwide, even though this is not the best option from an environmental point of view. Thus, the factor (d) mentioned above has lost some of its relevance in recent years, and is of significance only for concrete for airport and highway pavements. Furthermore, most of the high-performance/high-strength concrete in use today incorporates 3/4 or 3/8 in. (19 or 10 mm) maximum size aggregate.

Approximately 70 years after Abrams' w/c-strength pronouncement and approximately 30 years after Gilkey's suggested modifications, ACI published a paper in *Concrete International*. The paper by Barton [5] was titled, "Water-Cement Ratio is Passé." The title is misleading because Barton did not question the w/c principle, but stated "...the traditional w/c values as given in ACI 318 were no longer applicable because of the availability and use of superplasticizers, retarders, fly ash and silica fume." A later discussion of the paper further stated that "water-cement ratio is not passé, It is more vitally important than ever."

In modern-day parlance, Abrams' classical paper, which an average concrete engineer can follow, can be summarized in just a few words: It is w/c or w/cm, stupid.

Let us now consider some of the other issues discussed by Abrams in his report. Abrams does not advocate the use of specific fixed grading for concrete, and rightly so. He writes in his paper, "...the problem is to put together the aggregates available in order to have the best concrete mixture we can for a given cost or at a minimum cost."

It is amazing that we still have a large number of agencies and jurisdictions that have not caught up, and still approve specifications that demand the use of a "fixed grading" even though it may involve transporting aggregates from a long distance.

How environmentally unfriendly!

A number of recent reports published by FWHA, NIST, and NSF have indicated that fixing our deteriorating infrastructure would require billions of dollars. Part of the deterioration is due to the fact that structures were designed to meet strength criteria, regardless of other considerations such as exposure to sulphates and chlorides or moisture and temperature fluctuations. So, now it has become fashionable to ask for "design for durability not for strength alone." Why has it taken us so long to realize this? Abrams had warned us about this 90 years ago. This is what he wrote in his paper: "A structure which is exposed to wide ranges of temperature, wide variations in moisture and probably exposed to the destructive agencies must have considerable degree of resistance if it is to give a good account ... That is entirely aside from the matter of strength."

Until recently, it has been the mantra of the construction industry that increasing the quantity of cement in concrete will take care of all the ills associated with poor quality concrete. Paradoxically, increasing the cement content without reducing the w/c only makes a bad situation worse in terms of shrinkage cracking and heat of hydration. Once again, Abrams had the answer. Here is a quote from his paper. "However if adding cement is not accompanied by a reduction in water-ratio, it does not serve any useful purpose." Why is that these gems of advice never filtered to contractors and the construction industry? Perhaps we all share the blame for not getting these messages across to the concrete industry.

The comprehensive nature of Abrams' paper is mind boggling. The conclusions drawn in his paper are based on 100,000 tests performed over a period of 8 years, and indicate the broad areas addressed in the paper. It is unfortunate that, these days, literature is full of so-called research papers that are based on limited data. Researchers and authors will do well to read Abrams' paper.

At the time of publication of the paper by Abrams, the role of statistical concepts in developing specifications was not known. Notwithstanding the above, Abrams does elude to this where he mentions that only those test results that habitually fall out of line need to be rejected. For example, he states that if the specifications call for 6 in. (150 mm) slump concrete, then test results showing 7 in. (178 mm) slump need not cause alarm. However, if test results consistently show 12 in. (305 mm) slump, then action needs to be taken. Modern statisticall-based specifications imply much the same thing, basing these acceptance/rejection criteria on mathematical considerations.

To some of the readers, it may come as a surprise to know that Abrams my have been an environmental visionary. Abrams never used the word environment in his paper because environment was not an issue in the 1920s, but his observations and conclusions implicitly point to conservation of energy and resources. He emphatically discourages the use of unnecessarily high cement contents,[1] advocates the use of control of water, and obliquely mentions that where there is potential for attack by aggressive elements (read sulfates), the mixture proportions for

---

1 * The manufacture of one ton of portland cement clinker produces approximately one ton of CO_2 – a green house gas.

compressive strength development alone are not adequate and that the mixture should be proportioned for durability consideration. This means long service life and less need for repairs, thus resulting in conservation of energy and resources.

Considering that Abrams' outstanding paper was published in the early 1920s, it is amazing that the concepts and principles he elucidated then are equally applicable today. His emphasis on strict control of water content of concrete, and hence on w/c, his emphasis on the unwise use of large quantities of cement, and observation that long-term performance of concrete exposed to various aggressive elements is not solely dependent on compressive strength are words of wisdom that all concrete engineers will do well to remember. This paper, along with Gilkey's paper, must be a required reading for all students specializing in concrete technology.

References

1.   Malhotra, V.M., "Superplasticizers: Their Effects on Fresh and Hardened Concrete", *Concrete International*, Vol. 3, No. 5, May 1981, pp. 66 – 81.

2.   Abrams, Duff A., "Proportioning of Concrete Mixtures", Bulletin No. 1, Structural Materials Research Laboratory, Lewis Institute, Chicago, December 1918.

3.   Gilkey, Herbert J., "Water-Cement Ratio Versus Strength – Another Look", ACI JOURNAL, *Proceedings*, V. 57. No. 4, April 1961, discussion of the paper, ACI JOURNAL *Proceedings* Vol. 57, Sept. 1961.

4.   Neville, A.M., *Properties of Concrete*, Fourth Edition, 1995, pp. 269 – 272.

5.   Barton, Robert B., "Water-Cement Ratio is Passé", *Concrete International*, Vol. 11, No. 11, November 1989, pp. 75 – 78, discussion by Bryant Mather and others, p. 78.

V.M. Malhotra, *Scientist Emeritus, CANMET, Natural Resources Canada, Ottawa, Ontario, Canada.*

PROPORTIONING CONCRETE MIXTURES.

BY DUFF A. ABRAMS.*

A discussion preceding a demonstration of actual field proportioning of concrete by Stanton Walker. Mr. Walker has prepared a resumé of the methods used which appears on p. 182 of this volume.

Many different methods have been used and several theories have been advanced as a basis for proportioning concrete. I need only refer to a few of these to refresh your memory. We have the present custom (almost universal, I regret to say) of proportioning concrete by arbitrary quantities; that is, we use, say a 1 : 2 : 4 mix regardless of the particular type of materials available and regardless of the quantity of mixing water used and take little or no account of the strength of concrete produced. Needless to say, this method is extremely crude, and does not recommend itself to thoughtful engineers.

The maximum-density-of-aggregate method has been advocated and used to some extent. Here the endeavor was to grade aggregates in such a way as to give an aggregate mixture of maximum density, and then supply the quantity of cement that was considered necessary to produce the concrete desired for a particular purpose.

Another method which has been used in the proportioning of concrete is based on the voids in the aggregates. The voids in the coarse aggregates were determined, a sufficient quantity of sand was supplied to fill those voids, then a sufficient quantity of cement was used to fill the voids in the combined aggregates. This is a little more rational than the purely arbitrary method. It is not, however, on a scientific basis. It will, in general, give fairly good concrete, but it has been shown by our investigations and the tests of others, that the voids in the aggregate is not the determining factor in concrete mixtures.

EXPERIMENTAL STUDIES OF CONCRETE.

A great deal of experimental work has been done in endeavoring to arrive at a proper basis for proportioning concrete. Much of the early work of R. Feret,† a French engineer, was devoted to a study of this problem. Feret confined his studies almost entirely to sand mortars, so that it is not easy to apply his methods directly to a concrete mixture.

Allen Hazen** did some very interesting work in his studies of the use of sands in water filtration. He made use of the "effective size" and "uniformity coefficient" of sands. These have undoubtedly served a useful purpose in that connection, but many engineers have endeavored to apply

---

*Professor in Charge, Structural Materials Research Laboratory, Lewis Institute, Chicago.
†Ann. Ponts et Chaussees ; also Etude Experimentale du Ciment Arme, 1906.
**24th Annual Report Mass. State Board of Health ; reprinted in "State Sanitation" ; Harvard Univ. Press, v. 2, p. 232, 1917.

the same factors to concrete aggregates with no obvious reason why they should be applicable. It is apparent that these functions cannot serve any useful purpose so far as concrete aggregate is concerned, since they are based on separations made by one or two sieve sizes and consequently are quite inadequate to show the value for concrete of aggregate which covers a wide range in size. A good idea may be gained of the ·wide range in sizes in concrete aggregate when we consider that the diameter of a 3-in. pebble is over 500 times that of a particle of sand which passes the 100-mesh sieve.

The work of Fuller and Thompson[*] is a source of valuable information. However, our experiments have shown that the grading given by Mr. Fuller in his "maximum-density curve" is too coarse for the ordinary mixtures; in other words, for the usual quantities of cement, the grading he suggests gives a harsh-working concrete. Another corollary of Mr. Fuller's method indicates that the aggregates should be separated into a number of sizes and recombined in order to approximate this so-called maximum-density curve. Our investigations show that the separation of aggregates into a number of different sizes and recombining, is seldom, if ever, necessary or desirable; and especially in the case of the fine materials involves a great expense and many difficulties. I believe that this method has been used to some extent, but the practical difficulties in the way have barred it from general application.

A number of other experimentors have been studying this problem during the past few years. I might mention Captain L. N. Edwards[1], R. B. Young[2], Prof. A. N. Talbot[3], F. L. Roman[4], formerly of the Illinois Division of Highways, and R. W. Crum[5], of the Iowa State Highway Department. All these men have furnished valuable information, so that we are able to approach the subject from many different angles.

At the Structural Materials Research Laboratory we have been engaged in experimental studies of concrete and concrete materials for nearly 8 years. These tests are being carried out through the co-operation of the Portland Cement Association and Lewis Institute. It was apparent at the beginning of this work that a proper basis for proportioning concrete was not available; consequently, among our first investigations were a number of studies of the general subject of proportioning. These studies have been continued up to the present.

The studies carried out thus far which deal with the many phases of proportioning concrete reach a total of about 100,000 tests. These tests fall under the following categories:

---

[*]Trans. Am. Soc. C. E., v. 59, 1907; also "Concrete Plain and Reinforced," by Taylor and Thompson, 1916.
[1]Proc. A. S. T. M., v. XVII, Part II, p. 301, 1917; also Proc. v. XVIII, Part II, p. 303, 1918.
[2]Proc. A. S. T. M., v. XX, Part II, p. 137, 1920.
[3]Proc. A. S. T. M., v. XXI, Part II, p. 940.
[4]Eng. & Cont., May 5, 1915, p. 403; also Bull. 14, Ill. State Highway Department, 1917.
[5]Proc. A. S. T. M., v. XIX, p. 458, 1919.

1. Standardization of test methods,
2. Effect of grading of aggregates,
3. Effect of consistency of concrete,
4. Effect of quantity of cement,
5. Relative merits of different types of fine and coarse aggregates,
6. Comparison of concrete and mortar tests,
7. Effect of curing condition,
8. Effect of age of concrete,
9. Effect of powdered admixtures in concrete,
10. Studies of methods of measuring plasticity or workability of concrete,
11. Comparisons of compressive strength, tension, flexure, wear, yield and absorption of concrete.

THEORY OF CONCRETE MIXTURES.

The real problem in proportioning concrete mixtures is to take advantage of the characteristics of the materials available. At the present time aggregate materials cannot be transported long distances; we may know ever so much about the ideal characteristics of sand and coarse aggregates, but we may not be able to get that type of aggregate. In other words, we must make the best we can of the materials available.

Our investigations have led us to the following fundamental principles:

1. The strength of a concrete mixture depends on the quantity of mixing water in the batch, expressed as a ratio to the volume of cement *so long as the concrete is workable,* and the *aggregates are clean and structurally sound.*

2. The effect of differences in the quantity of cement is reflected by differences in the water-ratio.

3. The sieve analysis of the aggregate is the basis on which proportioning must be done. There is an intimate relation between the size and grading of the aggregate and the quantity of water required to produce concrete of a given workability.

4. It is not necessary, or desirable, that the aggregate be proportioned according to any fixed grading; wide variations in gradings of aggregate may occur without affecting the quantity of mixing water or the quality of the concrete.

5. Plasticity or workability is an essential requirement of concrete for structural purposes.

The sieve analysis expresses the life history of the material, so far as its concrete-making properties are concerned. It is only necessary for us to interpret this information in order to use the material to the best advantage.

The mixing water in concrete serves two distinct purposes, although we do not always recognize those distinctions. One purpose is to supply the water necessary for the hydration of cement. The second purpose is to produce a plastic mixture. I do not believe anyone has determined just how much water is required for hydration, but such information as we have indicates that it is a relatively small percentage as compared to the quantity we must use in the concrete; probably not more than a quarter or a third of the water that is usually placed in the concrete. The excess of water over and above that required for hydration of the cement simply goes to produce a plastic mixture and is removed later by evaporation.

The water-ratio seems to be the factor which ultimately governs the strength and wearing resistance of the concrete. If we use one cubic foot of water (about 7½ gal.) to each sack of cement, we would have a water-ratio of 1; a smaller quantity of water per sack would give a water-ratio of less than 1, etc. The usual water-ratio for ordinary conditions is about 0.8 or 0.9, or about 6 to 6¾ gal. per sack of cement. In dealing with water-ratio we disregard water absorbed by the aggregates, although water mechanically held by the aggregate would be considered. A great many tests carried out in our laboratory, and those made by others, have shown that the water-ratio is a reliable factor in studying the characteristics of concrete. Anything that can be done in improving the grading of the aggregate, in the use of more cement or different methods of finishing or placing concrete, in order that it may be placed with a lower quantity of mixing water—all of these things are simply means to an end; namely, to produce a plastic concrete with a lower water-ratio.

This brings us to a point which is generally overlooked in our building codes and other documents of that kind. It seems to be the opinion that increasing the quantity of cement is the cure for all the difficulties of weak or inferior concrete. However, if adding cement is not at the same time accompanied by a reduction in the water-ratio, it does not accomplish any useful purpose. The water-ratio may be changed due to changes in the relations of the quantity of cement, grading of aggregate, or changes in relative consistency of the concrete; however, we arrive at the same result, indicating that the water-ratio is the thing that actually controls the strength and other properties of concrete.

It is not necessary, or desirable, that the aggregate be proportioned according to any fixed grading; wide variations in gradings of aggregate may occur without affecting the quantity of mixing water or the quality of the concrete.

PLASTICITY OF CONCRETE.

The question of plasticity or workability of concrete is a very important one. We are hedged about on all sides by the requirement of plasticity. We could not use concrete at all if it were not for the fact that it can be mixed in a plastic condition and placed as such. We must put in enough water to make our concrete plastic so that it can be worked into place. Now, as to the method of measuring or controlling the plasticity of concrete; this is one of the questions which is giving engineers more concern today than probably any other one thing. A number of methods have been suggested and a great deal of experimental work is now under way. The method which probably has met with most common use, because of its simplicity, is the slump test. This test will be described more in detail in Mr. Walker's discussion. The Bureau of Standards is responsible, I believe, for a method which is known as the flow-test, in which a sample of the concrete is placed on a horizontal table which is raised and dropped 15 times in about 10 seconds, thus flattening out the concrete. The spread or increase in diameter is taken as a measure of the plasticity of the concrete.

There is a great need for constructive research in developing a satisfactory and practical method of determining the plasticity of concrete. Any method which is used for this purpose in the field should not be interpreted too strictly. In other words, if our specification indicates that the concrete should be mixed to a slump, say, of 6 in., we would not be justified in rejecting a batch of concrete simply because it gave a slump of 7 in. The purpose is to take care that the concrete does not habitually go beyond the quantity fixed by the specification. In most building construction, if you attempted to make a slump test, you would get nearer 12 in. than anything else. That is the type of concrete that we must guard against, and I believe that the big thing this test can do is to bring home the importance of the water control on building construction. I know that a great many people are skeptical as to the practicability of such control; some may still doubt whether an excess of water does produce an inferior concrete; but I can say with all the emphasis of which I am capable that I am very sure it does, and that in many cases the concrete produced on the job has a strength of probably not more than 20 to 30% of the strength it should have, and probably not more than 60 or 70% of the strength upon which the design was based. So, under these conditions we should not be surprised to find inferior concrete, and we do find it too often.

APPLICATION OF PRINCIPLES.

The foregoing principles lead us to a number of practical features of concrete-making.

The quantity of mixing water used to produce concrete of the condition of workability necessary is of major importance. Every care should be taken to restrict the mixing water to a minimum. An excess of mixing water produces the same result as omitting a large portion of the cement from the batch.

Methods have been developed whereby aggregates may be scientifically proportioned on the basis of sieve analysis without separation into a large number of sizes. Aggregates may be used with good results regardless of the fact that they do not conform to our older ideas of what concrete aggregate should be. For example, the Iowa State Highway Department has embodied in their specifications for concrete roads a method whereby so-called pit run gravels, can be used in almost any proportions in which they occur, so long as they are clean, regardless of the fact that there may be a great excess of sand. Their method requires an increase in the quantity of cement in proportion to the quantity of sand in excess of a certain minimum. The specifications would permit the use of a mixture of one part sand and one part coarse aggregate or of a sand only, providing the cement content were increased to such an extent as to produce concrete of the strength and wearing resistance aimed at by the specification. This instance is not an isolated one. The Illinois Division of Highways permits the same thing. In many sections of Kansas and Nebraska great quantities of sand and very little coarse aggregate are available; here a 1 : 3 sand mixture has been used with good results. Of course this procedure would have been frowned upon a short time ago, but I believe it has proven its value and will become general practice in the future.

Our problem is to put together the aggregates available in order to get the best concrete mixture we can for a given cost or at a minimum cost.

QUALITY OF CONCRETE.

A great deal has been said with reference to the compressive strength of concrete and we have come to accept the compressive strength as a measure of the other desirable qualities of concrete.

The strength of concrete is an important factor in building construction and in other types of construction; however, the quality of concrete has a wider bearing than strength. A structure which is exposed to the weather, with wide ranges of temperature, wide variations in moisture content, and probably exposed to other destructive agencies, must have a very considerable degree of resistance if it is to give a good account of itself. That is entirely aside from the matter of strength. It is true, however, that the strength of concrete reflects to a very large degree the ability of concrete to withstand these other agencies. Our experiments have shown that so far as wearing* resistance is concerned, it is true that the strength is the proper measure of the quality. The tests which I showed here yesterday indicated that the flexural strength** of concrete is not influenced in exactly the same way as the compressive strength, but the relation is in the same direction. The variation in water content did not affect the modulus of rupture so much as the compressive strength. However, we may consider that the compressive strength of concrete is an entirely satisfactory measure of its quality.

---

*See "Effect of Curing Condition on the Wear and Strength of Concrete," Bull. 2, Structural Materials Research Laboratory; also "Wear Tests of Concrete," Proc. Am. Soc. Testing Mat., 1921.
**Flexural Strength of Plain Concrete; see page 20 of this volume.

TABLES OF PROPORTIONS AND QUANTITIES.

As a result of our experimental studies of concrete and concrete aggregates we have prepared a set of tables of quantities and proportions of materials for concrete of a given strength.* Some of these tables appeared in the Joint Committee report; others have been added. The purpose of these tables is to show proportions and quantities which, under average conditions, may be expected to give concrete of a given compressive strength under normal conditions of curing.

Their chief value is in the selection of proportions for preliminary investigations and in making changes in proportions required by variations in materials, after a basic mixture has been determined upon. It is not expected that the tables will give as exact information as may be obtained by preliminary investigations of materials and mixtures, followed by control tests made during the progress of the work.

STANDARD TESTS OF CONCRETE AND CONCRETE MATERIALS.

I wish to add a few words on the work of standardization which is being done by the American Society for Testing Materials. During the past year or two that Society has published in their "Standards" and "Proceedings" the following *new* standards or tentative standards which are of interest to all concrete engineers:

1. Standard Method of Making and Storing Specimens of Concrete in the Field;

2. Tentative Method of Making Compression Tests of Concrete;

3. Tentative Specifications for Workability of Concrete for Concrete Pavements;

4. Tentative Method of Test for Sieve Analysis of Aggregate for Concrete;

5. Tentative Method of Test for Organic Impurities in Sands for Concrete;

6. Tentative Method of Securing Specimens of Hardened Concrete from the Structure;

7. Standard Method of Test for Unit Weight of Aggregate for Concrete;

8. Tentative Specifications for Concrete Aggregate;

9. Tentative Method of Test for Voids in Fine Aggregate for Concrete.

Those of you who have not looked up these standards recently will be well repaid for doing so. Many of the concrete tests made in the past are of little or no value, due to the fact that sound principles of

---

*"Quantities of Materials for Concrete," by Duff A. Abrams and Stanton Walker, Bull. 9, Structural Materials Research Laboratory.

testing were violated. It is frequently impossible to properly interpret indications of concrete tests, due to lack of proper standard methods of manipulation. The tentative standard method for making tests of concrete should be consulted and followed so far as possible by all who have occasion to make tests. In those standards the details are given whereby consistent results can be secured in different laboratories and in different sections of the country; something we have not been able to do heretofore.

We have been floundering around for 40 years and for the first time we now have some semblance of a standard method for making sieve analysis of aggregates. Heretofore practically every laboratory used a different set of sieves or used a different method of recording sieve analysis, and consequently the results have been so divergent that it has been almost impossible for one person to make anything out of the work done by others; standard sieves and methods are very important steps in advance.

CONCLUDING REMARKS.

Considerable progress is being made in many directions in improving and standardizing concrete tests and practices, all of which will exert an important influence on the quality of work, and will in the near future result in a higher batting average of good concrete.

A TRIBUTE TO

"The Influence of Gypsum on the Hydration and Properties of Portland Cement Pastes"

by W. Lerch

Foreword by Anton K. Schindler

Lerch worked for the Portland Cement Association (PCA) for most of his professional career and became an Honorary Member of ACI in 1960. He was a recipient of the Sanford E. Thompson Award for a paper of outstanding merit by the American Society for Testing and Materials (ASTM) in 1948. Mr. Lerch published works with distinguished researchers in concrete materials that included the likes of W.C. Hansen, H.F. Gonnerman, and R.H. Bogue.

In this pioneering work, William Lerch clearly describes the nature of the reactions of gypsum with portland cement and the manner in which gypsum affects the rate of heat liberation and the physical properties of the hardened paste. Lerch conclusively showed through the collective consideration of the early-age hydration, strength, and volume-change behavior that the quantity of gypsum required for portland cement varies with C_3A content, alkali content, and fineness of each cement. Until the publication of this paper, this issue had been a topic of controversy and, based on his recommendation, the cement industry allowed an increase in the amount of gypsum added during manufacturing of cement. At the time this paper was published, the SO_3 content of portland cement had been limited to 1.9% since 1911 by relevant ASTM standards. In this era of portland cement production, this limit was apparently used to prevent delayed excessive expansion. In this landmark paper, Lerch shows that gypsum can be added to portland cements in considerably larger amounts than was permitted by specifications of that era without danger of abnormal expansion.

Twelve commercial clinkers that cover the range of chemical composition generally encountered in the 1940s were used in this investigation. The clinkers with various additions of gypsum (SO_3) were ground to the same specific surface and the rate of heat liberation was determined for the cements. In addition, five of the clinkers were ground to varying degrees of fineness while holding the SO_3 constant.

99

Prior to this publication, most previous investigations on how to regulate the setting behavior of portland cement was mostly done by evaluating time of setting results as determined by penetration tests. Lerch made extensive use of isothermal calorimetry that provides a continuous indication of the progress of hydration at early ages. The innovative use of isothermal calorimetry allowed Lerch to evaluate the effect of various gypsum contents on the rate of hydration of portland cement pastes at early ages.

Mortar specimens were used to assess the effect of the various additions of gypsum on strength development and dimensional stability of the hardened paste. The results of this paper show that proper regulation of the reaction of early hardening is of much greater importance than merely regulating setting. The gypsum content not only influences the rate of hydration, but affects the strength and the volume-change characteristics of the hardened cement paste. With some cement compositions, gypsum retards the initial hydration and set, while with others it acts as an accelerator. These results showed that for many cements, the strengths can be increased and the drying shrinkage decreased by the use of larger additions of gypsum than were permitted by the ASTM SO_3 limits of that era. For the first time, Lerch also revealed a close relationship between the early-age heat of hydration and strength data.

The paper has had a significant impact on the concrete industry and is routinely referenced by leading text books on concrete material science. The results of this work led to changes in worldwide cement standards, and today sulfate levels are based on achieving the maximum 1-day strength. This paper is also frequently cited when authors of various journal articles discuss the effect of gypsum on the hydration of portland cement. Through this paper, William Lerch introduced a new paradigm in our understanding of the role of gypsum on the reactions of portland cement, and the manner in which gypsum affects the rate of heat liberation and the physical properties of portland cement pastes.

ACI Member **Anton K. Schindler** *is the Gottlieb Associate Professor in the Department of Civil Engineering at Auburn University, Alabama. He received his MSE and PhD from the University of Texas at Austin. His research interests include nondestructive testing, concrete properties, early-age behavior of concrete structures, and self-consolidating concrete. He received the ACI Wason Medal for Materials Research in 2006.*

THE INFLUENCE OF GYPSUM ON THE HYDRATION AND PROPERTIES OF PORTLAND CEMENT PASTES*

By William Lerch[1]

Synopsis

The manner in which the added gypsum controls the setting of cement has been the subject of many investigations and of some controversy. It is generally agreed, however, that its effect is to stop the rapid reaction normally shown by the calcium aluminates. In the absence of precise information relative to the function of gypsum in regulating the initial hydration and in order to provide ample protection against the abnormal expansion that might result from the use of excess amounts of gypsum it has been the custom from the beginning to place a limit on the SO_3 content of portland cement in standard specifications. In the A.S.T.M. specification for cement this limit has not been changed since 1917[2] except to permit a higher value for high early strength cement. In the belief that the quantity of gypsum required to regulate properly the hydration and hardening would vary with cement composition and fineness, the studies described in this paper were undertaken.

Twelve commercial clinkers covering the range of chemical composition generally encountered in portland cements were selected for study. Each of these compositions was used with various SO_3 contents with fineness held uniform at about 1900 sq. cm. per gram. In addition five of the clinkers were ground to varying degrees of fineness with SO_3 constant at about 1.8 per cent.

The effect of SO_2 on the rate of hydration was measured with a conduction calorimeter on neat cement pastes. Mortar prisms were used for physical tests. These studies have shown that a proper regulation of the reaction of early hardening is of much greater importance than merely regulating the time of setting. Such regulation not only influences the rate of hydration, but affects the strength and the volume-change characteristics of the hardened cement paste. With some cement compositions the gypsum retards the initial hydration and set, while with others it acts as an accelerator.

For many cements the strengths can be increased and the contraction on drying decreased by the use of larger additions of gypsum than are permitted by current specifications. The quantity required to obtain the best strength and the least contraction can be used without danger of abnormal expansion in water storage. The results show that the fineness, the alkalies, and the $3CaO \cdot Al_2O_3$ content all influence the gypsum requirements.

The paper contains a discussion of the function of gypsum in regulating the reactions of hydration and hardening.

When portland cement clinker is

* Presented at the Forty-ninth Annual Meeting of the Society, June 24–28, 1946.
[1] Research Chemist, Research Laboratory of the Portland Cement Assn., Chicago, Ill.
[2] Standard Specifications for Portland Cement (C 9 – 17), 1916 Book of A.S.T.M. Standards, p. 429.

ground without the addition of a retarder, the reactions with water are usually so rapid that quick set occurs. Of the phases normally present in portland cement clinker, the alumina-containing phases appear to be those which react with sufficient rapidity to give rise to the undesirable quick set. Since alumina-containing phases are always present, it is the common practice in the manufacture of portland cement to add some material to control the rate of the initial reactions. At present, gypsum is the retarder generally used. The manner in which the added gypsum controls the setting of cement has been the subject of many investigations and of much controversy. It is generally agreed, however, that its effect is to stop the rapid reaction normally shown by the aluminate phases, and that it causes the formation of calcium sulfoaluminate in place of hydrated calcium aluminates.

The problem of retarders and accelerators for portland cement is of importance, not alone for the effect which they may have upon the rate of hardening, but also for their effect upon the structure developed by the paste at early ages and the manner in which this structure may alter the physical properties of the hardened paste at subsequent ages.

It seems apparent that the fineness of the cement would be an important consideration in determining the quantity of gypsum required to obtain proper retardation. However, bodies responsible for cement specifications do not seem to have taken this into account. For example, the Standard Specifications for Portland Cement adopted by the A.S.T.M. effective January 1, 1917, (C 9 – 17)[2] limited the SO_3 content to 2.0 per cent and permitted a residue of 22 per cent on the No. 200 sieve. Since that date there has been a progressive increase in the fineness of portland cement, and in the most recent A.S.T.M. Specifications (C 150 – 44)[3] a minimum limit of fineness has been imposed of 1600 sq. cm. per g. specific surace (1).[4] This limit would be equivalent

to approximately a 5.0 per cent residue on the No. 200 sieve. Despite this large change in fineness there has been no change in the specifications to permit larger additions of gypsum to compensate for the increase in fineness—except that for high early strength cement an SO_3 content of 2.5 per cent is permitted.

The present investigation was undertaken to examine the influence of gypsum on the hydration and properties of portland-cement pastes when using cements of different composition and with fineness varied. Twelve commercial clinkers, representing the range in chemical composition encountered in portland cements, were used in the investigation. The clinkers with various additions of gypsum were ground to the same specific surface and the rate of heat liberation was determined for the cements. The cements were also used in the preparation of mortar specimens to determine the effect of the various additions of gypsum on the physical properties of the hardened paste. For five of the clinkers additional tests of the rate of heat liberation were made in which the specific surface was varied while holding the SO_3 constant. The discussion of the data contains a description of the nature of the reactions of gypsum with portland cement, and the manner in which gypsum affects the rate of heat liberation and the physical properties of the hardened paste.

APPARATUS AND METHODS OF TEST

The Conduction Calorimeter:

In previous investigations of retarders for portland cement the work has often been confined to a determination of the effect of retarders on the time of set by the conventional penetration tests. In the present investigation, the rate of hydration at early ages was adopted as a means of studying the effect of gypsum. For this purpose the rate of heat libera-

---

[2] Standard Specifications for Portland Cement (C 150 – 44), 1944 Book of A.S.T.M. Standards, Part II, p. 1.
[4] Boldface numbers in parentheses refer to the list of references appended to this paper, see p. 1292.

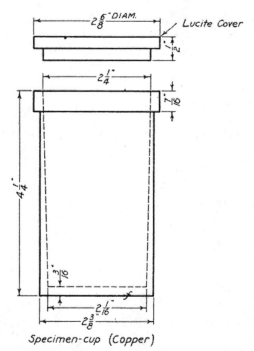

Specimen-cup (Copper)

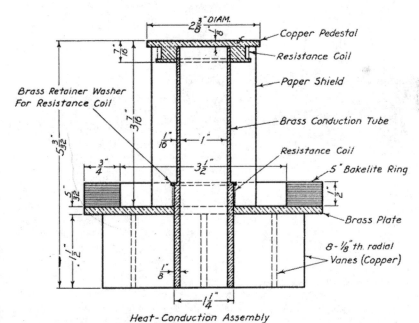

Heat-Conduction Assembly

Fig. 1.—The Conduction Calorimeter: Specimen-Cup and Heat-Conduction Assembly.

tion was used as a means of measuring the rate of hydration. The calorimetric methods were similar to those used by Carlson (2) and Forbrich (3).

A conduction calorimeter designed according to recommendations of R. W. Carlson[5] was used for the determination of the rate of heat liberation during the first 72 hr. The calorimeter proper con-

tion, the specimen cup, containing neat paste (water-cement ratio = 0.40 by weight), is placed on the copper pedestal and a vacuum flask is placed over the apparatus to minimize loss by radiation and by air-convection. Thus virtually all the heat generated by the hydration of the cement in the specimen cup is conducted to the water bath. The complete assembly of six units is shown in Fig. 3.

FIG. 2.—One of the Heat Conduction Units.

FIG. 3. Assembly of Six Units in Operation.

sists of four essential parts which are shown in Figs. 1 and 2: (1) a copper cup to contain the cement paste, (2) a brass tube to conduct the heat away from the specimen cup, (3) resistance thermometers intimately secured to the two ends of the conduction tube, and (4) a heat-dispersing base immersed in a water bath. When the calorimeter is in opera-

The rate at which heat is conducted away from the specimen is proportional to the difference in temperature between the specimen cup and the water bath. The difference in temperature is measured by means of a Leeds and Northrup instrument which records the difference between the temperatures (in terms of resistance) at the ends of the conduction tube. The instrument records the resistance difference for each of six calorimetera at 6-min. intervals. A detailed description of the method of calibration, and computation of data are given in a previous paper by Carlson (4).

[5] Personal communication.

The Temperature Rise in the Cement Pastes:

Among the cements used in this investigation the temperature rise varied over a wide range; the maximum was 23 F.; the minimum was 4 F. Carlson (2) has shown that in 10-in. slabs with one surface insulated and the other maintained at a uniform temperature, the temperature rise in concrete containing 1.5 bbl. of cement per cu. yd. would range from 10.5 F. for a low-heat cement to 32 F. for a high early strength cement. Thus, the temperature rise in the conduction calorimeter for the neat cement pastes used in these tests is of the same order as the temperature rise in relatively thin concrete slabs and no undue acceleration of the rate of hydration results from the temperature rise in the calorimeter specimen.

Determination of Heat of Immediate Hydration:

Since cement liberates an appreciable amount of heat immediately upon being mixed with water, the heat liberated before the first measurement with the conduction calorimeter must be determined by an independent method. The heat liberated during this initial period is referred to as the heat of immediate hydration. It is determined with a simple bottle calorimeter. The bottle used for these determinations has a capacity of about 300 ml. Three hundred grams of cement and 120 ml. of water are used for the determination. The initial temperature of the water is adjusted in such a manner that the paste at the completion of a determination will be approximately at room temperature. The measured quantity of water is placed in the bottle and the initial temperatures of the water and cement are recorded. The cement is then poured into the bottle, the stopper and thermometer inserted and the contents shaken vigorously for 5 min. Readings of the paste temperature are taken at 5-min. intervals for 30 min. The heat of hydration is then calculated from the temperature rise and the heat capacity of the system (cement, water, and bottle) and designated the heat of immediate hydration.

SELECTION AND PREPARATION OF THE CEMENTS

Twelve commercial clinkers were selected to represent the range of chemical composition found in portland cements. The chemical analysis and calculated compound composition (5, 6) of the twelve clinkers are given in Table I. Clinkers Nos. 16839, 16843, and 16890 are the products of one plant; clinkers Nos. 16827 and 16831 are the products of another plant; and the remaining 7 clinkers are each from a different plant. Five of the clinkers were ground in commercial mills to obtain cements of widely different specific surface: approximately 1200, 1800, and 2300 sq. cm. per g. For these grinds gypsum was added to the clinker before grinding to give about 1.8 per cent SO_3. These cements were used to study the influence of fineness on the rate of hydration of cements with SO_3 constant.

For a study of variations in SO_3 contents, additional cements were ground in a laboratory mill from the twelve clinkers mentioned above. A natural rock gypsum was used which by chemical analysis was known to be almost pure $CaSO_4 2H_2O$. Three grinds were made with each clinker: (1) without gypsum, (2) with gypsum added to give an SO_3 content of 1.90 per cent, and (3) with gypsum added to give an SO_3 content of 5.00 per cent. The cements were then blended in the proper proportions to give the desired intermediate SO_3 contents. In these laboratory grinds the clinker with no added gypsum was ground to 1800 ± 25 sq. cm. per g. The specific surface of the cements containing gypsum were ground finer by 50 sq. cm. per g. for each 1.0 per cent of added SO_3, in an attempt to maintain the same fineness for the clinker in all grinds. This procedure was based on previous work by Swenson and Flint (7) who found that approximately 70 per cent of the gypsum in cement was present in the 0 to 7 μ

mined for the twelve commercial clinkers ground with various SO_3 contents as described above. The pastes were mixed and cured at 75 F. and the rate of heat liberation was determined for the first 72 hr. The temperatures of the cement and water were adjusted so that the temperature of the paste would be 75 F. when placed in the calorimeter. The room containing the calorimeters was maintained at 75 F.

TABLE I.—CHEMICAL ANALYSES AND CALCULATED COMPOUND COMPOSITIONS OF CLINKERS.

Clinker	Oxide Analyses									Calculated Compound Composition						
	SiO_2	Al_2O_3	Fe_2O_3	Total CaO	MgO	SO_3	Ignition Loss	Na_2O	K_2O	C_3S	C_2S	C_3A	C_4AF	$CaSO_4$	Free CaO	MgO
CLINKERS OF HIGH $3CaO \cdot Al_2O_3$ AND LOW ALKALI CONTENT																
No. 15367	21.87	6.83	2.23	65.30	2.63	0.41	0.15	0.17	0.16	45.5	28.4	14.3	6.7	0.7	0.98	2.63
No. 16823	21.17	6.35	2.51	68.33	0.87	0.05	0.26	0.05	0.25	70.0	8.0	12.5	7.6	0.1	0.21	0.87
CLINKERS OF HIGH OR MODERATELY HIGH $3CaO \cdot Al_2O_3$ AND HIGH OR MODERATELY HIGH ALKALI CONTENT																
No. 15900	22.14	6.46	2.38	63.66	3.78	0.22	0.50	0.36	0.50	41.4	32.2	13.1	7.3	0.4	0.46	3.78
No. 15498	20.92	5.82	2.53	67.71	1.36	0.19	0.85	0.31	0.42	62.5	13.0	11.2	7.7	0.3	2.71	1.36
No. 16843	22.34	5.76	2.57	65.22	1.95	0.52	0.52	1.03	0.06	48.2	27.8	11.0	7.8	0.9	1.07	1.95
No. 15699	22.72	5.38	2.48	64.06	3.43	0.20	0.37	1.17	0.46	47.9	29.0	10.1	7.6	0.3	Nil	3.43
No. 16827	22.81	4.99	3.03	63.74	2.70	0.39	0.60	0.04	1.37	46.0	30.6	8.1	9.3	0.7	0.25	2.70
CLINKERS OF LOW $3CaO \cdot Al_2O_3$ AND LOW ALKALI CONTENT																
No. 16890	26.07	3.93	3.16	63.99	1.28	0.46	0.57	0.32	0.02	28.0	53.5	5.1	9.6	0.8	0.44	1.28
No. 15623	23.30	4.58	4.35	65.01	1.44	0.03	1.05	0.05	0.18	47.6	30.9	4.8	13.2	0.1	0.73	1.44
No. 15670	27.95	2.07	1.87	65.61	1.83	0.17	0.26	0.05	0.23	37.4	51.9	2.4	5.7	0.3	0.23	1.83
CLINKERS OF LOW $3CaO \cdot Al_2O_3$ AND HIGH ALKALI CONTENT																
No. 16839	24.02	5.28	4.60	62.13	1.56	0.67	0.53	1.01	0.10	26.0	49.1	6.2	14.0	1.1	0.12	1.56
No. 16831	21.28	5.27	4.84	61.87	3.12	0.53	1.29	0.05	1.37	46.0	26.3	5.7	14.7	0.9	0.07	3.12

* Corrected for free CaO, but not corrected for minor constituents.
NOTE: Clinker No. 15699 was made from a special batch of slurry prepared to produce a clinker of unusually high Na_2O content. The clinkers normally produced at the plant do not have this high Na_2O content.

fraction. Thus, if all were ground to the same specific surface, with increasing quantities of gypsum, the gypsum would contribute a disproportionate share of the total specific surface with the result that the specific surface of the clinker would become progressively lower as the SO_3 content increased.

THE INFLUENCE OF GYPSUM UPON THE
RATE OF HEAT LIBERATION

Typical Results:

The rate of heat liberation was deter-

A few typical results of the rates of reaction of the different cements are given in Figs. 4, 5, and 6, the rates of reaction being expressed in terms of the rate of heat liberation. The reactions of all cements undergo two cycles of increasing and decreasing rates, and cements of high or moderately high $3CaO \cdot Al_2O_3$ regardless of their alkali content or cements of low $3CaO \cdot Al_2O_3$ that are high in alkalies sometimes undergo a third cycle; whether the third cycle will occur depends on the SO_3

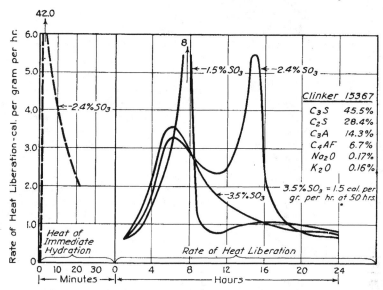

FIG. 4.—Rate of Hydration of Cements of High 3CaO·Al₂O₃ and Low Alkali Content With SO₃ Varied.

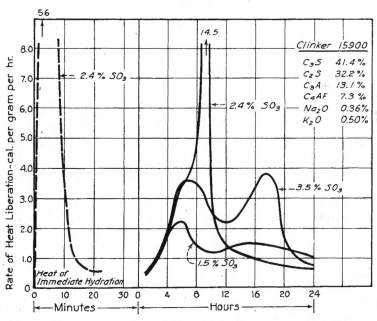

FIG. 5.—Rate of Hydration of Cements of High 3CaO·Al₂O₃ and Moderately High Alkali Content With SO₄ Varied.

content of the cement. During the first cycle shown by the broken line curves, the rate of heat liberation increases from zero to a relatively high value within the first five minutes and then decreases rapidly. This first cycle is designated the heat of immediate hydration. With cements of high or moderately high $3CaO \cdot Al_2O_3$ regardless of their alkali content or cements of high alkalies regardless of their $3CaO \cdot Al_2O_3$ content when ground without added gypsum or with small additions of gypsum 1.0 per cent SO_3 or less, the reactions are so rapid at this stage that flash-set occurs

ticity. Following the interval of slow hydration, the second cycle of increasing rates of hydration occurs as shown by the first ascending portion of the solid line curves in Figs. 4, 5, and 6. This is the stage of initial hardening. With the cement of low $3CaO \cdot Al_2O_3$ and low alkali without added gypsum, Fig. 6, the period of slow hydration is abnormally long and it is shortened by the addition of gypsum. The third cycle of increasing rates of reaction is shown by the second ascending portion of the solid line curve for the cement containing 2.4 per cent SO_3 in Fig. 4 and the cement

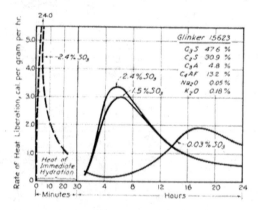

Fig. 6.—Rate of Hydration of Cements of Low $3CaO \cdot Al_2O_3$ and Low Alkali Content With SO_3 Varied.

during mixing. With larger additions of gypsum the heat-liberation is decreased (the reactions are slower) and the paste remains plastic. With cements of low $3CaO \cdot Al_2O_3$ and low alkali content even when ground without added gypsum the reactions are not sufficiently rapid to cause flash-set; however, gypsum will decrease their heat-liberation at this stage.

When the cements have sufficient gypsum to prevent the flash-set, the first cycle of rapid reaction is followed by a period of one or two hours of relatively slow reaction. During this period the paste retains much of its original plas-

with 3.5 per cent SO_3 in Fig. 5. The behavior during the second and third cycles of increasing rates of reaction may differ widely among different cements. The significant characteristics of a cement to develop its highest strength and lowest contraction are revealed by the characteristics of the heat-liberation curves during this period.

The Rate of Hydration of a Properly Retarded Cement:

The curve for the cement of low $3CaO \cdot Al_2O_3$ and low alkali content with 1.5 per cent SO_3, Fig. 6, shows two cycles of increasing and decreasing rates of reaction and larger additions of gypsum do not appreciably alter the shape of the curve. Similar curves are obtained with clinkers of high $3CaO \cdot Al_2O_3$ content by the use of larger additions of gypsum. These curves are similar to the curves obtained for the hydration of $3CaO \cdot SiO_2$ either with or without gypsum. From these considerations and on the basis of the results of physical tests to be given later, a properly retarded cement can be considered as one which contains the minimum quantity of gypsum required to give a curve that shows two cycles of ascending and descending rates of heat liberation and that shows no appreciable change with larger additions of gypsum during the first 30 hr. of hydration. It will be shown later that cements containing the proper amount of gypsum to give this type of heat-liberation curve are the cements that have the highest strength and lowest contraction on drying. With cements of low $3CaO \cdot Al_2O_3$ content the shape of the curve after 30 hr. will not be altered by larger additions of gypsum. With cements of high $3CaO \cdot Al_2O_3$ content larger additions of gypsum may cause the appearance of a third cycle of increasing rates of reaction after 30 hr. However, it will be shown later that these larger additions of gypsum give lower strengths, higher contractions and abnormal expansions. It is for these reasons that a properly retarded cement is defined on the basis of the shape of the curve showing the rates of hydration during the first 30 hr. and the use of the minimum quantity of gypsum which will give that shape.

THE FUNCTION OF GYPSUM IN CONTROLLING THE EARLY REACTIONS OF HYDRATION

It has been shown that gypsum influences the rate of hydration of portland cement and that its effect upon the rate of hydration is not the same for all cements. In the following discussion it will be shown that gypsum influences the rate of hydration by its presence in solution and that a saturated lime-gypsum solution retards the hydration of cements of high $3CaO \cdot Al_2O_3$ content and accelerates the hydration of cements of low $3CaO \cdot Al_2O_3$ content.

The Influence of Gypsum Upon the Rate of Hydration of Cements of High $3CaO \cdot Al_2O_3$ and Low Alkali Content:

In an investigation of the reactions of water on the calcium aluminates, Wells (8) observed that in aqueous solutions containing only lime and alumina, the solubility of alumina decreased with increasing concentrations of calcium hydroxide. He observed also that in a saturated calcium hydroxide solution, alumina reacts with calcium hydroxide to form hydrated calcium aluminates. Lerch, Ashton, and Bogue (9) have shown that alumina is less soluble in a lime-gypsum solution than in lime-water and that the alumina reacts with lime and gypsum to form calcium sulfoaluminate.

With these facts on solubility in mind, the action of gypsum as a retarder can be explained on the basis of the solubility of alumina in the aqueous solutions with the aid of the curve obtained for the cement containing 2.4 per cent SO_3 in Fig. 4. When water is added to the cement there is an initial rapid solution of the anhydrous aluminates and a rapid crystallization of hydrated calcium aluminates. These are the rapid reactions which occur before the mixing water becomes saturated with lime and gypsum. Evidence of these reactions is given by the high rate of heat liberation observed during the first 5 min.—the rising portion of the broken-line curve. Simultaneously, the concentration of lime and gypsum increases and rapidly halts the reactions by decreasing the solubility of alumina—the descending portion of the broken-line curve. This prevents the immediate flash-set. The solution of lime alone is not enough to prevent flash-set, for experiments have shown that flash-set occurs in the absence of gypsum.

When the solution has become saturated with lime and gypsum, the anhydrous aluminate phases continue to dissolve slowly and react with gypsum to form calcium sulfoaluminate, and the creases. At the same time the hydration products are precipitated on the surface of the remaining anhydrous particles, partially sealing the grains. By a combination of these conditions, the rate of hydration decreases to the eleventh hour. As the gypsum continues to be used up in the formation of calcium sulfoaluminate, the gypsum eventually becomes depleted and its concentration in the solution decreases. When this

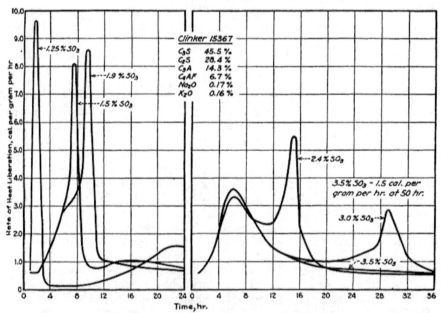

FIG. 7.—Rate of Hydration of Cements of High 3CaO·Al₂O₃ and Low Alkali Content With SO₃ Varied.

anhydrous calcium silicates dissolve and form hydrated calcium silicates. These are the reactions of hydration in the retarded state. As these reactions occur, the rate of heat liberation again increases and reaches a maximum at about the sixth hour as shown by the solid-line curve. As the hydration proceeds the smaller anhydrous particles may become completely hydrated and the larger particles become smaller, that is, the surface area of anhydrous phases de-condition is reached, the solubility of alumina again increases and a rapid reaction will occur if sufficient unhydrated calcium aluminates are available. This is shown by the third cycle of increasing rates of reaction from the eleventh to the fifteenth hour. The reactions that occur at this stage appear to be identical with those of the immediate flash-set that occurs in the absence of gypsum, but they are less rapid because of the decrease in surface area of the anhydrous particles and because of the presence of the protective film of hydration products.

From what has just been said, it would be expected that the time at which the rapid hydration of the aluminate phases may occur will depend on the gypsum content of the cement. That this is actually the case is illustrated by the curves in Fig. 7 obtained with additional cements prepared from this same clinker of high $3CaO \cdot Al_2O_3$ content (clinker No. 15367). In Fig. 7 the peak appears at the second hour with 1.25 per cent SO_3, the tenth hour with 1.9 per cent SO_3, the fifteenth hour with 2.4 per cent SO_3, the twenty-ninth hour with 3.0 per cent SO_3 and at the fiftieth hour with 3.5 per cent

in glass vials and allowed to harden. At ages of 6 and 24 hr. the pastes were pulverized and 200 g. of paste was mixed with 100 ml. of water. After a mixing period of 10 min., some of the clear water was filtered off and analyzed. Table II gives the partial analysis of the solutions. After 6 hr. of hydration, the concentration of dissolved SO_3 is approximately equal to that of saturated solution of gypsum, and with the cements of relatively high alkali content, Nos. 15900 and 15699, the concentration is even higher. The higher SO_3 concentrations can be accounted for by the presence of alkali sulfates formed by a reaction of the alkalies with gypsum. After 24 hr. of hydration, the concentration of dissolved

TABLE II.—PARTIAL ANALYSIS OF EXTRACTS OBTAINED FROM HARDENED PASTES.
The cements used in the preparation of the pastes contained 3.0 per cent SO_3

Clinker	Partial Composition of Clinker, per cent			Partial Analysis of Extract after Period of Hydration Indicated, g. per 100 ml.					
				6 hr.			24 hr.		
	C_3A	Na_2O	K_2O	SO_3	Na_2O	K_2O	SO_3	Na_2O	K_2O
No. 15367	14.3	0.17	0.16	0.1207	0.0304	0.0582	0.0117	0.0381	0.0582
No. 15900	13.1	0.36	0.50	0.1576	0.0391	0.1457	trace	0.1952	0.2963
No. 15699 ...:......	10.1	1.17	0.46	0.2142	0.1643	0.1351	0.0055	0.4333	0.2088
No. 15670	2.4	0.05	0.23	0.1120	0.0003	0.0216	0.1140	0.0116	0.0370
Saturated gypsum solution........................				0.1220					

SO_3. It is also shown that the peaks become lower with each progressive increase in SO_3 content.

From these considerations it appears that the action of calcium sulfate as a retarder for cements of high $3CaO \cdot Al_2O_3$ content depends upon the decreased solubility of the anhydrous calcium aluminate in a saturated lime-gypsum solution. This observation was further confirmed by chemical analysis of the liquid phase extracted from hardened pastes and by expansion data obtained from mortar prisms.

Four cements, each containing gypsum equivalent to 3.0 per cent SO_3 were mixed in pastes with a water-cement ratio of 0.40 by weight. The pastes were placed

SO_3 in the extracts from the three cements of high $3CaO \cdot Al_2O_3$ content is very low, and with the cement of low $3CaO \cdot Al_2O_3$ content, the concentration is very nearly that of a saturated gypsum solution. Thus, the results give further evidence of the rapid depletion of the gypsum in the pastes prepared from cements of high $3CaO \cdot Al_2O_3$ content, and the relatively slow depletion of the gypsum with cements of low $3CaO \cdot Al_2O_3$ content.

The reactions involved in the formation of calcium sulfoaluminate are known to be accompanied by expansion of the test specimen. Such expansion would be expected to continue as long as gypsum is available for the formation of calcium sulfoaluminate. With this in mind, mortar prisms containing cement 1.0 part, powdered silica 0.3 parts and standard Ottawa sand 2.3 parts by weight were made for length-change measurements. The pulverized silica was added to improve the plasticity of the otherwise harsh standard Ottawa sand mix. Cements of high $3CaO \cdot Al_2O_3$ content with SO_3 varied were used. The prisms were removed from the molds at 8 hr., and length-change measurements were made with the specimens cured in water at 70 F. The results are recorded in Table III which shows: (1) the time at which the gypsum was depleted as indicated by the heat-liberation curves,

TABLE III.—EXPANSION OF MORTAR PRISMS CLINKER NO. 15367, SO_3 VARIED.
Mix: Cement 1.0, powdered silica 0.3, standard Ottawa sand 2.3 by weight.

SO_3 Content, per cent	Specific Surface, sq. cm. per g.	Hour When Gypsum Was Depleted (from heat curves)	Expansion, per cent	
			8 to 24 hr.	24 hr. to 7 days
1.5........	1850	6th	0.005	0.009
1.9........	1870	8th	0.006	0.009
2.4........	1890	12th	0.012	0.007
3.0........	1940	24th	0.032	0.005
3.5........	2000	50th	0.043	0.026

Fig. 7; (2) the expansion observed from 8 hr. to 24 hr., and from 24 hr. to 7 days. The length-change measurements do not register expansion that occurs before the initial measurement at 8 hr.

These data show that: (1) when the heat curves indicate that the gypsum is depleted in 8 hr. or less (as with 1.5 or 1.9 per cent SO_3), the expansions from 8 hr. to 24 hr. and from 24 hr. to 7 days are low; (2) when the heat curves indicate that the gypsum is not depleted within 8 hr., the expansions between 8 and 24 hr. increase progressively with increasing SO_3 contents; (3) when the heat curves indicate that the gypsum is depleted within 24 hr., the expansions between 24 hr. and 7 days are low; (4) when the heat curves indicate that the gypsum is not

depleted within 24 hr. (3.5 per cent SO_3), the expansions between 24 hr. and 7 days are greater than that obtained from similar compositions of lower SO_3 content. Thus the results obtained by the two methods of observation, rate of heat liberation and rate of expansion, are in excellent agreement as to the time at which the gypsum is depleted. The results also indicate the need of an upper limit on the gypsum content to avoid undue expansion. This will be discussed in more detail below.

Discussion of Previous Theories:

In an investigation of retarders reported in 1934 Roller (10) concluded that retardation results from the formation of a protective film of hydrated tetracalcium aluminate around the cement grains and that added gypsum reacts with the alkalies in the aqueous solution to form calcium hydroxide which promotes the formation of the tetracalcium aluminate. Forsen (11) concluded that retardation resulted from the formation of a protective film of tetracalcium aluminate or calcium double salts (calcium sulfoaluminates, etc.) He concluded also that in the absence of alkalies, lime alone was an adequate retarder, but with alkalies present gypsum was required to neutralize the alkalinity resulting from the solution of the alkalies. These investigators arrived at their conclusions from studies of the time of set as measured by the conventional penetration tests.

The theory of the formation of a protective film of hydration products does not adequately explain the data presented above on the rates of heat liberation. The hydration products may partially seal the particles and thereby partially be responsible for the reduction in rate of subsequent reactions. However, this phenomenon would not explain the occurrence of the subsequent rapid reactions that are coincident with the depletion of gypsum. For example, in Fig. 4 the curve for the cement with 2.4 per cent SO₃ shows a peak at 6 hr. followed by a decrease in the rate of reaction. If this decrease in the rate of heat liberation were to be explained entirely on the basis of the formation of a protective film of hydration products, it would be difficult to explain the subsequent disappearance of the protective film, as would be necessary, to permit the later rapid reaction and high rate of heat liberation. The peak in the curve at 15 hr. is actually higher than that at 6 hr.

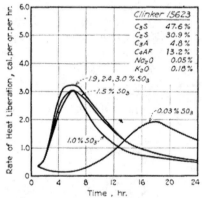

FIG. 8.—Rate of Hydration of Cements of Low $3CaO \cdot Al_2O_3$ and Low Alkali Content With SO₃ Varied.

However, these conditions can be explained from a consideration of the decreased solubility of alumina in a lime-gypsum solution.

The results obtained with another clinker of high $3CaO \cdot Al_2O_3$ and low alkali content, clinker No. 16823, are similar to those shown in Fig. 7. The clinker has a higher $3CaO \cdot SiO_2$ content than the one shown in Fig. 7. The higher $3CaO \cdot SiO_2$ appears to accelerate the over-all hydration with the result that the delayed rapid reaction occurs earlier and the peaks are somewhat higher for comparable SO₃ contents.

The Influence of Gypsum upon the Rate of Hydration of Cements of Low $3CaO \cdot Al_2O_3$ and Low Alkali Content:

The effect of SO₃ content upon the rate of hydration of cements prepared from a clinker of low $3CaO \cdot Al_2O_3$ content (4.8 per cent) and low alkali content, clinker No. 15623, is shown in Fig. 8. As stated previously there is no evidence of a flash-set in the absence of gypsum; and the addition of gypsum accelerates the rate of heat-liberation at early ages. To explain this acceleration, some additional facts must be called to mind. In a previous investigation (12) the author observed the accelerating effect of gypsum and explained the reactions on the basis of the formation of amorphous hydrated calcium ferrite and crystalline calcium sulfoferrite hydrate. In the absence of gypsum, $4CaO \cdot Al_2O_3 \cdot Fe_2O_3$ hydrates to form *crystalline* hydrated calcium aluminate and an *amorphous* hydrated calcium ferrite. It seems probable that the amorphous hydrated calcium ferrite, by precipitation on the cement particles, retards the subsequent hydration of the particles. It may be observed from the immediate heats of hydration, Fig. 15, the diagram at the right, that in the absence of gypsum the heat liberated within the first 5 min. is relatively high. It is apparently during this interval that rapid hydration of the $4CaO \cdot Al_2O_3 \cdot Fe_2O_3$ occurs and the hydrated calcium ferrite precipitates. MacIntire and Shaw (13) found that in the system $CaO—Fe_2O_3—SO_3—H_2O$ a crystalline calcium sulfoferrite is formed. It is probable that when gypsum is added to the clinker of low $3CaO \cdot Al_2O_3$ content, crystalline calcium sulfoferrite is formed in the cement paste and that in this state this compound does not seal the cement particles.

The results obtained with cements prepared from two additional clinkers of low $3CaO \cdot Al_2O_3$ and low alkali content (clinker Nos. 15670 and 16890) are very similar to those obtained from clinker No. 15623 in Fig. 8.

The Effect of the Alkalies on the Gypsum Requirements of Cements:

The effect of the alkali content of the cement upon the gypsum required for proper retardation cannot be definitely explained at this time. However, the experimental data will be presented and a tentative explanation will be given. The results obtained with cements of different $3CaO \cdot Al_2O_3$ content and varying alkali content indicate that the alkalies influence the rate of reaction of the cement. The characteristic differences brought about by the higher alkali content are: (1) That at some of the lower SO_3 contents the cement may give a heat-liberation curve somewhat similar to that of a properly retarded cement, whereas additional tests with higher SO_3 contents will show that they are not properly retarded; (2) That gypsum reacts more rapidly with the cements of higher alkali content; and (3) That higher SO_3 contents are required for proper retardation of such cements.

It seems probable that both the phase composition of the clinker and the concentration of alkalies in the aqueous solution influence the rate of hydration of the cement. The phase systems of portland cement clinker have not been completely solved and the state of combination of alkalies in the clinker is not entirely known. Insley and McMurdie (14) believe that at least part of the alkalies are combined as a lime-alumina-alkali compound with a small amount of $4CaO \cdot Al_2O_3 \cdot Fe_2O_3$ in solid solution. Some unpublished data obtained by the author have shown that the alkalies are readily soluble in the liquid phase of portland cement clinker and that a part of the alkalies are thus likely to be present in the glass. Kalousek, Jumper, and Tregoning (15) and Taylor (16) have found evidence that part of the K_2O in the clinker may be present as K_2SO_4. Taylor (17) reports that under conditions of crystalline equilibrium the compound $K_2O \cdot 23CaO \cdot 12SiO_2$ was found to exist in the region of the K_2O—CaO—Al_2O_3—SiO_2—Fe_2O_3 system in which portland cement compositions fall. Probably, however, not all of the K_2O is present as K_2SO_4 or $K_2O \cdot 23CaO \cdot 12SiO_2$ in commercial clinker since a state of crystalline equilibrium is seldom if ever fully attained.

That at least some of the alkali-containing phases are attacked rapidly by water is evidence by the relatively large amounts of alkalies in the aqueous solution within a few minutes after mixing. Roller (10) observed this phenomenon and Kalousek, Jumper and Tregoning (15) found that of the total alkalies present in the clinker from 1 to 53 per cent of the K_2O and from less than 1 to as much as 30 per cent of the Na_2O dissolved in the mixing water in 7 min. Roller observed also that in the hydration of clinker the solution of alkalies produced a high pH and decreased the $Ca(OH)_2$ concentration of the aqueous solutions; with the addition of gypsum double decomposition occurs by reaction of the gypsum with the alkali hydroxides and the pH of the solution is decreased.

The Effect of Alkalies on the Rate of Hydration of Cements of High $3CaO \cdot Al_2O_3$:

The results obtained with cements prepared from a clinker of moderately high $3CaO \cdot Al_2O_3$ and high alkali content are shown in Fig. 9. This cement is low in Na_2O and high in K_2O. The curve for the cements containing 1.0 to 1.5 per cent SO_3 show only moderate peaks at the fourth hour. As the SO_3 content is increased to 2.4 or 3.0 per cent the peaks on the curves become abnormally high and occur later. This phenomenon of increasing rates of hydration with increasing SO₃ content cannot be definitely explained at this time though it appears to be associated with the alkali content alkali content. The curves for the cements of the latter type with low SO₃ contents have high peaks as shown in Fig. 7. With larger quantities of gypsum the abnormally high peaks are elim-

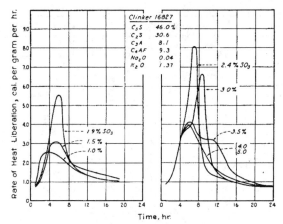

FIG. 9.—Rate of Hydration of Cements of Medium 3CaO·Al₂O₃ With Low Na₂O and High K₂O Content With SO₃ Varied.

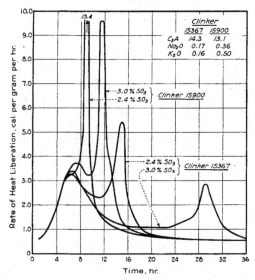

FIG. 10.—Effect of Alkali Content of the Cement in so far as it Influences the Effective SO₃ Content.

of the cement. It has been observed with several cements of high or moderately high 3CaO·Al₂O₃ and high alkali content but has not been observed with cements of high 3CaO·Al₂O₃ and low inated with the cement of high alkali content and with 4.0 per cent SO₃ the curves meet the requirements of a properly retarded cement.

The results obtained with cements

prepared from four additional clinkers of high or moderately high $3CaO \cdot Al_2O_3$ and high alkali content (clinker Nos. 15900, 15699, 16843, and 15498) are similar to those described in Fig. 9.

obtained with cements of very similar composition except for a difference in alkali content. With the clinker of higher alkali content (No. 15900) the gypsum becomes depleted at the seventh

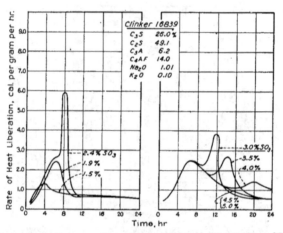

FIG. 11.—Rate of Hydration of Cements of Low $3CaO \cdot Al_2O_3$ With High Na_2O and Low K_2O Content With SO_3 Varied.

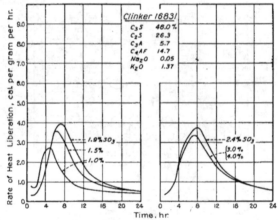

FIG. 12.—Rate of Hydration of Cements of Low $3CaO \cdot Al_2O_3$ With Low Na_2O and High K_2O Content With SO_3 Varied.

With cements of high $3CaO \cdot Al_2O_3$ content the gypsum reacts more rapidly with cements of high or moderately high alkali content than it does with cements of low alkali content. This is illustrated by Fig. 10 which compares the results

hour for the cement containing 2.4 per cent SO_3 (indicated by the rapidly ascending portion of the curve at the seventh hour) and at the tenth hour with 3.0 per cent SO_3. On the other hand, with the clinker of low alkali content (No. 15367) the gypsum does not become depleted until the eleventh hour for the cement with 2.4 per cent SO_3 and the twenty-third hour with 3.0 per cent SO_3. With cements of high or moderately high $3CaO \cdot Al_2O_3$ content larger additions of gypsum are required for proper retardation as the alkali content of the cement increases. From what has just been said, it seems probable that at least part of the alkalies are present in the aluminate phases, and that aluminate phases containing alkalies react with gypsum more rapidly than do similar phases which are alkali free or of lower alkali content.

The Effect of Alkalies on the Rate of Hydration of Cements of Low $3CaO \cdot Al_2O_3$:

The results obtained with cements prepared from clinkers of low $3CaO \cdot Al_2O_3$ and high alkali content (Nos. 16839 and 16831) are shown in Figs. 11 and 12. The cements shown in Fig. 11 are high in Na_2O and low in K_2O, those in Fig. 12 are low in Na_2O and high in K_2O. These cements require large additions of gypsum for proper retardation and the cement high in Na_2O requires more gypsum than the cement high in K_2O. As the SO_3 content is increased from 1.0 or 1.5 per cent to 2.4 per cent the peaks on the curves become higher and occur somewhat later. The cements of high Na_2O content, Fig. 11 shows the third cycle of ascending and descending rates of hydration (the first cycle for the heat of immediate hydration is not shown) with 3.0, 3.5, and 4.0 per cent SO_3. The cements high in K_2O, Fig. 12, do not show the third cycle. With the clinkers of low $3CaO \cdot Al_2O_3$ content, the one high in Na_2O (Fig. 11) requires 4.5 per cent SO_3 to give the curve of a properly retarded cement, the one high in K_2O (Fig. 12) requires 3.0 per cent

SO_3, while that of low alkali content (Fig. 8) require only 1.9 per cent SO_3.

The Effect of Alkalies on the Rate of Reaction of Gypsum with the Calcium Aluminates:

In the earlier discussion the action of gypsum in retarding the hydration of the aluminate phases was attributed to the fact that alumina is less soluble in a lime-gypsum solution than in a saturated lime solution. In the presence of the saturated lime-gypsum solution the aluminate phases dissolve at a retarded rate and react with lime and gypsum to form an insoluble calcium sulfoaluminate. By this process the gypsum eventually becomes depleted and its concentration in the aqueous solution decreases. When this condition is reached, the solubility of alumina again increases and a rapid reaction will occur if sufficient unhydrated calcium aluminates are available. This rapid reaction causes the abnormal peaks on the heat-liberation curves, sometimes observed as an abnormally high peak during the second cycle of ascending and descending rates and sometimes as a third cycle of ascending and descending rates. At this stage hydrated calcium aluminates are being formed in the paste. To bring out more clearly the relationship between the SO_3 concentration of the aqueous solutions and the appearance of the abnormal peaks on the curves some additional analyses were made of the aqueous solutions extracted from hydrating pastes. For this purpose two cements prepared from clinker No. 16839 were used, one with 3.5 per cent SO_3 and the other with 5.0 per cent SO_3. For these tests 200 g. of cement was mixed with 225 ml. of water and the paste was agitated continuously until the time of test. The clear liquid was then filtered off and analyzed. The partial analyses of the extracts are given in Table IV.

The results show that up to the seventh hour the compositions of the liquid extracts obtained from the two cements are almost identical, and during this time the rates of hydration of the two cements are identical, Fig. 11. At the twelfth hour the SO_3 concentration of the liquid extract obtained from the cement with 3.5 per cent SO_3 is considerably lower than it was at the seventh hour, and at the eighteenth hour it is practically nil. On the other hand, the SO_3 concentration of the liquid extract obtained from the cement with 5.0 per cent SO_3 increases from the seventh to

at the time the gypsum becomes depleted and its concentration in the aqueous solution decreases.

With cements of similar $3CaO \cdot Al_2O_3$ content the alkalies influence the rate of reaction of gypsum with the cements, those of high alkali content reacts with gypsum more rapidly than those low in alkalies. This observation is based on the results of analysis of liquid extracts given in Table V.

With the cement of high alkali content (No. 16839) the gypsum, equivalent to 3.5 per cent SO_3, has completely reacted

TABLE IV.—PARTIAL ANALYSES OF LIQUID EXTRACTS OBTAINED FROM HYDRATING PASTES.

Cements prepared from clinker No. 16839; C_3A, 6.2; Na_2O, 1.01; K_2O, 0.10 per cent.

Time of Extraction	Analysis, g. per liter			
	SO_3	CaO	Na_2O	K_2O
CEMENT WITH 3.5 PER CENT SO_3				
10 min.	2.181	1.325	1.974	0.402
4 hr.	2.137	1.370	2.214	0.425
7 hr.	2.404	1.235	2.567	0.450
12 hr.	1.444	0.485	3.259	0.518
18 hr.	0.002	0.130	4.949	0.560
CEMENT WITH 5.0 PER CENT SO_3				
10 min.	2.209	1.295	1.924	0.409
4 hr.	2.144	1.380	2.167	0.396
7 hr.	2.444	1.225	2.542	0.415
12 hr.	3.027	1.010	3.220	0.499
18 hr.	3.243	0.865	3.681	0.495

TABLE V.—THE EFFECT OF THE ALKALIES ON THE RATE OF REACTION OF GYPSUM WITH CEMENTS OF SIMILAR $3CaO \cdot Al_2O_3$ CONTENT.

Time of Extraction, hr.	Partial Analyses of Liquid Extracts Obtained from Hydrating Pastes, g. per liter			
	SO_3	CaO	Na_2O	K_2O
CLINKER NO. 16839—C_3A, 6.2; Na_2O, 1.01; K_2O, 0.10; SO_3, 3.5 PER CENT				
4	2.14	1.37	2.21	0.43
7	2.40	1.24	2.57	0.45
12	1.44	0.49	3.26	0.52
18	0.00	0.13	4.95	0.56
30	0.00	0.12	5.19	0.55
CLINKER NO. 16890—C_3A, 5.1; Na_2O, 0.32; K_2O, 0.02; SO_3, 3.5 PER CENT				
4	1.19	2.08	0.35	0.06
7	1.20	1.90	0.49	0.06
12	1.26	1.70	0.64	0.10
18	1.31	1.57	0.77	0.09
30	0.93	1.22	0.86	0.11

the twelfth hour and from the twelfth to the eighteenth hour. The heat-liberation curves, Fig. 11 show that the rates of hydration of the two cements are almost identical up to the tenth hour. At the twelfth hour the third cycle of ascending rate of heat liberation is just starting for the cement with 3.5 per cent SO_3 and its rate of hydration then becomes higher than that of the cement with 5.0 per cent SO_3. Thus these results give further evidence that the gypsum functions as a retarder by its presence in the aqueous solution, and that the delayed rapid reaction occurs

in 18 hr. or less as shown by the absence of SO_3 in the extract, whereas with the cement of low alkali content (No. 16890) the gypsum has not completely reacted in 30 hr. These results seem to indicate that at least part of the alkalies are present in the aluminate phases, and that the aluminate phases containing alkalies hydrate more quickly than do aluminate phases which are alkali free or of lower alkali content. Thus, it seems probable that the effect of the alkalies on the gypsum requirements of cements of similar $3CaO \cdot Al_2O_3$ content may be accounted for on the basis of their influence on the rate of hydration of the aluminate phases.

The Relative Effect of Gypsum and Plaster of Paris:

Forsen (11) concluded that, used as retarders, gypsum ($CaSO_4 \cdot 2H_2O$) and plaster of Paris ($CaSO_4 \cdot \frac{1}{2}H_2O$) would not behave in the same manner. He believed that with the addition of gypsum a saturated calcium sulfate solution was formed and under these conditions $3CaO \cdot Al_2O_3 \cdot CaSO_4 \cdot 12H_2O$ precipitated as a protective film on the cement particles; but with the addition of plaster of Paris a supersaturated calcium sulfate solution was formed with the result that

TABLE VI.—EFFECT OF DEHYDRATION OF GYPSUM UPON THE HEATS OF IMMEDIATE HYDRATION.

Cement	SO_3 Content, per cent	Specific Surface, sq. cm. per g.	Condition of Cement	Immediate Heat of Hydration, cal. per g.			
				5m.	10m.	15m.	30m.
CLINKER No. 15367—C_3S, 45.5; C_2S, 28.4; C_3A, 14.3; C_4AF, 6.7							
No. 15754...	2.4	1800	Original	3.9	4.3	4.5	4.8
No. 15754...	2.4	1800	Heated at 250 F. for 18 hr.	4.1	4.6	4.7	5.0

$3CaO \cdot Al_2O_3 \cdot 3CaSO_4 \cdot 31\frac{1}{2}H_2O$ crystallized from the solution without forming a protective film. Thus Forsen concluded that gypsum retards the set but that plaster of Paris does not.

To examine Forsen's hypothesis of the effect of gypsum and plaster of Paris upon the rate of heat liberation, a cement was selected which had been ground in a laboratory mill at a low temperature, 75 F. Little, if any, dehydration of gypsum would be expected at such a low grinding temperature. A portion of the cement was heated to 250 F. for 18 hr. to dehydrate the gypsum. The rates of heat liberation were determined for the original cement and the heated cement; the results are given in Table VI and

Fig. 13. These results show that the dehydration of the gypsum caused no appreciable change in the rates of heat-liberation. Thus it appears that the difference in the time of set, as observed by Forsen, resulted from the set of plaster of Paris *per se*, and not from any difference in the chemical reaction of the cement.

The Effect of Specific Surface upon the Rate of Hydration:

The five commercial clinkers ground at the plant to three degrees of fineness

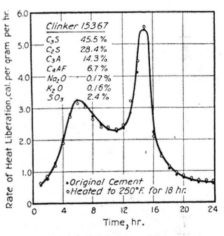

FIG. 13.—Relative Effect of Gypsum and Plaster of Paris Upon the Rate of Hydration.

were used to determine the effect of fineness upon the rate of heat liberation. The pastes were mixed and cured at 75 F. and the rates of heat liberation were determined for the first 72 hr. It will be shown from the results of these tests that: (1) The maximum rate of heat liberation becomes higher as the specific surface increases. (2) With cements of high $3CaO \cdot Al_2O_3$ content the maximum rate of heat liberation becomes abnormally high at the higher specific surface when the SO_3 content is maintained constant. When the SO_3 content of the cements in

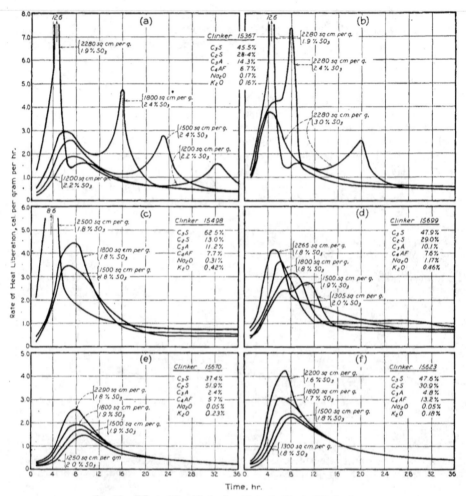

Fig. 14.—Effect of Specific Surface Upon the Heat of Hydration.

Al_2O_3 content, gypsum in amounts equivalent to 2.0 per cent SO_3 provides normal retardation for the range of specific surfaces investigated. Such increases in the rate of heat liberation as are observed are to be expected from the increased rate of hydration resulting from the higher specific surface. With cements of higher $3CaO \cdot Al_2O_3$ content it appears that with increasing specific surface, a larger portion of the aluminate phases becomes available for reaction at early ages and larger quantities of gypsum are required for proper retardation as measured by rates of heat-liberation.

The Heat of Immediate Hydration:

The curves showing heat of immediate hydration includes the heat liberated within 30 min. after water is added to the cement. The heats of immediate hydration were determined by means of the bottle calorimeter. The effect of SO_3 content upon the heats of immediate hydration for cements of the same specific surface is shown in Fig. 15. The heats of immediate hydration are higher for cements of high $3CaO \cdot Al_2O_3$ content than for cements of low $3CaO \cdot Al_2O_3$ content and become lower with increasing SO_3 contents. For cements of the same $3CaO \cdot Al_2O_3$ content variations in alkali content appear to have very little effect on the heats of immediate hydration. The effect of specific surface is shown in Fig. 16. The heats of immediate hydration become higher as the specific surface increases. A large percentage of the total heat liberated within the first 30 min. is liberated within the first 5 min.

The results obtained for the heats of immediate hydration are in accord with the theory that the lime-gypsum solution is the effective retarder. With increasing quantities of gypsum the solution becomes saturated with gypsum more quickly, and the heat of immediate hydration is decreased. As the specific surface is increased with the gypsum constant, a larger portion of the aluminate phases is available for immediate reaction with the mixing water—before the solution becomes saturated with gypsum—and the heats of immediate hydration become larger.

Effect of Gypsum on the Cumulative Heats of Hydration:

Since gypsum alters the rate of hydration at early ages, it would be expected that the cumulative heats of hydration would be altered likewise. That this is true is shown by the date given in Table VII. The first additions of gypsum increase the heats of hydration while with larger additions of gypsum the values decrease. The quantity of gypsum required to obtain the highest heats of hydration is not the same for all clinkers, nor is it the same at all ages for the same clinker. The relationship between the heats of hydration at 1 and 3 days and the strengths at these ages will be discussed later.

THE INFLUENCE OF GYPSUM ON THE
PHYSICAL PROPERTIES OF THE
HARDENED PASTE

In the data already presented it has been shown that varying the gypsum content of the cement very definitely alters the rate of hydration at early ages and alters the hydration products that are formed. It seems probable that such changes in the hydration process would produce differences in the structure of the hardened paste and thereby alter the physical properties of the hardened paste. Previous investigators have found that gypsum influences the properties of portland cements. Kühl and Lu (18) found that shrinkage can be reduced by proper additions of gypsum and that the quantity of gypsum required to obtain the lowest shrinkage would increase with the $3CaO \cdot Al_2O_3$ content of the cement. Haegerman (19)

TABLE VII.—THE EFFECT OF GYPSUM ON THE CUMULATIVE HEATS OF HYDRATION—SERIES 287.
Neat cement pastes, water-cement ratio = 0.40 by weight.

SO_3, per cent	Heat of Hydration, cal. per g. for Period Indicated										
	5 min.	10 min.	30 min.	2 hr.	4 hr.	8 hr.	12 hr.	16 hr.	24 hr.	48 hr.	72 hr.
CLINKERS OF HIGH $3CaO\cdot Al_2O_3$ AND LOW ALKALI CONTENT Clinker No. 15367, C_3A, 14.3; Na_2O, 0.17; K_2O, 0.16 per cent											
1.5	4.1	4.6	5.3	6.6	9.0	24.8	28.2	32.4	39.8	54.3	63.5
1.9	3.8	4.2	5.0	6.3	9.3	20.9	35.8	39.7	46.2	59.2	68.1
2.4	3.5	3.9	4.6	6.1	9.5	21.5	31.1	45.9	53.0	65.5	73.8
3.0	3.3	3.8	4.5	5.9	9.2	20.9	28.8	33.7	42.3	65.1	72.8
3.5	3.3	3.7	4.5	6.1	10.0	23.1	30.9	35.6	42.2	59.8	75.1
Clinker No. 16823, C_3A, 12.5; Na_2O, 0.05; K_2O, 0.25 per cent											
1.0	3.6	4.1	5.3	6.9	10.5	17.7	19.4	22.6	33.7	58.6	72.1
1.5	3.3	3.9	4.8	6.4	10.5	32.4	37.4	42.8	51.4	67.0	76.1
1.9	3.1	3.7	4.6	6.1	10.6	37.5	44.3	49.1	56.3	68.8	77.1
2.4	3.1	3.6	4.4	5.9	10.3	30.0	51.0	55.5	61.9	72.8	79.5
3.0	3.1	3.5	4.4	5.8	10.1	28.8	42.4	51.8	60.4	71.7	79.5
3.5	3.0	3.5	4.4	5.8	9.8	28.2	40.4	47.5	57.3	71.5	78.8
4.0	3.1	3.5	4.3	5.7	9.6	27.5	39.7	45.8	53.4	69.5	77.6
CLINKERS OF HIGH OR MODERATELY HIGH $3CaO\cdot Al_2O_3$ AND HIGH OR MODERATELY HIGH ALKALI CONTENT Clinker No. 15900, C_3A, 13.1; Na_2O, 0.36; K_2O, 0.50 per cent											
1.5	4.3	4.8	5.4	6.7	9.4	16.8	23.4	27.0	37.0	53.6	66.1
1.9	4.7	5.4	5.9	7.1	9.7	27.0	33.2	38.1	45.5	60.6	70.3
2.4	4.7	5.0	5.8	7.1	10.2	24.3	44.2	48.4	54.4	68.4	74.7
3.0	4.2	4.6	5.3	6.6	9.8	23.5	45.1	53.4	59.3	69.7	75.6
3.5	4.0	4.5	5.1	6.6	10.0	23.9	34.0	45.2	60.2	70.6	76.6
Clinker No. 15498, C_3A, 11.2; Na_2O, 0.31; K_2O, 0.42 per cent											
1.0	3.7	4.1	4.8	8.0	14.3	21.8	28.1	32.1	42.0	60.1	72.8
1.5	3.5	3.9	4.6	7.1	13.9	29.3	35.5	39.2	45.2	59.3	70.0
1.9	3.2	3.5	4.3	6.8	13.2	29.2	39.1	43.6	49.4	63.1	73.7
2.4	3.2	3.6	4.3	6.9	14.2	31.1	39.7	45.5	53.8	69.5	78.4
3.0	2.9	3.2	4.1	6.9	15.0	32.4	40.4	45.5	52.9	66.2	76.1
Clinker No. 16843, C_3A, 11.0; Na_2O, 1.03; K_2O, 0.06 per cent											
1.5	4.0	4.6	5.7	8.0	12.2	17.8	22.6	28.1	37.1	55.2	67.2
1.9	4.0	4.4	5.3	7.1	12.0	24.6	30.4	35.0	42.1	59.2	68.7
2.4	3.7	4.3	5.2	7.4	13.0	33.0	41.1	45.6	52.1	67.8	73.3
3.0	3.7	4.1	5.1	7.6	13.9	28.4	40.3	48.7	59.3	69.0	72.9
3.5	3.7	4.1	4.9	7.0	12.9	27.7	35.8	42.1	52.7	67.7	72.0
4.0	3.6	4.0	4.8	7.0	13.3	28.0	35.2	39.8	47.0	65.3	72.1
4.5	3.3	3.8	4.6	6.7	14.3	29.9	37.0	40.9	46.1	53.8	57.9
Clinker No. 15699; C_3A, 10.1; Na_2O, 1.17; K_2O, 0.46 per cent											
1.0	2.6	3.5	4.6	6.7	10.1	19.5	27.1	32.6	40.6	59.9	68.9
1.5	2.6	3.4	4.2	5.7	9.9	22.8	28.6	33.3	41.8	61.4	68.9
1.9	2.8	3.4	4.1	6.2	10.8	26.8	33.1	38.2	46.5	65.2	71.5
2.4	2.7	3.3	4.0	5.8	10.1	31.4	39.5	45.0	53.6	70.5	74.7
3.0	2.8	3.3	4.0	5.8	10.1	27.6	42.6	48.1	56.3	69.0	73.0
Clinker No. 16827, C_3A, 8.1; Na_2O, 0.04; K_2O, 1.37 per cent											
1.0	3.3	5.1	6.8	9.8	14.9	23.8	29.7	34.7	42.6	57.8	65.4
1.5	3.6	4.4	5.2	7.2	11.6	22.2	28.4	34.2	42.8	58.3	65.9
1.9	3.4	4.1	5.3	7.2	12.9	28.3	34.2	39.4	47.2	61.9	69.3
2.4	3.3	4.0	4.8	6.9	12.2	34.6	41.1	45.5	52.0	64.9	70.6
3.0	3.3	3.9	4.7	6.6	11.4	28.7	43.2	47.4	53.3	63.4	67.8
3.5	3.2	3.8	4.7	6.9	12.1	27.5	40.2	47.5	55.0	65.1	69.7
4.0	3.3	3.8	4.7	6.6	11.4	25.5	33.6	39.2	47.4	61.9	69.1
CLINKERS OF LOW $3CaO\cdot Al_2O_3$ AND LOW ALKALI CONTENT Clinker No. 16890, C_3A, 5.1; Na_2O, 0.32; K_2O, 0.02 per cent											
1.0	2.6	3.0	3.7	4.9	6.5	8.9	12.1	15.3	20.8	29.7	34.8
1.5	2.4	2.8	3.4	5.1	9.3	18.8	22.7	24.9	28.4	34.9	39.0
1.9	2.4	2.9	3.5	5.2	9.8	18.9	24.8	28.4	32.4	37.9	41.2
2.4	2.6	2.9	3.5	5.1	9.6	18.7	23.9	27.2	31.8	38.9	41.8
3.0	2.3	2.7	3.4	5.4	10.3	19.3	24.1	27.1	31.0	37.7	42.5
3.5	2.4	2.8	3.5	5.3	9.6	18.8	23.9	26.8	31.4	36.3	39.4
4.0	2.3	2.7	3.4	4.7	9.1	17.9	22.6	25.3	28.5	33.5	37.0

TABLE VII.—*Continued*

SO₃, per cent	Heat of Hydration, cal. per g. for Period Indicated										
	5 min.	10 min.	30 min.	2 hr.	4 hr.	8 hr.	12 hr.	16 hr.	24 hr.	48 hr.	72 hr.
Clinker No. 15623, C₃A, 4.8; Na₂O, 0.05; K₂O, 0.18 per cent											
0.03	4.0	4.5	5.0	5.6	5.9	6.7	9.1	15.0	28.1	44.6	51.9
1.0	2.3	2.5	3.1	4.0	7.7	18.5	·24.4	27.8	32.8	39.4	44.1
1.5	2.0	2.3	2.9	3.9	7.8	19.2	27.1	31.6	37.0	45.2	49.6
1.9	1.9	2.2	2.8	3.8	7.9	20.3	28.4	33.6	39.8	48.5	53.4
2.4	2.0	2.3	2.8	4.1	8.1	20.5	28.2	32.9	38.9	48.2	53.7
Clinker No. 15670, C₃A, 2.4; Na₂O, 0.05; K₂O, 0.23 per cent											
0.17	2.0	2.4	3.1	3.5	3.8	5.0	9.1	14.2	20.2	29.4	33.2
1.0	1.8	2.0	2.6	3.0	3.7	10.7	17.8	21.3	25.1	30.2	33.5
1.5	1.5	1.7	2.3	2.7	3.5	11.0	18.3	22.5	27.5	33.7	37.3
1.9	1.4	1.5	2.1	2.5	3.5	11.9	19.4	23.6	28.6	35.3	38.9
2.4	1.4	1.6	2.2	2.6	3.5	11.6	19.3	23.6	28.2	34.2	36.9
CLINKERS OF LOW 3CaO·Al₂O₃ AND HIGH ALKALI CONTENT Clinker No. 16839, C₃A, 6.2; Na₂O, 1.01; K₂O, 0.10 per cent											
1.5	3.9	4.7	5.5	6.8	9.2	12.6	15.4	18.2	23.3	34.2	42.5
1.9	3.9	4.5	5.0	5.8	8.2	16.2	18.8	21.2	26.4	36.6	43.9
2.4	3.9	4.4	5.2	6.2	8.8	21.8	26.5	29.3	33.8	45.1	49.9
3.0	3.7	4.2	5.0	6.2	8.7	18.1	29.8	35.0	39.7	48.5	52.2
3.5	3.7	4.2	5.0	6.0	8.8	18.4	26.0	35.2	41.0	47.1	49.5
4.0	3.7	4.1	4.8	6.3	9.1	18.9	25.9	30.5	40.2	49.0	53.8
4.5	3.6	4.0	4.8	6.1	9.4	19.6	26.4	30.5	37.2	45.0	50.2
Clinker No. 16831, C₃A, 5.7; Na₂O, 0.05; K₂O, 1.37 per cent											
1.0	1.5	2.3	3.7	5.2	9.6	17.8	21.2	23.7	27.3	37.6	44.2
1.5	2.0	2.6	3.7	4.4	6.9	19.5	26.9	30.5	35.1	43.6	48.5
1.9	2.0	2.7	3.7	4.5	7.1	21.0	31.0	36.0	40.9	49.6	54.3
2.4	2.0	2.6	3.7	4.7	7.7	21.0	32.3	38.0	43.8	53.2	58.3
3.0	2.0	2.7	3.6	4.3	7.5	20.3	29.9	35.9	42.8	53.3	58.5
3.5	2.0	2.7	3.5	4.5	7.1	18.5	27.0	32.1	38.5	48.9	54.9
4.0	1.5	2.2	3.4	4.4	7.3	19.2	27.9	32.5	38.1	47.5	52.6

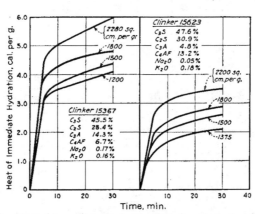

FIG. 16.—Heat of Immediate Hydration With Specific Surface Varied.

found that the quantity of gypsum required to obtain the highest strength and lowest shrinkage would depend on the 3CaO·Al₂O₃ content of the cement. With cements of high 3CaO·Al₂O₃ content the quantity of gypsum required would be larger than that permitted by present specifications.

No attempt was made in the tests reported here to examine the structure of

TABLE VIII.—STRENGTH AND MODULUS OF ELASTICITY OF MORTAR PRISMS—SERIES 287

One 2 by 2 by 9½-in. prism made on each of two days for each age of test.
Each flexural strength value and Young's modulus is the average of two tests, each compressive strength value is the average of four tests—modified 2-in. cubes.
Mix: Cement 1.0, pulverized silica 0.3, standard Ottawa sand 2.3.
Water content to give approximately 1-in. slump using a 6-in. cone.

SO_3, per cent	Water, gal. per sack	Flexural Strength, psi.						Compressive Strength, psi.						Young's Modulus of Elasticity, E, psi. $\times 10^{-6}$					
		1 day	3 days	7 days	28 days	3 months	1 yr.	1 day	3 days	7 days	28 days	3 months	1 yr.	1 day	3 days	7 days	28 days	3 months	1 yr.
CLINKERS OF HIGH $3CaO \cdot Al_2O_3$ AND LOW ALKALI CONTENT — Clinker No. 15367, C_3A, 14.3; Na_2O, 0.16; K_2O, 0.17 per cent																			
1.5	5.02	195	575	770	890	845	880	630	2700	4610	6650	6940	6990	1.7	3.7	4.6	5.3	5.3	5.6
1.9	5.02	290	675	815	1000	960	960	1000	2970	4830	7250	8240	8380	2.3	3.9	4.7	5.3	5.5	5.7
2.4	5.02	320	670	860	1025	970	980	1380	3440	5320	7830	8370	8840	2.7	4.1	4.8	5.5	5.7	6.0
3.0	5.02	275	640	870	1030	1100	1045	1300	3530	5610	7830	8940	8700	2.5	4.1	5.0	5.5	5.9	6.0
3.5	5.02	270	640	905	990	1010	1020	1180	3740	5580	7680	8370	8530	2.4	4.3	5.1	5.5	5.8	5.9
Clinker No. 16823, C_3A, 12.5; Na_2O, 0.05; K_2O, 0.25 per cent																			
1.0	4.82	105	805	1095	1035	1075	840	560	4360	6810	8440	8640	8310	1.6	5.0	5.7	6.1	6.4	6.2
1.5	4.82	380	865	1185	1000	1045	945	1750	5360	7620	9140	9580	9350	3.3	5.2	6.0	6.3	6.5	6.4
1.9	4.82	530	905	1055	1050	1050	1010	2160	5840	7910	9980	10080	9180	3.6	5.3	6.0	6.5	6.5	6.4
2.4	4.82	590	935	1300	1245	1160	1110	2870	6330	8630	10280	10180	10000	4.0	5.4	6.2	6.5	6.6	6.7
3.0	4.82	665	935	1050	990	1105	1040	3290	6460	8780	9790	10140	10030	4.4	5.5	6.2	6.4	6.7	6.5
3.5	4.82	585	950	1085	1140	1120	1120	3250	6400	7990	9780	9320	9960	4.4	5.5	6.2	6.4	6.4	6.5
4.0	4.82	510	925	1050	1130	1100	1060	2720	6360	8230	9350	9540	9980	3.7	5.5	6.0	6.3	6.4	6.6
CLINKERS OF HIGH OR MODERATELY HIGH $3CaO \cdot Al_2O_3$ AND HIGH OR MODERATELY HIGH ALKALI CONTENT — Clinker No. 15900, C_3A, 13.1; Na_2O, 0.36; K_2O, 0.50 per cent																			
1.5	4.85	215	565	720	890	1025	1015	700	3020	4440	6850	7940	7980	1.9	4.0	4.6	5.8	5.9	6.1
1.9	4.85	325	635	795	885	960	990	1140	3330	4880	6790	8320	8290	2.7	4.3	4.9	5.5	5.9	6.1
2.4	4.85	420	725	795	975	1055	950	1600	3760	5070	7090	8010	8620	3.1	4.3	4.9	5.4	5.9	6.2
3.0	4.85	430	795	815	1005	1125	1095	2030	4210	5570	7510	8440	8960	3.3	4.6	5.0	5.7	6.1	6.2
3.5	4.85	450	790	870	1045	1065	1085	2140	4410	5710	7480	8420	9190	3.6	4.7	5.2	5.7	6.1	6.2
5.0	4.86	330	515	795	985	1115	1155	1610	3290	5220	7760	9280	10390	2.9	4.2	5.1	5.8	6.3	6.4
Clinker No. 15498, C_3A, 11.2; Na_2O, 0.31; K_2O, 0.42 per cent																			
1.0	4.90	215	720	1030	975	855	915	900	4150	6800	7820	8200	8140	1.7	4.2	5.3	5.6	5.6	5.8
1.5	4.90	360	785	1000	980	915	940	1480	4420	6860	8360	8490	8620	2.6	4.4	5.4	5.7	5.8	6.0
1.9	4.90	445	830	1015	1085	995	955	1980	4720	7190	8070	8790	9030	3.3	4.7	5.6	5.8	6.0	6.2
2.4	4.90	455	845	1125	1060	1020	1055	2140	5230	7280	8390	8950	9300	3.4	4.9	5.7	5.9	6.0	6.2
3.0	4.90	380	835	1015	1170	1170	1035	2040	5240	7290	8660	9250	9290	3.2	4.9	5.7	6.0	6.1	6.2
Clinker No. 16843, C_3A, 11.0; Na_2O, 1.03; K_2O, 0.06 per cent																			
1.5	4.70	285	750	920	1065	1045	1110	1010	3720	5360	7030	7460	8380	2.4	4.7	5.6	6.3	6.6	6.7
1.9	4.70	400	860	925	960	1005	1105	1540	4180	5500	7270	7820	8430	3.2	4.8	5.8	6.4	6.5	6.7
2.4	4.70	570	900	940	1050	1025	1025	2100	4640	5820	7190	7780	8700	3.7	5.3	6.0	6.4	6.5	6.7
3.0	4.70	575	875	965	985	1085	1165	2640	4740	5820	7110	7560	8420	4.1	5.5	6.1	6.3	6.5	6.8
3.5	4.70	555	850	1035	1030	1125	1105	2640	4880	5930	7070	7830	8630	4.2	5.5	6.0	6.3	6.6	6.7
4.0	4.70	435	815	965	1020	1110	1170	2260	4960	6300	7430	8180	8980	3.8	5.5	6.2	6.2	6.5	6.7
4.5	4.70	405	740	940	1040	1135	1180	2060	4530	6090	7870	8650	9500	3.6	5.4	5.9	6.2	6.5	6.7
Clinker No. 15699, C_3A, 10.1; Na_2O, 1.17; K_2O, 0.46 per cent																			
1.0	5.00	215	635	850	880	875	860	940	3350	5200	6130	6620	6880	2.0	4.3	5.1	5.5	5.7	5.8
1.5	5.00	265	655	880	880	980	960	1030	3490	5240	6420	6800	7060	2.2	4.2	5.0	5.5	5.7	5.9
1.9	5.00	295	705	870	935	980	935	1200	3530	5200	6180	6340	6790	2.4	4.4	5.2	5.3	5.5	5.8
2.4	5.00	310	660	910	945	925	950	1400	3550	5020	5990	6220	6430	2.7	4.1	5.0	5.3	5.5	5.7
3.0	5.00	350	750	885	920	980	990	1560	3570	4940	5530	6100	6330	2.9	4.3	5.0	5.1	5.3	5.6
5.0	4.96	390	855	920	1110	1065	1080	1860	4720	6140	6480	7450	8200	3.1	4.9	5.6	5.9	5.1	6.2
Clinker No. 16827, C_3A, 8.1; Na_2O, 0.04; K_2O, 1.37 per cent																			
1.0	5.26	270	640	830	870	935	910	1000	3280	5120	6540	6760	6990	2.1	4.2	5.0	5.5	5.9	5.9
1.5	5.12	285	705	865	960	980	970	950	3540	5360	6820	6960	7520	2.2	4.3	5.2	5.7	5.8	6.0
1.9	5.00	345	740	915	855	1030	975	1310	3860	6070	7060	7260	8020	2.8	4.6	5.5	5.8	6.0	6.1
2.4	5.00	405	840	995	1065	1070	950	1680	4150	5900	7140	7480	8190	3.2	4.7	5.6	5.9	6.1	6.2
3.0	5.00	525	785	1010	1065	1105	1085	2090	4350	5910	7160	7800	7840	3.7	5.0	5.5	5.9	6.1	6.3
3.5	4.86	525	810	1140	1160	1090	1070	2380	4790	6130	6940	7700	8230	4.0	5.2	5.8	6.2	6.3	6.4
4.0	4.86	390	860	1005	1050	1110	1230	2080	4620	5960	7160	7710	8220	3.7	5.4	5.8	6.1	6.2	6.4

TABLE VIII.—*Continued*

SO_3, per cent	Water, gal. per sack	Flexural Strength, psi.						Compressive Strength, psi.						Young's Modulus of Elasticity, E, psi. 10^{-6}					
		1 day	3 days	7 days	28 days	3 months	1 yr.	1 day	3 days	7 days	28 days	3 months	1 yr.	1 day	3 days	7 days	28 days3	3 months	1 yr.
CLINKERS OF LOW $3CaO \cdot Al_2O_3$ AND LOW ALKALI CONTENT																			
Clinker No. 16890, C_3A, 5.1; Na_2O, 0.32; K_2O, 0.02 per cent																			
1.0	4.36	145	440	530	935	1010	1010	480	1570	2410	6360	9530	10680	1.3	3.2	4.4	5.6	6.5	6.9
1.5	4.36	230	440	600	960	1190	1245	770	1700	2620	6360	9540	10600	2.5	3.5	4.4	5.7	6.7	7.0
1.9	4.36	270	465	580	980	1225	1245	990	1860	2740	6480	9590	10660	2.9	4.0	4.7	5.9	6.8	7.0
2.4	4.36	260	490	660	995	1220	1225	920	1970	2880	6450	9280	10640	2.6	4.2	4.7	5.9	6.7	7.1
3.0	4.36	230	405	680	1025	1235	1240	820	1780	2990	6280	8860	10320	2.3	3.8	4.8	6.0	6.7	7.1
3.5	4.36	200	380	610	995	1160	1160	820	1620	2840	6130	9160	10290	2.3	3.6	4.7	6.0	6.8	7.0
4.0	4.50	215	375	560	920	1385	1125	780	1600	2540	6190	9100	10370	2.1	3.4	4.5	5.9	6.5	7.0
Clinker No. 15623, C_3A, 4.8; Na_2O, 0.05; K_2O, 0.18 per cent																			
0.03	4.60	140	545	685	895	1005	1095	590	2820	4510	7220	8580	9280	1.1	4.2	5.0	5.5	6.1	6.3
1.0	4.60	275	620	850	1055	1080	1165	1250	3180	4560	7170	9200	9820	2.6	4.5	5.3	5.7	6.1	6.6
1.5	4.60	315	635	885	960	1193	1120	1410	3420	4910	7060	9140	10020	2.8	4.5	5.2	5.7	6.2	6.5
1.9	4.60	315	625	810	970	1150	1255	1400	3460	4960	7280	9110	9960	2.8	4.6	5.3	5.7	6.2	6.7
2.4	4.60	310	600	780	980	1115	1090	1480	3360	5100	7360	9270	10370	2.7	4.4	5.2	5.7	6.3	6.5
Clinker No. 15670, C_3A, 2.4; Na_2O, 0.05; K_2O, 0.23 per cent																			
0.17	4.39	100	295	445	770	945	1090	390	1200	1980	4710	8020	8560	1.5	2.8	3.7	5.2	6.2	6.3
1.0	4.39	215	390	545	945	1195	1190	780	1650	2390	6120	10150	10320	2.1	3.4	4.2	5.5	6.0	6.8
1.5	4.39	210	410	585	895	1225	1235	840	1980	2780	6170	10250	10670	2.3	3.8	4.4	5.7	6.6	6.8
1.9	4.39	190	385	580	1070	1205	1250	820	1880	2990	6250	10090	11140	2.0	3.5	4.5	5.7	6.5	6.9
2.4	4.39	195	355	510	745	1060	1100	790	1500	2480	6080	10090	11130	1.9	3.0	4.1	5.5	6.5	6.9
CLINKERS OF LOW $3CaO \cdot Al_2O_3$ AND HIGH ALKALI CONTENT																			
Clinker No. 16839, C_3A, 6.2; Na_2O, 1.01; K_2O, 0.10 per cent																			
1.5	4.70	65	360	490	835	1040	1040	360	1480	2400	5230	6940	8040	1.1	3.0	3.9	5.4	6.1	6.4
1.9	4.61	40	405	585	940	1025	1005	460	1630	2640	5250	7500	8520	1.4	3.2	4.1	5.6	6.3	6.7
2.4	4.70	145	490	610	910	995	1035	720	1840	2880	5520	6990	8020	2.1	3.6	4.4	5.5	6.1	6.5
3.0	4.70	285	510	650	1110	1130	1065	950	2120	3130	5500	7140	8520	2.6	3.9	4.6	5.7	6.3	6.6
3.5	4.70	345	535	715	1040	1030	970	1200	2240	3130	5580	7350	8430	3.2	4.2	4.8	5.7	6.4	6.5
4.0	4.75	355	505	745	1135	1245	1150	1280	2270	3190	5490	6990	8010	3.2	4.2	4.7	5.8	6.2	6.6
4.5	4.81	250	570	725	1040	1230	1305	1050	2290	3260	5600	7460	8360	2.6	4.2	4.9	5.8	6.2	6.8
Clinker No. 16831, C_3A, 5.7; Na_2O, 0.05; K_2O, 1.37 per cent																			
1.0	4.61	230	485	750	1030	1015	1045	880	2320	4030	6010	7150	7530	2.3	4.0	5.0	5.9	6.0	6.4
1.5	4.51	360	720	960	975	1000	1120	1550	3160	4800	6480	7280	7800	3.3	5.0	5.7	6.2	6.3	6.6
1.9	4.51	490	775	905	1025	1015	1125	1920	3660	5080	6470	7660	8100	3.8	5.1	5.8	6.2	6.4	6.7
2.4	4.51	510	790	995	1115	1125	1160	2100	4090	4960	6580	7180	7820	4.1	5.3	5.8	6.2	6.4	6.6
3.0	4.56	455	825	925	1095	1075	1235	2220	4260	5400	7000	7830	8560	4.0	5.4	5.8	6.2	6.6	6.7
3.5	4.56	425	745	915	1135	1070	1085	2030	4310	5680	6970	7880	8880	3.7	5.3	5.9	6.2	6.6	6.6
4.0	4.56	375	655	730	985	1035	1150	1740	3470	4930	6920	8160	9050	3.3	4.9	5.5	6.1	6.5	6.7

the hardened paste by direct methods. However, physical tests were made to determine the effect of variations in gypsum content upon the physical properties of the hardened paste. Mortar prisms were prepared for the physical tests. The properties determined for the prisms included: compressive strength, flexural strength, Young's modulus of elasticity by the electrodynamic method, expansion in water, and contraction in air. Miscellaneous tests of the cements included: specific surface, normal consist-ency, time of set, soundness and expansion in the autoclave test.

Preparation of Test Specimens:

The specimens used for the physical test were 2 by 2 by 9½-in. mortar prisms. Two specimens of a kind were used for each type of test. These were made in two rounds on different days. Those used for expansion in water and contraction in air were provided with gage points, one at each end of the long axis, for measurement of changes in length.

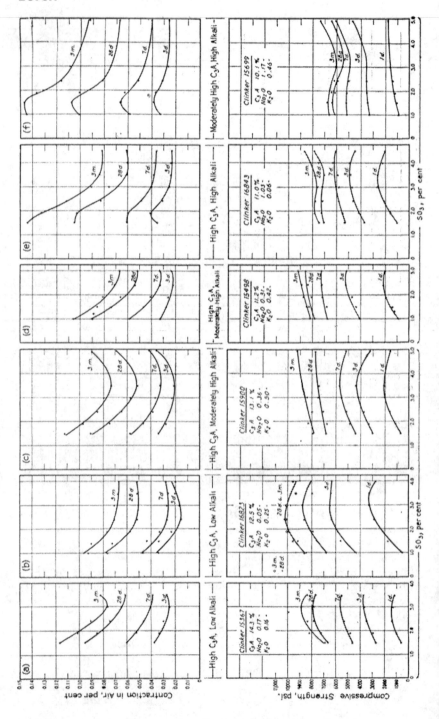

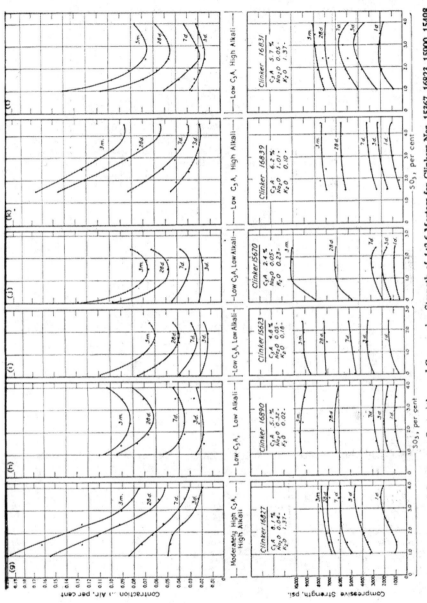

Fig. 17.—Influence of Gypsum on Contraction and Compressive Strength of 1:2.6 Mortars for Clinkers Nos. 15367, 16823, 15900, 15498, 16843, 15699, 16827, 16890, 15623, 15670, 16939, and 16831.

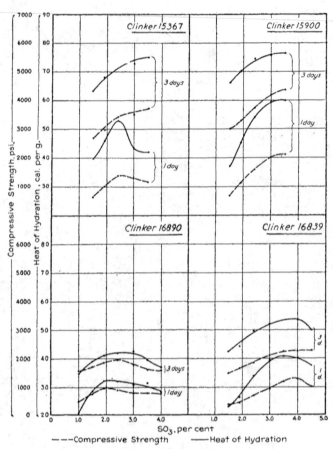

FIG. 18.—Relationship Between Heats of Hydration and Compressive Strengths at Early Ages.

TABLE IX.—THE INFLUENCE OF GYPSUM ON THE STRENGTH OF DIFFERENT 3CaO·Al₂O₃ AND ALKALI.

SO₃, per cent	Compressive Strength of Modified Cubes, psi.											
	Clinker No. 15367 High 3CaO·Al₂O₃ Low Alkali			Clinker No. 15900 High 3CaO·Al₂O₃ Moderately High Alkali			Clinker No. 15623 Low 3CaO·Al₂O₃ Low Akali			Clinker No. 16839 Low 3CaO·Al₂O₃ High Alkali		
	1 day	7 days	1 yr.	1 day	7 days	1 yr.	1 day	7 days	1 yr.	1 day	7 days	1 yr.
0.03........							590	4510	9 280			
1.0........							1250	4560	9 820			
1.5........	630	4610	6990	700	4440	7980	1410	4910	10 020	360	2400	6960
1.9........	1000	4830	8380	1140	4880	8290	1400	4960	8 960	460	2460	7500
2.4........	1380	5320	8840	1600	5070	8620	1480	5100	10 370	720	2880	6990
3.0........	1300	5610	8700	2030	5570	9960				950	3130	7140
3.5........	1180	5580	8530	2140	5710	9190				1200	3130	7350
4.0........										1280	3190	6990
4.5........										1050	3260	7450

The mix used was: cement 1.0 part, powdered silica 0.3 part, standard Ottawa sand 2.3 parts, by weight. The pulverized silica had a specific surface of 6000 sq. cm. per cu. cm. (Wagner method), which was very nearly the same as that of the cements.

The water content was adjusted with the intent of maintaining the slump (6-in. cone) approximately constant at 1 in. However, with only a limited quantity of cement available for trial mixes, the slumps obtained varied from 1 in. by as much as 0.5 in. For cements prepared from any one clinker, with the SO_3 content varied, the water content was maintained constant with only slight variations in the slump. However, for cements prepared from the different clinkers it was necessary to make rather large changes in water content to maintain a slump of approximately 1 in.

Each batch was mixed 1 min. dry, 2 min. wet, allowed to rest 3 min. and remixed 2 min. This schedule was adopted to eliminate the effect of premature stiffening, if any, on the water requirement. The slump tests were made in duplicate, two operators working simultaneously on one batch from each round.

The specimens were cured in the molds in saturated air at 70 ± 2 F. for the first 2 hr.; the molds and contents were then immersed in water at the same temperature and allowed to remain there until the specimens were removed from the molds.

The Influence of Gypsum on Strength:

The strength tests at 1 day were made immediately after the prisms were removed from the molds. At the later ages they were made with prisms which were cured continuously in water at 70 ± 2 F. until the time of test. The flexural strength and Young's modulus of elasticity were determined on two prisms (one from each round) for each age, and the compressive strength was determined on the four half-prisms resulting from the flexural tests—tested as modified cubes. The results of the strength tests are given in Table VIII and Fig. 17.

The general characteristic of the influence of gypsum is that it increases the strength. However, the quantity of gypsum required to obtain the highest strength varies with the different clinker compositions. The results show that the alkalies as well as the $3CaO \cdot Al_2O_3$ influence the gypsum requirements of the cements. For cements of low alkali content those of high $3CaO \cdot Al_2O_3$ require larger additions of gypsum to give the highest strength than do those of low $3CaO \cdot Al_2O_3$ content. For cements of the same $3CaO \cdot Al_2O_3$ content those high in alkalies require larger additions of gypsum than those of low alkali content. Even cements of low $3CaO \cdot Al_2O_3$ content require relatively large amounts of gypsum when they are high in alkalies. These observations are illustrated by the compressive strength data in Table IX taken from the more complete data given in Table VIII.

With the two clinkers of low alkali content the best strengths are obtained for the one of high $3CaO \cdot Al_2O_3$ (No. 15367) with 2.4 to 3.0 per cent SO_3 and for the one of low $3CaO \cdot Al_2O_3$ (No. 15623) with 1.5 to 2.4 per cent SO_3. With clinkers of the high $3CaO \cdot Al_2O_3$ content the best strengths are obtained for the one low in alkalies (No. 15367) with 2.4 to 3.0 per cent SO_3 and for the one high in alkalies (No. 15900) with 3.5 per cent SO_3. With clinkers of low $3CaO \cdot Al_2O_3$ the best results are obtained for the one low in alkalies (No. 15623) with 1.5 to 2.4 per cent SO_3 and for the one high in alkalies (No. 16839) with 3.5 to 4.5 per cent SO_3.

Relationship Between the Heats of Hydration and Strength:

It has been shown that the first additions of gypsum increase the heats of hydration and strength at early ages whereas with larger additions of gypsum the values decrease. The relationship between the heats of hydration at 1 and 3 days and the compressive strengths at these ages for cements of different SO_3 contents is shown for four of the clinkers in Fig. 18. The results show a close relationship between the heats of hydration and strengths at these ages, that is, as the heats of hydration increase with increasing SO_3 contents the strengths increase, and as the heats of hydration

TABLE X.—HEATS OF HYDRATION AND STRENGTH OF CEMENTS OF DIFFERENT GYPSUM CONTENT.

SO_3, per cent	Heat of Hydration, cal. per g.				Compressive Strength, psi.			
	Clinker No. 15367		Clinker No. 15900		Clinker No. 15367		Clinker No. 15900	
	28 days	3 months	28 days	3 months	28 days	3 months	28 days	3 months
1.5	107.7	112.7	99.0	100.8	6650	6940	6850	7940
2.4	106.6	109.3	94.9	96.7	7380	8370	7090	8010
3.5	103.4	106.3	90.3	97.4	7680	8370	7480	8420

decrease with the highest SO_3 contents the strengths decrease. Thus it appears that the effect of gypsum on the strengths at early ages can be accounted for, at least in part, by its effect on the hydration of the cements. However, results obtained at later ages show that a similar relationship no longer exists. The heats of hydration were determined at 28 days and 3 months for a few of the cements by the heat of solution method (20). The relationship between the heats of hydration and compressive strength at these ages is shown in Table X.

At these later ages the heats of hydration decrease while the strengths increase with increasing SO_3 contents. Thus it

is evident that the effect of gypsum on strength cannot be accounted for entirely on the basis of its effect on the extent of hydration of the cements. It seems probable that the beneficial results obtained by the larger additions of gypsum are, at least in part, the result of its effect on the structure of the hardened paste.

The Influence of Gypsum on Expansion:

It appears that the purpose of limiting the SO_3 content of portland cement was to avoid a possible delayed expansion which may result from the reaction of gypsum with the calcium aluminates to form calcium sulfoaluminate. There does seem to be some basis for such a precaution as will be shown in data to be presented below. Furthermore in an investigation of the effect of finer grinding and higher SO_3 contents upon the physical properties of portland cement Bates (21) observed that for neat cement pastes increasing the SO_3 to 2.5 per cent increased the expansion of the coarse cements. However, in the same series of tests it was observed that with the finer cements there was very little increase in expansion with the higher SO_3 content up to the limit 2.5 per cent, the highest SO_3 content used in the series.

The results of the heat-liberation data and the extraction data cited previously have shown that, for cements of medium to high $3CaO \cdot Al_2O_3$ regardless of their alkali content, and cements high in alkalies regardless of their $3CaO \cdot Al_2O_3$ content, amounts of gypsum up to 3.5 per cent become depleted within 24 hr. when the cements are ground to a specific surface of 1800 sq. cm. per g. From these results it appears that the SO_3 content may be increased beyond the limit of present specifications without danger of delayed expansions from this source. The results of expansion measurements confirm this observation.

TABLE XI.—EXPANSION OF MORTAR PRISMS STORED IN WATER—SERIES 287.

One 2 by 2 by 9½-in. prism made on each of two days for each age of test.
Mix: Cement 1.0, pulverized silica 0.3, standard Ottawa sand 2.3.
Water content to give approximately 1-in. slump using a 6-in. cone.

SO_3, per cent	Water, gal. per sack	Expansion of Specimen Stored Continuously in Water for Period Indicated, per cent					
		7 days	14 days	28 days	3 mo.	1 yr.	2 yr.

CLINKERS OF HIGH 3CaO·Al₂O₃ AND LOW ALKALI CONTENT
Clinker No. 15367, C_3A, 14.3; Na_2O, 0.16; K_2O, 0.17 per cent

1.5	5.02	0.009	0.011	0.016	0.021	0.027	0.028
1.9	5.02	0.008	0.011	0.015	0.020	0.025	0.027
2.4	5.02	0.007	0.010	0.013	0.018	0.022	0.024
3.0	5.02	0.005	0.007	0.009	0.015	0.021	0.021
3.5	5.02	0.026	0.028	0.032	0.036	0.043	0.043

Clinker No. 16823, C_3A, 12.5; Na_2O, 0.05; K_2O, 0.25 per cent

1.0	4.82	0.002	0.003	0.005	0.007	0.007	.....
1.5	4.82	0.001	0.000	0.003	0.006	0.006	.....
1.9	4.82	0.001	0.001	0.003	0.006	0.006	.....
2.4	4.82	0.001	0.004	0.005	0.009	0.008	.....
3.0	4.82	0.000	0.001	0.002	0.004	0.004	.....
3.5	4.82	0.001	0.004	0.004	0.006	0.007	.....
4.0	4.82	0.003	0.002	0.002	0.006	0.009	.....

CLINKERS OF HIGH OR MODERATELY HIGH 3CaO·Al₂O₃ AND HIGH OR MODERATELY HIGH ALKALI CONTENT
Clinker No. 15900, C_3A, 13.1; Na_2O, 0.36; K_2O, 0.50 per cent

1.5	4.85	0.007	0.009	0.013	0.023	0.039	0.039
1.9	4.85	0.005	0.009	0.015	0.021	0.038	0.038
2.4	4.85	0.006	0.010	0.012	0.018	0.034	0.034
3.0	4.85	0.005	0.007	0.011	0.017	0.033	0.032
3.5	4.85	0.002	0.005	0.009	0.015	0.033	0.030
5.0	4.86	0.053	0.053	0.060	0.061	0.071	0.073

Clinker No. 15498, C_3A, 11.2; Na_2O, 0.31; K_2O, 0.42 per cent

1.0	4.90	0.020	0.020	0.027	0.032	0.043	0.042
1.5	4.90	0.017	0.017	0.025	0.031	0.038	0.035
1.9	4.90	0.015	0.016	0.023	0.028	0.038	0.035
2.4	4.90	0.013	0.013	0.020	0.026	0.037	0.034
3.0	4.90	0.022	0.022	0.026	0.033	0.042	0.039

Clinker No. 16843, C_3A, 11.0; Na_2O, 1.03; K_2O, 0.06 per cent

1.5	4.70	0.004	0.016	0.022	0.027	0.034	.....
1.9	4.70	0.008	0.011	0.014	0.020	0.025	.....
2.4	4.70	0.010	0.011	0.012	0.017	0.022	.....
3.0	4.70	0.009	0.012	0.013	0.016	0.021	.....
3.5	4.70	0.003	0.004	0.004	0.006	0.011	.....
4.0	4.70	0.005	0.010	0.012	0.016	0.021	.....
4.5	4.75	0.011	0.017	0.018	0.021	0.027	.....

Clinker No. 15699, C_3A, 10.1; Na_2O, 1.17; K_2O, 0.46 per cent

1.0	5.00	0.006	0.009	0.013	0.020	0.034	0.033
1.5	5.00	0.005	0.006	0.010	0.017	0.029	0.027
1.9	5.00	0.004	0.006	0.011	0.017	0.030	0.029
2.4	5.00	0.005	0.006	0.010	0.015	0.030	0.029
3.0	5.00	0.004	0.006	0.008	0.013	0.027	0.026
5.0	4.96	0.020	0.022	0.025	0.028	0.037	0.037

TABLE XI.—*Continued*

SO_3, per cent	Water, gal. per sack	Expansion of Specimen Stored Continuously in Water for Period Indicated, per cent					
		7 days	14 days	28 days	3 mo.	1 yr.	2 yr.

Clinker No. 16827; C_3A, 8.1; Na_2O, 0.04; K_2O, 1.37 per cent

1.0	5.26	0.009	0.014	0.014	0.023	0.031	.....
1.5	5.12	0.010	0.010	0.012	0.019	0.027	.....
1.9	5.00	0.007	0.010	0.010	0.021	0.028	.....
2.4	5.00	0.007	0.009	0.011	0.020	0.026	.....
3.0	5.00	0.007	0.008	0.013	0.015	0.026	.....
3.5	4.86	0.008	0.008	0.011	0.016	0.019	.....
4.0	4.86	0.009	0.011	0.014	0.017	0.022	.....

CLINKERS OF LOW 3CaO·Al₂O₃ AND LOW ALKALI CONTENT
Clinker No. 16890, C_3A, 5.1; Na_2O, 0.32; K_2O, 0.02 per cent

1.0	4.36	0.010	0.012	0.016	0.021	0.025	.....
1.5	4.36	0.008	0.008	0.012	0.015	0.023	.....
1.9	4.36	0.014	0.010	0.012	0.018	0.024	.....
2.4	4.36	0.014	0.010	0.013	0.017	0.024	.....
3.0	4.36	0.025	0.020	0.022	0.028	0.032	.....
3.5	4.36	0.030	0.027	0.028	0.033	0.040	.....
4.0	4.50	0.023	0.027	0.029	0.037	0.045	.....

Clinker No. 15623, C_3A, 4.8; Na_2O, 0.05; K_2O, 0.18 per cent

0.03	4.60	0.005	0.007	0.011	0.022	0.019
1.0	4.60	0.006	0.007	0.007	0.012	0.022	0.020
1.5	4.60	0.001	0.002	0.002	0.006	0.016	0.013
1.9	4.60	0.001	0.002	0.002	0.006	0.014	0.011
2.4	4.60	0.004	0.004	0.004	0.007	0.017	0.014

Clinker No. 15670, C_3A, 2.4; Na_2O, 0.05; K_2O, 0.23 per cent

0.17	4.39	0.011	0.013	0.017	0.022	0.035	0.033
1.0	4.39	0.004	0.002	0.007	0.013	0.025	0.023
1.5	4.39	0.002	0.004	0.007	0.012	0.024	0.022
1.9	4.39	0.006	0.007	0.009	0.015	0.028	0.025
2.4	4.39	0.005	0.009	0.010	0.016	0.029	0.027

CLINKERS OF LOW 3CaO·Al₂O₃ AND HIGH ALKALI CONTENT
Clinker No. 16839, C_3A, 6.2; Na_2O, 1.01; K_2O, 0.10 per cent

1.5	4.70	0.007	0.009	0.010	0.015	0.023	.....
1.9	4.61	0.011	0.013	0.014	0.021	0.026	.....
2.4	4.70	0.010	0.011	0.015	0.018	0.027	.....
3.0	4.70	0.004	0.008	0.011	0.015	0.021	.....
3.5	4.70	0.005	0.007	0.008	0.014	0.019	.....
4.0	4.75	0.005	0.005	0.009	0.013	0.018	.....
4.5	4.81	0.007	0.007	0.010	0.015	0.019	.....

Clinker No. 16831, C_3A, 5.71; Na_2O, 0.05; K_2O, 1.37 per cent

1.0	4.61	0.011	0.011	0.014	0.019	0.029	.....
1.5	4.51	0.008	0.011	0.014	0.017	0.025	.....
1.9	4.51	0.007	0.009	0.012	0.016	0.025	.....
2.4	4.51	0.005	0.017	0.008	0.014	0.020	.....
3.0	4.56	0.007	0.010	0.010	0.016	0.020	.....
3.5	4.56	0.008	0.008	0.010	0.014	0.022	.....
4.0	4.56	0.012	0.015	0.016	0.021	0.027	.....

The results of the length changes of the mortar prisms cured continuously in water at 70 ± 2 F. for 2 yr. are given in Table XI. The initial measurement was made at one day and the results are

TABLE XII.—CONTRACTION OF MORTAR PRISMS STORED IN AIR—SERIES 287.

One 2 by 2 by 9½-in. prism made on each of two days for each age of test.

Mix: Cement 1.0, pulverized silica 0.3, standard Ottawa sand 2.3.

Water content to give approximately 1-in. slump using a 6-in. cone.

SO_3, per cent	Water, gal. per sack	Contraction in Air Storage for Period Indicated after Preliminary Curing 1 Day in Molds, 6 Days in Water, per cent						
		1 day	3 days	7 days	14 days	28 days	3 months	1 yr.

CLINKERS OF HIGH $3CaO \cdot Al_2O_3$ AND LOW ALKALI CONTENT

Clinker No. 15367, C_3A, 14.3; Na_2O, 0.16; K_2O, 0.17 per cent

1.5	5.02	0.022	0.038	0.061	0.088	0.096	0.117	0.125
1.9	5.02	0.018	0.034	0.053	0.075	0.086	0.102	0.107
2.4	5.02	0.018	0.030	0.047	0.066	0.075	0.091	0.100
3.0	5.02	0.014	0.025	0.041	0.057	0.065	0.077	0.089
3.5	5.02	0.015	0.027	0.039	0.054	0.062	0.083	0.094

Clinker No. 16823, C_3A, 12.0; Na_2O, 0.05; K_2O, 0.25 per cent

1.0	4.82	0.017	0.034	0.047	0.054	0.077	0.093	0.100
1.5	4.82	0.018	0.034	0.044	0.053	0.073	0.090	0.094
1.9	4.82	0.012	0.023	0.033	0.036	0.058	0.077	0.081
2.4	4.82	0.008	0.015	0.027	0.032	0.052	0.071	0.078
3.0	4.82	0.009	0.017	0.027	0.032	0.051	0.071	0.080
3.5	4.82	0.013	0.020	0.026	0.036	0.052	0.068	0.080
4.0	4.82	0.015	0.020	0.028	0.038	0.052	0.067	0.081

CLINKERS OF HIGH OR MODERATELY HIGH $3CaO \cdot Al_2O_3$ AND HIGH OR MODERATELY HIGH ALKALI CONTENT

Clinker No. 15900, C_3A, 13.1; Na_2O, 0.36; K_2O, 0.50 per cent

1.5	4.85	0.017	0.034	0.058	0.080	0.091	0.113	0.115
1.9	4.85	0.015	0.028	0.047	0.064	0.075	0.097	0.098
2.4	4.85	0.013	0.025	0.039	0.055	0.065	0.086	0.088
3.0	4.85	0.013	0.023	0.037	0.050	0.058	0.080	0.080
3.5	4.85	0.013	0.022	0.033	0.043	0.052	0.074	0.078
5.0	4.86	0.021	0.036	0.042	0.061	0.070	0.090	0.097

Clinker No. 15498, C_3A, 11.2, Na_2O, 0.31; K_2O, 0.42 per cent

1.0	4.90	0.016	0.033	0.059	0.082	0.090	0.106	0.105
1.5	4.90	0.017	0.028	0.047	0.065	0.074	0.086	0.086
1.9	4.90	0.015	0.026	0.041	0.059	0.066	0.081	0.083
2.4	4.90	0.013	0.022	0.033	0.047	0.054	0.071	0.074
3.0	4.90	0.017	0.023	0.033	0.047	0.052	0.067	0.073

Clinker No. 16843, C_3A, 11.0; Na_2O, 1.03; K_2O, 0.06 per cent

1.5	4.70	0.011	0.035	0.061	0.085	0.105	0.144	0.161
1.9	4.70	0.020	0.041	0.060	0.085	0.103	0.133	0.146
2.4	4.70	0.012	0.031	0.049	0.064	0.083	0.112	0.122
3.0	4.70	0.013	0.025	0.040	0.051	0.076	0.091	0.106
3.5	4.70	0.012	0.024	0.038	0.049	0.061	0.084	0.098
4.0	4.70	0.016	0.024	0.038	0.047	0.060	0.082	0.097
4.5	4.75	0.013	0.023	0.036	0.047	0.061	0.082	0.096

Clinker No. 15699, C_3A, 10.1; Na_2O, 1.17; K_2O, 0.46 per cent

1.0	5.00	0.017	0.033	0.059	0.085	0.101	0.145	0.160
1.5	5.00	0.021	0.039	0.067	0.092	0.108	0.147	0.161
1.9	5.00	0.018	0.037	0.063	0.086	0.101	0.137	0.152
2.4	5.00	0.015	0.031	0.052	0.069	0.082	0.117	0.133
3.0	5.00	0.015	0.027	0.047	0.064	0.075	0.109	0.126
5.0	4.96	0.012	0.026	0.040	0.054	0.067	0.093	0.110

TABLE XII.—Continued

SO_3, per cent	Water, gal. per sack	Contraction in Air Storage for Period Indicated after Preliminary Curing 1 Day in Molds, 6 Days in Water, per cent						
		1 day	3 days	7 days	14 days	28 days	3 months	1 yr.

Clinker No. 16827, C_3A, 8.1; Na_2O, 0.04; K_2O, 1.37 per cent

1.0	5.26	0.025	0.050	0.085	0.118	0.155	0.201	0.230
1.5	5.12	0.023	0.048	0.073	0.099	0.126	0.163	0.177
1.9	5.00	0.017	0.046	0.064	0.089	0.113	0.148	0.165
2.4	5.00	0.023	0.037	0.054	0.074	0.093	0.126	0.143
3.0	5.00	0.014	0.026	0.041	0.055	0.066	0.101	0.119
3.5	4.86	0.014	0.023	0.035	0.045	0.058	0.082	0.105
4.0	4.86	0.012	0.019	0.031	0.040	0.052	0.075	0.097

CLINKERS OF LOW $3CaO \cdot Al_2O_3$ AND LOW ALKALI CONTENT

Clinker No. 16890, C_3A, 5.1; Na_2O, 0.32; K_2O, 0.02 per cent

1.0	4.36	0.008	0.025	0.054	0.079	0.095	0.110	0.110
1.5	4.36	0.008	0.018	0.040	0.062	0.077	0.091	0.100
1.9	4.36	0.006	0.018	0.035	0.053	0.067	0.087	0.093
2.4	4.36	0.009	0.022	0.035	0.048	0.063	0.083	0.094
3.0	4.36	0.013	0.022	0.035	0.047	0.063	0.085	0.097
3.5	4.36	0.009	0.026	0.043	0.057	0.071	0.090	0.107
4.0	4.50	0.010	0.022	0.044	0.062	0.080	0.103	0.114

Clinker, No. 15623, C_3A, 4.8; Na_2O, 0.05; K_2O, 0.18 per cent

0.03	4.60	0.011	0.020	0.038	0.060	0.076	0.109	0.11
1.0	4.60	0.010	0.016	0.027	0.038	0.047	0.071	0.077
1.5	4.60	0.007	0.013	0.023	0.032	0.039	0.061	0.066
1.9	4.60	0.007	0.013	0.025	0.032	0.039	0.060	0.066
2.4	4.60	0.011	0.017	0.028	0.038	0.044	0.065	0.071

Clinker No. 15670, C_3A, 2.4; Na_2O, 0.05; K_2O, 0.23 per cent

0.17	4.39	0.006	0.020	0.044	0.076	0.097	0.128	0.135
1.0	4.39	0.009	0.017	0.031	0.045	0.050	0.070	0.077
1.5	4.39	0.009	0.022	0.032	0.039	0.048	0.065	0.071
1.9	4.39	0.007	0.017	0.029	0.040	0.048	0.067	0.075
2.4	4.39	0.009	0.020	0.037	0.054	0.063	0.081	0.080

CLINKERS OF LOW $3CaO \cdot Al_2O_3$ AND HIGH ALKALI CONTENT

Clinker No. 16839, C_3A, 6.2; Na_2O, 1.01; K_2O, 0.10 per cent

1.5	4.70	0.011	0.045	0.083	0.117	0.145	0.166	0.171
1.9	4.61	0.013	0.040	0.068	0.099	0.121	0.140	0.150
2.4	4.70	0.007	0.029	0.052	0.081	0.101	0.124	0.140
3.0	4.70	0.006	0.022	0.041	0.058	0.083	0.112	0.124
3.5	4.70	0.011	0.025	0.041	0.054	0.074	0.106	0.120
4.0	4.75	0.008	0.018	0.029	0.040	0.055	0.086	0.103
4.5	4.81	0.009	0.019	0.030	0.042	0.054	0.086	0.104

Clinker No. 16831, C_3A, 5.7; Na_2O, 0.05; K_2O, 1.37 per cent

1.0	4.61	0.010	0.026	0.051	0.077	0.107	0.141	0.161
1.5	4.51	0.014	0.024	0.037	0.055	0.069	0.097	0.115
1.9	4.51	0.009	0.019	0.030	0.045	0.057	0.082	0.100
2.4	4.51	0.005	0.014	0.019	0.032	0.046	0.067	0.082
3.0	4.56	0.007	0.016	0.022	0.032	0.046	0.066	0.080
3.5	4.56	0.008	0.019	0.027	0.037	0.051	0.070	0.084
4.0	4.56	0.008	0.021	0.033	0.044	0.058	0.077	0.091

recorded as the percentage expansion calculated from the length at 1 day. The results show that only a few specimens developed larger expansions as a result of the higher SO_3 content and that for these specimens the larger expansion occurs during the first few days. Clinker No. 15367 with 3.5 per cent SO_3, clinker No. 16890 with 3.0 to 4.0 per cent SO_3, and clinkers Nos. 15900 and 15699 with 5.0 per cent SO_3 show higher expansions at 7 days than do the corresponding cements of lower SO_3 contents prepared from the same clinkers. With these exceptions the expansions up to 1 yr. with as much as 3.5 to 4.5 per cent SO_3

urements are recorded as the percentage contraction calculated from the length at the time the specimens were placed in air. The results are shown in Table XII and in Fig. 17.

The general characteristics of the influence of gypsum on contraction is that the addition of gypsum decreases the contraction. However, the quantity of gypsum required to obtain the lowest contraction varies with different clinker compositions. The results show that the alkalies as well as the $3CaO \cdot Al_2O_3$ influence the gypsum requirements of the cements. For cements of low alkali content those of high $3CaO \cdot Al_2O_3$ content

TABLE XIII.—THE INFLUENCE OF GYPSUM ON THE CONTRACTION OF MORTAR PRISMS.

SO₃, per cent	Contraction During Storage in Air for Period Indicated, per cent							
	Clinker No. 16823 $3CaO \cdot Al_2O_3 = 12.5$ $Na_2O = 0.05$ $K_2O = 0.25$		Clinker No. 16843 $3CaO \cdot Al_2O_3 = 11.0$ $Na_2O = 1.03$ $K_2O = 0.06$		Clinker No. 16890 $3CaO \cdot Al_2O_3 = 5.1$ $Na_2O = 0.32$ $K_2O = 0.02$		Clinker No. 16839 $3CaO \cdot Al_2O_3 = 6.2$ $Na_2O = 1.01$ $K_2O = 0.10$	
	7 days	3 months	7 days	3 months	7 days	3 months	7 days	3 months
1.0	0.047	0.093			0.054	0.110		
1.5	0.044	0.090	0.061	0.144	0.040	0.091	0.083	0.166
1.9	0.033	0.077	0.060	0.133	0.035	0.087	0.068	0.140
2.4	0.027	0.071	0.049	0.112	0.035	0.083	0.053	0.124
3.0	0.027	0.071	0.040	0.091	0.035	0.085	0.041	0.112
3.5	0.026	0.068	0.038	0.084	0.043	0.090	0.041	0.106
4.0	0.028	0.067	0.038	0.082	0.044	0.103	0.029	0.086
4.5			0.036	0.082			0.031	0.086

are in no instance significantly higher than those with 1.9 per cent SO_3. Actually the least expansion is usually obtained with SO_3 contents greater than 1.9 per cent. Thus the results show that gypsum can be added to portland cements in considerably larger amounts than is permitted by current specifications without danger of abnormal expansion.

The Influence of Gypsum on Contraction:

The mortar prisms for contraction in air were cured in the molds 1 day, in water 6 days, and then continuously in air at approximately 75 F. and 50 per cent relative humidity. Contraction meas-

require larger additions of gypsum to give the lowest contraction than those of low $3CaO \cdot Al_2O_3$ content. For cements of the same $3CaO \cdot Al_2O_3$ content those of high alkali content require larger additions of gypsum than those of low alkali content. These observations are illustrated by the contraction data in Table XIII taken from the more complete data given in Table XII.

For cements of low alkali content, clinker No. 16823 with 12.5 per cent $3CaO \cdot Al_2O_3$ shows the least contraction with 2.4 to 4.0 per cent SO_3, whereas clinker No. 16890 with 5.1 per cent $3CaO \cdot Al_2O_3$ shows the least contraction with 1.9 to 3.0 per cent SO_3. On the

TABLE XIV.—MISCELLANEOUS TESTS OF CEMENTS GROUND WITH DIFFERENT PROPORTIONS OF GYPSUM—SERIES 287.

SO₃ Content, per cent	Specific Surface			Normal Consistency, per cent	Time of Setting				Expansion During Autoclave Tests, per cent	
	Turbidimeter, sq. cm. per g.	Air Permeability, sq. cm. pre g.	Ratio, Air to Turbidimeter		Vicat Needle		Gillmore Needle		One 5-hr. Cycle	Two 5-hr. Cycles
					Initial, hr.:min.	Final, hr.:min.	Initial, hr.:min.	Final, hr.:min.		
CLINKERS OF HIGH 3CaO·Al₂O₃ AND LOW ALKALI CONTENT Clinker No. 15367, C₃A, 14.3; Na₂O, 0.16; K₂O, 0.17 per cent										
1.5	1850	3210	1.74	24.0	2:35	4:40	3:15	4:50	0.127	0.167
1.9	1870	3330	1.78	24.0	2:35	6:00	3:30	6:15	....	....
2.4	1890	3460	1.83	24.5	2:30	6:00	3:30	6:15	0.058	0.097
3.0	1940	3780	1.95	24.0	2:50	6:00	3:25	6:30	....	....
3.5	2000	3980	1.98	24.0	2:50	6:10	3:20	6:30	....	....
5.0	2070	4850	2.34	23.0	....	....	....	....	0.096	0.142
Clinker No. 16823, C₃A, 12.0; Na₂O, 0.05; K₂O, 0.25 per cent										
1.0	1870	3280	1.75	25.0	2:15	9:50	4:00	9:50	0.190	....
1.5	1900	3440	1.81	25.0	2:05	6:00	3:30	6:00	0.246	....
1.9	1930	3560	1.84	25.0	2:00	5:30	3:30	5:30	0.222	....
2.4	1940	3790	1.95	25.5	2:40	6:10	4:00	6:10	0.189	....
3.0	1950	3970	2.04	25.5	2:35	6:25	4:10	6:25	0.219	....
3.5	1960	4160	2.12	25.5	2:40	6:40	4:30	6:40	0.241	....
4.0	1970	4320	2.19	25.5	3:00	6:35	4:20	6:35	0.234	....
CLINKERS OF HIGH OR MODERATELY HIGH 3CaO·Al₂O₃ AND HIGH OR MODERATELY HIGH ALKALI CONTENT Clinker No. 15900, C₃A, 13.1; Na₂O, 0.36; K₂O, 0.50 per cent										
1.5	1880	3290	1.75	24.5	2:00	4:10	3:00	4:25	0.568	....
1.9	1910	3440	1.80	24.0	2:20	5:25	3:20	5:30	....	....
2.4	1930	3640	1.88	24.0	2:20	5:30	3:30	5:45	0.380	....
3.0	1950	3870	1.98	24.0	2:50	5:20	4:05	5:45	....	....
3.5	1970	4050	2.06	24.0	3:00	5:00	4:40	5:25	....	....
5.0	2010	4650	2.25	23.0	....	....	....	....	0.649	....
Clinker No. 15498, C₃A, 11.2; Na₂O, 0.31; K₂O, 0.42 per cent										
1.0	1840	3200	1.74	24.5	2:35	6:15	3:30	6:30	0.530	....
1.5	1860	3270	1.76	24.5	2:30	5:45	3:30	6:00	....	....
1.9	1870	3360	1.80	24.5	2:20	5:45	3:30	6:00	....	....
2.4	1900	3580	1.88	24.5	2:20	5:45	3:30	6:00	0.320	....
3.0	1940	3810	1.97	24.0	2:10	5:30	3:30	5:45	....	....
5.0	2020	4580	2.24	23.5	....	....	....	....	0.430	....
Clinker No. 16843, C₃A, 11.0; Na₂O, 1.03; K₂O, 0.06 per cent										
1.5	1860	3350	1.80	25.0	0:40	2:10	1:00	3:10	0.112	....
1.9	1890	3500	1.85	25.0	1:50	4:30	3:20	4:30	0.092	....
2.4	1890	3700	1.96	25.0	2:00	4:30	3:30	4:30	0.066	....
3.0	1890	3930	2.08	25.0	2:10	5:15	3:40	5:15	0.018	....
3.5	1900	4100	2.16	25.0	2:10	5:00	3:45	5:00	0.008	....
4.0	1900	4280	2.25	25.0	2:15	4:40	3:40	4:40	0.014	....
4.5	1900	4460	2.35	25.0	2:10	5:00	3:15	5:00	0.006	....
Clinker No. 15699, C₃A, 10.1; Na₂O, 1.17; K₂O, 0.46 per cent										
1.0	1840	3220	1.75	23.5	1:20	3:40	2:00	4:00	0.187	....
1.5	1850	3390	1.82	23.5	1:15	3:40	2:20	4:00	....	....
1.9	1860	3510	1.88	23.5	1:35	4:00	2:40	4:15	....	....
2.4	1900	3680	1.93	23.5	1:40	4:15	2:50	4:25	0.141	....
3.0	1940	3830	1.97	23.5	1:45	4:20	3:00	4:30	....	....
5.0	2050	4400	2.15	....	....	....	....	....	....	....
Clinker No. 16827, C₃A, 8.1; Na₂O, 0.04; K₂O, 1.37 per cent										
1.0	1860	3220	1.73	27.0	0:20	1:30	0:30	1:50	0.085	....
1.5	1900	3350	1.76	25.0	2:00	3:40	2:30	3:50	0.101	....
1.9	1940	3450	1.78	25.5	2:40	6:00	3:20	6:00	0.101	....
2.4	1950	3650	1.87	25.5	2:25	5:50	3:40	5:50	0.085	....
3.0	1960	3890	1.98	25.0	2:50	4:30	3:45	4:50	0.082	....
3.5	1970	4070	2.07	25.0	2:40	6:30	3:40	6:30	0.077	....
4.0	1980	4250	2.15	25.0	2:30	5:40	3:35	5:40	0.071	....

TABLE XIV.—*Continued*

SO₃ Content, per cent	Specific Surface			Normal Consistency, per cent	Time of Setting				Expansion During Autoclave Test, per cent	
	Turbidimeter, sq. cm. per g.	Air Permeability, sq. cm. per g.	Ratio, Air to Turb.		Vicat Needle		Gillmore Needle		One 5-hr. Cycle	Two 5-hr. Cycles
					Initial, hr.:min.	Final, hr.:min.	Initial, hr.:min.	Final, hr.:min.		
CLINKERS OF Low $3CaO \cdot Al_2O_3$ AND Low ALKALI CONTENT Clinker No. 16890, C_3A, 5.1; Na_2O, 0.32; K_2O, 0.02 per cent										
1.0	1870	2960	1.58	23.0	3:40	7:40	4:00	7:40	0.010	....
1.5	1890	3090	1.63	23.5	3:50	7:20	4:00	7:20	−0.010	....
1.9	1900	3190	1.68	23.0	3:40	7:45	4:00	7:45	−0.023	....
2.4	1920	3410	1.78	23.0	2:40	5:20	4:00	5:20	−0.029	....
3.0	1950	3640	1.87	23.0	3:30	7:00	4:30	7:00	−0.031	....
3.5	1980	3870	1.95	23.0	3:30	6:40	4:30	6:40	−0.031	....
4.0	2000	4060	2.03	23.5	3:20	6:50	4:30	6:50	−0.029	....
Clinker No. 15623, C_3A, 4.8; Na_2O, 0.05; K_2O, 0.18 per cent										
0.03	1800	2860	1.59	23.0	8:20	12:00	9:20	13:00	0.005	0.007
1.0	1840	3120	1.70	22.0	3:15	6:00	4:10	6:00	....	....
1.5	1860	3260	1.76	22.0	3:15	5:50	4:30	6:00	....	....
1.9	1880	3410	1.81	22.0	3:00	5:45	4:20	5:50	....	....
2.4	1910	3620	1.90	22.0	2:50	5:40	4:00	5:40	−0.045	−0.042
Clinker No. 15670, C_3A, 2.4; Na_2O, 0.05; K_2O, 0.23 per cent										
0.17	1800	2630	1.46	20.0	8:20	12:00	9:00	13:00	0.033	0.038
1.0	1870	2920	1.56	19.5	5:00	8:50	5:15	8:50	....	....
1.5	1910	3080	1.62	20.0	5:25	8:45	5:50	8:45	....	....
1.9	1950	3220	1.65	20.0	5:10	8:40	5:30	8:40	....	....
2.4	1970	3390	1.72	20.0	5:00	8:30	5:00	8:40	−0.017	−0.017
CLINKERS OF Low $3CaO \cdot Al_2O_3$ AND HIGH ALKALI CONTENT Clinker No. 16839, C_3A, 6.2; Na_2O, 1.01; K_2O, 0.10 per cent										
1.5	1890	3190	1.69	24.0	0:30	4:15	1:50	4:15	0.032	....
1.9	1910	3380	1.77	24.0	2:15	5:00	2:50	5:00	0.032	....
2.4	1940	3600	1.86	24.5	2:05	5:40	3:40	5:40	0.013	....
3.0	1980	3890	1.96	25.0	2:15	6:20	4:00	6:20	−0.007	....
3.5	2010	4050	2.01	25.5	2:30	5:35	3:40	5:35	−0.021	....
4.0	2030	4250	2.09	25.5	1:45	5:15	3:30	5:15	−0.017	....
4.5	2060	4460	2.17	25.5	2:10	5:20	3:30	5:20	−0.009	....
Clinker No. 16831, C_3A, 5.7; Na_2O, 0.05; K_2O, 1.37 per cent										
1.0	1840	3510	1.91	26.0	3:15	5:00	3:45	5:00	0.102	....
1.5	1820	3580	1.97	24.5	3:30	5:30	3:45	5:30	0.090	....
1.9	1810	3630	2.01	24.0	3:00	6:10	4:30	6:10	0.074	....
2.4	1820	3820	2.10	23.5	3:15	6:20	4:30	6:20	0.056	....
3.0	1830	4040	2.21	23.5	3:15	6:20	4:30	6:20	0.044	....
3.5	1850	4220	2.28	23.0	3:00	6:00	4:00	6:00	0.038	....
4.0	1860	4400	2.37	23.0	2:45	5:50	4:00	5:50	0.031	....

other hand, for cement of high $3CaO \cdot Al_2O_3$ content the clinker with low alkalies, No. 16823, shows the least contraction with 2.4 to 4.0 per cent SO_3, whereas the clinker with high alkalies, No. 16843, shows the least contraction with 3.5 to 4.5 per cent SO_3. Likewise, for cements of low $3CaO \cdot Al_2O_3$ content the clinker with low alkalies, No. 16890, shows the least contraction with 1.9 to 3.0 per cent SO_3, and the clinker with high alkalies,

No. 16839, shows the least contraction with 4.0 to 4.5 per cent SO_3.

Figure 19 shows that the contractions of the different cements are very nearly equalized by the use of proper amounts of gypsum. When the cements are compared on the basis of an SO_3 content of 1.9 per cent, the different cements show contractions ranging from 0.025 to 0.068 per cent at 7 days and 0.060 to 0.148 per cent at 3 months—spread of 0.043 and

0.088 percentage points, respectively. When the same cements are compared on the basis of the amount of gypsum that gives the least contraction the values range from 0.019 to 0.040 per cent at 7 days and from 0.060 to 0.093 per cent at 3 months—here the spread is reduced to 0.021 and 0.033 percentage points at the respective ages.

Thus, the results indicate that, for cement of high $3CaO \cdot Al_2O_3$ regardless of

which gives the lowest contraction in air is likewise the SO_3 content which gives the highest strength.

Miscellaneous Tests of the Cements:

The results of miscellaneous tests of the cements are given in Table XIV. For cements prepared from the different clinkers there is considerable difference in the water required for normal consistency. The cements of high $3CaO \cdot$

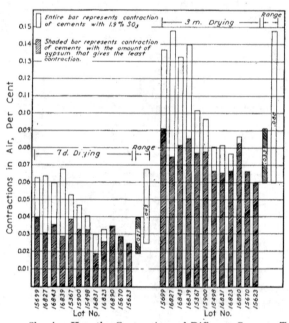

Fig. 19.—Diagram Showing How the Contractions of Different Cements Tend to Be Equalized by the Use of Proper Amounts of Gypsum.

their alkali content or cements high in alkalies regardless of their $3CaO \cdot Al_2O_3$ content, the contraction on drying can be decreased as much as 30 to 50 per cent by the use of larger additions of gypsum than are permitted by the current A.S.T.M. Specifications C 150 – 44.[3] For cements of low $3CaO \cdot Al_2O_3$ and low alkali content the contraction would not be decreased by larger additions of gypsum. For each clinker the SO_3 content

Al_2O_3 content require more water than do the cements of low $3CaO \cdot Al_2O_3$ content. For cements prepared from any one clinker, with SO_3 content varied, the water required for normal consistency does not vary appreciably except that the cement with 5.0 per cent SO_3 requires less water than do the corresponding cements of lower SO_3 content.

As the SO_3 content is increased, the time of set is generally increased for cements of high $3CaO \cdot Al_2O_3$ content and decreased for cements of low $3CaO \cdot Al_2O_3$ content. All cements meet the requirements of the A.S.T.M. Methods C 191 – 44[6] for time of set except the clinkers of low $3CaO \cdot Al_2O_3$, (Nos. 15623 and 15670) when tested without added gypsum. Under this condition the cements are very slow setting. All cements pass the pat test for soundness. Increasing the SO_3 content does not greatly

face by the two methods can be accounted for on the basis that the Wagner method does not adequately account for all of the surface of the minus 7.5 μ particles. Thus, since a large percentage of the gypsum is present as $-$ 7.5 μ particles, the ratio of the specific surfaces determined by the air permeability method to those determined by the Wagner method would increase with larger additions of gypsum.

TABLE XV.—OPTIMUM SO_3 CONTENT OF CLINKERS OF DIFFERENT COMPOSITION.

Clinker	C_3A	Na_2O	K_2O	For Proper Retardation (Heat Curves)	For Highest Strength	For Lowest Contraction	To Avoid Abnormal Expansion	Optimum SO_3, per cent
Clinkers of High $3CaO \cdot Al_2O_3$ and Low Alkali Content								
No. 15367	14.3	0.17	0.16	3.0	2.4 to 3.0	3.0	3.5	3.0
No. 16823	12.5	0.05	0.25	3.5	2.4 to 3.0	2.4 to 3.0	>4.0	3.0
Clinkers of High or Moderately High $3CaO \cdot Al_2O_3$ and High or Moderately High Alkali Content								
No. 15900	13.1	0.36	0.50	4.0	3.5	3.5	5.0	3.5
No. 15498	11.2	0.31	0.42	3.0	2.4 to 3.0	2.4 to 3.0	>3.5	3.0
No. 16843	11.0	1.03	0.06	4.0	3.5 to 4.5	3.5 to 4.5	>4.5	4.0
No. 15699	10.1	1.17	0.46	4.5	5.0	5.0	5.0	4.5
No. 16827	8.1	0.04	1.37	4.0	3.0 to 4.0	3.5 to 4.0	>4.0	3.5
Clinkers of Low $3CaO \cdot Al_2O_3$ and Low Alkali Content								
No. 16890	5.1	0.32	0.02	1.9	1.9 to 2.4	1.9 to 3.0	3.0	1.9
No. 15623	4.8	0.05	0.18	1.9	1.5 to 2.4	1.5 to 1.9	>2.4	1.9
No. 15670	2.4	0.05	0.23	1.9	1.5 to 1.9	1.5 to 1.9	>2.4	1.9
Clinkers of Low $3CaO \cdot Al_2O_3$ and High Alkali Content								
No. 16839	6.2	1.01	0.10	4.5	3.5 to 4.5	4.0 to 4.5	>4.5	4.0
No. 16831	5.7	0.05	1.37	3.0 to 3.5	3.0 to 3.5	2.4 to 3.0	>4.0	3.0

alter the expansion in the autoclave test though there is a general trend of slightly lower expansions with increasing SO_3.

The specific surface was determined by the Wagner turbidimeter and by the air permeability method (22, 23). The results obtained by these methods are given in Table XIV. It is shown that for each clinker the ratio of the specific surfaces determined by the air permeability method to those determined by the Wagner method increases progressively with increasing SO_3 content. It is probable that such variations in specific sur-

The Optimum SO_3 Content for the Different Clinkers:

In the studies described in this report four methods of test have been used to determine the optimum SO_3 content for the different clinkers. The rate of heat-liberation curves were used to determine the minimum SO_3 content required to give the type of curve that would meet the definition of a properly retarded cement, strength tests were made to determine the SO_3 content required for the best strengths, contraction measurements were made to determine the SO_3 content required for the lowest contraction, and expansion measurements were

---

[6] Methods of Test for Time of Setting of Hydraulic Cement by the Vicat or Gillmore Needles (C 191 – 44), 1944 Book of A.S.T.M. Standards, Part II, p. 66.

made to detect the occurrence of abnormal expansion resulting from the use of larger additions of gypsum. The results of these tests are summarized in the Table XV. It is seen that the SO_3 values by the different methods are in relatively good agreement. A suggested value for an optimum percentage is shown which is not higher than that indicated by any of the four methods.

These data show that results obtained by calorimetric methods, and the tests for strength, contraction and expansion are all in very good agreement in showing the optimum SO_3 content for the different clinkers. The relationship between the SO_3 contents required for the highest strength and lowest contraction is shown also in Fig. 17.

Previous investigators (24, 25, 26) have studied the influence of cement composition on the contraction with the SO_3 content of the cements maintained constant at 1.8 to 1.9 per cent. From the results of such investigations it has been concluded that the $3CaO \cdot Al_2O_3$ has the greatest influence on contraction and the contraction of hardened cement pastes stored in air increases with increasing $3CaO \cdot Al_2O_3$ content. The results of the present investigation show that the high coefficients of contraction of the $3CaO \cdot Al_2O_3$ and alkalies can be very considerably reduced and that the contraction of different cement compositions can be equalized, or very nearly equalized, by a proper adjustment of the gypsum content.

SUMMARY AND CONCLUSIONS

Twelve commercial clinkers, representing the range of chemical composition found in portland cements, were ground in a laboratory mill with various additions of gypsum. The resulting cements were used to study the influence of gypsum on the hydration and properties of portland-cement pastes. Five of the clinkers were ground in commercial mills with approximately 1.8 per cent SO_3 to three widely different specific surfaces. The latter cements were used to study the influence of fineness upon the rate of hydration with SO_3 constant.

A conduction calorimeter was used to determine the rate of hydration of neat cement pastes, mortar prisms were used to determine the physical properties of the hardened paste.

A properly retarded cement is defined on the basis of the shape of the heat-liberation curve during the first 30 hr. of hydration. A properly retarded cement is one that contains the minimum quantity of gypsum required to give a heat-liberation curve that shows two cycles of ascending and descending rates and that shows no appreciable change with larger additions of gypsum. The results of the physical tests show that when considering cements ground from a given clinker, those containing the proper amount of gypsum to give this type of curve will develop the highest strength and the lowest contraction.

The quantity of gypsum required to obtain a properly retarded cement varies with the composition and fineness of the cement. The results show that the alkalies as well as the $3CaO \cdot Al_2O_3$ content influence the gypsum requirements of the cements. With cements of low alkali content those of high $3CaO \cdot Al_2O_3$ content require larger additions of gypsum than those of low $3CaO \cdot Al_2O_3$. For cements of the same $3CaO \cdot Al_2O_3$ content those high in alkalies react with gypsum more rapidly and require larger additions of gypsum than those low in alkalies. There is some evidence that cements containing Na_2O require larger amounts of gypsum than do similar cements containing an equivalent quantity of K_2O.

Gypsum retards the early hydration of cements of high or moderately high

$3CaO \cdot Al_2O_3$ content and accelerates the hydration of cements of low $3CaO \cdot Al_2O_3$. Without added gypsum, cements of high or moderately high $3CaO \cdot Al_2O_3$ regardless of their alkali content and cements of low $3CaO \cdot Al_2O_3$ that are high in alkalies react with water so rapidly that an immediate flash-set occurs. This phenomenon is the result of the rapid solution of the anhydrous aluminate phases and the rapid crystallization of hydrated calcium aluminates. With added gypsum, the gypsum dissolves in the mixing water together with lime formed by the hydrolysis of compounds present in the cement. The saturated lime-gypsum solution depresses the solubility of alumina in the aqueous solution and thereby retards the hydration of the aluminate phases.

In the presence of the saturated lime-gypsum solution the aluminate phases dissolve at a retarded rate and react with the lime and gypsum to form an insoluble calcium sulfoaluminate. By this process the gypsum may eventually become depleted and its concentration in the aqueous solution decreased. If at this time there is still present a quantity of unhydrated aluminate phases, a rapid reaction will ocur. Such a rapid reaction appears to be the same as that which occurs in the immediate flash-set, that is, a rapid solution of the anhydrous aluminate-phases and a rapid crystallization of hydrated calcium aluminates. With larger additions of gypsum this rapid reaction is eliminated and larger amounts of calcium sulfoaluminate are formed in place of hydrated calcium aluminates.

It appears that at least part of the alkalies of the cement are present in the aluminate phases, and that aluminate phases containing alkalies react with water more rapidly than do similar phases which are alkali-free or of lower alkali content. Thus the cements of higher alkali content require larger additions of gypsum for proper retardation than do similar cements of lower alkali content.

Increasing the specific surface of the cement increases the quantity of aluminate phases available for reaction with water at early ages and thereby increases the quantity of gypsum required for proper retardation of cements of moderately high or high $3CaO \cdot Al_2O_3$ content.

Cements of low $3CaO \cdot Al_2O_3$ and low alkali content without added gypsum can be mixed with water without the occurrence of a flash-set. With cements of this type an amorphous hydrated calcium ferrite precipitates on the surface of the cement particles and seals the surface in a manner such as to retard subsequent hydration. With added gypsum a crystalline hydrated calcium sulfoferrite is formed which does not seal the surface and the hydration is accelerated.

The results show that varying the gypsum content of the cement will alter the rate of hydration at early ages and alter the hydration products that are formed. It seems probable that such changes in the hydration process would alter the structure of the hardened paste. No attempt was made to examine the structure of the paste by direct methods. However, the results of physical tests indicate that the structure of the hardened paste is altered.

The results of the physical tests show that for many cements the strengths can be increased and the contraction on drying or the expansion in water storage decreased by the use of larger additions of gypsum than are permitted by current specifications. In some instances in the present investigation the strengths were increased by as much as 20 to 50 per cent and the contraction decreased by as much as 30 to 50 per cent. For cements of low $3CaO \cdot Al_2O_3$ and low alkali content the strengths were not increased nor was the contraction decreased by larger additions of gypsum. The cements high in $3CaO \cdot Al_2O_3$ regardless of their alkali content or cements high in alkalies regardless of $3CaO \cdot Al_2O_3$ content require the larger additions of gypsum.

Gypsum could be added in larger amounts than is permitted by present specifications without danger of delayed expansion.

REFERENCES

(1) L. A. Wagner, "A Rapid Method for the Determination of the Specific Surface of Portland Cement," *Proceedings*, Am. Soc. Testing Mats., Vol. 33, Part II, p. 553 (1933).

(2) R. W. Carlson, "The Significance of Early Heat Liberation of Cement Paste," *Proceedings*, Highway Research Board, Vol. 17, p. 360 (1937).

(3) L. R. Forbrich, "The Effect of Various Reagents on the Heat Liberation Characteristics of Portland Cement," *Journal*, Am. Concrete Inst., Vol. 12, p. 161 (1940).

(4) R. W. Carlson, "The Vane Calorimeter," *Proceedings*, Am. Soc. Testing Mats., Vol. 34, Part II, p. 322 (1934).

(5) R. H. Bogue, "Calculation of Compounds in Portland Cement," *Industrial and Engineering Chemistry* (Anal. Ed.), Vol. 1, p. 92 (1929).

(6) L. A. Dahl, "A Slide Rule for Calculating Compounds in Portland Cement," *Rock Products*, Vol. 32, No. 23, p. 50 (1929).

(7) J. A. Swenson and E. P. Flint, "Distribution of Compounds in Portland Cement," *Journal of Research*, Nat. Bureau Standards, Vol. 17, p. 261 (1936). (*RP* 910).

(8) L. S. Wells, "Reaction of Water on Calcium Aluminates," *Journal of Research*, Nat. Bureau Standards, Vol. 1, p. 915 (1928). (*RP* 34).

(9) William Lerch, F. W. Ashton, and R. H. Bogue, "The Sulfoaluminates of Calcium," *Journal of Research*, Nat. Bureau Standards, Vol. 2, p. 715 (1929). (*RP* 54).

(10) P. S. Roller, "The Setting of Portland Cement," *Industrial and Engineering Chemistry*, Vol. 26, p. 669 (1934).

(11) L. Forsen, "The Chemistry of Retarders and Accelerators," *Proceedings*, Symposium Chem. of Cement, Stockholm, · p. 298 (1938).

(12) R. H. Bogue and William Lerch, "Hydration of Portland Cement Compounds," *Industrial and Engineering Chemistry*, Vol. 26, p. 837 (1934).

(13) W. H. MacIntire and W. M. Shaw, "The Ternary System $CaO-Fe_2O_3-CaSO_4$ and $CaO-Al_2O_3-CaSO_4$ as Explaining the Retention of Sulfates by Heavily Limed Soil," *Soil Science*, Vol. 19, p. 125 (1925).

(14) Herbert Insley and H. F. McMurdie, "Minor Constituents in Portland Cement Clinker," *Journal of Research*, Nat. Bureau

Standards, Vol. 20, p. 173, (1938). (*RP* 1074).

(15) C. L. Kalousek, C. H. Jumper, and J. J. Tregoning, "Potassium Sulfate in Cement Clinkers," *Rock Products*, Vol. 44, No. 4, p. 52 (1941).

(16) W. C. Taylor, "Further Phase-Equilibrium Studies Involving the Potash Compounds of Portland Cement," *Journal of Research*, Nat. Bureau Standards, Vol. 29, p. 437 (1942). (*RP* 1512).

(17) W. C. Taylor, "The System $2CaO \cdot SiO_2$-$K_2O \cdot CaO \cdot SiO_2$ and Other Phase-Equilibrium Studies Involving Potash," *Journal of Research*, Nat. Bureau Standards, Vol. 27, p. 311 (1941). (*RP* 1421).

(18) H. Kuhl and D. H. Lu, "The Influence of Sulfates on the Chemical and Physical Properties of Portland Cement," *Tonind. Z.*, Vol. 59, No. 70, p. 843 (1935).

(19) G. Haegermann, "The Influence of Sulfates on the Shrinkage of Portland Cement," *Zement*, Vol. 28, No. 40, p. 599 (1939).

(20) William Lerch, "Heat of Hydration of Cement by Simple Apparatus," *Engineering News-Record*, Vol. 113, p. 523 (1934).

(21) P. H. Bates, "The Effect of Finer Grinding and a Higher SO_3 Content Upon the Physical Properties of Portland Cement," *Proceedings*, Am. Soc. Testing Mats., Vol. 15, Part II, p. 128 (1915).

(22) F. M. Lea and R. W. Nurse, "The Specific Surface of Fine Powders," *Journal*, Soc. Chem. Ind., Vol. 58, No. 9, p. 277 (1939).

(23) R. L. Blaine, "Studies of the Measurement of Specific Surface by Air Permeability," ASTM Bulletin No. 108, January, 1941 p. 17.

(24) H. Woods, H. R. Stark, and H. H. Steinour, "Effect of Composition of Portland Cement on Length and Weight Changes of Mortars," *Rock Products*, Vol. 36, No. 6, p. 42 (1933).

(25) H. F. Gonnerman, "Study of Cement Composition in Relation to Strength, Length Changes, Resistance to Sulfate Waters and to Freezing and Thawing of Mortars and Concretes," *Proceedings*, Am. Soc. Testing Mats., Vol. 34, Part II, p. 244 (1934).

(26) R. H. Bogue, William Lerch, and W. C. Taylor, "Portland Cement Pastes," *Industrial and Engineering Chemistry*, Vol. 26, p. 1049 (1934).

DISCUSSION

MR. BENJAMIN WILK.[1]—What would be the effect on the hardening of concrete, if it were cured at higher temperatures?

MR. WILLIAM LERCH (author).—The tests described in this report were made at a temperature of 75 F. Some additional tests have been made to study the effect of temperature on the rate of hydration. Higher temperatures have an effect approximately similar to that of increasing the fineness; that is, the hydration is accelerated.

MR. G. L. KALOUSEK[2] (by letter).—The results presented by the author on the effect of gypsum on properties of hydrating cements and concretes comprise a distinctive contribution to the knowledge of cement technology. The paper presents information long needed to answer many questions regarding the correct amounts of gypsum required for retardation or acceleration of the reactions of setting and hardening.

The twelve cements used in the tests give a good representation of composition and alkali contents among commercial cements. However, because of the peculiarities in behavior of many cements due to unknown factors, the proper choice of "representative" cements is not always realized. It is not the intent to criticize the report on the ground that too few cements were used or the data are limited; the data for most tests are given in large numbers. It is felt, nonetheless, that the inclusion of certain other cements may have altered some of the interpretation made of the data.

Principally on the basis of the thermal behavior of the cements during hydration, the author advances a theory to explain the mechanism of setting and hardening as related to the alumina-bearing phase, tricalcium aluminate. This theory appears inadequate to account satisfactorily for many data published by other investigators. It is true that such data probably in most instances were obtained on cements differing in many respects from those of the author. However, a theory to be general should be applicable to all cements. It is with this thought in mind that this discussion is presented.

Lea[3] in commenting on the theories of setting of cements states, "it cannot be said that at the present time any definite decision as to the correctness of these various theories can be made as it seems not unlikely that certain elements of the whole truth reside in many of them." One of these "elements of truth," as it would appear to be from an abundance of prevailing data, observations, and deductions, is the generally accepted hypothesis of the formation of a slightly permeable hydrous film on the surface of cement grains to retard the reactions of setting and hardening. The author discards this concept in explaining the retardation of setting by gypsum, stating that it is due to the decreased solubility of the anhydrous

---

[1] Standard Building Products Co., Detroit, Mich.
[2] Chemist, Research Dept., Owens-Illinois Glass Co., Toledo, Ohio.

[3] F. M. Lea and C. H. Desch, "Chemistry of Cement and Concrete," Edward Arnold and Co. (London), (1935).

aluminates in presence of $CaSO_4$ in solution. The cause of the appearance of the third maximum in his rate-of-heat – evolution-time curves he ascribes to an acceleration of the hydration of the alumina phase which results from an increase in solubility of the aluminate upon depletion of gypsum in solution. Reasons are advanced in the following paragraphs why it is believed that such a theory is less tenable than one based on the formation of semipermeable membranes of probably a metastable nature.

The author does not report any values for the concentrations of alumina in the aqueous phase of his cement pastes. Since such values have a pertinent bearing on the theory, some of the previously published data will be considered briefly. Attention has to be called first to the fact that the anhydrous phases as such have no true solubility in water because they are decomposed; hence, the solubility of the products (hydrates) formed is in reality the determining factor when discussing the solubility of the anhydrous phase. The author's statement that calcium sulfoaluminates (phases formed in presence of soluble sulfates) are less soluble than the hydrated calcium aluminates (phases formed in presence of $Ca(OH)_2$) is correct, but the amounts in solution are very small for both types of salts. The writer[4] has reported values of about 0.0002 g. per liter of Al_2O_3 as the solubility of the sulfoaluminates in saturated or nearly saturated lime-gypsum solutions. The value for the hydrated calcium aluminates has variously been reported from 0.0004 to 0.004 g. per liter of Al_2O_3 in saturated or nearly saturated lime solution. These concentrations, however, are so markedly smaller than those of the other constituents in so-lution that, from the standpoint of theories of solution, it would be difficult to differentiate among the values given or to ascribe any real meaning to the small difference observed. Inasmuch as the alkalies have an effect on the solubility of the hydrous aluminates and sulfoaluminates,[4] it might seem that in the aqueous phase of hydrating cements a significant difference might be found in the solubility of the phases mentioned. Examination of extensive data published by the writer jointly with others[5] on the compositions of aqueous extracts from cement clinkers, showed that within limits of experimental errors, and making allowance for any Cr_2O_3 present, no significant difference could be found in extracts obtained from pastes, with and without additions of gypsum, filtered immediately after mixing and 2 hr. after mixing. The values, ranging between 0.002 to 0.010 g. per liter of Al_2O_3, are very small compared to the concentrations of the other constituents.

The author in explaining the heat of immediate hydration, the first maximum in the heat curves, states that the mixing water during about the first 5 min. is not saturated with lime and gypsum, and that during this period the anhydrous aluminates are being dissolved and the hydrated calcium aluminate is being precipitated. This claim for the rate of solution is not borne out by the data of other investigators. Forsen[6] has shown that gypsum dissolves rapidly, and also that the solutions from cement pastes are almost instantly saturated or supersaturated with $Ca(OH)_2$ and saturated with respect to gypsum. Data obtained by the writer on the solution of

[4] G. L. Kalousek, "Study of a Portion of the System $CaO-Al_2O_3-SO_3-Na_2O-H_2O$ at 25 C.," Dissertation, University of Maryland, College Park, Md. (1941).

[5] G. L. Kalousek, C. H. Jumper, J. J. Tregoning, "Composition and Physical Properties of Aqueous Extracts from Portland Cement Clinker Pastes Containing Added Materials," Journal of Research, Nat. Bur. Standards, Vol. 30, p. 215 (1943).

[6] L. Forsen, "The Chemistry of Retarders and Accelerators," Symposium on the Chemistry of Cements (Stockholm), p. 298 (1938).

$Ca(OH)_2$ in the mixing water agreed with that of Forsen. Although such results would contradict sharply the author's contention on the rates of solution during the first few minutes, it should be pointed out that cements which have been in storage a long time and are partially hydrated might show a slower rate of solution of $Ca(OH)_2$. Because gypsum dissolves rapidly it would be available for sulfoaluminate formation, and it is highly probable that calcium sulfoaluminate is precipitated instead of a calcium aluminate hydrate, immediately upon the addition of the mixing water. This statement is based on tests and observations by Forsen,[6] results of comprehensive studies by Jones[7] on systems involving $CaO-Al_2O_3-SO_3-Na_2O-K_2O-H_2O$, and by results of the writer[4].

In order to discuss the postulate of the formation of protective films and contrast it with the author's explanation, a brief résumé is given of some of the theories advanced. Forsen[6] presented an extensive amount of experimental data to support the hypothesis that a film of a sulfoaluminate, specifically the monosulfate form of the salt, is formed and retards the reaction of the hydration of the aluminous phases. Jones[7] in a recapitulation of his studies likewise favors the formation of a film of sulfoaluminate, but he considers that the solid solution of the sulfoaluminate is the product formed. Roller[8] expressed the belief that a film of tetracalcium aluminate hydrate was formed even in the presence of gypsum in solution. As already stated, it appears doubtful that hydrated calcium aluminate precip-

itates in the presence of sulfate in solution.

In what manner the deposit of sulfoaluminate as a film may retard the hydration of the anhydrous alumina phases is not known, especially in cements where the presence of silicates may play a part. Thus, additions of alkali sulfate to cement clinkers,[9] or the K_2SO_4 already present in some clinkers[10,11], do not retard the reactions of hydration even though sulfoaluminates are being formed[11]. Actually alkali salts[9] and hydroxides[3] accelerate the reactions of setting. Evidently certain conditions favoring the stability of the film must prevail. Roller[8] pointed out that $Ca(OH)_2$ must be present in solution to stabilize the film, Forsen[6] called attention to the fact that a large decrease in $Ca(OH)_2$ in solution is caused by NaOH and KOH of even moderate concentration, and this confirms Roller's finding.

The preceding considerations would permit the deduction that the nature of the aqueous phase has a marked influence on the course of the reaction of hydration. It should follow that as the composition of the solutions changes, a change occurs in the nature of the solid products. In studies of systems pertaining to cements, the writer[12] has shown that even relatively low concentrations of NaOH (5 g. per liter as Na_2O) decrease markedly the lime content of the hydrous lime silicate gel formed compared to the composition found without the NaOH.

[7] F. E. Jones, "The Formation of the Sulfoaluminates and Sulfoferrites of Calcium in the Portland Cement-Water System," *Journal of Physical Chemistry*, Vol. 49, No. 4, p. 344 (1945).
[8] P. S. Roller, "The Setting of Portland Cement," *Industrial and Engineering Chemistry*, Vol. 26, p. 669 (1934).

[9] C. H. Jumper and G. L. Kalousek, "Effect of Admixtures on Temperature Rise of Cement Pastes," *Rock Products*, Vol. 54, April, May, and June, 1942.
[10] W. C. Taylor, "Further Phase-Equilibrium Studies Involving the Potash Compounds of Portland Cement," *Journal of Research*, Nat. Bur. Standards, Vol. 29, p. 437 (1942).
[11] G. L. Kalousek, C. H. Jumper, and J. J. Tregoning, "Potassium Sulfate in Cement Clinkers," *Rock Products*, April, 1941.
[12] G. L. Kalousek, "Studies of Portions of the Quaternary System Soda-Lime-Silica-Water at 25 C.," *Journal of Research*, Nat. Bur. Standards, Vol. 32, p. 285 (1944).

Also it was found that NaOH in moderate concentration results in the formation of the solid solution form of the sulfoaluminates. Direct evidence is not yet available as to the alterations that may take place in the composition of the hydrous film in cements. However, it is likely that as the composition of the solution is changed there results a change in the film. Certain deductions by inference regarding these changes may be drawn from the heat curves for the hydration of $3CaO \cdot SiO_2$ without any additions. The author has mentioned that this compound in reacting with water gives a rate-of-heat-liberation curve similar to that of cements of low $3CaO \cdot Al_2O_3$ and low alkali. That is, there is first a rapid evolution of heat during the first few minutes, termed the heat of immediate hydration, followed by much lower rate for a few hours, and then there occurs a more rapid evolution of heat for a while. The explanation of these variations in the rate of heat liberation may be according to the following reasons. During the first few minutes the reaction is rapid and a deposit of a lime silicate is formed on the surface of the crystals. The gel first formed must contain less lime than that formed later because initially a part of the lime is required to saturate the solution. After the solution is saturated, in a few seconds for pastes of normal consistency, the gel subsequently formed is richer in lime. Why the film deposited retards the hydration for a while, as indicated by the slower rate of heat evolution, is not known. It must be more impervious to the water than that deposited later, but upon changing over to a product of different composition it becomes more pervious to the water and the rate of hydration is increased.

A rate-of-heat-liberation curve for $3CaO \cdot Al_2O_3$ cannot be determined as for $3CaO \cdot SiO_2$, because of the very rapid rate at which the reaction occurs. Ap-parently no film is deposited. This compound when in cements shows a markedly slower rate of reaction, due probably to the effect of the other constituents in cements. The author has shown that the curve for cements of moderate or high $3CaO \cdot Al_2O_3$, depending on the amount of gypsum added, may show three maxima, the first two being similar to those for $3CaO \cdot SiO_2$ except they are higher and the second occurs sooner. As already mentioned, the author ascribed the first to the formation of hydrous calcium aluminate, but it could be due also to the formation of the sulfoaluminates. The cause for the second maximum is not given. The third maximum occurs if insufficient gypsum had been added and is explained as being the result of the rapid hydration of the remaining $3CaO \cdot Al_2O_3$ above that required to combine with all the sulfate. The author could not account for the third maximum if the hypothesis of the film formation were adopted. The following statement from his report summarizes the ground for the rejection of the film hypothesis: "If this decrease in the rate of heat liberation were to be explained entirely on the basis of the formation of a protective film of hydration products it would be difficult to explain the subsequent disappearance of the protective film, as would be necessary, to permit the rapid reaction and high rate of heat liberation."

Any explanation of the third maximum merits consideration of the change in the aqueous phase. Prior to the occurrence of this rapid liberation of heat, the sulfate disappears from solution and there is left essentially a solution of alkali hydroxides for cement of even moderate alkali contents. This change in solution (from calcium and alkali sulfates and hydroxides to only alkali hydroxides with little lime) could result in a chemical as well as physical change in the reaction products leading to an increased permeability of the film. Not only would the reaction be accelerated by the availability of more water to the anhydrous particles, but as already mentioned the reactions of hydration of cements are accelerated by addition of alkali salts.

The explanation of the second maximum in the heat-liberation curves would appear to deserve more consideration than given it. Neither the hydration of $3CaO \cdot Al_2O_3$ alone, nor $3CaO \cdot SiO_2$ alone, accounts for this maximum. It does not seem unlikely that both these phases are hydrating simultaneously. It is possible that the hydration of the siliceous phases affects that of the aluminous phases and conversely the hydration of the siliceous phases may be altered by the reactions of the aluminous phases. This point is of interest in connection with the author's claim that the alkalies may be associated with the aluminous phases and that these alkali-containing phases, as indicated by heat-liberation characteristics, react more rapidly with gypsum than do similar phases free of alkalies. One may raise the question whether the alkalies could not originate equally as well from the siliceous phases since they are probably hydrating relatively fast at the point of the second maximum. Once in solution, these would be expected to accelerate the reaction of the aluminous phases with gypsum. The author may be correct in his deductions, but it seems that too little is known about the hydrolysis of the alkali-containing lime silicates to permit any conclusion as to the origin of the alkalies. Furthermore, the presence of the alkali sulfates in clinker also may be expected to accelerate the rate of reaction.

A TRIBUTE TO

"Theory of Volume Changes in Hardened Portland-Cement Paste during Freezing"

by T.C. Powers and R.A. Helmuth

Foreword by Kenneth C. Hover

T.C. Powers is an icon of our industry. Hailing from the State of Washington and holding a BA in chemistry, he was later awarded an honorary DSc. Prior to his creative and prolific career at the Portland Cement Association (for which we are truly in Powers' and PCA's debt) he had worked for the Oregon State Highway Commission, and then managed a ready mixed concrete operation until the depression of 1929. Early in 1930 F.R. McMillan invited him to come to PCA with these fateful words "Our work is tending more and more toward the fundamental approach and away somewhat from the customary method of making and breaking specimens." When an early assignment involved the qualitative evaluation of mortar cubes with various degrees of freeze-thaw damage, a young T.C. Powers recalled the often quoted words of Lord Kelvin: "When you can measure what you are talking about and express it in numbers, you know something about it, and when you cannot measure it, when you cannot express it in numbers, your knowledge is of a meager and unsatisfactory kind." Kelvin's words became Powers' operating philosophy, and the result is a cascade of quantitative studies, of which the subject paper is part, that have laid a firm foundation for much of our current understanding of concrete in general, and specifically, the basis for our current practice in specifying, producing, and evaluating air entrained concrete in particular.

The years cannot improve on Powers' own abstract for the subject paper:
"New experimental data are presented on the freezing of hardened portland-cement pastes with and without entrained air. They are explained in terms of two mechanisms: (1) the generation of hydraulic pressure as water freezes in capillary cavities and (2) the growth of the bodies of ice in the

Keywords: air entrainment; air voids; capillaries; diffusion; durability; freezing; gel; hydraulic pressures; paste; portland cement; pressure; thawing; volume changes

capillary cavities or air voids by diffusion of water from the gel. Air voids limit the hydraulic pressure and shorten the period during which the ice in the cavities can increase. The closer the air voids are to each other the more effective they are in controlling either mechanism."

The paper is best understood and appreciated as one in a series of publications by Powers and his respected colleagues, such as Richard Helmuth, on the topic of freeze-thaw durability, published over the critical period from 1935 to 1975. The use of air entrained concrete that resists damage due to freezing and thawing developed from infancy to maturity over that same period, thanks largely to the work of Powers and his associates who inspired, and continue to inspire, a floodtide of high quality scientific investigation. One might suggest that while new studies in the post-Powers era have added immensely to our appreciation and understanding of the challenge of freeze-thaw durability, there have been relatively few fundamental changes in North-American practice for specifying, producing, or evaluating concrete intended to resist damage due to freezing and thawing since Powers' introduced and then elaborated on his Hydraulic Pressure Theory in 1945, 1949, and in the subject paper in 1953.

Immediately prior to publication of Powers and Helmuth [1953], our understanding of freezing phenomena in concrete was centered on Powers' concept of ice crystals expanding in saturated capillaries, driving as-yet unfrozen water towards empty air voids as in a piston-type pump. The pressure generated in this process was understood to increase with rate of freezing, viscosity of the porewater, the length of the flow path to the air void, and with a decrease in permeability of the paste. The notion of a critical length of the flow path was connected to an approximate index of air void spacing known as the spacing factor, and an acceptable value of 0.010 in. "or thereabouts" was recommended. The 1953 paper records the beginning of what was to become a significant transition in thinking about how, where, and when water freezes in concrete with and without air voids, and what happens as a consequence. While the hydraulic pressure theory and its associated critical spacing factor of the air-void system had already been rapidly accepted, endorsed, and confirmed, this paper announced that there was at least one more mechanism to be considered: diffusion of unfrozen water from gel pores to both capillary pores and air voids, and diffusion from capillary pores to air voids. (But even this idea was not exclusively new, as the possibility of diffusional mechanisms had been raised 8 years earlier based on consideration of the physics of soil behavior.) This diffusion model (although Powers did not use the word model) explained the experimental observation that saturated specimens continued to contract with decreasing sub-freezing temperature (freeze drying), more rapidly than could be explained by thermal contraction alone. However, far from minimizing or recanting hydraulic pressure, the authors included an extended commentary on hydraulic pressure that clarified the 1949 paper. In "general remarks" near the close of the paper we find these words: "It was gratifying to find that the original hydraulic pressure hypothesis was correct with respect to its major premise and that the principle deductions from that premise are borne out by the experimental results.[1] To make that theory complete, it was necessary to develop further the observation made in 1945 to the effect that diffusion could play a part. Experiments showed that it played a prominent role and could not be regarded simply as an auxiliary phenomenon."

Thus, after careful study of this densely packed paper that yields more with each reading,[2] one might extract the timeless generalization that multiple mechanisms are associated with freezing and thawing concrete. The predominant mechanism and the subsequent consequences for any given case will depend on:

- Specific material properties of the hardened paste including porosity (as a function of w/c and degree of hydration as of the onset of freezing), permeability, strength, characteristics of the air void system, and degree of saturation.
- Specifics of the freezing environment including factors contributing to the degree of saturation of the concrete, the rate of cooling, and the sub-freezing time-temperature history.

Having once discovered at least one additional freeze-thaw mechanism, the game was afoot and Powers and his co-workers brought us many subsequent papers introducing developments such as osmotic pressure, effects of deicer salts, frost-resistance of aggregates, and the vulnerability of recently-cast concrete. We are fortunate in having Powers' own summaries of his freeze-thaw findings in both the ASTM Stanton Walker Lecture of 1965 (NSGA/NRMCA), and with a little more perspective in time, in the ACI publication *Freezing Effects in Concrete* [1975]. The extent of his scientific pursuit is indicated by his 1975 statement that while hydraulic pressure is generated by flow away from the freezing sites, it "became evident that most of the effects of freezing in cement pastes were due to the movement of unfrozen water to the freezing sites." Further, by late in his studies he recommended a spacing factor as low as 0.006 in. to avoid damage due to osmotic pressure effects.

In the Stanton Walker Lecture (1965) Powers stated that it "has been shown experimentally that if the bubbles are close enough together...we see how entrained air converts what otherwise would be destructive dilation to harmless shrinkage." Of course the key question is, how close is close enough? Early work by Powers et al. showed that when the freezing rate is rapid and temperatures do not drop far below freezing nor stay there for long, the dominant mechanism is hydraulic pressure,

---

1 While citing the critical influence of the air-void spacing factor, Powers took a more moderate approach to its value than do many modern day practitioners, reinforcing his earlier recommendations. "It seems, therefore, that a spacing factor of 0.01 is about that required to produce the practical maximum effect of entrained air [on his paste specimens]." "This is also about optimum spacing factor found from freezing and thawing tests on concrete."
2 The paper itself is light on experimental details, which are subsequently provided in papers by Helmuth published 7 and 8 years later.

and air voids with a spacing factor of 0.010 in. "or thereabouts" are effective in preventing damage. Later work demonstrated that at slower freeze rates and longer and colder "cold-soaks," other mechanisms are at work and spacing factors closer to 0.006 in. are required. Multiple recommended values are not to be interpreted as contradictory, and in applying Powers' work to modern practice we need to remember his terse yet profound statement from the Stanton Walker Lecture: "The key word is SITUATION." As Powers and his colleagues predicted, and as subsequent research and field experience has demonstrated, we should not expect rigidly fixed criteria to apply to different types of concrete with varying w/cm, paste compositions, admixtures, and type and extent of curing, nor to widely varying exposures as defined by moisture, degree of saturation, and variations of temperature with time.

References

1. Powers, T. C., "Basic Considerations Pertaining to the Freezing and Thawing Tests," Proceedings, ASTM, V. 55, 1935, pp. 1132-1155.

2. Powers, T. C., "A Working Hypothesis for Further Studies of Frost Resistance of Concrete," ACI JOURNAL, Proceedings V. 41, No. 3, Feb. 1945, pp.245-272.

3. Powers, T. C., Discussion of Reference I, ACI JOURNAL, Proceedings V. 41, No. 5, Nov. 1945, pp. 272-1 to 272-20.

4. Powers, T. C., and Brownyard, T.L., "Studies of the Physical Properties of Hardened Portland Cement Paste," ACI JOURNAL, Proceedings V. 43, Oct. 1946 - Apr. 1947.

5. Powers, T. C., "The Air-Requirement of Frost Resistant Concrete," Proceedings, Highway Research Board, V. 29, 1949, 184-211.

6. Powers, T. C., and Helmuth, R. A., "Theory of Volume Changes in Hardened Portland Cement Paste During Freezing," Proceedings, Highway Research Board, V. 32, 1953, pp. 285-297.

7. Powers, T. C., "Void Spacing as a Basis for Producing Air Entrained Concrete," ACI JOURNAL, Proceedings V. 50, No. 9, May 1954, pp.741-760.

8. Powers, T. C., "Resistance of Concrete to Frost at Early Ages," Proceedings, RILEM Symposium on Winter Concreting, (Copenhagen, 1956), Danish National Institute of Building Research, Copenhagen, 1956, pp. C1-C47. Also, Research Bulletin No.71, Portland Cement Association.

9. Helmuth, R. A., "Capillary Size Restrictions on Ice Formation in Hardened Cement Pastes," Proceedings, Fourth International Symposium on the Chemistry of Cement, Washington, D. C., V.2,.1960, pp. 855-869, (National Bureau of Standards, Monograph 43, Sept. 1962).

10. Helmuth, R. A., "Dimensional Changes of Hardened Cement Pastes Caused by Temperature Changes, "Proceedings, Highway Research Board, V. 40, 1961, pp. 315-336.

11. Powers, T. C., "The Mechanism of Frost Action in Concrete," Stanton Walker Lecture No. 3, National Sand and Gravel Association, Silver Spring, Maryland, 1965, 35 pp.

12. Powers, T. C., "The Thermodynamics of Volume Change and Creep," Materials and Structures/Research and Testing (Paris), V.6, Nov.-Dec. 1968, pp. 487-507.

13. Powers, T. C. "Freezing Effects in Concrete," Durability of Concrete, ACI SP-47, American Concrete Institute, Farmington Hills, MI, 1975, pp. 1-11.

Kenneth C. Hover, *PE, is a Professor of civil & environmental engineering and the Weiss Presidential Fellow at Cornell University, where he teaches undergraduate concrete design and construction management, and graduate courses on fresh and hardened concrete. His research interests include concrete at early ages and air-entrained concrete, earning ASCE's Best Basic Research Paper Award with Snyder and Natesaiyer for work on air void systems.*

Theory of Volume Changes in Hardened Portland-Cement Paste During Freezing

T. C. Powers, *Manager of Basic Research,* and
R. A. Helmuth, *Junior Research Physicist*
Portland Cement Association

New experimental data are presented on the freezing of hardened portland-cement pastes with and without entrained air. They are explained in terms of two mechanisms: 1) the generation of hydraulic pressure as water freezes in capillary cavities and 2) the growth of the bodies of ice in the capillary cavities or air voids by diffusion of water from the gel. Air voids limit the hydraulic pressure and shorten the period during which the ice in the cavities can increase. The closer the air voids are to each other the more effective they are in controlling either mechanism.

● IN two previous papers (*1, 2*) a hypothesis was advanced to explain the mechanism by which freezing may damage hardened cement paste in concrete and by which air voids may prevent that damage. The hypothesis was based on the assumption that damage is due to hydraulic pressure generated during the process of freezing. Work done in the laboratories of the Portland Cement Association during the last 2 yr. has, we think, advanced the basic assumption of that hypothesis to the status of established fact. At the same time we have learned that hydraulic pressure does not account for all the phenomena produced by freezing. Part of the effect of freezing is apparently due to the tendency of microscopic bodies of ice to grow by drawing water from the gel.

This paper is not intended to be a complete report of the laboratory research on which it is based. Additional details will be given in other papers as soon as the work is finished. The present paper will deal with the salient features of the experimental results and give our interpretation of them.

VOLUME CHANGES DUE TO FREEZING

Several-hundred experiments were made in which the length changes of cement-paste specimens were measured simultaneously with measurements of temperature. Arrangements were such that the temperature could be held constant or could be caused to change at any desired rate through a range extending from +25 to −25 C. Changes in length as small as 1 microinch per in. could be detected.

The temperature measurement was sensitive to about 0.1 C. Length change, temperature change, and elapsed time were recorded automatically.

The specimens were composed of neat cement paste, some made with and some without entrained air. They were tubular, about 2 in. long; outside diameter, 1 in.; inside diameter, ½ in. Most of them contained a Type I cement. Various water-cement ratios were used ranging from 0.45 to 0.70 by weight. The specimens were cured so as to maintain the highest possible degree of saturation throughout the curing period. Ages at test ranged from 3 weeks to about 3 mo. for most of the work. Some specimens, however, were about 2-yr. old when tested.

The results of a test on a specimen containing no air voids[1] is shown in Figure 1. The left-hand scale of ordinates gives the change in length and the right-hand scale, the change in temperature. The scale of abscissas gives the elapsed time after the beginning of the experiment. In most respects the features shown are typical of all relatively porous pastes made without entrained air.

Beginning at room temperature, the specimen was cooled about 0.25 deg. per min. In this case the specimen contracted linearly (the contraction is usually not linear) until the temperature was −6.6 C. At the time when this temperature was reached, freezing oc-

---

[1] Air voids are not considered to be a part of the paste; the paste is the substance surrounding the air voids. The paste is porous (see later) and its pores may contain either air or water. In this paper, we deal only with water-saturated paste, but in no case would we speak of an empty pore in the paste as an air void.

curred, as shown by the sudden rise in temperature. At the instant that freezing began, the specimen began to expand rapidly and with continued cooling it continued to expand.

The particular specimen represented by Figure 1 supercooled about 6 deg. before freezing began. Usually the degree of supercooling is less, often negligible. For specimens of the same kind, the greater the degree of supercooling, the greater the initial expansion. Without supercooling, expansion begins gradually, and apparently in such a case, too, it begins at the same time that freezing begins.

the temperature reached -8.3 C, the cooling was stopped and the temperature held practically constant for about 22 min. During this period of constant temperature the specimen containing entrained air (bottom curve) continued to contract for about 12 min. of the 22-min. constant-temperature period. When cooling was resumed, the specimen resumed contracting.

The dashed-line curve shows the behavior of a similar specimen without air voids as it followed the same temperature schedule. The behavior is like that shown in Figure 1,

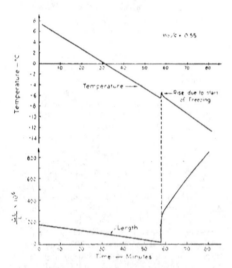

Figure 1. Coincidence of initial expansion with freezing; paste porosity, 0.46.

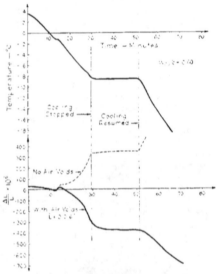

Figure 2. Freezing of pastes with and without air voids; paste porosity, 0.45.

For a specimen containing no entrained air and for rates of cooling 0.25 deg. per min. or higher, the expansion that occurs during freezing is smaller the smaller the porosity of the sample. The porosity of the sample also influences the temperature at which pronounced expansion begins.

Similar data for a specimen containing entrained air are shown in Figure 2, lowest curve. In this case freezing began at about -1 C. and it was accompanied by a small expansion (about 30 microinches). Then as the temperature continued to fall at a nearly constant rate the specimen contracted. When

modified by the difference in supercooling. As the temperature fell the specimen expanded at an increasing rate. At the time when cooling was stopped and the constant-temperature period began, the specimen without entrained air continued to expand slightly while the specimen with entrained air was contracting. After a small expansion the specimen without entrained air then remained almost at constant length.

At the start of the second period of cooling, the specimen without entrained air began abruptly to expand, whereas that made with entrained air began gradually to contract.

Figure 3 is presented to show the effect, on a sample containing no air voids, of holding the temperature constant after the freezing process starts. The sample, a relatively dense one, did not begin to expand until the temperature reached −19 C. The graph includes a record of the experiment for a period beginning 30 min. before expansion began and continuing for more than 6 hr. after that time. For the first 40 min. the temperature was decreased at nearly constant rate. When the temperature had reached −21.3 C, cooling was stopped and the temperature was held constant. During the constant-temperature period the specimen continued to expand. Finally, cooling was resumed, whereupon

geometry of the specimen, i.e., no point in the specimen can be more than 0.1 in. from a boundary. The spacing factors for the specimens containing entrained air were based on the calculated mean distance between voids, the calculations being made by a method previously published (2).

The feature to be noted is that at a given low temperature, say −20 C, the expansion produced by freezing is smaller the smaller the spacing factor. In the low range of spacing factors, the specimens expand slightly and then they contract more than can be ac-

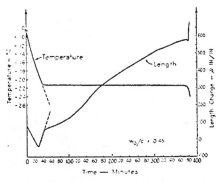

Figure 3. Effect of holding temperature constant after freezing starts in a relatively dense paste.

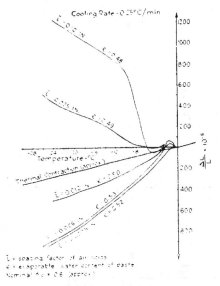

Figure 4. Effect of entrained air.

there was a slight contraction followed by an abrupt increase in the rate of expansion.

The principal point to be noticed in this graph is the expansion during the constant-temperature period. This same tendency is discernible in the dashed line of Figure 2; but for reasons associated with the dimensions and porosity of the sample, the effect was small and of short duration.

Figure 4 shows the relationship between length change and temperature change in the freezing range for pastes containing different amounts of entrained air and, hence, for different void-spacing factors, L. The pastes represented by the different curves all had approximately the same porosity. The uppermost curve represents a specimen containing no entrained air. The indicated spacing factor for such a specimen is based on the

counted for by normal thermal contraction alone.

Many variants of these curves were found among the several-hundred obtained. But it is not necessary to deal with those variants here, for they are such as would be expected from the mechanisms that may be deduced from the curves presented above. The data chosen were those that illustrate with a minimum of complication the mechanisms producing the volume changes.

The principal phenomena may be summarized as follows: (1) In all water-soaked pastes not containing air voids expansion begins at the instant that freezing begins. (2) When air voids are present and closely spaced, initial expansion, if any, begins with freezing and is followed by contraction. (3) When cooling is stopped in the midst of the freezing process and the temperature is held constant, pastes without air voids continue to expand, and those with closely spaced air voids continue to contract, for limited periods. (4) When cooling is resumed after a constant-temperature period, pastes without voids begin abruptly to expand and those with voids begin gradually to contract. (5) On freezing water-soaked pastes of given porosity, expansion is smaller the smaller the spacing factor of the air voids. With spacing factors such as those found in air-entrained concrete, the specimens contract.

INTERPRETATION OF EXPERIMENTS

Knowledge of the submicroscopic structure of hardened portland-cement paste is prerequisite to an understanding of the phenomena under discussion. We shall see that these phenomena can occur only in a material that holds some freezable water in pores so small that the water cannot freeze while it is in those pores, together with some water so situated that it can freeze in place. Experimental evidence has already been published showing that hardened portland cement paste is such a material (3a). Its pores are of two kinds, gel pores and capillary pores. Water cannot freeze in gel pores but can freeze in the capillary pores.

Physical Structure of Paste

In 1947 data were published (3c) showing that the ultimate particles in cement paste (ultimate with respect to water penetration) were exceedingly small, their average diameter being about 140 Å.[2] The calculation of size was based on measured specific surface of the ultimate particles. A few months ago we obtained data on the low-angle scattering of X rays that confirmed this calculation of average size. More recently, in coöperation with the National Bureau of Standards, we obtained electron photomicrographs showing that the ultimate particles were roughly spherical and ranged in size from 50 to

[2] 140 angstrom units equal 0.014 micron, or 0.6 micro-inch. On the basis of current work, this figure is being revised downward. The average diameter is now believed to be between 85 and 100 Å.

200 Å, the apparent average being as previously calculated. The Bureau of Standards also obtained low-angle X-ray data confirming the average size. The tiny spheres are evidently linked together to form the cohesive mass we call *cement gel*. Points of contact are believed to be bonded chemically, as if the spheres were spotwelded together.

Other data published in 1947 showed that when the cement gel completely fills the space available to it, the porosity of the specimen is about 25 percent. From this we deduced that the interstitial spaces are about 25 percent of the over-all volume, a figure now seen to be consistent with the shape of the particles and their limited size range.

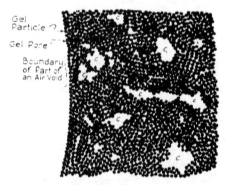

Figure 5. Simplified diagram of paste structure; *C* indicates capillary cavity.

In most pastes the volume of the gel does not equal the apparent volume of the paste. The unfilled space in the paste occurs as cavities in the otherwise continuous mass of gel. These spaces are called capillary pores or capillary cavities. The gel pores are the interstitial spaces among the massed spheres that surround these cavities.

With this knowledge at hand we are able to construct a diagram on which a discussion of the mechanism of freezing can be based. This is given in Figure 5. The gel particles are indicated by the black spots and the capillary pores by the empty spaces. So as not to obscure the gel pores, we have indicated the dense regions to be much less dense than they really are.[3]

[3] Ca(OH)₂ crystals and residues of unhydrated cement are not represented. These are comparatively few and far between and of no significance here.

The curved boundary at the left is supposed to represent a part of the wall of an air void and is intended to suggest that air voids such as those in air-entrained concrete are extremely large as compared with the capillary cavities and gel pores in the paste. If the air void were drawn to scale and were of average size, the curvature would hardly be discernible.

The capillary cavities are more numerous and larger the higher the original water-cement ratio and the shorter the period of curing. Such cavities are the only places where ice can exist within the boundaries of the paste.

Experimental data show that a very-small amount of water freezes near the normal freezing point, but in most specimens a significant amount of freezing occurs only after the temperature falls well below the normal freezing point. This behavior (as well as other evidence) indicates that most of the capillary cavities are quite small. They are so small that the ice crystals they contain cannot exist except when the temperature is below the normal freezing point. The reason for this is too complex to be dealt with here. A simple explanation is that the surface tension of the bodies of ice in capillary cavities puts them under a pressure that is higher the smaller the body. Hence, the smaller the cavity and, of necessity, the smaller the ice body the higher the pressure and the lower the freezing point.[4] (The gel pores are so small that freezing cannot occur at any temperature, at least not at any temperature above -78 C.)

Freezing starts at the temperature required by the largest cavity, and as the temperature continues to fall, the water in the smaller cavities progressively becomes frozen. Freezing curves, such as the dashed line in Figure 2, indicate that the water is held in cavities of various sizes.

The foregoing remarks pertain to freezing in a saturated specimen, in which case the free energy of the unfrozen water is at a maximum. Owing to adsorption and capillary forces and to dissolved substances, principally the alkalies, the free energy of the water in hardened paste is a function of its degree of

saturation (3). The same is true of the cement gel considered by itself. The maximum free energy is somewhat below that of pure water in bulk, because of the solute concentration. When water is removed from the paste or the gel, the free energy of the residual water becomes progressively lower. Hence, the highest temperature at which the remaining water can freeze becomes lower as water is extracted from the paste.

Capillary size, limiting as it does the size of the ice crystal, fixes the least amount by which the free energy of ice in a capillary exceeds that of bulk ice. (When the capillary ice is subjected to pressure, its free energy rises above the minimum.) Desiccation of the paste lowers the free energy of the freezable water and fixes the highest temperature at which the freezable water can be in equilibrium with bulk ice. The temperature at which freezing can occur in a given capillary cavity is determined by the free energy of the ice and the free energy of the freezable water; thus, it is controlled both by cavity size and degree of desiccation.

In the following discussion we shall assume, for the sake of simplicity, that the concentration of soluble material is negligible, hence, that the free energy of the water in saturated gel is practically the same as the free energy of pure water in bulk at the same temperature. This condition is not entirely hypothetical; it has been produced in the laboratory.

Freezing in Capillaries and Generation of Hydraulic Pressure

In a water-soaked paste the capillary pores and the gel pores are full, or nearly full, of water. When the temperature falls to the point where freezing can begin, ice crystals should appear, presumably in the largest capillary cavities only. Consider the capillary cavity marked C_1 in Figure 5. When the water it contains begins to change to ice, the volume of water plus ice will exceed the original capacity of the cavity. This comes about, of course, because 1 cc. of water occupies about 1.09 cc. of space after freezing. Therefore, during the time when the water in C_1 is changing to ice, the cavity must dilate or the excess water must be expelled from it.

As indicated by the diagram, cement paste is a permeable material (though the coefficient of permeability is extremely low). Hence, there is a possibility that the excess water can escape from C_1 during the process of freezing. If we consider Figure 5 to represent half of a layer between two voids, we can see that there is a possibility for the excess in C_1 to escape into the air void at the left. We may think of the growing ice body in C_1 as a sort of pump forcing water through the paste toward the void boundary. Obviously, such a pumping out of water involves the generation of pressure. The factors controlling this pressure have been dealt with in detail in a previous paper (2). The most important factors are: (1) the coefficient of permeability of the material through which the water is forced; (2) the distance from C_1 to the void boundary; and (3) the rate at which freezing occurs.

Let us now consider freezing in the capillary marked C_2. Clearly, the excess water can escape from C_2 more readily than from C_1. Therefore, the maximum pressure reached during freezing in C_2 must be less than the maximum reached in C_1. In general, we can see that during the process of freezing hydraulic pressure will exist throughout the paste, and this pressure will be higher the farther the point in question from the nearest escape boundary. If a point in the paste is sufficiently remote from an escape boundary, the pressure may be high enough to stress the surrounding gel beyond its elastic limit, or beyond its strength, and thus may produce permanent damage.

It becomes clear that every air void enveloped by the paste must be bordered by a zone or shell in which the hydraulic pressure cannot become high enough to cause damage. Theoretically, the pressure increases approximately in proportion to the square of the distance from the void, the pressure being zero at the void boundary. By reducing the distance between voids to the point where the protected shells overlap, we can prevent the generation of disruptive hydraulic pressure during the freezing of water in the capillaries.

The foregoing is the essence of the hydraulic-pressure hypothesis that has been developed in detail previously. Experimental data of the kind already presented advance the hypothesis to the status of established fact. To see how this is so, consider again the capillary cavity represented in C_1 in Figure 5.

Hydraulic pressure must appear in this cavity at the very instant that freezing begins. Therefore, the specimen as a whole (acted on simultaneously by all similar cavities) should begin to expand at the instant that freezing begins. Figure 1 shows that this is exactly what happens. No other mechanism that we can think of can account for this coincidence of events. This evidence alone, when all its implications are evaluated, is enough to confirm the hydraulic-pressure hypothesis. Other evidence will be brought out further on pertaining to responses to changes in rate of cooling.

However, generation of hydraulic pressure through the mechanism just described does not account for all phenomena illustrated in Figures 1 to 4. In particular, it does not account for shrinkage that accompanies freezing when air voids are present nor for certain responses to change in rate of cooling. To account for these phenomena, we must consider what may happen after the water in a given capillary cavity becomes frozen.

Diffusion and Freezing of Gel Water

With the water in cavity C_1 turned to ice, we have to consider the relationship of that ice to the unfrozen water in the surrounding gel. (Remember that water cannot freeze in the gel.) If the gel is saturated, the gel water has the same free energy as that of ordinary water in bulk. Therefore, it can be in thermodynamic equilibrium with the ice in C_1 at 0 C if both the ice and the gel water are under a pressure of 1 atmosphere and if C_1 is so large as to have negligible surface energy. If now the temperature drops below the temperature at which the water in C_1 became frozen (we here assume it to be 0 C), the gel water is no longer in thermodynamic equilibrium with the ice; its free energy is higher than that of the ice. We know this because we know that the water that can be extracted from a saturated gel has a higher entropy than that of ice (3b). When such a difference in entropy exists, it is a direct thermodynamic consequence that lowering the temperature will cause the water to gain free energy faster than does the ice. As a consequence, the gel water acquires an energy potential enabling it to move into the cavity and cause the ice crystal to grow and enlarge the cavity. Our conclusions regarding the mechanism by which this growth takes place will now be described.

As indicated in Figure 5, the walls of the capillary cavities are made up of gel particles. Each gel particle carries its adsorbed water "film" and the water film separates the gel particles from the ice, the degree of separation being submicroscopic, only a few molecular diameters. We attempt to show this boundary region between ice and cavity wall in Figure 6. The body of ice is shown to be separated from the cavity wall by an unfrozen film, the adsorbed layer, which film is continuous with the adsorbed layers within the gel.

The water molecules in the film tend to have the orientation demanded by the force field of gel particles. The same molecules are also

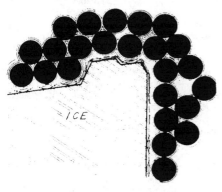

Figure 6. Disposition of water films.

subject to the force fields of the ice crystal which tend to produce the molecular orientation characteristic of the crystal. Thus, the water in the film is subject to competitive forces. At a given temperature below 0 C, the ice crystal is able to capture some of the film water and reduce the thickness of the film below what it would be if no ice were present. As the temperature becomes still lower, more of the molecules in the film are captured by the ice and the film becomes thinner. Since the films are identical with the adsorbed layers on the gel particles in the interior of the gel (the gel water), the depletion of the film in the capillary cavity by the ice in the capillary cavity produces a free-energy difference between the film in the cavity and the gel water. Consequently, water creeps along

the surfaces of the gel particles into the film in the ice-bearing cavity as required to reduce the free-energy potential created by depletion of the film in the cavity. The process is called surface diffusion.

Whenever the gel loses water it tends to shrink, no matter whether the water is lost by evaporation or by freezing. The tendency of the gel to shrink as water is extracted from it, by freezing and the growth of the ice body, places the ice in the capillary cavities and the film around the ice under pressure. Such pressure increases the free energy of the ice and of the water in the film between the ice crystal and the gel particles and tends to prevent the replenishment of that film by diffusion of water from the gel. However, the swelling pressure in the film is enough to produce dilation. For example, if the gel were saturated and if the capillary cavities contained ice at −5 C, the pressures in the film between the ice and the solid could be as much as 1,200 psi. This amount of pressure would surely cause the paste to dilate appreciably. Thus, expansion can be caused by diffusion of water from the gel to the capillary cavities.

Diffusion to Air Voids

Up to this point we have spoken mostly of the diffusion of gel water to capillary cavities. From the same considerations of thermodynamics, we can see that while gel water is diffusing to capillary cavities it is diffusing also to the ice in the air voids.

The amount of ice in the air voids is not equal to the capacity of the voids.[5] Consequently, as the ice grows and the gel shrinks, the ice in the air void may be under no significant pressure. Such would be the case when the ice exists as discrete crystals or as a thin shell lining the void, the shell having negligible rigidity. If the shell becomes thick enough, it might offer resistance to the contraction of the void. But it could not offer as much resistance as the ice in the completely filled capillary cavities. The point is that the pressures on the capillary ice may be much higher than the pressures on the air-void ice.

[5] Under some circumstances the air voids in cement paste or in concrete can become filled, or partly filled, with water prior to freezing. In practice, such circumstances are rare, as attested by the successful use of air-entrained concrete. In the present discussion we assume that the air voids contain no water except that received during the process of freezing. However, they could contain a considerable additional amount of water without appreciable alteration of their protective effect.

Since the pressure on the capillary ice may be higher than that on the air-void ice, its free energy may be correspondingly higher. Also, as we have already seen, the bodies of capillary ice are very small, and as a consequence, the free energy of the capillary ice is higher than that of the bulk ice in the air voids at the same temperature and pressure. Hence, at a given temperature the free energy of the capillary ice will be higher than that of the air-void ice, because of the smallness of the particles of capillary ice and, at times, because of higher pressure on the capillary ice.

The consequences of these differences in free energy can best be understood with the aid of Figure 5. Consider again capillary C_2. Let us suppose as before that a temperature has been reached at which the water

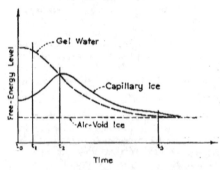

Figure 7. Free-energy changes in reaching equilibrium.

in this cavity becomes frozen. Because of the nearby air void, we may now assume that the excess water produced in this cavity has been forced into the air void where, along with the excess water from other cavities, it has produced a thin coating of ice on the void boundary. We shall suppose further that the hydraulic pressure has been relieved so that the ice in the air void, the water in the gel, and the ice in the cavity are under equal pressure. Now let us cool this region quickly to a lower temperature and then hold the temperature constant.[6] The effect of this change is illustrated in Figure 7.

This diagram shows the changes in free energy of the gel water, the capillary ice, and the air-void ice that will take place while the

[6] Lowering the temperature should cause other, smaller cavities to freeze, but we are considering only the small region indicated.

temperature is held constant. The upper curve represents the free energy of the gel water at a particular point within the gel, which we shall call Point A. This point is assumed to be nearer to C_2 than it is to the air void. The time, t_0, corresponds to the time at which the diffusion is assumed to begin. At this time the capillary ice and the air-void ice are assumed to be under the same pressure, but the free energy of the capillary ice is shown to be higher than that of the air-void ice, because the body of capillary ice is assumed to be very small. The free energy of the gel water is shown to be higher than either of the ice bodies, because in dropping from the first to the second temperature, it gained more free energy than did the bodies of ice.

The starting point of the curve for capillary ice relative to the other two points will depend upon the size of capillary void in question. The smaller the ice body, the smaller will be the initial difference between its free energy and that of the gel water and the greater will its free energy exceed that of the air-void ice. Figure 7, therefore, represents conditions pertaining to a particular size of capillary cavity.

Since at the start the free energy of the gel water exceeds that of the two ice bodies and since the gel separates the two, gel water will begin to diffuse in both directions, that is, to the air void and to the capillary cavity. As diffusion proceeds, the gel water at Point A is not immediately affected. After a certain time interval, t_0 to t_1, the amount of gel water at Point A begins to diminish and the free energy begins to decrease.

During the interval t_0 to t_1, the capillary ice increases and, through the mechanism already discussed, produces pressure on the walls of the cavity. As a consequence, the free energy of the capillary ice increases during this interval.

The air-void ice also receives water during this period; but, being at constant temperature and under negligible pressure, its free energy remains constant.

During the interval t_1 to t_2 the free energy of the gel water continues to decrease, because of continued desiccation of the gel. At the same time the free energy of the capillary ice rises until it equals the free energy of the residual gel water. At this time diffusion through Point A to the capillary cavity ceases. Thereafter, the gel water moves toward the air void only.

During the interval t_2 to t_4 the system comes close to equilibrium. In this period the free energy of the capillary ice is at all times higher than that of the residual gel water. Hence, the capillary ice loses water to the gel and eventually to the air-void ice. At equilibrium the gel has reached the required degree of desiccation, and the ice in the capillary cavities has been depleted enough to relieve the pressure.

During the interval t_0 to t_2, the capillary ice increases by approximately 1.09 times the volume of water it receives. The parts of the gel from which this water is received tend to shrink, but even when unrestrained the shrinkage is much less than the volume of water lost. Hence, the net effect is a tendency to expand.

The concomitant volume increase of the air-void ice either results in no expansive force at all or else in only a feeble one, as we have already pointed out. Consequently, the net effect of water lost from the gel to the air void is a tendency to shrink. Both tendencies coexist during the interval t_0 to t_2, that being the period of diffusion in both directions; but in the following interval gel water diffuses toward the air void only, and the net effect is shrinkage throughout the gel. Over-all expansion due to diffusion is possible while the capillary ice is still receiving gel water, though it may cease while diffusion to some capillary cavities is still going on.

In a paste of given characteristics, the amount of gel water that can enter a capillary cavity by diffusion and freezing will be a maximum if the paste contains no air voids and if the boundaries of the specimen are at a practically infinite distance from the cavity.[7] In this case, the capillary ice can grow for as long as necessary to reach equilibrium with the gel. If the stresses, whether from hydraulic pressure or from subsequent growth of capillary ice, rupture the gel and thus release the pressure on the ice, the growth will be limited only by the amount of water in the system freezable at the given temperature.

On the other hand, if the paste contains air voids and if the capillary cavity is adjacent to a void, the free energy of the gel water between

---

[7] An ice coating on a specimen is like the ice in the air voids within the specimen. It can receive water from the gel as its temperature falls below 0 C, and it can produce a tendency for the specimen to shrink.

---

the cavity and the void must decrease rapidly. The period of diffusion to the capillary cavity will be correspondingly brief (see C_2 of Fig. 5). If the cavity is remote from the void, depletion of the gel water in the vicinity of the cavity by diffusion to an air void will be correspondingly delayed and diffusion to the capillary cavity prolonged (see C_1 of Fig. 5). In terms of the relationships shown in Figure 7, this means that the farther the capillary cavity is from the nearest air void, the longer the interval t_0 to t_2 and the greater the proportion of total freezable water received by the capillary cavity.

Application to Test Data

Let us now apply this theory to the data presented in Figures 1 to 4. First, the evidence of expansion due to hydraulic pressure:

As already mentioned, the instantaneous expansion shown in Figure 1 seems to be explainable only in terms of the hydraulic pressure generated during the freezing of capillary water, that is, by water freezing in place. Because of the relatively high porosity of the sample and because of supercooling, a relatively large amount of water was able to freeze at one time. (The only escape for the excess water was the outer boundaries of the specimen.) The continued expansion accompanying further cooling was also due mostly to hydraulic pressure, but the evidence for this conclusion does not appear in Figure 1 (see discussion of Fig. 4).

In Figure 2 the first rising part of the dashed-line curve represents expansion due to hydraulic pressure, though again the proof does not appear in this diagram. This part of the curve is mentioned, however, as an illustration of the fact that expansion due to hydraulic pressure is not always greatest at the start of the freezing process, though the start of expansion is always coincident with the start of freezing. The clearest indication of freezing in place is shown at the end of the constant-temperature period: when the temperature began to drop, expansion at a relatively high rate began abruptly.

In Figure 3, resumption of cooling at the end of the 6-hr. constant-temperature period gave evidence of freezing in place and expansion due to hydraulic pressure. Notice that the sample showed a momentary contraction, probably thermal, followed by abrupt expansion, when cooling started.

In Figure 4 the topmost curve representing an air-free paste represents expansion primarily due to the generation of hydraulic pressure, as already mentioned. Various experiments show that if at any time during the production of such a curve the rate of cooling is suddenly increased, the rate of expansion is also suddenly increased. This response to a change in rate is characteristic of the hydraulic pressure mechanism; expansion due to diffusion to a capillary cavity responds in the opposite way.

Now we shall examine evidence of expansion due to diffusion and freezing of gel water:

The clearest example is that shown in Figure 3. These data were from a relatively dense specimen in which an appreciable amount of freezing did not begin until the temperature reached −19 C. After freezing started, the specimen was allowed to expand for 10 min., during which time cooling was continued. This expansion is characteristic of that due to hydraulic pressure. At the end of the 10-min. period, cooling was stopped and the temperature held constant for 6 hr., as described before. At the start of this constant-temperature period we have a limited amount of ice in capillary cavities in contact with saturated gel at a temperature of −21 C. This corresponds to time t_0 of Figure 7. The capillary ice is probably under pressure, but it is not under enough pressure to raise its free energy to that in the saturated gel. In this case the "air-void ice" is represented by whatever ice may be on the exterior surfaces of the specimen. This ice is too far away from the interior parts to have any discernible effect in a specimen as impermeable as this one. As the capillary ice grows, the pressure on it increases and it undergoes corresponding increases in free energy. Thus we see that the expansion during the 6-hr. constant-temperature period corresponds in Figure 7 to the rising part of the energy curve for capillary ice.

The process of diffusion is relatively slow. Hence, when the temperature is falling ¼ deg. or so per min., an experiment such as that shown in Figure 1 can be completed before an appreciable amount of diffusion takes place. Diffusion phenomena are apparent only when the temperature is kept constant

for a considerable length of time or when closely spaced air voids are present. They should be apparent, too, when the cooling is very slow.

The influence of air voids is shown by the bottom curve of Figure 2. As stated before, the small initial expansion is probably due to hydraulic pressure. As the temperature falls, more capillary cavities freeze and tend to cause expansion while, at the same time, the ice in capillaries already frozen tends to draw water from the gel. With the air voids only a few thousandths of an inch apart and with the ice they contain under no pressure, diffusion from the gel can occur at a relatively high rate. Very soon after freezing starts, the relationship between the capillary ice, air-void ice, and gel water must be as indicated for the time interval t_2 to t_3 of Figure 7 for most of the capillary cavities in the paste surrounding the air voids. Hence, the over-all effect is contraction.[8]

A study of responses to change in rate of cooling was rewarding. The process of diffusion must always lag behind the development of potential causing the diffusion, that is, it lags behind the drop in temperature. Consequently, when the cooling is stopped, the lag is manifested by a continued contraction. This is shown clearly in Figure 2, bottom curve. The rate of contraction decreases in the manner expected. At the end of the constant-temperature period, probably little potential between air-void ice and gel water remained. When cooling was resumed, the potential began to increase, probably linearly with the decrease in temperature. As would be expected, continued shrinkage developed only gradually, the rate of shrinkage increasing with the increase in potential. The gradual beginning of shrinkage on resumption of cooling is to be contrasted with the abrupt expansion that occurred for the paste without air voids (dashed-line curve). This difference in behavior is one of the clearest means of distinguishing between a volume change controlled by diffusion and one controlled by hydraulic pressure.

Under certain conditions the tendency to expand from the freezing of capillary cavities is about equal to the thermal contraction plus the tendency to contract due to diffusion

[8] Valore (6) observed this previously. Specimens of air-entrained concrete or of plain concrete partially dried showed shrinkage at constant temperature after fast cooling.

to ice bodies. While such conditions exist, the specimen does not change in volume as the temperature falls. Also, if the rate of cooling is varied, the specimen does not respond in a manner distinctive of either mechanism. Among the many experimental curves obtained almost every possible variation has been observed.

In Figure 4 we see the effect of differences in void-spacing factor. The results are as would be expected from the two mechanisms discussed above. However, curves such as these alone do not tell whether hydraulic pressure or diffusion to cavities is the principal factor causing expansion, when expansion occurs. Auxiliary experiments were necessary to observe the effects of changes in cooling rate, as already discussed.

When considering the curves of Figure 4, we must remember that the volume changes shown are those that occur during the course of cooling. When the specimens are returned to their original temperature, some return to approximately their original dimensions, if given enough time; others show residual expansion. Specimens undergoing as much expansion as the two represented by the upper curves will show a considerable residual expansion. For a specimen to show no residual expansion the spacing factor must be small enough to produce over-all contraction throughout practically all the freezing-temperature range.

We noted that with various families of curves, such as that shown in Figure 4, reductions in the spacing below 0.01 in. produced relatively little additional shrinkage. It seems, therefore, that a spacing factor of 0.01 in. is about that required to produce the practical maximum effect of entrained air. This is also about the optimum spacing factor found from freezing-and-thawing tests on air-entrained concrete.

It is of some interest to speculate as to why to protect the paste we must produce a spacing factor that gives a substantial amount of contraction. Why is it that a factor that just prevents expansion is not enough? We have already seen reasons to believe that although freezing may produce no over-all expansion, a tendency to expand may nevertheless be present in some regions. The regions tending to contract offset the regions tending to expand. On repeated freezings the tendency

to expand, opposed by the tendency to contract, may gradually produce mechanical damage. The paste evidently can be fully protected only when the regions tending to expand approach the vanishing point. From these considerations, admittedly speculative, test results on neat cement pastes, like those shown in Figure 4, seem to be in excellent agreement with test results on air-entrained concrete.

GENERAL REMARKS

The two earlier papers dealing with the theory of frost resistance, previously referred to, gave the development of a hypothesis. As such, they aimed to be a logical development of a stated premise. They were not based on experimental data and consequently could be no more valid than the premise on which they were based. In contrast, the present paper is based on experimental data. The data are those obtained not only from freezing experiments on hardened cement paste but also from studies pertaining to the submicroscopic structure of hardened paste and the thermodynamics of the physical interactions between the solids and the evaporable water in the paste. Therefore, the theory presented here is more than a hypothesis; it rests on experimental results and known physical principles. Moreover, it is able to account for the phenomena observed.

It was gratifying to find that the original hydraulic-pressure hypothesis was correct with respect to its major premise and that the principal deductions from that premise are borne out by the experimental results. To make the theory complete, it was necessary to develop further the observation made in 1945 to the effect that diffusion could play a part. Experiments showed that it played a prominent role and could not be regarded simply as an auxiliary phenomenon.

In this paper we devoted much space to developing the theory of diffusion and freezing of gel water and relatively little to the freezing of capillary water· and the generation of hydraulic pressure. As already indicated, this does not mean that we hold the diffusion theory to be the more important or to displace the hydraulic-pressure theory. Both are indispensable parts of a general theory, and neither part alone can account for all the observed phenomena. We did not need to devote much space here to the theory of hydraulic pressure, because that was treated rather exhaustively in the earlier papers.

Although the experimental evidence of hydraulic pressure is easily observed, the basis for the diffusion part of the theory may not be as clear, because the experimental evidence is less direct. The data reported in Reference 3b pertaining to the energy of binding of evaporable water in hardened paste is the starting point. Figures 4 to 9, p. 571 of the paper referred to, give the results of calculations of the change in entropy that water undergoes when it enters a dry paste. The data show that the water first to enter dry paste undergoes more entropy change than the entropy change of freezing, but they show also that as the paste nears saturation the increments of water undergo a negligible change in entropy. It is thus experimentally established that the entropy of the water that might be extracted from the gel by freezing at a given temperature within the range of temperatures of interest here is greater than the entropy of ice at the same temperature.

One of the fundamental thermodynamic relationships is

$$\left(\frac{\partial F}{\partial T}\right)_P = -S$$

which says that the change in free energy of a given component produced by a change in temperature with pressure held constant is equal to its entropy but opposite in sign to the change in temperature. Therefore, if the entropy of the ice is smaller than the entropy of water to be extracted from the gel, a decrease in temperature will produce a greater change in the free energy of the ice than the change in free energy of the gel water. Hence, if the starting point is one of equilibrium (where the two free energies are equal), lowering the temperature will destroy the equilibrium and create a free-energy potential.

The energy data already cited show that such a potential is produced between the unfrozen gel water and the capillary ice when the temperature is lowered. This demonstrates that a change in the system will take place in such a way as to restore equilibrium. In the present case, the theoretically possible change would produce either a contraction or an expansion, according to circumstances, as discussed in this paper. The expected changes were observed to take place.

Thus, though the experimental evidence for diffusion is more complicated than that for hydraulic pressure, it is just as conclusive.

The beginnings of the diffusion theory developed here were mentioned in the 1945 paper in connection with the hypothesis advanced by Collins (6), which was, in turn, based upon the "segregation" theory of Taber (4). It was pointed out that a transfer of gel water to capillary ice is thermodynamically possible and that it should result in expansion. However, at that time it did not seem possible to account for the protective effect of air by such a mechanism. Since air voids did control frost action and since the method of control of hydraulic pressure by air voids was clear, it seemed necessary to assume that hydraulic pressure was the principal cause of damage. Confronted with data such as given in this paper, we reconsidered the diffusion theory and found that it, too, could account for the protective effect of air and that the explanation was compatible with that given for the control of hydraulic pressure.

The explanation of pressure generation through the adsorbed film between the ice body and the solid is essentially like that advanced by Taber in 1930 for the growth of ice lenses in soils (4). However, the "lenses" in paste are microscopic bodies, and the forces set up are of a nature peculiar to cement paste.

Both mechanisms of frost action on cement paste are predicated on the peculiarities of the paste. Hydraulic pressure would be no factor at all if it were not for the particular combinations of permeability, strength, and porosity found in paste, together with typical distances between air voids in non-air-entrained concrete. Also, diffusion phenomena of the kind described are possible because cement pastes are capable of holding some freezable water that cannot be frozen in place, along with some that can be frozen in place.

Although we did not bring it out explicitly in the preceding discussions, the reader may have seen that the water movements discussed are reversible, or mostly so. When water is extracted from the paste to the air voids during a period of freezing, it will return from the voids to the paste during a period of thawing. Thus, water that was expelled or that diffused to the air voids during freezing will be extracted from the air voids during thawing. This accounts for the persistence of the protective effect of entrained air. When air voids are absent, water extracted from the gel to the capillary cavities will return to the gel during thawing.

A question remains as to which of the two mechanisms is principally responsible for expansion when expansion occurs. It is clear that the answer will depend mainly upon the rate at which the sample is cooled and the length of time it remains at a subfreezing temperature and the permeability of the paste. At the rates of cooling normally used in laboratory freezing-and-thawing tests, most of the expansion of average non-air-entrained concrete that takes place while the cooling is going on at customary rates may be due to hydraulic pressure. If, however, the specimen is held in the freezer for a time after the minimum temperature is reached, continued expansion may take place through the other mechanism. Concrete in the field cools slowly, and low temperatures may be maintained for many hours or days. If the paste is not protected with entrained air, it is liable to be damaged by both mechanisms: first, by hydraulic pressure, and then by growth of the ice bodies. The lower the temperature, the more severe the final effect.

With air-entrained concrete, the role played by hydraulic pressure will depend upon the degree to which the paste is protected by the air voids. If the air voids are close together and if the rate of cooling is not excessive, hydraulic pressure is exceedingly transitory, and diffusion to the air voids dominates the process almost immediately. If the air voids are too far apart for adequate protection of the paste, hydraulic pressure may play a more prominent role. The dominant influence of the spacing factor cannot be overemphasized.

SUMMARY

Water freezing in capillary cavities produces hydraulic pressure and consequent dilation. At any temperature below the temperature at which the ice in a cavity was formed, gel water can diffuse to that cavity and cause the ice body to grow, producing expansion. Both processes can occur simultaneously in different parts of the paste. Since diffusion is slow, expansion is due mainly to hydraulic pressure when freezing is rapid, as in laboratory tests.

When air voids are present, they limit the hydraulic pressure according to the thickness of the layers of paste between them. Also, the ice they contain draws water from the paste, causing the paste to shrink. Since the ice in the capillary cavities generally has a higher free energy than that in the air voids, the ice in the air void may eventually draw the excess from both the gel and the frozen cavities, producing over-all contraction. Expansion due to growth of ice in the capillary cavities is prevented if the air voids are close enough together, as is also expansion due to hydraulic pressure.

During thawing, the water that was extracted from the paste by the ice in the air voids diffuses back. In a paste free of air voids, the ice in the capillary cavities melts progressively, and the water drawn from the gel during freezing is returned to the gel.

Expansion or contraction during cooling at constant rate occurs in the manner expected from the theory. Also, the effects of changes in rate of cooling are in accord with the theory.

The function of the air voids is to limit hydraulic pressure and to limit the time during which capillary ice can increase by diffusion of gel water. The spacing factor controls the effectiveness of the voids for either mechanism.

REFERENCES

1. T. C. Powers, "A Working Hypothesis for Further Studies of Frost Resistance of Concrete," *Proceedings*, Am. Concrete Inst. *41*, 245 (1945); PCA Bulletin 5.
2. T. C. Powers, "The Air Requirement of Frost-Resistant Concrete," Proceedings, Highway Research Board *29*, 184 (1949): PCA Bulletin 33.
3. T. C. Powers and T. L. Brownyard, "Studies of the Physical Properties of Hardened Portland Cement Paste," *Proceedings*, Am. Concrete Inst. *43*, (1947); PCA Bulletin 22. (a) Part 8, p. 933. (b) Part 4, p. 549. (c) Part 3, p. 469. (d) Part 2, p. 277, Fig. 2–6.
4. Stephen Taber, "The Mechanics of Frost Heaving," *J. Geol. 38*, 303–17 (1930). See also *J. Geol. 37*, 428 (1929); *Public Roads 11*, 113 (1930).
5. R. C. Valore, "Volume Changes Observed in Small Concrete Cylinders during Freezing and Thawing Using a Mercury Displacement Dilatometer," *Jl. of Res. NBS*, *43*, July 1949, Res. Paper RP2000.
6. A. R. Collins, "The Destruction of Concrete by Frost," *J. Inst. Civ. Engrs. 23*, 29 (1944).

A TRIBUTE TO
"Causes and Prevention of Crack Development in Plastic Concrete"
by C.A. Menzel

Foreword by Jason Weiss

Overview

It has been my distinct pleasure to be asked by the ACI Publications and History Committees to write the foreword for this paper that was selected for this landmark series. The paper titled "Causes and Prevention of Crack Development in Plastic Concrete" was authored by Carl Menzel and introduced the concrete community to an illustrative graph that could be used to help minimize plastic cracking by identifying conditions that are responsible for rapid evaporation in fresh concrete. Though this graph has taken on different forms since its original publication, it marks a distinct attempt to relate fundamental scientific theory from one field to the solution of problems in concrete construction. In my opinion this paper has several features that every author should strive for:

1) The paper adopts science from another field to solve practical problems;
2) The paper is easy to read by authors with a variety of backgrounds; and
3) The paper is clearly related to field concerns and data are gathered from practice that provide evidence that the approach may have validity.

Mission of the Paper

Menzel begins his paper with a clear mission: "... cracking, can be practically eliminated if appropriate measures to minimize the causes are taken at the right time." [1] This paper discusses many of the factors that can cause cracking at early ages before focusing on the cracking that occurs before the concrete sets (that is, when it is in the plastic state). The paper describes how plastic shrinkage cracking is greatly dependent on the relationship between the rate of evaporation and the rate of bleed water reaching the surface. If the volume of bleed water reaching the surface is greater than that which evaporates, water stays on the surface of the concrete and it is protected from cracking. However, when evaporation causes a greater volume of water to evaporate than has bled to surface, the potential for plastic shrinkage cracking is high.

It is known that the rate of bleeding and rate of evaporation can vary widely, depending on materials used (for example, slump, section depth, water content, and cement fineness) and the environmental conditions (for example, temperature, wind speed, and relative humidity). Toward this end, Menzel introduced a chart that can provide "a quick indication of the drying tendency for the air for any set of conditions." This chart uses the temperature of the concrete surface, the wet-bulb temperature of the environment, and the wind speed to estimate the rate of evaporation from the concrete surface. Menzel provides a discussion of conditions that should cause concern for a contractor, such as hot dry weather and high winds often found during summer, which produce rates of evaporation that are higher than the normal rates of bleeding from concrete. Conditions are discussed that indicate examples from construction projects that provide evidence for how this type of graph could be used to indicate when caution should be taken by contractors.

While Menzel's paper does not provide the full theoretical background for the graph, excellent reviews on the evaporation of water from concrete surfaces have recently been written by Uno [2] and Hover [3]. In a follow-up article, Lerch [4] used Menzel's graph to demonstrate good concreting practices that minimizes cracking. These practices are recommended by PCA to this day [5].

Impact and Influence on the Technical Community

The impact of Menzel's paper on the concrete community is substantial. While many are unaware of the original document, a nomograph was developed using the approach discussed by Menzel in work by Lerch and Bloem [6]. The Nomogrpah that was used by Bloem was adopted by PCA [5], NRMCA [7], and ACI [8]. This nomograph is synonymous with plastic shrinkage cracking for many, despite the fact that this only describes the potential rate of evaporation.

This nomograph represents a simple approach and provides rapid information to concrete professionals on site. This document demonstrates the need for increased documentation at construction sites and this information is frequently kept in construction journals. Many contractors now use inexpensive equipment on site to measure wind speed, relative humidity, and temperature. This information can be used to designate when precaution should be taken [8]. For example, ACI 305 suggests that this should occur when the rate of evaporation exceeds 1.0 kg/m²/hr [8]. This rate likely comes from work by Powers that indicated typical bleed rates experienced by pastes and mortars [9].

It should also be noted that the approach presented by Menzel (adopted by ACI, NRMCA, PCA, and others) has also been criticized because it does not provide a comprehensive prediction of whether plastic cracking will occur. In my opinion, this criticism points to the fact that many fundamental aspects of this problem are still not significantly understood, and further work is needed to improve the prediction of plastic shrinkage cracking. It is my opinion that many of these developments will take place toward a better understanding of the bleed rate as well as a better understanding of other factors that influence the potential for cracking including autogenous shrinkage, thermal resistance, and a material's resistance to cracking.

Current State of the Field

Unfortunately, problems of early age cracking have not disappeared over the last 50 years. In fact, it has been suggested that cracking at early ages has increased in recent years [10]. As a result, the concrete community has had a great deal of renewed interest in quantifying volume change and cracking potential in early age concrete.

Menzel [1] discussed how finer cement (that is, smaller particles) decreased the rate of bleeding. As cements have become finer over the last five decades, the problem of early age cracking has continued to increase [11,12]. Cohen et al. [13] also identified how fine powders (silica fume) can significantly reduce the rate of bleeding and lead to an increased potential for cracking. Work continues to better understand how changes in material properties influence bleed rate.

Substantial research has been performed recently that focuses on the development of a better understanding of the factors that lead to early age cracking. A recent state of the art report discusses the influences of material properties and testing techniques [14]. In addition, new standardized tests have been developed to quantify early age shrinkage including ASTM C1579 (plastic shrinkage), C1581 (restrained shrinkage), and C1608 (chemical shrinkage) while other test procedures are currently being developed to systematically assess autogenous shrinkage. Further research aims at the development of computer models to automatically predict early age cracking [15-18].

References

1   Menzel, C. A., (1954) "Causes and Prevention of Crack Development in Plastic Concrete," Proceedings of the Portland Cement Association, November 1954, pp. 130-136

2   Uno, P. J. (1998) "Plastic Shrinkage Cracking and Evaporation Formulas," *ACI Materials Journal*, V. 95, No. 4, July-August 1998, pp. 365-375

3   Hover, K. C., (2006) "Evaporation of Water from Concrete Surfaces," V. 103, No. 5, pp. 384389

4   Lerch, W., (1957) "Plastic Shrinkage," ACI Journal, *Proceedings* V. 28, No. 8, February 1957, p. 797-802

5   Kosmatka, S. H., Kerkhoff, B., Panarese, W. C., (2002) PCA Design and Control of Concrete Mixtures EB 001, 14th Edition, Portland Cement Association, p. 385

6   Bloem, D. (1960) "Plastic Cracking of Concrete," National Ready Mixed Concrete Association/National Sand and Gravel Association, July 1960, p.2

7   NRMCA (1960) : "Plastic Cracking of Concrete," Engineering Information, NRMCA, Silver Springs, Md, July 1960, p. 2

8   ACI 305R-96 "Hot Weather Concreting," *Manual of Concrete Practice*, V. 2, American Concrete Institute, Farmington Hills, MI.

9   Powers, T. C. (1968) "The Properties of Fresh Concrete," John Wiley and Sons, p. 664

10 Shah, S. P., Weiss, W.J., and Yang, W., (1998) "Shrinkage Cracking-Can It Be Prevented?" *Concrete International*, Vol. 20, No. 4, 51-55

11 Chariton, T., and Weiss, W. J. (2002). "Using Acoustic Emission to Monitor

Damage Development in Mortars Restrained from Volumetric Changes." Proc., Concrete: Material Science to Application, A Tribute to Surendra P. Shah, Eds. P. Balaguru, A. Namaan, W. J. Weiss, ACI SP-206, pp. 205-218.

12 Bentz, D. P., Sant, G., and Weiss, J. (in press) "Early-Age Properties of Cement-Based Materials: I. Influence of Cement Fineness," ASCE Journal of Civil Engineering Materials

13 Cohen, M. D., Olek, J., Dolch, W. L., (1990) "Mechanisms of Plastic Shrinkage Cracking in Portland Cement and Portland Cement-Silica Fume Paste and Mortar," Cement and Concrete Research, Vol. 20, pp. 103-119, 1990, pp. 103-119

14 Early Age Cracking In Cementitious Systems – RILEM State of the Art Report TC-EAS, ed. A. Bentur, 2002

15 Weiss, W. J, Yang, W., and Shah, S. P., (2000) "Influence of Specimen Size and Geometry on Shrinkage Cracking." Journal of Engineering Mechanics Division, American Society of Civil Engineering, Vol. 126, No. 1, pp. 93-101

16 Information about Recent Developments in Femmasse (2007). Retrieved December 24th, 2007, from the Femmasse site: http://www.femmasse.nl/home.htm

17 J. Mauricio Ruiz, Robert O. Rasmussen, George K. Chang, Jason C. Dick, Patricia K. Nelson, Ted R. Ferragut Computer-Based Guidelines for Concrete Pavements Volume I-Project Summary. Federal Highway Administration Report FHWA-HRT-04-121, Washington, September 2004.

18 Raoufi, K., Radlinska, A., Nantung, T., and Weiss, W. J., (2008) "Practical Considerations To Determine The Time And Depth Of Saw-Cuts In Concrete Pavements," Transportation Research Board

Jason Weiss *is a Professor and Associate Head for the School of Civil Engineering at Purdue University. Jason received his BAE from Pennslyvania State University and his MS and PhD from Northwestern University. He is Chair of ACI Committee 123, Research and Current Development, and a member of ACI Committee 209, Creep and Shrinkage in Concrete; 231, Properties of Concrete at Early Ages; 365, Service Life Prediction; 446, Fracture Mechanics; and 522, Pervious Concrete. He is a recipient of the ACI Young Member Award and the ACI Walter P. Moore Jr. Faculty Achievement Award.*

CAUSES AND PREVENTION OF CRACK DEVELOPMENT IN PLASTIC CONCRETE

By CARL A. MENZEL*

Cracks often develop in the surface of fresh concrete soon after has been placed or finished and while it is still in the plastic state. Th development of such cracks, commonly referred to as *plastic crackin* can be practically eliminated if appropriate measures to minimize th causes are taken at the right time. The development, location an extent of cracks in fresh concrete may be readily observed if they occu in the exposed top surface. However, cracks may also develop, thoug much less frequently, in the vertical surfaces of fresh concrete place in narrow, deep forms or in the bottom surface of fresh concrete slab in horizontal forms. Cracks in vertical surfaces are seldom due t drying shrinkage, which is the most frequent cause of top-surface crack

Generally speaking, plastic cracking is the result of restrained move ments at the surface or within the concrete, or between the concret and the subgrade or form in which it is placed. Cracks are forme when the restrained movements develop tensile stresses which excee the ability of the fresh concrete to hold together. Any factor whic causes movement is a potential cause of crack development. Followin is a list of such factors:

A. *Constructional movements*
   1. Movements of subgrade.
   2. Movements of forms.

B. *Movements within concrete after placing*
   1. Settlement of concrete mass.
   2. Disturbances.
   3. Temperature changes in concrete mass.

C. *Movements at surface of concrete*
   1. Drying shrinkage.
   2. Thermal contraction.
   3. Strike-off and finishing.

Drying shrinkage is the most common cause of plastic crackin and often occurs in combination with other causes. Cracks from dry ing shrinkage are likely to develop soon after the rate of evaporatio of moisture from the top surface of fresh concrete exceeds the rate a which moisture is supplied to the surface. In general, drying shrink age can be reduced by preventing or minimizing moisture loss. How

---

* Concrete Technical Problems Consultant, PCA.

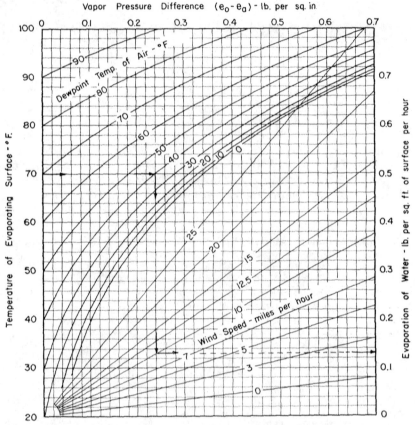

Fig. 2. Chart Indicating Rate of Evaporation and Drying Tendency of Air.

Chart is based on Equation $W = 0.44 (c_o-c_a) (0.253 + 0.096V)$, where

$W =$ lb. of water evaporated per sq.ft. of surface per hour.

$c_o =$ pressure of saturated vapor in lb. per sq.in. at temperature of evaporating surface.

$c_a =$ vapor pressure of the air in lb. per sq.in. This can be obtained from dry-bulb and wet-bulb temperatures to give the dew-point temperature of the air. For this purpose dry- and wet-bulb temperature should be measured at a level about 4 to 6 ft. higher than the evaporating surface on its windward side and shielded from the sun's rays.

$V =$ average horizontal air or wind speed in miles per hour. This should be measured at a level about 20 in. higher than the evaporating surface.

Example Illustrating Use of Chart, assuming:

1. Temperature of top surface of concrete .... 70 deg. F.
2. Dry-bulb temperature of air .... 50 deg. F.
   Wet-bulb temperature of air .... 45 deg. F.
3. Dew-point temperature of air (from item 2 and psychro-

excessively high during the critical period after bleeding stops. Now suppose that the wind speed increases from 10 mph to 25 mph. In that case the chart indicates that the rate of evaporation has increased from 0.13 to 0.30 lb., or over two times. On the other hand, if the wind speed decreases from 10 mph to 0 the chart indicates that the rate of evaporation would be reduced to about one-quarter of its value at 10 mph.

In a similar manner we can determine the effect of variations in wind speed, relative humidity and concrete and air temperatures on drying tendency of concrete from Table 1.

For example, the values for Group 1 show that as the wind speed increases from 0 to 25 mph the drying tendency is increased from 0.015 to 0.135 lb. per sq ft. per hour, or about nine times. The values for Group 2 show that as the relative humidity is decreased from 90 per cent to 10 per cent the drying tendency is increased from 0.020 to 0.175 lb., or over eight times. Group 3 shows that an increase in the concrete and air temperature from 50 to 100 deg. F. increases the drying tendency about seven times. On the other hand, Group 4 shows that evaporation is practically eliminated when the temperature of the concrete and the dew point of the air are equal, regardless of wind speed.

Even though the air may be cool and in a saturated condition at 100 per cent humidity, there is a marked tendency for drying if the concrete is placed at normal temperatures of about 70 deg. F. This may explain why cracks were formed during heavy fog when warm concrete was placed on a cold, windy day on coal docks jutting out into Lake Superior at Duluth, Minn. Under these conditions the drying shrinkage from rapid evaporation plus the contraction with cooling were each tending to produce cracks in the plastic concrete.

A combination of hot, dry weather and high winds often found during the summer produces a drying tendency well above the normal bleeding rate. It is apparent why sunshades and windbreakers are sometimes used on important paving projects to reduce the surface temperature of the concrete and the wind movement across the surface to lower the rate of drying. Sometimes it is desirable to reduce the temperature of

---

metric chart) .... 40 deg. F.
4. Average horizontal wind speed .... 10 mph.

First, locate temperature of concrete (70 deg. F.) on vertical scale at left of chart (temperature of evaporating surface). Then follow the 70 deg. line horizontally to right (as shown by arrow) until it intersects the dew-point curve at 40 deg. F. (From scale at top of chart, this point indicates a vapor pressure difference of 0.24 lb. per sq.in.) Next follow down a vertical line through this point until it intersects the straight inclined line indicating a wind speed of 10 mph. Then follow a horizontal line through this intersection to the scale at right of chart where the evaporation or drying tendency is indicated to be about 0.13 lb. per sq.ft. of surface per hour.

Table 1. Effect of Variations in Concrete and Air Temperatures, Relative
Humidity and Wind Speed on Drying Tendency of Air at Job Site

Case no.	Concrete temp., deg. F.	Air temp., deg. F.	Relative humidity, per cent	Dew point, deg. F.	Wind speed, mph.	Drying tendency lb./sq.ft./hr.
(1) Increase in Wind Speed						
1	70	70	70	59	0	.015
2	70	70	70	59	5	.038
3	70	70	70	59	10	.062
4	70	70	70	59	15	.085
5	70	70	70	59	20	.110
6	70	70	70	59	25	.135
(2) Decrease in Relative Humidity						
7	70	70	90	67	10	.020
8	70	70	70	59	10	.062
9	70	70	50	50	10	.100
10	70	70	30	37	10	.135
11	70	70	10	13	10	.175
(3) Increase in Concrete and Air Temperatures						
12	50	50	70	41	10	.026
13	60	60	70	50	10	.043
14	70	70	70	59	10	.062
15	80	80	70	70	10	.077
16	90	90	70	79	10	.110
17	100	100	70	88	10	.180
(4) Concrete at 70 deg. F.; Decrease in Air Temperature						
18	70	80	70	70	10	.000
19	70	70	70	59	10	.062
20	70	50	70	41	10	.125
21	70	30	70	21	10	.165
(5) Concrete at High Temperature; Air at 40 deg. F. and 100 per cent R.H.						
22	80	40	100	40	10	.205
23	70	40	100	40	10	.130
24	60	40	100	40	10	.075
(6) Concrete at High Temperature; Air at 40 deg. F.; Variable Wind						
25	70	40	50	23	0	.035
26	70	40	50	23	10	.162
27	70	40	50	23	25	.357
(7) Decrease in Concrete Temperature; Air at 70 deg. F.						
28	80	70	50	50	10	.175
29	70	70	50	50	10	.100
30	60	70	50	50	10	.045
(8) Concrete and Air at High Temperature; 10 per cent R.H.; Variable Wind						
31	90	90	10	26	0	.070
32	90	90	10	26	10	.336
33	90	90	10	26	25	.740

primarily to poor aggregate, high slump and improper construction methods. These features were pointed out to the contractors and the remedies were discussed with them. The need was stressed for prompt and adequate application of a good curing compound to prevent plastic cracks from developing when conditions were favorable for rapid drying.

Cracks caused by normal drying shrinkage in *hardened* concrete are often thought to be plastic cracks, although the two frequently occur together on the same job and in combination with other causes. Both can be practically eliminated by taking appropriate steps to minimize the causes.

A TRIBUTE TO

"Properties of Cements and Concretes Containing Fly Ash"

by R.E. Davis, R.W. Carlson, J.W. Kelly, and H.E. Davis

Foreword by Kevin MacDonald

The proof of the fundamental nature and quality of a technical paper is the relevance of the findings beyond their time. Applying this standard of quality to this paper is easy. The statements made in the conclusions are still those made in reference to the utilization of fly ash in concrete in 2008.

All of the modern engineering reasons for using fly ash as a pozzolan are well described. Only the details of their use have changed, as new technologies are reduced to practice and implemented on a wider scale.

The paper ties its data to other materials then in use by making comparisons to natural pozzolans, and to limestone as a (somewhat) inert filler. The breadth and scope of the test results presented and the materials tested completely presents the situation for the practitioner, not merely for the academic. The overarching theme to the paper is allowing the practitioner to incorporate fly ash into concrete in practice. The paper also marks a milestone in that the use of fly ash is described to benefit the resulting concrete – increasing both durability and strength at later ages with respect to similar mixtures without fly ash. Rather than disposing of a waste, or acting as an inert filler, fly ash increases later age strengths and improves resistance to sulphates in soil and freezing and thawing. Concrete made with fly ash will have better properties than that containing only portland cement or other available pozzolans. The water-reduction effect of fly ash is detailed with respect to both the achievement of lower water-cement ratios with the resulting improved strength, water tightness and shrinkage (volume consistency), and improved workability at fixed water-cement ratio. These properties define the arena for the use of pozzolanic materials today. The recommended replacement level of 30% or more for the right fly ash is a level not seen in many modern concretes.

Significantly, there is a discussion that the chemical and physical properties of the fly ash are the underlying causes of the differences in concrete properties, and that the chemistry of the portland cement is also a major driver of concrete performance. High fineness in fly ash increases water demand, and low fineness decreases water demand. This is a concept that is still not well understood by practitioners, and is nowhere better described than in the paper below.

The first use of fly ash as a pozzolan was in mass concrete, and appropriately the paper examines this aspect, as well as the effect on elastic modulus. The comments made with respect to the effect of 50% replacement generating less heat than any low-heat portland cement are more appropriate today than they were 70 years ago.

The discussion of shrinkage may surprise some, as this topic has seen renewed significant interest in recent decades. The shrinkage is compared not only with mixtures containing only portland cement, but also with concrete containing natural pozzolans. The minor effect of fly ash compared with that of pozzolans is quite revealing as to the rapid replacement in practice of the latter by the former.

The paper presents a prescriptive- as well as performance-based specification for fly ash that sets out many properties still found in the relevant specifications for modern fly ash.

The method of delivery of pozzolans in the cementitious fraction of concrete is today a matter of some debate, that is, whether fly ash is best interground with cement or added as an admixture at the concrete production plant. The paper addresses this issue by examining strength gain of both interground and admixed materials, finding that the blending was as good as, if not better, than intergrinding. There have been major changes in materials and methodology in the decades following the paper's publication, many of which have changed the use of fly ash. Changes in the setting and strength gain of portland cement, driven by chemical and physical changes, increased the effect of reduced early-age strength gain. The use of organic Vinsol resins to build stable air-void systems in concrete have made the employment of high carbon content fly ash impractical if not impossible. The extensive use of deicing chemicals and the resultant scaling limit the use of fly ash in concrete flatwork exposed to freezing and thawing. There have also been positive changes. The use of high-efficiency water reducers was found to compliment the water-reduction properties of the fly ash. Concretes containing both these materials have realized the goal of very low water:cement. Fly ash can also be employed to combat alkali-silica reaction, which had not been described at the time this paper was written.

Today structures are constructed incorporating concrete with fly ash contents as high as 80% of the mass of the cementitious materials. As these structures are constructed to modern schedules, high early strength is desirable. The existence of modern high volume fly ash concrete, with 1-day strengths in excess of 3000 psi, find their origin in this paper.

The paper, some 70 years after publication, continues to illuminate the difficult process of using pozzolanic materials in concrete. As the interest and need for sustainability in concrete construction grows, many more will find themselves referencing this paper, and the thousands it inspired, in reducing the ground clinker fraction of hydraulic binders in the concrete of the future.

Kevin A. MacDonald, PhD, PE, FACI
MacDonald received a master's degree and Doctor of Philosophy degree in engineering materials from the University of Windsor, Ontario, Canada.
He has served the Minnesota Chapter of ACI as Education Coordinator, Vice President, and President. He has been actively involved in the certification process in Ontario and Minnesota. He received the ACI Young Member Award for Professional Achievement in 2000 and is a fellow of the Institute.

Vol. 33 PROCEEDINGS OF THE AMERICAN CONCRETE INSTITUTE

JOURNAL
of the
AMERICAN CONCRETE
INSTITUTE

7400 SECOND BOULEVARD, DETROIT, MICHIGAN . . . . . MAY-JUNE 1937

Properties of Cements and Concretes Containing Fly Ash*

By RAYMOND E. DAVIS[1], ROY W. CARLSON[2], J. W. KELLY[3],
AND HARMER E. DAVIS[4]

MEMBERS AMERICAN CONCRETE INSTITUTE

SUMMARY

THIS paper presents the results of tests to determine the effect of using fly ash as a replacement for portland cement upon the properties of mortars and concretes.

In the test program were included fly ashes from 15 different sources and portland cements of seven compositions. Fly ashes in percentages up to 50 were blended with the portland cements. Other variables under investigation included chemical composition and fineness of fly ash and chemical composition and fineness of portland cement. The properties investigated included strength, elasticity, volume change, durability as indicated by resistance to freezing and thawing and by resistance to the action of sodium sulfate, plastic flow, and heat of hydration.

The results of the investigation indicate that fly ashes of moderately low carbon content and moderately high fineness exhibit a high degree of puzzolanic activity as compared with most natural puzzolans. When such fly ashes are used in moderate percentages as a replacement for portland cement, there can be produced concretes which exhibit qualities equal and in some respects superior to those exhibited by concretes containing corresponding portland cement without fly ash.

As compared with concretes containing portland cements, corresponding concretes containing properly constituted fly-ash cements exhibit (1) about the same water requirement to produce a given con-

*Presented by Raymond E. Davis at the 33rd Annual Convention, Amer. Concrete Inst., New York, February, 23-26, 1937.
[1]Professor of Civil Engineering, University of California, Berkeley.
[2]Associate Professor of Civil Engineering, Massachusetts Institute of Technology, Cambridge.
[3]Research Engineer, Engineering Materials Laboratory, University of California, Berkeley.
[4]Assistant Professor of Civil Engineering, University of California, Berkeley.

sistency; (2) somewhat lower compressive strength at the early ages but substantially higher compressive strength at the later ages under normal conditions of moist curing (70° F.); (3) compressive strengths which are substantially higher even at the relatively early age of 28 days when the temperature of curing is 100° F.; (4) shrinkage, for sections of normal thickness and normal drying conditions, which is likely to be no more and may be less; (5) lower heat of hydration; (6) about the same or somewhat less resistance to freezing and thawing; and (7) greater resistance to sulfate action.

In general the performance of fly-ash cements appears to be most satisfactory when the portland-cement constituent is of normal fineness and of normal or high-lime composition.

For ordinary construction it appears that fly ashes of moderately low carbon content and moderately high fineness may be employed as replacements for portland cement in percentages up to 30 without in any way impairing the qualities of the concrete. For heavy concrete construction it appears that such fly ashes may be employed as replacements for portland cements in percentages as high as 50, with the advantages of substantially lower temperature rise due to hydration of the cement and of higher ultimate compressive strength.

Suggested specification requirements for fly ash include limitations on the chemical composition, fineness, water requirement, and activity in the presence of lime.

INTRODUCTION

The residue from the burning of powdered coal is commonly designated as "fly ash." As the powdered coal passes through the zone of high temperature within the boiler, the carbon is burned and the residue remains in suspension in the form of fused particles. These particles, still in suspension, are quickly carried to a zone of comparatively low temperature where they solidify to form the fly ash; for some fly ashes many of the particles are of spherical shape. The ash, which if discharged from the stack into the atmosphere would constitute a dust nuisance, is caught by precipitators.

Between fly ashes derived from various coals there exist differences in chemical composition, but the principal compounds are silica, alumina, iron oxide, and lime. In all cases the compound present in the largest percentage is silica, and in all cases there is present in the ash some carbon, but under proper plant conditions it appears that the carbon content will be low. Fly ashes from most plants burning powdered coal are characterized by their extreme fineness, the surface area per unit of weight being on the average perhaps twice that of a normal portland cement.

It is known that certain finely divided siliceous materials of volcanic origin when mixed with lime produce a hydraulic cement. The pozzuolana of ancient Rome was a volcanic ash possessing such characteristics. It is generally recognized that, during the process of hydration of portland cement, lime is liberated. In exposed concrete structures, this free lime is frequently leached from the concrete and appears on the surface in the form of efflorescence. In the case of concretes subjected to the action of percolating water which is evaporated as it reaches the surface, there frequently appear incrustations of lime carbonate having a thickness of an inch or more.

Portland-puzzolan cements are composed of a mixture of portland cement and a siliceous material which in the presence of water possesses the property of combining with the lime liberated during the hydration of the portland-cement constituent, *i.e.*, a material which posseses puzzolanic activity. It is usually considered that the principal compound formed by reaction between the puzzolan and the lime liberated by the portland cement is monocalcium silicate. This compound, which is insoluble in water, forms slowly and contributes to a long-continued gain in strength of concrete as well as to watertightness.

Natural materials which exhibit puzzolanic activity to a marked degree are pumicites, trasses, tuffs, diatomaceous earths, and shales. These materials are either interground with the portland-cement clinker during the process of manufacture or used as a replacement for cement, being added in a finely divided state either at the concrete mixer or in a blending plant. The proportion of natural puzzolan which has been used as a replacement for cement varies considerably, but perhaps averages 25 percent.

Portland-puzzolan cements containing suitable natural puzzolans appear to possess certain advantages over normal portland cement. Concretes in which they are employed are generally observed to possess greater workability, with less tendency towards segregation of the aggregates, than portland-cement concretes. Although at the early ages the compressive strength of concrete is lower than that of corresponding concrete containing normal portland cement, there is generally a long-continued gain in strength, so that at the later ages the compressive strength may exceed that of a concrete containing normal portland cement. Also, concretes containing portland-puzzolan cements are characterized by a high degree of impermeability and by excellent resistance to the action of aggressive waters. However, in general, concretes containing portland-puzzolan cements require the long-continued presence of water for satisfactory development of strength; and concretes containing some portland-puzzolan cements shrink considerably more upon drying than do concretes containing corresponding portland cements.

Since the conditions under which fly ash is produced are similar to those under which volcanic ash is produced, it was considered possible that fly ash of reasonably low carbon content and high fineness might prove to be an artificial puzzolanic material of satisfactory activity and that, because of the generally spherical shape of the particles and their extreme fineness, through its use there might be produced a portland-puzzolan cement of superior properties.

In order to investigate these possibilities, quantities of fly ash were obtained from 15 power plants in the East and Middle West (Table 1),

TABLE 1—SOURCE OF PUZZOLANS

Puzzolan	Source	Location
Chicago fly ash	Chicago District Electric Generating Corp.	State Line Plant, Hammond, Ind.
Cleveland fly ash	Cleveland Electric Illuminating Co.	Avon Plant, Cleveland, Ohio
Indiana fly ash	Northern Indiana Public Service Co.	Michigan City, Ind.
West Penn fly ash	West Penn Power Co.	Springdale, Pa.
Union Electric fly ash	Union Electric Light and Power Co.	Cahokia Station, St. Louis, Mo.
Detroit fly ash	Detroit Edison Co.	Trenton Channel Plant, Detroit, Mich.
Duquesne fly ash	Duquesne Light Co.	Colfax Station, Cheswick, Pa.
Long Island fly ash	Long Island Lighting Co.	Glen Cove, Long Island, N. Y.
Potomac fly ash	Potomac Electric Power Co.	Buzzard Point Station, Washington, D. C.
New York Edison fly ash	New York Edison Co.	14th St. (East River) Station, New York, N. Y.
Cos Cob fly ash	N. Y., N. H., & Hartford R. R.	Cos Cob, Conn.
Stamford fly ash	Stamford Gas & Electric Co.	Stamford, Conn.
New York Steam fly ash	New York Steam Corp.	Kips Bay Station, New York, N. Y.
Hell Gate fly ash	New York Edison Co.	Hell Gate Station, New York, N. Y.
Boston fly ash No. 1	Boston Elevated Railway Co.	Boston, Mass.
Boston fly ash No. 2	Boston Elevated Railway Co.	Boston, Mass.
Pumicite	——	Fresno Co., Calif.
Limestone dust	——	Colton, Calif.

and these fly ashes, together with portland cements, were utilized in the manufacture of portland-puzzolan cements varying from one another as to chemical composition and fineness of the fly ash and of the portland-cement constituent, as to the proportion of fly ash (10 to 50 percent by weight), and as to the method of blending (by admixing or by intergrinding). In order to make the comparisons more complete, cements similar to the fly-ash cements were prepared using a natural puzzolan (pumicite) and an inert material (limestone dust).

The cements were utilized in three series of tests to determine strength, elasticity, volume changes, heat of hydration, resistance to the action of freezing and thawing, resistance to the action of sodium sulfate, etc. The total number of cements was 81, the total number of specimens was approximately 5000, and the total number of tests and observations exceeded 11,000.

General Investigation

The first of the three series of tests was undertaken in order to determine the properties of cements, mortars, and concretes in which fly ashes having a wide range in composition and fineness were used as a replacement for portland cement. While the majority of tests were made on fly-ash cements containing a portland cement of a moderate-lime, low-alumina composition and of a moderately high degree of fineness, there was also investigated the effect upon various properties of composition and fineness of the portland cement, the proportion of fly ash, and the method of blending.

The distinguishing characteristics of the portland cements were as shown in Table 2:

TABLE 2—TYPES OF PORTLAND CEMENT

Portland Cement	Tricalcium Silicate, Per Cent	Tricalcium Aluminate, Per Cent	Specific Surface, sq. cm. per gram
High-early-strength	60	8	2220
Normal	53	12	1590
General-purpose	50	6	2220
			1600
			1170
Low-heat	42	4	1600

In general the fly-ash cements contained 20 percent of fly ash, but several cements contained 30 percent and one cement contained 10 percent of fly ash. For most of the cements, the fly ash and portland cement were blended by simply admixing at the mixer, but for four of the fly-ash cements the materials were interground.

The general scope of the investigation is indicated by Tables 3 and 4. The results of tests to determine selected important properties of all cements are shown in Table 3, and the results of tests to determine additional properties of selected cements are shown in Table 4.

Table 3—RESULTS OF TESTS ON PORTLAND-PUZZOLAN CEMENTS CONTAINING
(Table continued opposite page)

Cement				Neat Paste[2]			Standard Mortar	
% of Puzzolan	Puzzolan	% Carbon in Fly Ash	Specific Surface, sq. cm. per gram[1]	Norm. Cons., % water by wt.	Time of Setting, hr.:min. (Gillmore) Init.	Final	Water-Cement Ratio, by wt.	Tensile Strength, p.s.i. (Briquets)[3] 28 da.
1	2	3	4	5	6	7	8	9
0	None	——	1600	22.5	2:15	4:00	0.41	365
10	Chicago fly ash	1.1	1760	22.5	2:45	4:40	0.41	390
20	Chicago fly ash	1.1	1920	22.2	3:00	5:00	0.41	350
	Cleveland fly ash	1.1	1770	23.3	3:40	5:00	0.42	430
	Indiana fly ash	3.3	1800	22.8	3:10	5:00	0.41	390
	West Penn fly ash	6.4	1900	24.5	3:05	5:10	0.42	375
	Union Elec. fly ash	7.4	1810	22.5	3:40	5:45	0.41	380
	Detroit fly ash	7.5	1890	25.0	3:25	5:35	0.43	370
	Duquesne fly ash	9.3	1800	26.5	3:30	4:45	0.44	350
	Long Island fly ash	10.4	2040	28.0	4:10	6:30	0.45	370
	Potomac fly ash	11.9	1760	25.5	3:25	5:20	0.43	330
	N. Y. Edison fly ash	13.6	1770	29.5	3:25	5:25	0.46	415
	Cos Cob fly ash	13.9	1910	28.5	3:45	6:00	0.45	325
	Stamford fly ash	15.7	1880	27.5	4:55	6:45	0.44	330
	N. Y. Steam fly ash	16.6	1800	27.5	3:45	5:50	0.44	355
	Hell Gate fly ash	19.3	1670	30.0	3:00	5:25	0.46	335
	Boston fly ash No. 1	26.4	1580	29.0	3:30	5:20	0.45	310
	Boston fly ash No. 2	30.2	1620	30.0	3:50	5:45	0.46	335
	Average for 16 fly ashes	12.1	1810	26.4	3:35	5:30	0.44	360
	Pumicite	——	1940	26.0	3:10	4:40	0.43	375
	Limestone dust	——	2130	22.5	1:55	3:15	0.41	350
30	Chicago fly ash	1.1	2090	22.0	3:20	6:20	0.41	410
	West Penn fly ash	6.4	2040	24.0	3:30	6:15	0.42	330
	Long Island fly ash	10.4	2260	30.0	4:25	6:45	0.46	365
	Potomac fly ash	11.9	1840	26.5	3:35	6:05	0.44	315
	Limestone dust	——	2390	23.0	2:00	3:25	0.41	330

[1]Specific surface of portland-puzzolan cements computed from specific surfaces of separate materials.
[2]All cements sound in standard steam test on neat-cement pat.
[3]Standard curing.

Tests on High-Early-Strength Portland-Puzzolan Cements

It is a general characteristic of portland-puzzolan cements that, compared with corresponding portland cements, they exhibit relatively low strength at the early ages. The results of the first series of tests indicated, however, that certain of the fly ashes possessed a high degree of activity even at the early ages, and that there existed the possibility of the development of a portland-puzzolan cement having high-early-strength characteristics even with replacements as high as 20 or 30 percent. Certain advantages would appear to result from the use of a portland-puzzolan cement having rapid-hardening characteristics: (1) reductions in cost of manufacture and grinding resulting from replacement of portland cement by an active puzzolan of an initially high degree of fineness, and (2) the long-continued gain in strength characteristic of portland-puzzolan cements in contrast

PUZZOLAN ADMIXED WITH GENERAL-PURPOSE PORTLAND CEMENT

(Table continued from opposite page)

Water-Cement Ratio, by wt.	Compressive Strength, p.s.i. (3 by 6-in. Cylinders)[3]				Init. Tan. Modulus of Elasticity, mill. p.s.i.[3]	Length Change, millionths (1½ by 1½ by 12-in. Bars)[5]				
						Exp. in Fog[3]	Net Contraction (Air Storage)[6]			
	7 da.	28 da.	3 mo.	1 yr.	1 yr.	28 da.	35 da.	56 da.	4 mo.	1 yr.
10	11	12	13	14	15	16	17	18	19	20
0.43	4040	5310	5790	6810	6.2	25	265	380	440	475
0.41	4010	5260	6110	7500	6.7	25	285	410	480	515
0.40	3760	5190	6230	7610	6.8	30	260	385	455	490
0.42	3720	4510	5700	6760	6.2	25	285	445	510	540
0.41	3540	5010	6330	7190	6.4	40	285	440	500	525
0.43	3370	4910	6260	7450	6.4	25	280	435	505	530
0.45	3330	4510	5620	6410	6.1	30	270	400	455	500
0.44	3170	4790	5870	6690	6.2	40	325	510	580	605
0.48	2890	4220	5200	6130	5.7	30	300	445	505	555
0.46	3220	4910	6390	7080	6.4	20	325	465	535	570
0.45	3270	4770	5830	6840	6.1	30	280	430	505	540
0.49	2940	4310	5360	6240	6.0	25	310	520	580	610
0.49	2830	3770	5400	6540	6.3	30	325	505	570	605
0.47	2980	4100	5480	6550	6.2	25	320	495	560	600
0.49	2820	4350	5330	5930	5.8	30	325	485	545	585
0.49	2810	3900	4940	5720	5.8	35	295	495	605	650
0.50	2620	3950	4970	5840	5.8	40	310	485	520	600
0.52	2640	3830	4700	5330	5.8	35	305	465	525	555
0.46	3090	4440	5600	6520	6.1	30	300	465	530	565
0.44	3180	4590	5200	6160	6.2	30	340	505	575	620
0.43	3600	4520	5150	6130	5.9	15	285	455	525	545
0.40	3210	4970	6400	7770	6.8	15	260	380	460	495
0.43	2850	4400	5900	7390	6.4	30	290	425	490	515
0.48	2640	4250	5800	6730	5.8	20	320	465	530	565
0.46	2590	3960	5250	6360	5.9	30	305	500	585	630
0.43	3120	4030	4680	5320	5.8	20	275	465	535	555

[4]Cement-aggregate ratio = 1:5.6 by wt.; 0 to ¾-in. aggregate; flow 60 per cent.
[5]All values referred to length at 3 days.
[6]Standard curing for 28 days, then storage at 70° F. in air of 50% relative humidity.

with the tendency of many high-early-strength portland cements to show retrogression in strength at the later ages. A probable disadvantage is the necessity for adequate moist curing in order to develop and maintain puzzolanic action.

Accordingly, a second series of tests was undertaken, in which two groups of cements were employed. For one group of cements a fly ash of low carbon content and moderately high fineness was interground with a portland cement (50 percent 3CS, 8 percent 3CA) in various percentages ranging from 10 to 40. For the second group of cements, a fly ash of low carbon content and moderately low fineness was interground with a portland cement (56 percent 3CS, 8 percent 3CA) in various percentages ranging from 10 to 40. For the latter group a natural puzzolan (pumicite) was also employed. The general features of this investigation are shown in Table 9, in which are given the results of the tests.

192 **Davis et al.**

TABLE 4—RESULTS OF ADDITIONAL TESTS ON SELECTED PORTLAND-PUZZOLAN
(Table continued opposite page)

Fly Ash in Portland-Puzzolan Cement	% Carbon in Fly Ash	Specific Surface of Cement, sq. cm. per gram[1]	Water-Cement Ratio, by wt.	Standard Mortar							
				Tensile Strength, p.s.i. (Briquets)							
				Standard Curing[3]						Air Storage[2,9]	
				1 da.	3 da.	7 da.	28 da.	3 mo.	1 yr.	3 mo.	1 yr.
1	2	3	4	5	6	7	8	9	10	11	12
None	——	1600	0.41	140	275	310	365	395	425	430	305
Chicago	1.1	1920	0.41	110	245	285	350	515	530	480	415
West Penn	6.4	1900	0.42	105	225	295	375	425	480	415	375
Long Island	10.4	2040	0.45	75	220	265	370	465	520	435	355
Potomac	11.9	1760	0.43	115	225	280	330	420	475	450	430
Hell Gate	19.3	1670	0.46	120	225	260	335	415	465	405	375
Avg. for 5 fly ashes	9.8	1860	0.43	105	230	275	350	450	495	435	390

Fly Ash in Portland-Puzzolan Cement	Water-Cement Ratio, by wt.	Concrete (3 by 6-in. Cylinders)[7]								
		Resistance to Sodium Sulfate[11]					Resist. to Freezing and Thawing			
		Appearance Rating[12]			Compressive Str. at 6 Mo.		Loss in Weight, %	Appearance Rating[12]	Compr. Str. at 6 Mo.	
		4 mo.	5 mo.	6 mo.	p.s.i.	Ratio[13]		6 mo.	p.s.i.	Ratio[13]
25	26	27	28	29	30	31	32	33	34	35
None	0.43	10	9	7	5560	0.88	0.2	9	6050	0.96
Chicago	0.40	10	10	8	7120	1.03	0.2	9	6780	0.98
West Penn	0.43	10	9	7	6580	0.97	0.1	9	5060	0.75
Long Island	0.46	10	10	8	6400	0.96	0.0	9	5490	0.83
Potomac	0.45	9	8	5	5830	0.91	0.1	9	4920	0.77
Hell Gate	0.49	10	9	6	5060	0.93	0.0	9	3560	0.65
Avg. for 5 fly ashes	0.45	10	9	7	6200	0.96	0.1	9	5160	0.80

[1]Specific surface of portland-puzzolan cements computed from specific surface of separate materials.
[2]Standard curing for 28 days, then storage at 70° F. in air of 50% R. H.
[3]Standard curing; specimens tested damp.
[4]Specimens standard-cured for 5 months, then subjected to thirty 24-hr. cycles of treatment; saturated.
[5]Ratio of compressive strength of standard-cured concrete at age indicated to heat of hydration of neat-cement paste at 28 days.
[6]Contraction referred to length at 28 days.
[7]1 Part of cement by weight to 5.6 parts of 0 to ¾-in. local gravel; flow 60 per cent.

Portland-Puzzolan Cements Containing High Replacements of Puzzolan

The results of the first series of tests indicated that through the use of a high replacement there might be produced a fiy-ash cement of very low heat of hydration, particularly suitable for mass-concrete construction. To investigate this possibility there were employed two fly ashes of low carbon content and (for comparison) a pumicite, in replacements of 30 and 50 percent. The portland cement was commercially ground from a general-purpose or modified type of clinker. The portland cements and puzzolans were blended by being admixed

CEMENTS CONTAINING 20 PER CENT OF FLY ASH ADMIXED WITH GENERAL-PURPOSE
PORTLAND CEMENT
(Table continued from opposite page)

Water-Cement Ratio by wt.	Concrete (3 by 6-in. Cylinders)[7]									Strength-Heat Ratio, p.s.i. per cal. per gram[5]		
	Compressive Strength, p.s.i.											
	Standard Curing[3]					70-100° F. Curing[8]					
	7 da.	28 da.	3 mo.	6 mo.	1 yr.	7 da.	28 da.	3 mo.	28 da.	3 mo.	1 yr.
13	14	15	16	17	18	19	20	21	22	23	24
0.43	4040	5310	5790	6310	6810	4300	5320	5790	63	69	81
0.40	3760	5190	6230	6950	7610	4200	6080	6750	69	83	101
0.43	3370	4910	6260	6800	7450	3850	6020	6380	61	78	93
0.46	3320	4910	6390	6650	7080	3700	5660	6110	62	81	90
0.45	3270	4770	5830	6420	6840	3800	5610	5880	60	74	86
0.49	2810	3900	4940	5480	5720	3220	4700	5140	51	65	75
0.45	3290	4740	5930	6460	6940	3750	5610	6050	61	76	89

Concrete (6-in. Cubes)[7]									Neat Paste			
Contraction, millionths (Parallel to Exposed Face and at Given Depth; All Other Faces Sealed)[2,6]									Heat of Hydration, Calories per gram (After 15 Min.)[10]			
¼ In. from Face			2 In. from Face			5¾ In. from Face						
35 da.	56 da.	1 yr.	35 da.	56 da.	1 yr.	35 da.	56 da.	1 yr.	1 da.	3 da.	7 da.	28 da.
36	37	38	39	40	41	42	43	44	45	46	47	48
180	255	515	35	65	290	0	-10	95	33	55	72	84
160	240	480	20	50	245	5	-5	30	29	51	62	75
155	290	570	30	90	310	5	-10	45	29	47	64	80
155	250	445	30	65	270	-5	-10	35	29	50	67	79
170	300	540	45	105	355	10	0	75	30	49	64	79
145	295	640	30	75	355	15	-10	60	32	51	64	76
155	275	535	30	75	305	5	-5	50	30	50	64	78

[8]Curing in sealed cans at 70° F. for 1 day, then at 100° F. until 1 day prior to test, and then at 70° F.; specimens tested damp.
[9]Specimens tested dry.
[10]Water-cement ratio 0.40 by wt.; Carlson vane calorimeter; control temperature 70°F.
[11]Specimens standard-cured for 28 days, then immersed in 10% solution of Na_2SO_4.
[12]Rating scale: 10 perfect, 9 excellent, 7 good, 6 intermediate, 3 poor, 1 very poor.
[13]Ratio of compressive strength of treated specimens to strength of untreated specimens standard-cured up to same age of test.

in a laboratory batch mill equipped with wooden vanes. In addition to the determination of strength of concretes made and tested under standard conditions, there was determined the strength of concretes under an accelerated curing cycle, designed to simulate mass-curing conditions, inasmuch as the response of a portland-puzzolan cement to mass curing may be much more favorable than to ordinary conditions.

The principal details of this series of tests are indicated by Table 10 which gives the results of the tests.

Chemical Composition of Fly Ashes

Except as regards the percentage of carbon, the differences in chemical composition of the various fly ashes under investigation were not large, even though the fly ashes were derived from widely scattered coal deposits. Table 5 shows the range and average values of the principal oxides present in two groups of fly ashes—one of low carbon content and the other of high carbon content. (The complete chemical analysis of the fly ashes is shown in Table 6.)

TABLE 5—CHEMICAL COMPOSITION OF FLY ASHES, BY GROUPS

Group		C	SiO₂	SiO₂ in Non-carbon Portion	Fe₂O₃	Al₂O₃	CaO
				Percentage			
3 Fly ashes of low carbon content	Range	1–3	42–44	43–45	12–19	16–28	3–7
	Avg.	2	43	44	16	22	5
5 Fly ashes of high carbon content	Range	16–30	28–38	40–45	7–14	18–25	1–8
	Avg.	22	33	42	10	22	4

It will be observed that the carbon content varied widely, ranging from 1 to 30 percent. For one fly ash not herein considered the carbon content was 54 percent. The silica content of the fly ashes as a whole ranged from 28 to 44 percent, but for the non-carbon portion of the fly ashes the silica content fell within the narrower limits of 40 to 45 percent. The lime content ranged from 1 to 8 percent. The percentages of the alkalies and of sulfur and its compounds were small.

Although the effects of differences in chemical composition other than carbon content are not discussed herein, it may be stated that as among the fly ashes of this investigation, except for carbon content the differences in chemical composition of fly ash appear to have no marked effect upon the properties of concretes.

Fineness of Fly Ashes

In general, the fly ashes of low carbon content were considerably finer than those of high carbon content, as indicated by the average values for two groups of fly ashes in Table 7. (Data regarding the fineness of individual fly ashes are shown in Table 6.)

The coarseness of the high-carbon fly ashes was due in part to the fact that the carbon particles were relatively large.

In the last column of Table 7, the fineness is expressed in terms of specific surface, which is a calculated value of the surface area of the particles per gram of fly ash. The calculations are based upon changes in density of a column of water in which a given quantity of fly ash was dispersed and then allowed to settle; the changes in density were observed with a sensitive hydrometer.* Although the calculated values may be open to question, they are at least comparative.

It will be observed that the average value of the specific surface of the fly ashes of low carbon content was 2750 sq. cm. per gram. The calculated specific surface of an average portland cement is perhaps 1400 sq. cm. per gram. This difference in specific surface indicates that the fly ashes contained a much larger number of very fine particles than does the average portland cement. The results of tests have indicated that in portland cement there are few, if any, particles of diameter less than 2 microns. For some of the fly ashes it appears that there may be a large number of particles of diameter less than 1 micron.

Activity of Fly Ashes

Of the several methods which have been employed in attempting to evaluate the puzzolanic activity (ability to combine with lime) of fly ashes, the one showing the highest degree of correlation with concrete strengths at the later ages consisted in determining the compressive strength of mortars composed of a mixture of 2 parts of fly ash, 1 part of hydrated lime (high-calcium finishing lime), and 9 parts of standard Ottawa sand. The test pieces, which were 2 by 4-in. cylinders, were cured in sealed containers at a temperature of 70° F. for the first 12 hr., 100° F. for the second 12 hr., and 130° F. thereafter. They were tested in compression at ages of 7 and 28 days. The elevated temperatures are considered to accelerate the chemical reaction between fly ash and lime, so that the results of the tests up to the age of 28 days may be taken as indicative of the contribution of the fly ash to the strength of concrete at the later ages.

In Table 8 are shown for two groups of fly ashes—one of low carbon content and the other of high carbon content—the maximum, minimum, and average compressive strengths of the puzzolan-lime-sand mortar cylinders. (Detailed results of the activity tests are shown for individual fly ashes in Table 6.)

It will be observed that on the average the strengths of puzzolan-lime-sand mortar were considerably higher for the fly ashes of low carbon content than for those of high carbon content.

While it does not appear that the results of the activity tests on a particular fly ash may be utilized in quantitatively determining the contribution of that fly ash to the strength of concrete, there appears to be a general relationship between the results of the activity test

*"A Hydrometer Method for Determining the Fineness of Portland-puzzolan Cement," by S. B. Biddle Jr. and Alexander Klein, A. S. T. M., 1936, p. 310.

TABLE 6—CHEMICAL AND PHYSICAL PROPERTIES OF PUZZOLANS

(Table continued opposite page)

Puzzolan[1]	SiO$_2$	FeO[4]	Fe$_2$O$_3$	Al$_2$O$_3$[5]	TiO$_2$	CaO	MgO	SO$_3$[7]	H$_2$O (240° F.)	CO$_2$	C	Na$_2$O
1	2	3	4	5	6	7	8	9	10	11	12	13
Chicago fly ash.........	44.18	4.23	17.45	16.44	0.83	7.14	0.92	2.34	0.32	0.16	1.13	2.17
Cleveland fly ash........	44.10	4.27	18.99	20.85	1.11	4.00	0.79	1.37	0.36	0.01	1.13	0.58
Indiana fly ash.........	41.70	4.23	11.77	27.88	1.21	3.44	0.89	0.92	0.27	0.07	3.27	0.67
West Penn fly ash.......	49.00	2.07	3.86	27.53	1.45	5.36	0.86	0.42	0.09	0.17	6.36	0.73
Union Elec. fly ash......	47.00	2.81	9.99	19.94	1.01	5.02	0.92	1.76	0.41	0.06	7.42	0.92
Detroit fly ash.........	46.40	2.20	6.29	27.49	1.51	2.48	1.02	0.77	0.35	0.02	7.54	1.93
Duquesne fly ash........	47.82	2.16	6.98	25.57	1.19	2.48	0.79	0.46	0.14	0.16	9.26	0.66
Long Island fly ash......	40.26	2.33	9.92	29.74	1.47	1.60	0.62	0.89	0.53	0.05	10.42	0.43
Potomac fly ash.........	35.24	2.85	7.74	22.87	1.27	10.59	1.82	1.50	0.15	0.32	11.94	1.03
N. Y. Edison fly ash.....	39.18	2.76	10.55	27.77	1.19	1.22	0.56	0.58	0.44	0.00	13.55	0.39
Cos Cob fly ash.........	40.40	1.28	3.91	30.65	1.04	1.78	1.17	0.97	0.13	0.01	13.89	1.03
Stamford fly ash........	37.84	2.35	9.96	24.41	1.00	1.68	1.15	1.28	0.13	0.00	15.68	1.15
N. Y. Steam fly ash.....	34.68	4.06	14.30	21.52	0.97	2.80	0.55	1.42	0.57	0.19	16.56	0.47
Hell Gate fly ash[3].......	32.84	3.63	11.75	25.42	0.84	1.00	0.57	0.52	0.18	0.08	19.26	1.26
Boston fly ash No. 1.....	30.32	1.58	7.00	18.54	0.90	8.32	1.91	1.27	0.08	0.13	26.36	0.90
Boston fly ash No. 2.....	28.10	1.62	6.96	17.84	0.90	7.28	1.73	1.46	0.20	0.15	30.25	0.74
Average for 16 fly ashes	39.94	2.78	9.84	24.03	1.12	4.14	1.02	1.12	0.27	0.10	12.13	0.94
Pumicite[2].............	72.34	—	1.35	13.27	[6]	0.66	0.38	Tr.	—	—	—	1.65
Limestone dust[2]........	6.90	—	1.06	2.22	[6]	48.54	2.16	Tr.	—	—	—	—

[1]All puzzolans tested as received, except as noted.
[2]Ground.
[3]Oven-dried before test; originally contained 43.8 per cent moisture.
[4]Total Fe and ferrous compounds as FeO.
[5]Including all of ammonia group except iron and titanium.
[6]Included with Al$_2$O$_3$.

and the strength of concrete, as illustrated by the foregoing tabulation in which are given the results of compression tests on standard-cured concretes. As between the two groups of fly ashes, high strength of concrete is paralleled by high strength of puzzolan-lime-sand mortar; and low strength of concrete is paralleled by low strength of puzzolan-lime-sand mortar.

TABLE 7—FINENESS OF FLY ASHES, BY GROUPS

Group		% Carbon	Percentage Passing a No. 325 Sieve (43 Microns)	Percentage Finer Than 10 Microns	Specific Surface, sq. cm. per gram
3 Fly ashes of low carbon content	Range	1–3	90–91	30–40	2460–3220
	Avg.	2	90	33	2750
5 Fly ashes of high carbon content	Range	16–30	62–84	7–37	1510–2980
	Avg.	22	70	20	2150

TABLE 6

(Continued from opposite page)

K₂O	Ign. Loss	Insol. Res.	Water Soluble	Sp. Gr.	No. 200 (74µ)	No. 325 (43µ)	% Finer Than 10 Microns	Specific Surface, sq. cm. per gram[8]	W/C, by wt.	7 da.	28 da.
14	15	16	17	18	19	20	21	22	23	24	25
1.82	1.50	71.53	6.72	2.54	95.6	90.5	40.0	3220	0.49	1120	1280
1.53	1.55	78.54	4.22	2.57	94.9	90.0	29.8	2460	0.51	1110	1390
2.56	3.91	77.87	3.12	2.46	95.8	90.8	30.0	2580	0.51	870	1160
2.09	6.56	85.54	2.56	2.29	95.5	89.3	36.0	3080	0.53	810	1350
1.89	7.89	77.10	5.44	2.27	74.2	67.4	30.3	2660	0.53	1110	1660
2.08	8.33	87.65	2.10	2.25	90.7	85.1	35.0	3060	0.56	1000	1220
1.85	9.82	88.51	2.12	2.21	72.0	64.5	27.2	2580	0.58	840	1270
1.11	11.87	86.24	1.66	2.38	94.7	90.9	50.2	3800	0.61	1050	1960
1.12	13.16	67.25	5.46	2.34	84.9	80.3	21.5	2390	0.55	600	730
1.14	14.66	85.75	1.22	2.33	86.8	79.6	34.6	2460	0.66	900	1310
1.82	15.30	89.21	1.43	2.18	86.0	78.0	35.0	3150	0.63	750	900
1.97	17.05	83.15	2.09	2.29	90.5	83.6	36.8	2980	0.59	1080	1290
1.20	18.12	81.28	3.12	2.33	72.8	63.5	28.0	2580	0.59	670	1010
0.72	20.98	81.53	2.70	2.27	85.9	74.0	18.0	1970	0.63	400	560
1.29	27.89	75.85	4.69	2.20	73.3	62.2	7.0	1510	0.65	390	730
1.24	31.56	76.14	4.75	2.21	78.3	68.8	11.0	1720	0.68	410	560
1.59	13.13	80.82	3.34	2.32	85.7	78.7	29.4	2640	0.58	820	1150
5.40	4.13	97.94	—	2.37	99.5	98.6	43.3	3280	0.54	780	810
—	38.14	—	—	2.73	95.5	12.3	48.0	4240	0.50	0	0

Header structure: Chemical Analysis, Per Cent (K₂O, Ign. Loss, Insol. Res., Water Soluble); Sp. Gr.; Fineness (% Passing Sieve (Wet): No. 200 (74µ), No. 325 (43µ); % Finer Than 10 Microns; Specific Surface, sq. cm. per gram[8]); Activity (W/C, by wt.; Puzzolan-lime-sand Mortar[9] Compr. Str. p.s.i. 7 da., 28 da.)

[7]Total sulfur and compounds as SO₃.

[8]By hydrometer; computed from area under particle-size distribution curve extended to 1 micron or to limiting size if above 1 micron.

[9]2 parts of puzzolan, 1 part of hydrated lime, 9 parts of standard Ottawa sand, by weight; puzzolans oven-dried before test; 2 by 4-in. cylinders; curing at 70° F. for 12 hr., then at 100° F. for 12 hr., and then at 130°F.

PROPERTIES OF CEMENTS AND CONCRETES

Physical Properties of Cements

Results of the standard physical tests on cements are shown in Tables 3, 9, and 10. All of the cements were sound, as indicated by

TABLE 8—ACTIVITY OF FLY ASHES, BY GROUPS

Group		Per Cent Carbon	Specific Surface, sq. cm. per gram	Activity (Compr. Str. of Puzzolan-Lime-Sand Mortar), p.s.i.		Compr. Str. of 1:5.6 Concrete Containing Portland-Puzzolan Cement, p.s.i. (80 per cent P. C., 20 per cent Puzzolan		
				7 da.	28 da.	28 da.	3 mo.	1 yr.
3 Fly ashes of low carbon content	Range	1–3	2460–3220	870–1120	1160–1390	—	—	—
	Avg.	2	2750	1030	1280	4900	6090	7190
5 Fly ashes of high carbon content	Range	16–30	1510–2980	390–1080	560–1290	—	—	—
	Avg.	22	2150	590	830	4030	5080	5870

TABLE 9—RESULTS OF TESTS ON HIGH-EARLY-STRENGTH CEMENTS
(Table continued opposite page)

Clinker Composition, %		Puzzolan			Cement			Neat Paste[3]		
3CS	3CA	Type	% Carbon	Specific Surface, sq. cm. per gram[1]	% of Puzzolan	% Pass. No. 325 Sieve (Wet)	Specific Surface, sq. cm. per gram	Norm. Cons., % water by wt.	Time of Setting, hr. : min. (Gillmore) Init.	Final
1	2	3	4	5	6	7	8	9	10	11
50	8	None	—	——	0	97.5	2350	24.5	1:00	1:45
50	8	Chicago fly ash[2]	1.1	3220	10	97.9	2570	25.0	1:15	2:05
					20	97.7	2430	24.8	1:20	2:20
					30	99.0	2350	25.8	1:40	2:35
					40	99.3	2400	26.5	2:05	3:20
56	8	None	—	——	0	98.0	2420	25.5	1:15	2:15
56	8	Indiana fly ash[2]	3.3	2580	10	98.6	2570	25.7	1:35	3:15
					20	99.1	2620	26.5	2:30	4:15
					30	99.4	2740	26.6	3:45	5:15
					40	99.7	2760	28.0	4:00	6:00
56	8	Pumicite[2]	——	3280	20	98.4	3090	27.0	2:00	3:15
					30	99.0	3210	29.0	3:00	4:30

the standard steam test on a neat-cement pat. All of the fly-ash cements set more slowly than the corresponding portland cements. Of the fly-ash cements containing 20 percent of fly ash, all except six which were high in carbon, low in fineness, or both, met the

TABLE 10—RESULTS OF TESTS ON ADMIXED PORTLAND-PUZZO

Clinker Composition of Portland Cement	Puzzolan[2]		Cement		Neat Paste[3]			Standard Mortar			
	Type	Spec. Surf., sq. cm. per gram	% of Puzzolan	Spec. Surf., sq. cm. per gram	Norm. Cons., % water by wt.	Time of Setting, hr.:min. (Gillmore) Init.	Final	Water-Cement Ratio, by wt.	Tensile Strength, p.s.i. (Briquets) 1 da.	7 da.	28 da.
1	2	3	4	5	6	7	8	9	10	11	12
58% 3CS, 6% 3CA[1]	None	——	0	1590	22.5	2:20	3:30	0.41	170	340	420
	Chicago fly ash	3220	30	2080	21.8	3:40	6:20	0.40	135	315	395
		3220	50	2400	22.0	3:40	7:30	0.41	60	325	335
	Cleveland fly ash	2460	30	1850	23.8	3:40	5:45	0.42	120	300	365
		2460	50	2030	24.2	4:20	7:40	0.42	55	235	330
	Pumicite	3280	30	2100	28.0	4:00	6:10	0.45	115	285	390–
		3280	50	2440	31.0	3:10	6:20	0.47	70	205	355

A.S.T.M. requirement for 28-day strength of standard mortar containing portland cement. A few fly-ash cements containing 30 or 50 percent of fly ash also failed to meet this requirement. On the average, at the age of 28 days the tensile strength of standard-cured mortar for the fly-ash cements containing up to 20 percent of fly ash was about the same as that for the corresponding portland cement,

TABLE 9
(Continued from opposite page)

	Standard Mortar					Concrete[4]			
Water-Cement Ratio, by wt.	Tensile Strength, p.s.i. (Briquets)[5]				Water-Cement Ratio, by wt.	Compressive Strength, p.s.i. (3 by 6-in. Cylinders)[5]			
	1 da.	3 da.	7 da.	28 da.		1 da.	3 da.	7 da.	28 da.
12	13	14	15	16	17	18	19	20	21
0.42	300	380	435	460	0.43	2570	3540	4740	5720
0.43	320	385	440	475	0.43	2330	3560	4720	5870
0.43	305	390	420	500	0.43	2490	3560	4590	5950
0.43	315	390	425	515	0.43	2130	2990	4040	5600
0.44	260	340	425	510	0.43	1680	2850	3560	5260
0.43	300	380	400	440	0.46	2680	4170	4470	5890
0.43	260	345	370	450	0.46	2720	4030	4410	6470
0.44	250	340	375	470	0.45	2380	4170	4190	6200
0.44	200	310	315	415	0.45	2040	3580	3800	5780
0.45	170	270	290	330	0.45	1600	3000	3300	5230
0.44	250	325	370	455	0.46	2520	3920	4050	6420
0.45	250	320	340	460	0.48	1890	3330	3700	5700

[1]Before blending.
[2]Puzzolan added to corresponding portland cement of specific surface 1600 sq. cm. per gram and mixture ground for same time as that required to increase specific surface of portland cement from 1600 sq. cm. per gram to specific surface shown (approximately 2400 sq. cm. per gram).
[3]All cements sound in standard steam test on neat-cement pat.
[4]1 Part of cement by weight to 5.6 parts of 0 to ¾-in. local gravel; flow 60 per cent.
[5]Standard curing.

LAN CEMENTS CONTAINING HIGH PERCENTAGES OF PUZZOLAN
(Continued from opposite page)

	1:5.6 Concrete[4]										Neat Paste[7]					
Water-Cement Ratio, by wt.	Compressive Strength, p.s.i. (3 by 6-in. Cylinders)					Length Change, millionths (1½ x 1½ × 12-in. Bars)[6]					Heat of Hydration After 15 Min., calories per gram				Strength-Heat Ratio, p.s.i.
	Standard Curing			70-100°F. Curing[5]		Exp. in Fog	Net Contraction (Air Storage)							calories per gram[8]
	7 da.	28 da.	3 mo.	28 da.	3 mo.	28 da.	35 da.	56 da.	4 mo.	1 da.	3 da.	7 da.	28 da.	28 da.	3 mo.
13	14	15	16	17	18	19	20	21	22	23	24	25	26	27	28
0.44	3310	4560	5440	4610	5270	20	265	415	515	32	49	65	80	57	68
0.41	3050	4420	6030	5660	6710	20	175	305	410	25	48	59	71	62	85
0.39	2400	3870	5350	5200	5790	20	185	320	435	16	39	49	62	62	86
0.41	2890	4410	5880	5700	6550	15	240	390	495	26	43	54	70	63	84
0.42	2120	3410	4930	5110	5640	30	205	340	425	17	37	45	58	59	85
0.46	1610	3550	4950	5020	5970	25	355	560	665	25	39	53	71	50	70
0.48	1370	2810	4100	4400	5130	30	365	625	725	19	32	43	59	48	70

[1]Commercially ground.
[2]Chicago fly ash and Cleveland fly ash as received contained 1.1 per cent of carbon.
[3]A. S. T. M. standard test; all cements sound in standard test on neat-cement pat.
[4]1 Part of cement by weight to 5.6 parts of 0 to ¾-in. local gravel; flow 60 per cent.
[5]In sealed metal cans; 1 da. at 70° F., then at 100° F. until $\begin{Bmatrix} 4 \text{ da.} \\ 8 \text{ da.} \end{Bmatrix}$ prior to test for $\begin{Bmatrix} 28\text{-da.} \\ 3\text{-mo.} \end{Bmatrix}$ tests, then cooled slowly to 70°F.
[6]Specimens standard-cured in fog to 28 da., then stored at 70°F. in air af 50% R. H.; all length changes referred to length at 3 days.
[7]Water-cement ratio 0.40 by wt.; Carlson vane calorimeter; control temperature 70°F.
[8]Ratio of compressive strength of standard-cured concrete at age indicated to heat of hydration of neat-cement paste at 28 days.
NOTE: All portland-puzzolan cements blended by admixing for 10 min. in laboratory batch mill equipped with wood vanes.

and at later ages it was greater than that for the corresponding portland cement. Further, at the age of 1 year the tensile strength of
briquets which were stored in air after 28 days was higher for the fly-
ash cements tested than for the portland cement (Table 4, column 12).

Water Requirement to Produce Concrete of Given Consistency

It is desirable that the amount of water required to produce concrete of given consistency be low. In the case of many cements containing natural puzzolans, however, it is observed that their water
requirement is higher than that of a corresponding portland cement.

In these investigations, the water requirement of concrete was determined by flow-table tests. In Table 11 are given typical results
showing the effect of carbon content and fineness of fly ash. (For
individual values of water-cement ratio, see Tables 3, 4, 9 and 10.)

TABLE 11—WATER–CEMENT RATIO REQUIRED TO PRODUCE 60 PER CENT FLOW OF 1:5.6
CONCRETE CONTAINING 0 TO ¾-IN. AGGREGATE

General-purpose portland cement; fly-ash cements contain 20 per cent of fly ash.

Fly Ash in Cement	Per Cent Carbon in Fly Ash	Specific Surface of Fly Ash, sq. cm. per gram	Water-Cement Ratio of Concrete, by wt.
None................................	—	—	0.43
Chicago.............................	1	3220	0.40
Cleveland...........................	1	2460	0.42
West Penn	6	3080	0.43
Long Island........................	10	3800	0.46
Avg. for 3 fly ashes low in carbon.........	2	2750	0.41
Avg. for 5 fly ashes high in carbon.........	22	2150	0.49
Avg. for 6 fine fly ashes.................	9	3220	0.45
Avg. for 3 coarse fly ashes..............	25	1730	0.50

It will be noted that for the cement containing a fly ash which was
low in carbon and of moderately high fineness (Chicago fly ash), the
water requirement was less than that for the corresponding portland
cement. The cement containing a fly ash which was moderately low
in carbon and of moderately high fineness (West Penn fly ash) required the same amount of water as the portland cement. The cement
containing a fly'ash which was moderately high in carbon and of high
fineness (Long Island fly ash) exhibited a high water requirement.
Further, the water requirement was less for the average of 3 fly ashes
low in carbon than for the average of 5 fly ashes high in carbon.

The effect of fineness of fly ash upon water requirement of concrete
is shown in Table 11. It is seen that the water requirement was
less for the average of 6 fine fly ashes than for the average of
3 coarse fly ashes. However, the comparison is not direct, as the
two groups of fly ashes had different carbon contents. A direct
comparison is obtained between Chicago fly ash, which was fine, and

Cleveland fly ash, which was fairly coarse. Each of these fly ashes contained 1 percent of carbon. In the tabulation, it is seen that the cement containing the finer fly ash exhibited the lower water requirement.

In general (as shown in Tables 3, 4, 9 and 10), for those fly-ash cements which required about the same amount of water as the corresponding portland cement, the water requirement was not appreciably affected by variation in the amount of fly ash. For those fly-ash cements which required more water than the portland cement, in general the larger the percentage of fly ash the greater the water requirement. For those fly-ash cements which required less water than the portland cement, the larger the percentage of fly ash the less the water requirement.

The foregoing comparisons point to the desirability of a fly ash of reasonably low carbon content and reasonably high fineness, and indicate that for a cement containing such a fly ash the water requirement to produce a concrete of a given consistency may be less than that for a portland cement. In this regard, such fly ashes differ from most other puzzolans, natural or artificial, since ordinarily a portland-puzzolan cement is recognized as requiring as much or more water than the corresponding portland cement. The obvious advantages which may accrue from the use of a fly ash of low water requirement as a puzzolanic replacement for portland cement are, first, those related to improved strength, watertightness, and volume constancy due to lowered water-cement ratio, and second, those related to improved workability on the basis of equal water-cement ratios.

Compressive Strength of Concrete

The effect of a moderate percentage—20 percent—of fly ash upon compressive strength of concrete is indicated by Table 12, in which are shown the compressive strengths of standard-cured concretes of the same mix and same consistency at various ages from 7 days to 1 year. The concrete contained 6.4 sacks of cement (94 lb. per sack) per cu. yd., and the maximum size of aggregate was ¾ in.; it might be compared to the mix normally employed in building construction. The same portland cement was used throughout, and the fly ash was mixed with the portland cement without grinding, so that the portland-cement constituent of the fly-ash cement was of the same fineness as the portland cement used without admixture.

Although at the ages of 7 and 28 days the compressive strength of concrete was higher for the portland cement than for any of the fly-ash cements, at the ages of 3 months and 1 year the concrete strength

TABLE 12—COMPRESSIVE STRENGTH OF STANDARD-CURED 1:5.6 CONCRETE CONTAINING
FLY ASHES OF DIFFERENT CARBON CONTENT AND DIFFERENT FINENESS
General-purpose portland cement; portland-puzzolan cements contain 20 per cent of puzzolan.

Puzzolan in Cement	Per Cent Carbon in Fly Ash	Specific Surface, sq. cm./g.		W/C of Concrete, by wt.	Compressive Strength of Concrete, p.s.i.			
		Puzzolan	Cement		7 da.	28 da.	3 mo.	1 yr.
None......................	—	———	1600	0.43	4040	5310	5790	6810
Chicago fly ash.............	1	3220	1920	0.40	3760	5190	6230	7610
Cleveland fly ash...........	1	2460	1770	0.42	3270	4510	5700	6760
West Penn fly ash..........	6	3080	1900	0.43	3370	4910	6260	7450
Long Island fly ash.........	10	3800	2040	0.46	3220	4910	6390	7080
Avg. for 3 fly ashes low in carbon..................	2	2750	1830	0.41	3520	4900	6090	7190
Avg. for 5 fly ashes high in carbon..................	22	2150	1710	0.49	2770	4030	5080	5870
Avg. for 6 fine fly ashes......	9	3220	1920	0.45	3220	4610	5940	6990
Avg. for 3 coarse fly ashes....	25	1730	1630	0.50	2690	3890	4870	5630
Pumicite...................	—	3280	1940	0.44	3180	4590	5200	6160

of the cements containing fly ash of low carbon content and high fineness was higher than that for the portland cement.

Between the ages of 7 days and 3 months, the gain in strength of the concretes containing the four selected fly-ash cements averaged about 2700 p.s.i., as against approximately 1800 p.s.i. for the portland cement and 2000 p.s.i. for the portland-pumicite cement. Between the ages of 28 days and 1 year, the gain in strength of the concretes containing the four fly-ash cements averaged about 2300 p.s.i., whereas the gain in strength was only 1500 p.s.i. for the portland cement and 1600 p.s.i. for the portland-pumicite cement.

Effect of Carbon Content and Fineness of Fly Ash.—The effect of carbon content of fly ash upon compressive strength of concrete is shown in Table 12, for two groups of fly ashes of different carbon content. It is seen that the group of cements containing fly ashes of low average carbon content (2 percent) exhibited considerably higher concrete strengths at all ages than did the group of cements containing fly ashes of high average carbon content (22 percent).

With regard to the groups of cements containing fly ashes of different degrees of fineness, the group of cements containing fine fly ashes (average specific surface 3220 sq. cm. per gram) exhibited considerably higher concrete strengths at all ages than did the group of cements containing coarse fly ashes (average specific surface 1730 sq. cm. per gram). However, the carbon content of the two groups of fly ashes differed widely, so that the comparison is not direct. A direct comparison is obtained between Chicago fly ash, which was moderately fine, and Cleveland fly ash, which was moderately coarse, since both of these fly ashes had the same carbon content. The cement containing the finer fly ash exhibited considerably higher concrete strength at all ages from 7 days to 1 year.

These results make it appear that a moderate amount of fly ash of reasonably low carbon content and reasonably high fineness, while contributing somewhat less to the early strength of concrete than would a corresponding weight of portland cement, contribute considerably more to the ultimate strength. The high strength of concretes containing fly-ash cement stamps the fly ashes of satisfactory composition and fineness as unique among the puzzolans.

Effect of Chemical Composition and Fineness of Portland Cement.— To investigate the effect of chemical composition of the portland-cement constituent upon certain properties of concrete, Chicago fly ash was admixed with each of four portland cements each of different chemical composition. The tricalcium-silicate (3CS) and tricalcium-aluminate (3CA) contents of these four portland cements are given in Table 13, together with the results of the compression tests of concrete. It is seen that as regards concrete strength, for the compositions and finenesses employed in this investigation the greatest benefit in substituting the fly ash for portland cement was in general obtained when the portland-cement constituent was moderately high or high in lime.

TABLE 13—COMPRESSIVE STRENGTH OF STANDARD-CURED 1:5.6 CONCRETE CONTAINING PORTLAND CEMENTS OF DIFFERENT COMPOSITION AND FINENESS ADMIXED WITH 20 PER CENT OF CHICAGO FLY ASH

Portland Cement				Compressive Strength of Concrete								
				p.s.i.						Ratio, % (Fly-Ash to Portland)		
Type	% 3CS	% 3CA	Spec. Surf., sq. cm./g.	Portland Cement			Fly-Ash Cement					
				28 da.	3 mo.	1 yr.	28 da.	3 mo.	1 yr.	28 da.	3 mo.	1 yr.
High-early-strength.....	60	8	2220	6030	6340	6920	6010	6880	7860	100	108	114
Normal........	53	12	1590	5460	6100	6620	4890	6450	7920	90	106	120
General-purpose	50	6	1600	5310	5790	6810	5190	6230	7610	98	108	112
Low-heat......	42	4	1600	4880	5770	6960	4020	5750	7170	82	100	103
			2220	5750	6390	7260	5120	6170	7420	89	97	102
General-purpose	50	6	1600	5310	5790	6810	5190	6230	7610	98	108	112
			1170	4070	4520	5710	3450	4770	6300	85	105	110

For three fly-ash cements each containing 20 percent of Chicago fly ash, the influence of fineness of the portland-cement constituent upon compressive strength of concrete is also indicated by the values given in Table 13. It will be observed that on the whole the greatest benefit to concrete strength in substituting the fly ash for portland cement was obtained in the case of the portland cement of normal fineness, *i.e.*, 1600 sq. cm. per gram.

High-Early-Strength Portland-Puzzolan Cements.—In Table 9 are given the results of a series of tests to investigate the possibilities of producing fly-ash cements having high-early-strength characteristics. The two portland cements employed in these tests were of a fineness represented by a nominal specific surface of 2400 sq. cm. per gram. The puzzolans—Chicago fly ash, Indiana fly ash, and pumicite—were the same as those used in the tests previously described. The fly ashes were employed as replacements in percentages of 10, 20, 30, and 40. The materials were blended by intergrinding, as follows: The portland cement was ground to a specific surface of 1600 sq. cm. per gram, then the puzzolan was added and the mixture was ground for the same length of time as that required to increase the specific surface of the portland cement from 1600 to 2400 sq. cm. per gram. This procedure resulted in specific surfaces of portland-puzzolan cement which were equal to, or higher than, that of the corresponding portland cement.

When the Chicago fly ash (low carbon, moderately high fineness) was used as a replacement for portland cement in amounts of 10 or 20 percent, at ages of 1 to 28 days the compressive strengths of concrete were substantially the same for the fly-ash cements as for the corresponding portland cements. When 30 percent of this fly ash was used as a replacement, at the early ages the concrete strengths were relatively low for the fly-ash cements but at the age of 28 days the concrete strengths were substantially the same for the fly-ash cements as for the portland cements.

When the Indiana fly ash (low carbon, moderately low fineness) was used as a replacement for 10 percent of the portland cement, at ages of 1 to 28 days the compressive strength of concrete for the fly-ash cement was equal to or greater than that for the portland cement. When 20 or 30 percent of this fly ash was used as a replacement, at the early ages the concrete strengths were relatively low for the fly-ash cements but at the age of 28 days the concrete strengths for the fly-ash cements were approximately equal to those for the portland cements. Similarly, the portland-pumicite cements exhibited relatively low strengths at early ages but relatively high strengths at the age of 28 days.

For the particular combinations of materials here considered, the tests indicate that replacement of these types of portland cement with fly ash up to perhaps 20 percent do not impair the compressive strength of concrete at early ages; and that the strength at ages as early as 28 days may be improved by replacements of fly ash up to perhaps 30 percent. It might be expected that, under satisfactory conditions of curing, the high-early-strength fly-ash cements would exhibit substantially higher concrete strengths at the later ages than would the corresponding high-early-strength portland cements.

Effect of Intergrinding.—Certain of the fly ashes were interground as well as admixed with the portland cement. Each mixture of clinker and puzzolan was ground under the same mill conditions and for the same period as that required to grind the portland cement to a specific surface of 1600 sq. cm. per gram. The effect of intergrinding is shown in Table 14.

TABLE 14—COMPRESSIVE STRENGTH OF STANDARD-CURED 1:5.6 CONCRETE CONTAINING INTERGROUND AND ADMIXED FLY-ASH CEMENTS

General-purpose portland cement.

Fly Ash			Per Cent of Fly Ash	Specific Surface, of Cement, sq. cm/g.	Compressive Strength of Concrete					
Type	Per Cent Carbon	Spec. Surf., sq. cm. /g.			7 da.				1 yr.	
					Adm.	Intg.	p.s.i.		p.s.i.	
							Adm.	Intg.	Ratio, Per Cent	Adm.	Intg.	Ratio, Per Cent
Chicago.......	1	3220	20	1920	2110	3760	4090	109	7610	7940	104
Long Island....	10	3800	20	2040	2790	3220	3390	105	7080	6480	92
Potomac.......	12	2390	20	1760	2320	3270	3600	110	6840	6970	102
Chicago.......	1	3220	30	2090	2570	3210	3150	98	7770	6930	89

In all cases the effect of intergrinding was to increase the fineness of cement. At the earliest age of test—7 days—the interground cements containing 20 percent of fly ash exhibited concrete strengths which were on the average 8 percent higher than the average strength for the corresponding admixed cements. At the age of 1 year, the average strengths for the interground cements containing 20 percent of fly ash were about equal to those for the admixed cements. For the interground cement containing 30 percent of Chicago fly ash (low carbon, moderately high fineness), the concrete strength at the age of 7 days was about the same as that for the corresponding admixed cement, and at the age of 1 year was lower than that for the admixed cement. For these materials and conditions of grinding, it appears that intergrinding is of benefit only at early ages.

Effect of Richness of Mix.—The effect of richness of mix upon the compressive strength of standard-cured concrete containing fly-ash cement is indicated in Table 15. The maximum size of aggregate was 3/4 in., and the concrete was of fixed consistency (flow 60 percent). The specimens were 3 by 6-in. concrete cylinders.

It will be seen that regardless of the richness of the mix the compressive strengths were higher for the concretes containing the fly-ash cements than for the concretes containing the portland cement. As between concretes of different cement content, the percentages of in-

TABLE 15—COMPRESSIVE STRENGTH OF CONCRETES CONTAINING VARIOUS AMOUNTS OF
CEMENT

General-purpose portland cement.

	Fly Ash		Per Cent of Fly Ash	Compressive Strength of Concrete at 3 Mo.					
				p.s.i.			Per Cent of Str. for P.C.		
Type	Per Cent Carbon	Spec. Surf., sq. cm. /g.		Rich 7.6 sks./c.y.	Normal 6.4 sks./c.y.	Lean 5.5 sks./c.y.	Rich 7.6 sks./c.y.	Normal 6.4 sks./c.y.	Lean 5.5 sks./c.y.
None........	—	——	0	6500	5790	5410	100	100	100
Chicago.....	1	3220	20	6770	6230	5550	104	108	103
West Penn...	6	3080	20	7320	6260	5640	113	108	104
Long Island..	10	3800	20	6770	6390	5570	104	110	103

crease in strength due to the use of fly ash did not differ greatly; it thus appears that the relations discussed herein for concrete of normal cement content would likewise apply to concretes of high and low cement content.

Effect of Percentage of Fly Ash.—The effect of the amount of fly ash in a cement upon the compressive strength of concrete is summarized in Table 16 for the combinations of fly ash and portland cement in various percentages. (The data are taken from Tables 3 and 10.) For the fly-ash cements, each value in the body of the tabulation represents the ratio, in percent, of the compressive strength of concrete containing the fly-ash cement to the compressive strength of concrete containing the corresponding portland cement.

At the early ages of 7 and 28 days, the larger the percentage of fly ash the lower the strength of concrete. At the ages of 3 months and 1 year, however, for the cements containing Chicago fly ash (low in carbon, moderately high in fineness) the greater the amount of fly ash up to 30 percent the higher the strength. For both the Chicago fly ash and the Cleveland fly ash (low in carbon, moderately low in fineness) the concrete strengths were lower for a 50-percent replacement of portland cement by fly ash than for a 30-percent replacement. However, it is interesting to observe that, even with half of the portland cement replaced by fly ash, concrete strengths were obtained which at the age of 3 months were of the order of 5000 p.s.i.

In Table 16, it is seen that for the fly ash which was moderately low in carbon (West Penn), at the age of 1 year the concrete strength for a 30-percent replacement of portland cement by fly ash was about the same as that for a 20-percent replacement. For the fly ashes which were moderately high in carbon (Long Island and Potomac), the concrete strengths were lower for a 30-percent replacement than for a 20-percent replacement. Similar findings

TABLE 16—EFFECT OF PERCENTAGE OF FLY ASH UPON COMPRESSIVE STRENGTH OF STANDARD-CURED 1:5.6 CONCRETE

	Compound composition	50 Per Cent 3CS; 6 Per Cent 3CA				58 Per Cent 3CS; 6 Per Cent 3CA		
Portland Cement	Specific surface, sq. cm./g.	1600				1590		
	Age of test	7 da.	28 da.	3 mo.	1 yr.	7 da.	28 da.	3 mo.
	Compr. strength of concrete, p.s.i.	4040	5310	5790	6810	3310	4560	5440

		Fly Ash		Per Cent of Fly Ash	Ratio, in Per Cent, of Compressive Strength of Concrete Containing Fly-Ash Cement to Compressive Strength of Concrete Containing Corresponding Portland Cement						
	Type	Per Cent Carbon	Spec. Surf., sq. cm. /g.								
Fly-Ash Cement	Chicago	1	3220	10	99	99	106	110	—	—	—
				20	93	98	108	112	—	—	—
				30	80	94	110	114	92	97	111
				50	—	—	—	—	73	85	98
	Cleveland	1	2460	30	—	—	—	—	87	97	108
				50	—	—	—	—	64	75	91
	West Penn	6	3080	20	83	92	108	109	—	—	—
				30	71	83	102	108	—	—	—
	Long Island	10	3800	20	80	92	110	104	—	—	—
				30	65	80	100	99	—	—	—
	Potomac	12	2390	20	81	90	101	100	—	—	—
				30	64	75	91	93	—	—	—

were shown in the high-early-strength tests discussed previously and reported in Table 9.

From the foregoing comparisons it may be concluded that in so far as compressive strength of concrete is concerned, the optimum percentage of a fly ash of low carbon content and moderately high fineness may be 30 or more; and that except for fly ashes which are of high carbon content or low fineness, or both, a 30-percent replacement will produce a concrete for which the compressive strength will within a few months equal or exceed that which will be produced by the corresponding portland cement.

A point of further interest is the fact that when a suitable fly ash was employed, replacements as high as 50 percent resulted in concrete strengths which were not unduly low, and even at the early ages the reduction in strength was considerably less than 50 percent. This fact is of importance in regard to the development of cements for mass-concrete construction.

Effect of Curing under Mass Conditions.—In order to determine the compressive strength of fly-ash concretes under conditions of hydration similar to those which obtain in mass-concrete structures, specimens in the form of 3 by 6-in. concrete cylinders were cured in sealed containers, at 70° F. for 1 day and thereafter at 100° F., and at various ages were tested in compression. The results of the tests are given in Table 17. For the fly-ash cements, each value represents the ratio, in percent, of the compressive strength of the concrete containing the fly-ash cement to the strength of the concrete containing the corresponding portland cement.

TABLE 17—COMPRESSIVE STRENGTH OF 1:5.6 CONCRETE CURED UNDER STANDARD AND MASS CONDITIONS

Portland Cement			Fly Ash			Per Cent of Fly Ash	Compressive Strength of Concrete, p.s.i.[1]					
Per Cent 3CS	Per Cent 3CA	Spec. Surf., sq. cm. /g.	Type	Per Cent Carbon	Spec. Surf., sq. cm. /g.		Standard Curing			70-100° F. Curing		
							7 da.	28 da.	3 mo.	7 da.	28 da.	3 mo.
			None	—	—	0	4040	5310	5790	4300	5320	5790
50	6	1600	Chicago	1	3220	20	93	98	108	98	114	117
			West Penn	6	3080	20	83	92	108	90	113	110
			Long Island	10	3800	20	80	92	110	86	106	106
			Potomac	12	2390	20	81	90	101	88	105	102
			Hell Gate	19	1970	20	70	73	85	75	88	89
			None	—	—	0	3310	4560	5440	—	4610	5270
58	6	1590	Chicago	1	3220	30	92	97	111	—	123	127
						50	73	85	98	—	113	110
			Cleveland	1	2460	30	87	97	108	—	124	124
						50	84	75	91	—	111	107

[1]For the fly-ash cements, values are percentages of the compressive strength exhibited by the corresponding portland cement.

A study of the values given in Table 17 shows that the conditions of mass curing are particularly favorable to the development of high strengths of fly-ash-cement concretes as compared with the strengths of corresponding portland-cement concretes.

It will be observed that under mass curing conditions, even at the relatively early age of 28 days, the strengths of the concretes containing fly ashes of low carbon content were considerably greater than those of the concretes containing corresponding portland cement without admixture, even for fly-ash replacements as high as 50 percent. The test results make it appear that, so far as strength is concerned, properly constituted fly-ash cements as a group are considerably superior to portland cements where the conditions of curing involve temperatures above normal. When (as shown later) it is considered that the larger replacements of fly ash result in a substantial reduction in the heat of hydration as compared with that which would be obtained with the corresponding portland cement, the possibilities of the use of high-replacement fly-ash cements for mass-concrete construction appear to be very attractive.

Elasticity of Concrete

For selected cements, the initial tangent modulus of elasticity of

TABLE 18—MODULUS OF ELASTICITY OF STANDARD-CURED 1:5.6 CONCRETE
General-purpose portland cement.

Type	Fly Ash			Per Cent of Fly Ash	Initial Tangent Modulus of Elasticity, million p.s.i.			
	Per Cent Carbon	Specific Surface, sq. cm/g			7 da.	28 da.	3 mo.	1 yr.
None..................	—	——		0	5.4	5.9	5.7	6.2
Chicago................	1	3220		20	5.8	6.0	6.1	6.8
West Penn	6	3080		20	5.2	5.9	6.0	6.4
Long Island...........	10	3800		20	4.9	5.7	6.1	6.4

standard-cured 1:5.6 concrete at ages of 7 days to 1 year is shown in Table 18.

In general, there was a close relation between the strength and the modulus of elasticity of the concretes, for the fly-ash cements as well as for the portland cements. On the average, at the early ages the modulus of elasticity was slightly lower for the fly-ash cements as a group than for the portland cements, and at the later ages it was somewhat higher; but the differences were not sufficiently great to become a factor in design.

Volume Changes of Concrete

In previous investigations it has been observed that concretes containing portland-puzzolan cements derived from natural puzzolans in general tend to shrink considerably more upon drying than do concretes of the same mix containing portland cement. This characteristic is considered undesirable, particularly in the case of thin concrete structures subjected to prolonged drying conditions, inasmuch as excessive shrinkage tends to produce cracks.

Since the drying shrinkage of concrete is related to the reduction in moisture content, which in turn is influenced by the area exposed to drying, by the size of the pore spaces within the concrete mass, and by the extent of hydration of the cement, it was felt that possibly the shrinkage of small concrete bars exposed on all sides to drying conditions might not be a true index to the shrinkage which would occur in ordinary concrete structures, where, as compared to the volume of the concrete mass, the areas exposed to drying are relatively small. In order to investigate the effect of the mass-area factor upon drying shrinkage, volume changes were determined for two types of concrete specimen—6-in. cubes and 1½ by 1½ by 12-in. bars.

All specimens were moist-cured up to the age of 28 days and thereafter were stored in air at 70° F. and 50 percent relative humidity. At the age of 28 days, five sides of each of the cubes were waterproofed so that all evaporation would take place from one face. Periodically measurements were taken to determine the change in length of concrete bars and the change in length of concrete cubes along planes parallel with the exposed face and at distances therefrom of ¼ in., 2 in., and 5¾ in. The results of the shrinkage tests up to the age of 1 year are summarized in Table 19. (For further details see Tables 3 and 4.)

TABLE 19—CONTRACTION OF 1:5.6 CONCRETE BARS AND CUBES CONTAINING FLY ASHES OF DIFFERENT CARBON CONTENT AND DIFFERENT FINENESS
General-purpose portland cement; portland-puzzolan cements contain 20 per cent of puzzolan.

Puzzolan in Cement	Per Cent Carbon in Fly Ash	Specific Surface, sq. cm./g.		Contraction, millionths (Storage at 70°F. in Fog to 28 Da., Then in Dry Air)							
				1½ x 1½ X 12-In. Bars[1]		6-In. Cubes[2]					
						¼ In. from Exposed Face		2 In. from Exposed Face		5¾ In.from Exposed Face	
		Puzzolan	Cement	4 mo.	1 yr.	4 mo.	1 yr.	4 mo.	1 yr.	4 mo.	1 yr.
None.............	—	——	1600	440	475	410	515	160	290	5	95
Chicago fly ash......	1	3220	1920	455	490	375	480	145	245	5	30
West Penn fly ash ...	6	3080	1900	505	530	445	570	180	310	10	45
Long Island fly ash ..	10	3800	2040	535	570	365	445	155	270	5	35
Avg. for 3 fly ashes low in carbon.....	2	2750	1830	490	520	——	—	——	—	——	—
Avg. for 5 fly ashes high in carbon.....	22	2150	1710	550	600	——	—	——	—	——	—
Avg. for 6 fine fly ashes.............	9	3220	1920	535	565	——	—	——	—	——	—
Avg. for 3 coarse fly ashes	25	1730	1620	550	600	——	—	——	—	——	—
Pumicite..........	—	3280	1940	575	620	——	——	—	——	—	——

[1]Net contraction, referred to the length at 3 days.
[2]Gross contraction, referred to the length at 28 days.

With regard to the results of tests on 6-in. cubes, it will be observed that at the age of 1 year, the shrinkage of the concretes containing fly-ash cements, at a distance of 5¾ in. from the exposed face, was on the average only about one third the shrinkage of the concrete containing the corresponding portland cement. Also, for the two finer fly ashes (Chicago and Long Island) the shrinkage of the cubes at distances ¼ and 2 in. from the exposed face was less than for the portland cement.

It is perhaps fair to assume that concretes containing properly constituted fly-ash cements possess a finer pore structure than do concretes containing normal portland cement, that due to this finer pore structure moisture is less readily withdrawn through evaporation from exposed surfaces, and that in ordinary structures containing fly-ash cement subjected to normal drying conditions the shrinkage may be no more, and perhaps may be less, than for corresponding structures containing portland cement.

With regard to the results of tests on 1½ by 1½ by 12-in. bars—which tests represent extreme conditions of drying, particularly when the relatively slow rate of hydration of puzzolanic cements is considered—it will be observed that at the age of 1 year the shrinkage was less for the portland cement than for any of the puzzolanic cements, although for the better fly ashes the differences were not great.

It will be observed that on the average, concretes containing fly ashes of low carbon content or high fineness shrank less than did corresponding concretes containing fly ashes of high carbon content or low fineness, and that the concrete containing pumicite (which among natural puzzolans exhibits a fairly low shrinkage) shrank more than did the corresponding concrete for any fly-ash cement.

A fact of further interest is that, as between the fly-ash cements, generally the higher the strength of concrete the less the contraction.

Effect of Percentage of Fly Ash.—The effect of the amount of fly ash in a portland-puzzolan cement on the contraction of concrete upon drying is shown in Table 20. The specimens were 1½ by 1½ by 12-in. bars. For the fly-ash cements, the values in the body of the table are ratios, in percent, of the contraction of concrete containing the fly-ash cement to the contraction of concrete containing the corresponding portland cement.

TABLE 20—EFFECT OF PERCENTAGE OF FLY ASH UPON CONTRACTION OF 1:5.6
CONCRETE BARS

Standard curing to 28 days, then storage at 70°F. in air of 50 per cent relative humidity. Contraction referred to length at 3 days.

	Compound composition	50% 3CS; 6% 3CA		58% 3CS; 6% 3CA
Portland Cement	Specific surface, sq. cm./g.	1600		1590
	Age of test	4 mo.	1 yr.	4 mo.
	Contraction of concrete, millionths	440	475	515

		Puzzolan		Per Cent of Puzzolan	Ratio in Per Cent, of Contraction for Portland-Puzzolan Cement to Contraction for Corresponding Portland Cement		
	Type	Per Cent Carbon	Specific Surface, sq. cm./g.				
Portland-Puzzolan Cement	Chicago fly ash	1	3220	10	109	108	—
				20	103	103	—
				30	104	104	80
				50	—	—	85
	Cleveland fly ash	1	2460	30	—	—	96
				50	—	—	83
	West Penn fly ash	6	3080	20	115	112	—
				30	111	108	—
	Long Island fly ash	10	3800	20	121	120	—
				30	121	119	—
	Potomac fly ash	12	2390	20	.115	114	—
				30	133	133	—
	Pumicite	—	3280	30	—	—	129
				50	—	—	141

For the fly ashes of low carbon content, within the limits of this investigation the percentage of fly ash had in general no great effect upon the amount of contraction. For the fly ash of high carbon content and low fineness (Potomac fly ash), the contraction increased as the percentage of replacement was increased.

TABLE 21—CONTRACTION OF BARS OF 1:5.6 CONCRETE CONTAINING VARIOUS PORT-
LAND CEMENTS ADMIXED WITH 20 PER CENT OF CHICAGO FLY ASH

Portland Cement				Contraction, millionths (Storage at 70°F. in Fog to 28 Da., Then in Air to 1 Yr.)[1]		Ratio, % (Fly-Ash to Portland)
Type	Per Cent 3CS	Per Cent 3CA	Spec. Surf., sq. cm. per g.	Portland Cement	Fly-Ash Cement	
High-early-strength............	60	8	2220	510	440	86
Normal........................	53	12	1590	495	505	102
General-purpose...............	50	6	1600	475	490	103
Low-heat......................	42	4	1600	530	490	92
			2220	530	510	96
General-purpose	50	6	1600	475	490	103
			1170	600	525	87

[1]Net contraction, referred to the length at 3 days.

Effect of Composition and Fineness of Portland Cement.—The shrinkage of 1½ by 1½ by 12-in. concrete bars containing several types of portland cement and the shrinkage of bars containing corresponding fly-ash cements are summarized in Table 21.

For the portland cements of normal fineness and normal composition as to tricalcium silicate, the replacement of fly ash had little influence upon the shrinkage of concrete bars. With the high-early-strength portland cement, a replacement of fly ash resulted in a substantial reduction in shrinkage of concrete. The same is true with the low-heat cement of normal fineness and the general-purpose cement of low fineness.

It will be observed that the least shrinkage occurred in the bars containing the high-early-strength fly-ash cement.

While the reasons for these differences in behavior are not altogether clear, it would seem reasonable to suppose that in the case of the high-early-strength cement, which is high in lime and of high fineness, conditions would be most favorable for an early combination between the fly ash and the lime liberated during the process of hydration of the portland-cement constituent; also, for portland cement of low fineness, the addition of fly ash would tend to reduce the size of the pore structure and hence to retard the rate of moisture loss through evaporation, insuring a more complete hydration of cement than would be possible if the moisture loss were rapid.

Durability of Concrete

For exposed structures the ability of concrete to resist the action of weather is important. Furthermore, certain concrete structures—notably harbor works and structures located in alkali ground—are subjected to the action of aggressive waters. It is known that among the factors which influence the durability of concrete under such conditions are the composition and fineness of cement.

Resistance to Freezing and Thawing.—To determine their relative resistance to the action of weather, concretes containing selected cements were subjected to an accelerated test which consisted in the alternate freezing and thawing of 3 by 6-in. cylindrical test specimens. The specimens were standard-cured for 5 months and then were subjected to thirty 24-hr. cycles of freezing and thawing while saturated. Each cycle comprised 16 hr. at 0° F. and 8 hr. at 70° F. The effect of the treatment was determined by visual inspection of the specimens and by their compressive strength as compared with the compressive strength of concretes of the same age which had not been subjected to the treatment. Results of the freezing-and-thawing test are given in Table 22. (The values are taken from Table 4.)

TABLE 22—RESISTANCE TO FREEZING AND THAWING OF 3 BY 6-IN. CYLINDERS
OF 1:5.6 CONCRETE

General-purpose portland cement; fly-ash cements contain 20 per cent of fly ash.

Fly Ash					Concrete		
Type	Per Cent Carbon	Specific Surface, sq. cm./g.	Loss in Weight, per cent	Appearance Rating	Compr. Strength at 6 Mo.		
					p.s.i.		Ratio, Treated to Untreated
					Untreated	Treated	
None..........	—		0.2	9	6310	6050	0.96
Chicago........	1	3220	0.2	9	6950	6780	0.98
West Penn.....	6	3080	0.1	9	6800	5060	0.75
Long Island.....	10	3800	0.0	9	6650	5490	0.83
Potomac........	12	2390	0.1	9	6420	4920	0.77
Hell Gate.......	19	1970	0.0	9	5480	3560	0.65

On the basis of appearance of the specimens there was no difference between the fly-ash cements and the corresponding portland cements. The loss in weight during the freezing-and-thawing treatment on the average was slightly less for the group of fly-ash cements than for the portland cement. For all cements, the compressive strength of the treated specimens was lower than that of the untreated specimens. The fly ash which was lowest in carbon and of moderately high fineness (Chicago fly ash) exhibited a higher compressive strength of treated specimens and a higher strength ratio than did the portland cement. The cement exhibiting the greatest loss in strength due to the treatment contained the fly ash highest in carbon content and of lowest fineness (Hell Gate fly ash).

Resistance to Sodium Sulfate.—To determine their relative resistance to the action of aggressive waters, concretes containing selected cements were subjected to an accelerated test which consisted in immersing the test specimens in a 10-percent solution of sodium sulfate. The specimens, which were 3 by 6-in. cylinders of 1:5.6 concrete, were standard-cured for 28 days, then immersed in the solution for 5 months. The effect of the treatment was determined by visual inspection of the specimens and by comparing their compressive strength with that of corresponding specimens of the same age which had been continuously standard-cured. Results of the tests are given in Table 23. (The values are taken from Table 4.)

TABLE 23—RESISTANCE TO SODIUM SULFATE OF 3 BY 6-IN. CYLINDERS OF 1:5.6 CONCRETE

General-purpose portland cement.

	Fly Ash			Concrete					
Type	Per Cent Carbon	Specific Surface, sq. cm. /g.	Per Cent of Fly Ash	Appearance Rating			Compressive Strength at 6 Mo.		
							p.s.i.		Ratio, Treated to Untreated
				4 mo.	5 mo.	6 mo.	Untreated	Treated	
None........	—	——	0	10	9	7	6310	5560	0.88
Chicago.....	1	3220	20	10	10	8	6950	7120	1.03
West Penn ...	6	3080	20	10	9	7	6800	6580	0.97
Long Island..	10	3800	20	10	10	8	6650	6400	0.96
Potomac.....	12	2390	20	9	8	5	6420	5830	0.91
Hell Gate....	19	1970	20	10	9	6	5480	5060	0.93

On the basis of appearance of specimens, the only two fly-ash cements which were not the equal of the corresponding portland cement were high in carbon and low in fineness as compared with the others. On the basis of the ratio of compressive strength of treated specimens to that of corresponding untreated specimens, all fly-ash cements were superior to the corresponding portland cement. It is significant that the Chicago fly ash exhibited a higher compressive strength for specimens which had been subjected to the sodium-sulfate treatment than for corresponding specimens which had been continuously standard-cured. Not only was the Chicago fly ash low in carbon and of moderately high fineness, but also among the fly ashes it was the lowest in alumina.

Heat of Hydration of Cement

In massive concrete structures it is desirable that the heat of hydration of the cement be low in order that the rise in temperature due to heat of hydration and the subsequent decline in temperature as the heat is gradually dissipated may be low. If this temperature change is large, stresses due to these thermal changes are likely to produce cracks. Even in walls having a thickness no greater than 2 or 3 feet,

Materials Landmark Papers 215

where standard portland cements have been employed, in many cases cracks of considerable frequency and magnitude have been observed soon after the forms were removed.

The rate and amount of the heat of hydration of portland-puzzolan cement is influenced by the chemical composition and the fineness of the portland-cement constituent and by the character of the puzzolanic material. In the case of natural puzzolans, it has been observed that their contribution to this heat is substantially less than that for a corresponding amount of portland cement.

In Table 24 (values from Tables 4 and 10) there are given the results of heat-of-hydration tests on fly-ash cements for which the portland-cement constituent would fall in the moderately low-heat class, together with values for the corresponding portland cements and for the low-heat portland cement tested in this investigation.

TABLE 24—HEAT OF HYDRATION OF CEMENTS

Portland Cement			Fly Ash			Per Cent of Fly Ash	Heat of Hydration at 70°F., calories per gram (After 15 Min.)			
Per Cent 3CS	Per Cent 3CA	Specific Surface, cm²/g.	Type	Per Cent Carbon	Specific Surface, sq. cm./g.		1 da.	3 da.	7 da.	28 da.
50	6	1600	None	—	——	0	33	55	72	84
			Chicago	1	3220	20	29	51	62	75
			West Penn	6	3080	20	29	47	64	80
			Long Island	10	3800	20	29	50	67	79
			Potomac	12	2390	20	30	49	64	79
			Hell Gate	19	1970	20	32	51	64	76
58	6	1590	None	—	——	0	32	49	65	80
			Chicago	1	3220	30	25	48	59	71
						50	16	39	49	62
			Cleveland	1	2460	30	26	43	54	70
						50	17	37	45	58
42	4	1600	None (low-heat p. c.)			0	30	45	58	73

For all of the fly-ash cements, the heat of hydration at ages of 1 to 28 days was less than that for the corresponding portland cements. The cements containing 30 to 50 percent of fly ash were low-heat cements; and those containing 50 percent of fly ash generated less heat than any of the low-heat portland cements which have so far been employed in construction.

Plastic Flow of Mortar

The plastic flow of mortars containing selected cements was determined by subjecting 3 by 3 by 40-in. mortar beams to sustained load and by observing the deflections at intervals. The mortar contained 1 part of cement by weight to 3.25 parts of a 0 to No. 4 graded local sand; the water-cement ratio was that required to produce a flow of 40 percent. The specimens were standard-cured in fog throughout the period of test, 3 months. The beams were loaded at the third-points on a span of 39 inches.

Beginning at the age of 7 days, half of the beams for each condition were subjected to total sustained load (including weight of beam and apparatus) as follows: From 7 to 14 da., 100 lb.; from 14 to 21 da., 150 lb.; from 21 to 28 da., 200 lb.; and from 28 da. to 3 mo., 250 lb. At the age of final test, 3 months, the load was released for 45 minutes, then load was applied at a normal testing speed until failure occurred. At the same age, the specimens which had not been subjected to sustained load were also loaded at a normal rate to failure. The center deflections of the beams were observed before and after the time of each change in sustained load and at intervals during the period of rapid loading. The plastic (total minus elastic) deflection between 7 and 28 days is shown in Table 25.

TABLE 25—PLASTIC DEFLECTION AT CENTER OF MORTAR BEAMS SUBJECTED TO SUSTAINED LOAD AT THE AGE OF 7 DAYS

Portland Cement			Fly Ash			Per Cent of Fly Ash	W/C of Mortar, by wt.	Plastic Deflection at Center of Beam per Pound of Total Load, millionths of inches (Between 7 and 28 Days)
Per Cent 3CS	Per Cent 3CA	Specific Surface, sq. cm. /g.	Type	Per Cent Carbon	Specific Surface, sq. cm. /g.			
60	8	2220	None........	—	—	0	0.41	22
			Chicago.....	1	3220	20	0.40	25
50	6	1600	None........	—	—	0	0.41	21
			Chicago.....	1	3220	20	0.40	24
			West Penn ..	6	3080	20	0.42	27
			Long Island..	10	3800	20	0.44	24
			Potomac....	12	2390	20	0.44	28

At these early ages, 7 to 28 days, the plastic deflection was consistently greater for the fly-ash cements than for the corresponding portland cements. At the later ages, however, the rate of hardening of the fly-ash cements exceeded that of the portland cements, so that the total flows to the final age of test (3 mo.) were not greatly different. This property of plastic flow at the early ages is considered desirable, in that differential stresses which may be set up in concrete during the early hardening period may be the more readily relieved.

Suggested Specification Requirements for Fly Ash

Throughout this paper, certain general comparisons have been drawn which make it appear that through the use of fly ashes of low carbon content and high fineness concretes can be produced which are at least equal, and in some respects superior, to concretes which can be produced with a corresponding portland cement.

In order that fly ash as an ingredient of concrete may be selected with the assurance that it will give satisfactory performance, it would seem desirable that there be prepared a specification containing, in addition to a definition of the material, certain chemical and physical requirements.

For use in moderate percentages in a cement for general purposes, it is believed that a fly ash which meets the following requirements would produce a concrete the equal of that which would be produced if the portland cement were used alone.

1. Specific surface not less than 2500 sq. cm. per gram and not more than 4000 sq. cm. per gram, as determined by the hydrometer method with dispersion in water. Further the fineness should be such that not more than 12 per cent of the material is retained on the No. 325 sieve when the method of wet-sieving is employed.

2. Loss on ignition not to exceed 7 per cent. This will insure a fly ash of low carbon content. For all fly ashes there is very close agreement between ignition loss and carbon content.

3. Magnesium oxide content not to exceed 3 per cent.

4. Sulfur and its compounds not to exceed 3 per cent.

5. Silica not less than 40 per cent.

6. Activity to be such that the compressive strength of fly-ash-lime-sand-mortar, when prepared, cured, and tested in accordance with the method described herein, will be not less than 700 p.s.i. at 7 days and not less than 1100 p.s.i. at 28 days.

7. The physical character of the fly ash to be such that a thoroughly blended mixture containing 80 per cent of portland cement and 20 per cent of fly ash will require a percentage of water which does not exceed by more than 3 the percentage of water required to produce normal consistency for the same portland cement without fly ash.

Given proper powdered-fuel equipment and proper conditions of combustion, it would appear that a fly ash meeting these requirements might be readily produced in any steam plant from a rather wide variety of coal deposits.

CONCLUSIONS

The following general conclusions as regards the suitability of employing fly ash as a replacement for portland cement are based upon the results of tests up to the age of one year on fly ashes from 15 different sources, blended in percentages up to 50 with portland cement of seven compositions. All fly-ash replacements were made by weight, and in general the cements were blended by mixing, though in a few cases the cements were blended by intergrinding.

1. Though the fly ashes were derived from widely scattered coal deposits, the differences in chemical composition are not large, except as regards carbon content.

2. In general, fly ashes are much finer than are portland cements, some of the particles perhaps being in the sub-micron size. In certain of the fly ashes, many of the particles are of spherical shape.

3. Fly ashes as a group exhibit high puzzolanic activity, as judged

by their ability to combine with lime to form strength-producing compounds. In general, the finer the fly ash and the lower the carbon content, the greater the activity and the greater the contribution to the strength of mortars and concretes.

4. For fly ashes of low carbon content and high fineness, the optimum percentage to be used as a replacement for portland cement under normal conditions of moist curing appears to be about 30.

5. Under conditions of curing such as would normally obtain in mass concrete, for fly ashes of low carbon content and high fineness it appears that there may be definite advantages in using replacements of fly ash as high as 50 percent.

6. In general, it appears that the most favorable results are obtained when the fly ash is blended with portland cements of normal or high fineness and of normal or high-lime composition.

7. On the whole, the results obtained by simply admixing the fly ash with the portland cement are as good as, or better than, those obtained by intergrinding the two materials.

8. Fly-ash cements set more slowly than do the corresponding portland cements, but the times of setting are within the usual specification limits.

The following conclusions refer to fly ashes of moderately low or low carbon content and moderately high or high fineness, blended with portland cements of normal or high fineness and normal or high-lime composition.

9. The water requirement to produce a given consistency of concrete is about the same for fly-ash cements as for corresponding portland cements, and is somewhat less than for most of the natural puzzolans.

10. For percentages of fly-ash replacement up to 30, the compressive strength of concrete cured under standard conditions is somewhat lower for the fly-ash cements than for the corresponding portland cements at the early ages, but is substantially higher at the later ages.

11. When concretes are cured under mass conditions (in sealed containers at 70° F. for one day and then at 100° F.), cements with fly-ash replacements as high as 50 percent exhibit compressive strengths greater than do the corresponding portland cements even at the relatively early age of 28 days. (For 30-percent replacements, more than 1000 p.s.i. higher at the age of 3 months.)

12. By replacing a cement of normal fineness with up to 20 percent of fly ash and by intergrinding this mixture, there may be produced fly-ash cements which at ages as early as 3 days exhibit substantially the

same concrete strength as the corresponding high-early-strength portland cement for which the same energy is consumed in grinding.

13. The contribution (in percent) of fly ash to the compressive strength of concrete is not markedly affected by richness of mix.

14. The modulus of elasticity of concretes containing fly-ash cements is slightly lower at the early ages and somewhat higher at the later ages than that of concretes containing corresponding portland cements, but the difference is not of sufficient magnitude to be a factor in design.

15. For masses of ordinary thickness, such as are normally found in highway slabs and in the walls and frames of buildings, the drying shrinkage at the exposed surfaces of concrete up to the age of one year is for fly-ash cements about the same as, or somewhat less than, that for corresponding portland cements. At a short distance from the exposed surface the drying shrinkage up to the age of one year is substantially less for concretes containing fly-ash cements than for concretes containing corresponding portland cements. For very thin sections and for cements of normal fineness the drying shrinkage of concrete may be expected to be slightly greater for fly-ash cements than for corresponding portland cements. It appears that the drying shrinkage of concretes containing finely ground high-early-strength cements may be somewhat reduced by the use of fly ash.

16. As compared with the corresponding portland cements, the fly-ash cements exhibit about the same or somewhat less resistance to freezing and thawing of concrete.

17. Concretes containing the fly-ash cements are more resistant to the action of sodium sulfate than are concretes containing the corresponding portland cements.

18. The heat of hydration of fly-ash cements is less than that of corresponding portland cements. It appears that the percentage of reduction of the heat of hydration up to the age of 28 days is roughly one half of the percentage of fly-ash replacement.

19. When subjected to sustained load, mortars containing fly-ash cements exhibit greater plastic flow at early ages than do mortars containing the corresponding portland cements.

ACKNOWLEDGMENTS

Acknowledgments for valuable services in connection with the investigations are due to G. E. Troxell, Associate Professor of Civil Engineering; to E. H. Brown, E. J. Garbarini, Alexander Klein, and C. M. Price, assistant research engineers in the Engineering Materials

Laboratory; and to G. E. Dillon and C. W. Thomson, senior students in Civil Engineering, all of the University of California.

Discussion of the foregoing paper will be welcomed if received in triplicate by the Secretary of the Institute by August 1, 1937. For such discussion as may develop readers are referred to a Supplement to be issued with the JOURNAL *for Sept.-Oct., 1937.*

A TRIBUTE TO

"Microcracking and Time-Dependent Strains in High Strength Concrete"

by A.S. Ngab, F.O. Slate, and A.H. Nilson

Foreword by Charles W. Dolan and Jennifer E. Tanner

Isaac Newton said "you can see farther standing on the shoulders of giants." In Newton's case, Michael Collins suggests that the giant's shoulders he was standing on were probably those of Edmund Hook, a scientist and engineer.[1] Not only is this a good analogy for the advancement of technology, it is also an apt reference for the execution of good research, where new ideas come from fundamental work completed by others. The Ngab, Slate, Nilson paper[2,3] is the last in a significant series of papers that define microcracking and its importance to fundamental understanding of the behavior of concrete.

Microcracking is the formation of fracture surfaces around and through aggregate and through the cement paste. Microcracks were initially identified by careful examination of thin concrete slices cut from cylinders that had been loaded to increasing levels of stress. Microcracking appeared in the literature in 1963 when a research group at Cornell that included George Winter and Floyd Slate proposed a microcracking hypothesis.[4] The growth of microcracks correlated well to the stress level applied to the cylinders and helped explain observed strength and creep behavior of concrete. This initial work suggested that microcracking provides a fundamental basis to explain the behavior and properties of concrete. Professors Floyd O. Slate and Arthur H. Nilson, Honorary Member of ACI, were involved in this initial research and then extended the initiative. Over the next 20 years, Slate, Nilson and their PhD students were able to expand and define the contribution of microcracking and its importance to overall concrete behavior. The Cornell research effort produced 13 papers that address microcracking behavior, which appeared in ACI publications between 1963 and 1982. These papers provide insight to the development of a coherent theory of concrete behavior and demonstrate how sustained research is critical to gain a comprehensive understanding of a concept.

Initial studies examined the mechanics of microcracking and its effect on the stress-strain curve of concrete. These first research efforts focused on the uniaxial behavior of normal-strength concrete cylinders under load. A critical part of that study determined that slicing of thin specimens did not affect the microcrack growth or alter microcrack formation under stress. Both X-ray analyses and microscopic studies were used to observe the crack growth. As their understanding grew, the research expanded to include inelastic behavior, short-term loading, and time dependent loading.

In the 1970s, microcracking concepts were extended to biaxial bending. Short-term and long-term loading conditions were examined and a strain theory of concrete strength was developed.[5] Long-term loadings assessed the expansion of microcracks in the concrete, the extension of microcracking to understand effects of shrinkage and creep on microcracking.

By the late 1970s, researchers were investigating the use of high-strength and high-performance concrete to improve the quality of reinforced concrete structures. The behavior of high-strength concrete appeared to be different than, and superior to, normal-strength concrete. As part of his doctoral research work, Ngab began a comprehensive assessment of microcracking in high-strength concrete: 9000 to 12,000 psi (62 to 83 MPa). The work concluded that high-strength concrete was different that normalweight concrete in both function and performance. Key findings of the Ngab, Slate, and Nilson work demonstrated that the quantity of microcracking extended in a nearly linear progression as the sustained loads approached 65% of f_c', while microcracking in normal strength concrete increased exponentially. The conclusions reinforced observations that the high-strength concrete stress-strain curve was more linear to a higher stress level than normal-strength concrete. Further, they observed that microcracks form at higher relative stress levels, confirming that high strength concrete exhibits fundamentally superior creep properties.

Once the concept and theory of microcracking evolved, numerous other researchers extended the ideas developed in the Cornell program. Papers explored the behavior of concrete from a multitude of perspectives, ranging from fracture mechanics to alkali aggregate reactions, to artificial intelligence. Over 1100 technical papers have been published on the behavior, properties, and effects of microcracking. The abstracts archive on the ACI website alone contains over 175 references to microcracking.

References

1 Collins, Michael, "In search of Elegance: The Evolution of Structural Engineering in the Western World," *Concrete International*, July 2001, pg. 57-72

2 Ngab, A. S., Nilson, A. H. and Slate, F., "Microcracking and Time-Dependent Strains in High Strength Concrete," ACI JOURNAL, *Proceedings* v. 78 n. 4, Jul 1981.

3 Ngab, A. S., Nilson, A. H. and Slate, F., "Shrinkage and Creep of High Strength Concrete" ACI JOURNAL, *Proceedings* v. 78 n. 4, Jul 1981

4 Hsu, T. T. C., Slate, F. O. Sturman, G. M. and Winter, G. "Microcracking of Plain Concrete and the Shape of the Stress-Strain Curve," ACI JOURNAL, *Proceedings* v. 60, n. 2, Feb, 1963, p 209-224

5 Carino, N. J. and Slate, F. O., "Limiting Tensile Strain Criterion for Failure of Concrete," ACI JOURNAL, *Proceedings* v, 73, n. 3, March 1976.

Charles W. Dolan, *FACI, is a member of ACI 318, Structural Building Code, and Joint ACI/ ASCE Committee 423, Prestressed Concrete. He has served as Chair of the ACI Technical Activities Committee and is a past member of the ACI Board of Direction. Along with Arthur H. Nilson and David Darwin, he is co-author of the text Design of Concrete Structures.*

Jennifer Tanner *is Secretary of ACI Committee 523, Cellular Concrete. She is a member of the Masonry Standards Joint Committee (MSJC) and is active on the Infills and Autoclaved Aerated Concrete Subcommittees. Her research interests include FRP durability, large-scale testing of masonry, and concrete systems and alkali silica reaction (ASR) in Wyoming.*

ACI JOURNAL   TECHNICAL PAPER

Title no. 78-23

Microcracking and Time-Dependent Strains in High Strength Concrete

by Ali S. Ngab, Floyd O. Slate, and Arthur H. Nilson

The relationship between time-dependent deformation and internal microcracking of high strength concrete was investigated experimentally. Direct comparison was made to the behavior of normal strength concrete subjected to similar relative uniaxial compressive stresses and under the same environmental conditions. Sealed and unsealed specimens were analyzed for microcracking after they were subjected to short-term loading, to shrinkage, and to sustained loading.

Results confirm that microcracking, always present even in unloaded specimens, is increased by short-term loading, shrinkage, and sustained loading. However, the amount of cracking, as well as the increase relative to the initial state, is significantly less in high strength concrete than in normal strength material. The amount of creep strain associated with internal cracking in high strength concrete is negligible, whereas such creep is significant in normal strength concrete, particularly at high stresses. The research also indicates that the ratio of the sustained load strength to the short-term strength is higher for high strength than for normal strength concrete. This also can be explained in terms of differences in microcracking.

Time-dependent engineering properties for high strength concrete, such as creep coefficient, specific creep, and shrinkage characteristics, are reported in a separate paper.

Keywords: compressive strength; creep properties; deformation; high strength concretes; loads (forces); microcracking; shrinkage; specimens; strains; stresses; stress-strain relationships.

Research at Cornell University[1-9,17] and elsewhere has shown that the heterogeneity of the concrete material system plays an important role with regard to its short-term and long-term behavior. The deformation of concrete under short-term loading has been shown to be directly related to progressive internal microcracking at the paste-aggregate interface and through the mortar. The nonlinearity of the stress-strain relation is related to the cumulative effects of this cracking, and not to creep, as has often been stated. Cracks are observed in specimens free of stress. These cracks increase in width, length, and number at stresses of about 30 to 50 percent of ultimate strength. At 70 to 80 percent of ultimate strength, cracks through mortar start to form, bridging between bond cracks to form parallel crack patterns leading to failure.

It has also been shown that internal cracking is increased by sustained compressive stress,[4] accounting for a portion of the irreversible creep deformation. The nonlinear stress-creep relation also is related to microcracking. In addition, at high sustained stresses, creep deformation and associated microcracking lead to failure under stresses less than the short-term strength.[21]

However, previous work has dealt mostly with normal concrete having compressive strength in the range from 3000 to 5000 psi (21 to 34 MPa). The research described in this paper was motivated by the suspicion that high strength concretes with f_c' from about 9000 to 12,000 psi (62 to 83 MPa), such as are presently used for many structures, may behave in fundamentally different ways. This has proven to be the case.

EXPERIMENTAL PROGRAM

Eighty-four specimens of normal and high strength concrete were subjected to varying environmental and stress histories, and analyzed for internal microcracking. Sealed and unsealed specimens were used to investigate separately the effects of shrinkage and creep on the microcracking of the concrete system. Designated specimens were also loaded short-term to the same stress-to-strength ratios used in the creep tests to evaluate the cracking associated with initial loading of the creep specimens.

The specimens were 3.5 x 3.5 in. (89 x 89 mm) in cross section and 10.5 in. (267 mm) long. They were prepared using Type I portland cement, with sand and crushed limestone aggregate from a deposit near Ithaca, N.Y. The sand-cement, coarse aggregate-cement, and water-cement ratios for the high strength mix were 1.23, 1.58, and 0.32, respectively. For the normal strength mix, these ratios were 2.79, 3.82, and 0.64,

Received July 7, 1980, and reviewed under Institute publication policies. Copyright © 1981, American Concrete Institute. All rights reserved, including the making of copies unless permission is obtained from the copyright proprietors. Pertinent discussion will be published in the May-June 1982 ACI JOURNAL if received by Feb. 1, 1982. 002-8061/81/040262-07$2.50.

ACI member Ali S. Ngab is lecturer in structural engineering at the University of El-Fatah in Tripoli, Libya. He received his BS from the University of Texas at Austin in 1972, MS from The Pennsylvania State University in 1975, and PhD from Cornell University in 1980.

Floyd O. Slate, FACI, is professor of civil engineering materials at Cornell University, Ithaca, N.Y. Dr. Slate did his undergraduate and graduate work in chemistry at Purdue University where he was associated with the Joint High-way Research Project until 1949, when he joined the faculty at Cornell. He worked on the Manhattan Project from 1944 to 1946. He is the author of a book and about 60 technical papers. He was a recipient of the ACI Wason Medal for Materials Research in 1957, 1965, and 1974.

Arthur H. Nilson, FACI, is professor and chairman of the department of structural engineering at Cornell University, Ithaca, N.Y. He received his BS from Stanford University in 1948, MS from Cornell in 1956, and PhD from the University of California at Berkeley in 1967. Prior to joining the faculty at Cornell in 1956, he was engaged in professional practice for 6 years. Dr. Nilson is a member of ACI Committees 435, Deflection of Concrete Building Structures; 114, Research and Development; and 363, High Strength Concrete. He is coauthor of the text Design of Concrete Structures, and author of Design of Prestressed Concrete, as well as numerous technical papers. He was co-recipient with Professor Slate of the ACI Wason Medal for Materials Research in 1974.

respectively. A polymer-type, non-air-entraining, water-reducing admixture, ASTM C 494-71 Type A, was used in the high strength concrete. A Type D may be preferable for larger specimens and for field work.

Specimens were loaded parallel to the long direction, at different ages after curing, to stress-to-strength ratios varying from 0.30 to 0.85.

The microcracking analysis of each specimen was carried out in the following manner. Before loading, and after loading to specified levels of short- or long-term stress, designated specimens were sliced using an automatic feed, diamond-blade masonry saw. A horizontal slice, 0.15 in. (4 mm) thick, perpendicular to the direction of the applied load, was cut. (Previous studies[1] have indicated that this cutting procedure, when carefully done, introduces no additional microcracking.) Unstressed specimens, used for shrinkage studies, were investigated for internal microcracking in the same manner.

The observed cracks of all specimens were mapped on full-size photographs of the slices, and the total length of the cracks was determined. The cracks were approximated by straight segments, and then the coordinates were read by a digitizer and printed automatically on computer cards. The crack length was evaluated using a simple computer program. By comparing crack lengths of shrinkage, short-term load, and sustained load specimens, the relationships between time-dependent deformations and microcracking were determined.

The details of the experimental program, the materials used, loading, and instrumentation are reported more fully elsewhere.[12,13,15]

EXPERIMENTAL RESULTS

The basic data obtained in the microcracking investigation are presented in Tables 1 and 2. Table 1 gives data on bond and mortar cracking for specimens loaded at age 2 days, and Table 2 gives the corresponding information for specimens loaded at age 28 days

Table 1 — Microcracking data for specimens loaded at 2 days after 28-day curing — Series A-1, A-2

Specimen*	f_c/f_c'	Duration of loading or drying, days	Bond cracks		Mortar cracks	
			Number	Length, in.†	Number	Length, in.†
AUH-1	0	0	6	1.45	2	0.34
AUH-2	0	0	3	0.58	1	0.13
AUH-3	0.45	0	1	0.25	0	0
AUH-4	0.45	0	5	1.01	0	0
AUH-5	0.65	0	3	1.52	0	0
AUH-6	0.65	0	8	1.88	0	0
BUH-7	0	75	6	1.38	3	0.39
BUH-8	0	75	9	1.98	0	0
BSH-9	0	75	3	0.99	0	0
BSH-10	0	75	7	1.23	2	0.25
CUH-11	0.45	60	11	2.71	2	0.24
CUH-12	0.45	60	4	1.35	3	0.37
CUH-13	0.65	60	11	3.05	2	0.35
CUH-14	0.65	60	8	2.24	0	0
CSH-15	0.45	60	3	0.41	1	0.14
CSH-16	0.45	60	2	0.82	0	0
CSH-17	0.65	60	2	0.29	0	0
CSH-18	0.65	60	—	—	—	—
AUN-19	0	0	11	2.60	1	0.13
AUN-20	0	0	16	4.75	0	0
AUN-21	0.45	0	17	4.23	0	0
AUN-22	0.45	0	—	—	—	—
AUN-23	0.65	0	21	9.04	1	0.31
AUN-24	0.65	0	32	10.8	0	0
BUN-25	0	75	18	4.79	3	0.43
BUN-26	0	75	—	—	—	—
BSN-27	0	75	—	—	—	—
BSN-28	0	75	5	1.06	2	0.19
CUN-29	0.45	60	32	15.64	0	0
CUN-30	0.45	60	16	10.94	0	0
CUN-31	0.65	60	32	16.93	0	0
CUN-32	0.65	60	73	24.82	4	0.56
CSN-33	0.45	60	22	4.90	1	0.21
CSN-34	0.45	60	—	—	—	—
CSN-35	0.65	60	17	14.26	0	0
CSN-36	0.65	60	—	—	—	—

*Specimen designation: First letter: A — Short-term loading
B — Shrinkage (nonloaded)
C — Sustained loading
Second letter: U — Unsealed
S — Sealed
Third letter: N — Normal strength concrete (4800-5800 psi) (33-40 MPa)
H — High strength concrete (9030-10,200 psi) (62-70 MPa)

†1 in. = 25.4 mm.

(in each case, days in laboratory air after the standard 28-day moist curing period). Data are given for non-loaded shrinkage specimens, short-term loading, and sustained loading cases. Stress ratios f_c/f_c' investigated were 0, 0.45, and 0.65. The duration of loading in creep tests was 60 days, followed by a 15-day creep recovery (nonloaded) period. Results for stress ratios f_c/f_c' of 0.70 and 0.85 are given in References 12 and 13.

Cracking maps for typical cases are reproduced in Fig. 1, 2, and 3. Fig. 1 shows cracking of shrinkage specimens for normal and high strength concrete; Fig. 2 gives cracking due to short-term loading for each; and Fig. 3 shows cracking for unsealed specimens sub-

Table 2 — Microcracking data for specimens loaded at 28 days after 28-day curing — Series A-3, A-4

Specimen*	f_c/f_c'	Duration of loading or drying, days	Bond cracks Number	Length, in.†	Mortar cracks Number	Length, in.†
AUH-49	0	0	9	2.81	1	0.12
AUH-50	0	0	8	1.61	0	0
AUH-51	0.45	0	3	0.49	0	0
AUH-52	0.45	0	6	1.90	0	0
AUH-53	0.65	0	11	5.74	0	0
AUH-54	0.65	0	—	—	—	—
ASH-55	0	0	3	0.84	0	0
ASH-56	0	0	1	0.80	0	0
ASH-57	0.45	0	2	0.29	0	0
ASH-58	0.45	0	6	1.46	1	0.59
ASH-59	0.65	0	7	1.22	0	0
ASH-60	0.65	0	4	0.98	4	1.38
BUH-61	0	102	16	3.49	0	0
BUH-62	0	102	14	4.64	0	0
BSH-63	0	102	7	1.80	0	0
BSH-64	0	102	6	1.20	2	0.24
CUH-65	0.45	60	3	3.09	0	0
CUH-66	0.45	60	—	—	—	—
CUH-67	0.65	60	21	5.57	1	0.10
CUH-68	0.65	60	19	4.77	1	0.12
CSH-69	0.45	60	2	0.63	0	0
CSH-70	0.45	60	5	1.24	2	0.21
CSH-71	0.65	60	7	1.52	1	0.30
CSH-72	0.65	60	24	6.08	4	0.46
AUN-73	0	0	—	—	—	—
AUN-74	0	0	24	9.05	4	0.58
AUN-75	0.45	0	22	5.90	1	0.21
AUN-76	0.45	0	—	—	—	—
AUN-77	0.65	0	25	9.12	0	0
AUN-78	0.65	0	—	—	—	—
ASN-79	0	0	11	2.60	0	0
ASN-80	0	0	—	—	—	—
ASN-81	0.45	0	6	1.97	2	0.09
ASN-82	0.45	0	27	9.11	0	0
ASN-83	0.65	0	22	8.06	1	0.20
ASN-84	0.65	0	—	—	—	—
BUN-85	0	102	30	9.68	0	0
BUN-86	0	102	26	9.28	0	0
BSN-87	0	102	9	2.32	0	0
BSN-88	0	102	4	1.06	0	0
CUN-89	0.45	60	32	15.06	2	0.34
CUN-90	0.45	60	34	14.27	1	0.33
CUN-91	0.65	60	49	19.07	0	0
CUN-92	0.65	60	38	13.20	0	0
CSN-93	0.45	60	29	14.90	0	0
CSN-94	0.45	60	—	—	—	—
CSN-95	0.65	60	—	—	—	—
CSN-96	0.65	60	—	—	—	—

*Specimen designation:
First letter:
A — Short-term loading
B — Shrinkage (nonloaded)
C — Sustained loading
Second letter:
U — Unsealed
S — Sealed
Third letter:
N — Normal strength concrete (4800-5800 psi) (33-40 MPa)
H — High strength concrete (9030-10,200 psi) (62-70 MPa)

†1 in. = 25.4 mm.

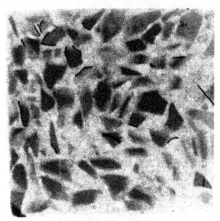

(a) High strength concrete

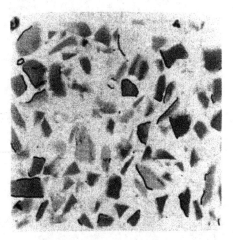

(b) Normal strength concrete

Fig. 1 — Typical cracking maps for shrinkage specimens

ject to sustained loading for 60 days, followed by a 15-day nonloaded period. In all cases, the cracks, identified by careful study of the x-ray negatives, have been traced by pen to enhance clarity in the reproduced illustrations.

Almost all observed cracking was at the interface between stone and mortar, defined as bond cracking. Fig. 4 and 5 show the relation between stress intensity (relative to f_c') and the total bond crack length observed in unsealed and sealed specimens, respectively. Results are plotted for normal and high strength concretes, for both short-term and long-term loadings.

In Fig. 6 and 7, the total crack length (bond plus mortar cracking in this case) is related to strain for unsealed and sealed specimens, respectively. Strain in this case may be that due to shrinkage, short-term loading, sustained loading, or a combination of these.

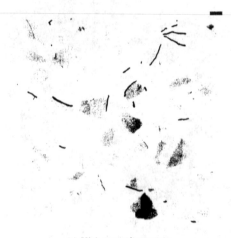

(a) High strength concrete

(a) High strength concrete

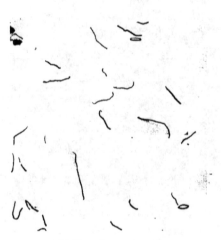

(b) Normal strength concrete

(b) Normal strength concrete

Fig. 2 — Typical cracking maps for specimens under short-term loading

Fig. 3 — Typical cracking maps for unsealed creep specimens loaded to $0.65f'_c$ for 60 days

DISCUSSION

Inspection of the cracking maps, Fig. 1, 2, and 3, indicates clearly that there is much less cracking in the high strength concrete specimens than in normal strength specimens. This is true for the nonloaded (shrinkage) tests, for short-term loads, and for sustained loads. Furthermore, by comparing the photos for normal strength concrete for these three states, it is evident that there is significant increase in cracking,

as the load is initially applied, and that the cracking is further increased as the load is held constant over a period of time. High strength concrete is notably different in that the small number of cracks initially present due to shrinkage are increased little, if any, as the load is applied and sustained.

Crack studies were quantified using a digitizer as noted, permitting the more specific comparisons of Fig. 4 and 5 showing total bond crack lengths for un-

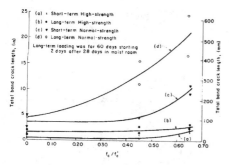

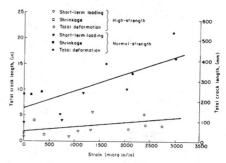

Fig. 4 — *Relation between crack length and* f_c/f_c' *for unsealed specimens*

Fig. 6 — *Relation between strain and cracking of unsealed specimens*

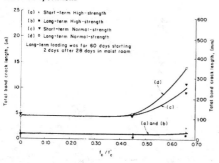

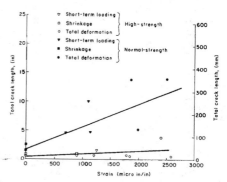

Fig. 5 — *Relation between crack length and* f_c/f_c' *for sealed specimens*

Fig. 7 — *Relation between strain and cracking of sealed specimens*

sealed and sealed specimens, respectively. Fig. 4 shows almost no increase in crack length for high strength concrete in the range from 0 to $0.65f_c'$, and little difference in crack length comparing sustained load with short-term load. In contrast, normal strength material shows substantially more cracking even before load, and a significant increase in cracking at about $0.45f_c'$. Furthermore, there is a significant increase in cracking due to sustained load, as seen by comparing the sustained load curve with the short-term loading curve for normal strength concrete.

Similar comparisons can be made for the sealed specimens of Fig. 5, except that in the absence of moisture loss to the environment there is little increase in the amount of cracking during the sustained loading period even for normal strength material, except at very high stress levels.

The much smaller total crack length for high strength concrete is clearly shown in Fig. 6 and 7, which also indicate that cracking may correlate with total strain in each case, whether that strain is caused by shrinkage no load, by short-term load, or by sustained load. A generally linear relationship is indicated in all cases. This substantiates earlier thoughts by Slate and Meyers,[3] and work by Carino and Slate,[3]

and indicates that a crack is formed when a limiting value of local tensile deformation is reached.

It is interesting to compare the relation between stress and creep strain for high strength concrete, shown in Fig. 8, with the known characteristics of normal concrete. It has been established by the present research[15] that for high strength material the linear range of the relation between stress and creep strain, i.e., the range of stress through which the creep coefficient or coefficient of specific creep is constant, extends at least up to 70 percent of f_c'. Nonlinearity for normal strength material begins at a stress between 30 and 50 percent of f_c'.[16,19,20] This can be directly related to the fact that there is much less cracking for high strength material.

The microcracking characteristics described may help to explain some of the anomalies of high strength concrete behavior under short-term and long-term loading. Under short-term uniaxial stress, the linear stress-strain relation is known to be directly related to the relative lack of internal microcracking.[1]

Under uniaxial sustained compressive stress, the linear stress-creep relation is also related to the amount of microcracking, in this case due to creep, which is significantly less in high strength concrete. The contribution of this small amount of microcracking to creep strain is negligible, explaining in part the observation that when creep is less the compressive strength of concrete is higher.[15]

As the concrete system continues to creep under the action of sustained load, the magnitude of the applied stress carried by the aggregate increases, while the stress carried by mortar decreases to maintain equilibrium.[16] However, if a crack at the aggregate-paste interface is formed under the action of the sustained stress, this reduces the effective stiffness of that local area, hence the stress on the uncracked region must increase. Since creep is proportional to stress, creep response of concrete is expected to increase as cracking increases. Due to the resistance of the aggregate to the creep of the paste, sufficient stress can develop at the aggregate-paste interface to introduce progressive microcracking.[2] This behavior takes place in normal strength concrete, which is more susceptible to internal microcracking. However, in high strength concrete, the increase in the elastic modulus of paste will itself result in less cracking at the interface because of the smaller differences in moduli of the aggregate and paste. The concrete system is more rigid and this reduces the formation of internal cracking under service stress levels. The stress redistribution due to creep will thus relieve the paste (the material which is more liable to creep) from some load. The aggregate particles will continue to carry a higher ratio of load as the concrete creeps. Consequently, the creep rate is reduced because of the effective reduction in load on the paste. Also, the contribution of microcracking to creep is small, leading to further reduction in the inelastic deformation of high strength concrete.

It was observed in the tests that the ratio of the long-term strength to the short-term strength is higher for high strength concrete than for normal strength. Normal strength concrete loaded to about 85 percent of its ultimate strength soon failed under sustained stress, whereas high strength concrete loaded to the same stress-to-strength ratio maintained the stress until the load was removed after 60 days. This must also be related to microcracking. The discontinuity stress represents the beginning of an unstable form of mortar cracking, and this cracking is self-propagating, leading to eventual failure under sustained stress.[4,10,18] Thus, the discontinuity stress and the sustained loading strength are considered to be identical.[7] Normal strength concrete loaded above its discontinuity stress failed under sustained stress. This is in agreement with previous findings.[21]

The discontinuity stress of high strength concrete is, however, considerably higher than that of normal strength concrete. This stress level may be as high as $0.95f_c'$[11] for high strength concrete, and its sustained loading strength may be very close to the short-term strength. The ratio of the sustained loading strength to the short-term strength is in the range of 0.85 to 0.95 for high strength concrete, whereas this ratio is in the range of 0.70 to 0.75 for the normal strength concrete. This behavior implies that, from a stress point of view, the high strength material may be able to carry an overload more safely than normal strength concrete.

The differences in the internal structural behavior of high strength concrete described here may provide an understanding of the differences in engineering properties of the material as established by other phases of the investigation.

CONCLUSIONS

The main conclusions of this phase of the Cornell University research on high strength concrete may be summarized briefly as follows:

1. The amount of microcracking in high strength concrete associated with shrinkage, short-term loading, and sustained loading is significantly less than in normal strength concrete.

2. The substantial time-dependent increase in cracking found in normal strength concrete subject to shrinkage conditions or sustained loading is far less in high strength concrete, explaining in part the much smaller creep of the latter.

3. The amount of microcracking for both normal and high strength concretes appears to be approximately linearly related to strain, regardless of whether the strain is caused by short-term or sustained loading, or by shrinkage.

4. High strength concrete exhibits a discontinuity stress that is a higher fraction of its short-term compressive strength than does normal strength concrete. It follows that the sustained load strength of high strength concrete is relatively higher.

5. The stress-creep relationship for high strength concrete is linear to a higher percentage of the compressive strength than that of normal strength concrete because of the smaller amount of microcracking of the former at high stress levels.

ACKNOWLEDGMENTS

This work was part of the PhD dissertation of the first author and was done at Cornell University under the direction of the second and third authors. The research was made possible through the support of the National Science Foundation. The authors would like to express their appreciation to Mr. Stanley Olsefski for his help in the laboratory. Valuable suggestions were made by Professor Emeritus Solomon C. Hollister.

REFERENCES

1. Hsu, Thomas T. C.; Slate, Floyd O.; Sturman, Gerald M.; and Winter, George, "Microcracking of Plain Concrete and the Shape of the Stress-Strain Curve," ACI JOURNAL, Proceedings V. 60, No. 2, Feb. 1963, pp. 209-224.

2. Meyers, Bernard L., and Slate, Floyd O., "Creep and Creep Recovery of Plain Concrete as Influenced by Moisture Conditions and Associated Variables," Magazine of Concrete Research (London), V. 22, No. 70, Mar. 1970, pp. 37-41.

3. Slate, Floyd O., and Meyers, Bernard L., "Deformation of Plain Concrete," Proceedings, Fifth International Symposium on the Chemistry of Cement (Tokyo, 1968), Cement Association of Japan, Tokyo, 1969, V. 3, pp. 142-151.

4. Meyers, Bernard L.; Slate, Floyd O.; and Winter, George, "Relationship Between Time-Dependent Deformation and Micro-

cracking of Plain Concrete," ACI JOURNAL, Proceedings v. 66, No. 1, Jan. 1969, pp. 60-68.

5. Meyers, B. L., "Time-Dependent Strains and Microcracking of Plain Concrete," PhD Thesis, Cornell University, Ithaca, 1967.

6. Hsu, Thomas T. C., and Slate, Floyd O., "Tensile Bond Strength Between Aggregate and Cement Paste or Mortar," ACI JOURNAL, Proceedings V. 60, No. 4, Apr. 1963, pp. 465-486.

7. Carino, Nicholas J., and Slate, Floyd O., "Limiting Tensile Strain Criterion for Failure of Concrete," ACI JOURNAL, Proceedings V. 73, No. 3, Mar. 1976, pp. 160-165.

8. Slate, Floyd O., and Meyers, Bernard L., "Some Physical Processes Involved in Creep of Concrete," Proceedings, Conference on Structure, Solid Mechanics and Engineering Design (Southampton, 1969), Wiley-Interscience, London, 1971, Part 1, pp. 769-774.

9. Shah, Surendra P., and Winter, George, "Inelastic Behavior and Fracture of Concrete," ACI JOURNAL, Proceedings V. 63, No. 9, Sept. 1966, pp. 925-930.

10. Newman, K., and Newman, J., "Failure Theories and Design Criterion for Plain Concrete," Proceedings, Conference on Structure, Solid Mechanics and Engineering Design (Southampton, 1969), Wiley-Interscience, London, 1971, Part 1, pp. 963-996.

11. Carrasquillo, R. L., "Microcracking and Engineering Properties of High-Strength Concrete," PhD Thesis, Cornell University, Ithaca, 1980.

12. Ngab, A. S., "Behavior of High-Strength Concrete Under Sustained Compressive Stress," PhD Thesis, Cornell University, Ithaca, 1980.

13. Ngab, A. S.; Slate, F. O.; and Nilson, A. H., "Behavior of High-Strength Concrete Under Sustained Compressive Stress," Research Report No. 80-2, Department of Structural Engineering, Cornell University, Ithaca, 1980, 201 pp.

14. Thomas, F. G., "Creep of Concrete Under Load," Proceedings (London Congress, Apr. 1937), International Association for Testing Materials, London, 1937, pp. 292-294.

15. Ngab, Ali S.; Nilson, Arthur H; and Slate, Floyd O., "Shrinkage and Creep of High Strength Concrete," ACI JOURNAL, Proceedings V. 78, No. 4, July-Aug. 1981, pp. 255-261.

16. Neville, A. M., Creep of Concrete: Plain, Reinforced, and Prestressed, American Elsevier Publishing Company, New York, 1970, 622 pp.

17. Slate, Floyd O., and Olsefski, Stanley, "X-Rays for Study of Internal Structure and Microcracking of Concrete," ACI JOURNAL, Proceedings V. 60, No. 5, May 1963, pp. 575-588.

18. Newman, K., "Criteria for the Behavior of Plain Concrete Under Complex States of Stress," Proceedings, International Conference on the structure of Concrete and Its Behavior Under Load (London, Sept. 1965), Cement and Concrete Association, London, 1968, pp. 255-274.

19. Roll, Frederic, "Long-Term Creep-Recovery of Highly Stressed Concrete Cylinders," Symposium on Creep of Concrete, SP-9, American Concrete Institute, Detroit, 1964, pp. 95-114.

20. Freudenthal, A. M., and Roll, Frederic, "Creep and Creep Recovery of Concrete Under High Compressive Stress," ACI JOURNAL, Proceedings V. 54, No. 12, June 1958, pp. 1111-1142.

21. Rusch, Hubert, "Researches Towards a General Flexural Theory for Structural Concrete," ACI JOURNAL, Proceedings V. 57, No. 1, July 1960, pp. 1-28.

A TRIBUTE TO

"Analysis of Crack Formation and Crack Growth in Concrete by Means of Fracture Mechanics and Finite Elements"

by A. Hillerborg, M. Modeer, and P.E. Petersson

Foreword by Barzin Mobasher

Arne Hillerborg was born in Stockholm, Sweden, in 1923. He graduated as a Civil Engineer from the Royal Institute of Technology in Stockholm in 1945, and obtained his PhD in 1951 from the same institute. His doctoral dissertation was titled: "Dynamic Influences of Smoothly Running Loads on Simply Supported Girders." Between 1955-1960 he was a lecturer at the technical college in Stockholm and 1960-1968 was head of the Siporex Central Laboratory conducting research on aerated autoclaved concrete. From 1968 until his retirement in 1989, he served as the professor of building materials at the Lund University of Technology. Hillerborg is well known for introducing the strip method of reinforced concrete of slabs in 1956 as a design method based on the lower bound theory of plasticity. This method was translated to English in 1975 and has seen widespread use. Arne Hillerborg got interested in Fracture Mechanics in the mid 1970s and published his work with Matz Modeer and Per Erik Petersson, two of his PhD students who graduated in 1979 and 1981, respectively. He continued his research on fracture mechanics thereafter and has made a significant contribution to the development of this field.

Fracture process in quasi-brittle materials such as concrete can be visualized as a two-step process, the initiation of cracks followed by their propagation. Microcracks may be initiated by many mechanisms such as temperature change, shrinkage, loading, aggregate-paste interface mismatch, and other factors, and serve as initiation sites for macroscopic cracks. Crack propagation in concrete, and in many quasi-brittle materials such as ceramics, rocks, and composites, are characterized by a nonlinear (dissipative) zone at the crack tip. This nonlinear zone is commonly referred to as fracture process zone (FPZ), whose size is not negligible compared with usual structural sizes. Thus, linear elastic fracture mechanics (LEFM), according to which the FPZ is a point, in general does not apply; so the behavior of the FPZ needs to be simulated directly.

The original attempt to apply linear elastic fracture mechanics to concrete materials was proposed in 1961 by Kaplan, who used the Griffith crack theory to explain the failure of concrete and mortar beams. One of the fundamental questions in this area deals with the processes that lead to the formation of the fracture process zone and subsequent propagation of the cracks. One of the ways to address this question is based on the energy approach, where the fracture energy is obtained by measuring the work of fracture concept: the total amount of energy dissipated in the formation of a single crack from a notched specimen loaded in a tension mode.

The Cohesive Crack Model (CCM) was introduced following the development of models for the fracture of metals. In this approach, the effect of plastic zone formation at the tip of a crack within a metal was incorporated in the original crack, and the energy dissipation due to the plastic work was also included in the energy balance criteria. The Dugdale/Barenblatt plastic crack tip model was used as a basis to develop the Cohesive Crack Model in the paper by Hillerborg, Modeer, and Petersson in 1976. This original approach enables one to apply a fracture mechanics approach in the finite element analysis of concrete structures and assumes that a crack longer than its observable length in an experiment exists. Preceding the crack tip, a smaller or larger process zone propagates where yielding takes place in the case of plastic metals and microcracking in materials like concrete and rock. The essential element in CCM is the inclusion of this process zone in the total crack length as a fictitious crack, and the assumption that a closing pressure acts over the process zone length.

In plastic metals, the closing pressure is assumed to be constant and equals the yielding stress of the metal; in concrete, according to the CCM, the closing pressure is governed by the softening curve measured in a stable displacement-controlled uniaxial tension test. The nature of this closing pressure, and the notion if it, represents a fundamental material property, has been the subject of much scientific discussion over the past 30 years. Hillerborg et al. showed that by measuring the stress-crack width and relating it to material parameters, one can introduce the closing pressure forces within a finite element approach. The softening function relates the stress transferred between the crack faces to the crack opening at each point, and it is considered, by hypothesis, to be a material property independent of geometry and size.

In the original paper, the applicability of the method was verified by simulating the bending of an unreinforced beam. This led to an explanation of the differences between bending strength and tensile strength, and of the variation in bending strength with beam depth. The broader applicability of the approach can be viewed in the context of many applications where tensile properties contribute to the overall behavior of the structure. Examples include determination of moment at first cracking and limit state of reinforced and unreinforced beams, crack spacing and crack width in bending, deflection in beams, formation of shear cracks and their effect on shear capacity, anchor pullout, microcrack formation, and compression failure. Effects due to multi-axial stress conditions, size effect, crack path trajectory, equivalent elastic crack models, and computation of the softening function by inverse analysis are just some of the research directions that have carried forward the fictitious crack approaches.

Interest in theoretical and analytical modeling, computer simulation, and experimental aspects of the fictitious crack modeling for quasi-brittle materials follows from this original work and continues to the present day. Many models have been proposed to take into account the physical and natural effects of softening. The cohesive or fictitious crack model has evolved to a general approach and provides a suitable macroscopic modeling of the nonlinear fracture processes in concrete, rock, ceramics, and other fiber reinforced brittle matrix composites. It describes physical processes intuitively as it simulates the microcracking and deterioration in the fracture process zone through the softening function. As a result, numerical simulation schemes, such as finite element analysis (FEA), have been increasingly applied to quasi-brittle materials by employing cohesive crack models.

Over the past 30 years, the basic assumptions and results of this model have been discussed and debated in fracture books and articles written by many authors, including Bazant, Wittmann, Shah, Mihashi, Planas and Elices, Karihaloo, Van Mier, and Carpinteri among others. These efforts have led to a much better understanding of theoretical and experimental techniques, and have aided the development of methods to measure the fracture energy, its properties, and influences on the structural response. Several RILEM technical committees were formed under the direction of Dr. Hillerborg to measure the fracture energy, and the flexural test conducted on the three-point bend specimen resulted from these technical committees.

The cohesive or fictitious crack model has had a profound effect on the thousands of publications and conferences that integrate fracture energy as a fundamental material property into everyday computational tools for concrete structures. This approach is by no means without criticism however: it has been shown that the softening response is a general interaction between the material and the test specimen size and geometry, and thus must be viewed as a structural response. The overly simplified approach of the model, in treating only the tension case, has also been criticized. One must however appreciate the elegance and simplicity of this method as one of its most important contributions to concrete materials research community. Finally, the number of citations to this single paper is in the thousands and is a clear and justifiable reason for the fundamental impact of this work on the concrete materials research community.

Barzin Mobasher *is Professor of materials and structural engineering at Arizona State University. His research interests include modeling the mechanical properties of materials, structural testing, experimental stress analysis, fracture mechanics, durability-hydration characteristics of blended cements, and fiber reinforced concrete. He is a member of ACI Committees 544, Fiber Reinforced Concrete; 549, Thin Section Cementitious Composites and Ferrocement; and 446, Fracture Mechanics of Concrete.*

CEMENT and CONCRETE RESEARCH. Vol. 6, pp. 773-782, 1976. Pergamon Press, Inc.
Printed in the United States.

ANALYSIS OF CRACK FORMATION AND CRACK GROWTH IN CONCRETE BY

MEANS OF FRACTURE MECHANICS AND FINITE ELEMENTS

A Hillerborg, M Modéer and P-E Petersson
Division of Building Materials
Lund Institute of Technology, Lund, Sweden

(Communicated by Z. P. Bazant)
(Received August 24, 1976)

ABSTRACT

A method is presented in which fracture mechanics is introduced into
finite element analysis by means of a model where stresses are assumed
to act across a crack as long as it is narrowly opened. This assumption may be regarded as a way of expressing the energy absorption G_c
in the energy balance approach, but it is also in agreement with results of tension tests. As a demonstration the method has been applied
to the bending of an unreinforced beam, which has led to an explanation of the difference between bending strength and tensile strength,
and of the variation in bending strength with beam depth.

Une méthode est présentée, par laquelle la méchanique des ruptures est
introduite dans l'analyse des éléments finis à l'aide d'un modèle, où
les contraintes sont supposées d'opérer sur les côtés d'une fissure
tant que cette fissure est étroite.
Cette hypothèse peut être considérée comme un moyen d'exprimer l'absorption G_c d'énergie en usant l'approche de l'équilibre d'énergie.
Cette hypothèse est aussi justifiée par les résultats des essais de
tension.
Pour en prouver la validité, cette méthode a été appliquée au fléchisse-
ment d'une poutre non armée et fournit une explication de la différence
entre la résistance au moment de flexion et la résistance à l'effort de
tension, ainsi que de la variation de la résistance au moment de flexion
en fonction de la profondeur de la poutre.

Importance of cracks and crack growth

Crack formation and crack growth play an important part in the performance of unreinforced and reinforced concrete. Examples of this are

crack spacing and crack width in bending

shear chracks and their effect on shear capacity

cracking moment of reinforced and unreinforced beams

microcracks in compression and compression failure.

A rational design in these cases ought to be based on realistic theoretical models, which take crack formation and crack propagation into account. So far no such models have been available. Consequently the design methods have had to be based on empirical research, supported by simplified models.

Recent advances within fracture mechanics and finite element methods (FEM) have now given us a possibility of analysing crack growth. Fracture mechanics gives the fundamental rules for crack propagation and FEM makes it possible to apply these rules to complicated cases.

The cases we wish to analyse are rather complicated, as they involve diverse phenomena, such as

formation and propagation of cracks

two or more parallel cracks

bent shear cracks

shrinkage strains

interaction between concrete and reinforcement

interaction between cement matrix and aggregate.

It is therefore necessary to use FEM and also to try and find a method which simplifies the analysis as much as possible.

Proposed approach

There are many methods to choose from fracture mechanics, e.g.

the stress intensity factor approach

the energy balance approach

the "strip-yield" model according to Dugdale

the cohesive force model according to Barenblatt.

The different methods are known to give coherent results.

In the stress intensity factor approach the stresses near the crack tip are studied. These stresses theoretically approach infinity at the crack tip according to the expression $\sigma = K/\sqrt{2\pi r}$, where r is the distance from the crack tip and K is a coefficient, the stress intensity factor, depending on the load, the crack dimensions, etc. When K reaches a critical value K_c, the crack propagates.

The stress intensity factor approach has been used a great deal in FEM analysis. The direct method requires a FEM mesh with very small elements close to the crack tip, which limits its applicability to complicated problems. Indirect and special methods permit the use of greater elements. The methods cannot explain the formation of cracks, only the propagation.

In the energy balance approach it is assumed that a certain amount of energy G_c is absorbed by the formation of a unit area of crack surface. When a crack propagates a certain amount of stored energy is released. The crack propagates when the released energy is equal to or greater than the absorbed energy. FEM has been used to determine the energy release rate in the energy balance approach, see e.g. /5/. This enables the use of a FEM mesh with rather large elements. The formation of cracks cannot be explained.

In the Dugdale model it is assumed that there is a plastic zone near the crack tip according to Fig. 1. Within the plastic zone a stress equal to the yield strength σ_y acts across the crack. The Barenblatt model is similar to the Dugdale model, but the stress is assumed to vary with the deformation. It does not seem to have been used in finite element analysis.

The basic idea of the model we propose is demonstrated in Fig. 2. It is in some respects similar to the Barenblatt model. The model is described only for mode I (the opening mode), but it may also be applied to modes II and III.

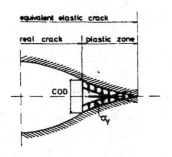

Fig. 1 The Dugdale model for   Fig. 2 Proposed model
         crack tip plasticity

The crack is assumed to propagate when the stress at the crack tip reaches the tensile strength f_t. When the crack opens the stress is not assumed to fall to zero at once, but to decrease with increasing crack width w, for example according to Fig. 3. At the crack width w_1 the stress has fallen to zero. For that part of the crack where $w < w_1$, the "crack" in reality corresponds to a microcraced zone with some remaining ligaments for stress transfer. As there is a stress to be overcome in opening the crack, energy is absorbed. The amount of energy absorbed per unit crack area in widening the crack from zero to or beyond w_1 is

$$\int_0^{w_1} \sigma \, dw$$

and corresponds to the area between the curve and the coordinate axis' in Fig. 3.

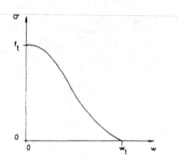

Fig. 3 Assumed variation of stress σ with crack width w, general case

We now choose the curve in Fig. 3 so that

$$\int_0^{w_1} \sigma dw = G_c \tag{1}$$

which means that the energy absorbed per newformed unit crack area is the same as in the energy balance approach. The model of Fig. 2 may thus be looked upon as a way of expressing the energy balance approach.

At the same time the assumption of Fig. 2 may be looked upon as a reality. Stresses may be present in a microcracked zone as long as the corresponding displacement is small. This has been clearly demonstrated in tension tests, using a very rigid testing equipment, e.g., by Evans and Marathe /4/; cf. Fig. 5.

By the application of the proposed model the curve $\sigma(w)$ may be chosen in different ways, e.g. according to Figs. 4a, b or c, which all show simple mathematical relations. For typical yielding materials, like mild steel, Fig. 4a seems to be the best choice. It corresponds exactly to the Dugdale model with $f_t = \sigma_y$ and w_1 = COD at initiation of crack growth. The discontinuity may give rise to some problems by the application in FEM, but they are not serious.

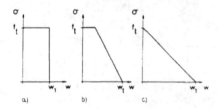

Fig. 4 Examples of possible assumptions of variation of stress σ with crack width w in practical applications

For concrete it seems that Fig. 4c is the best choice as it corresponds reasonably well with tension test results /4/, cf. Fig. 5. It is also simple, continuous and suitable for FEM analysis. For our purpose we have therefore chosen Fig. 4c.

We then obtain

$$\int_0^{w_1} \sigma dw = f_t w_1 / 2$$

or from (1),

$$w_1 = 2G_c / f_t \tag{2}$$

For ordinary concrete G_c/f_t seems to be of the order 0.005 -

0.01 mm, cf. /1/, and thus w_1 of the order 0.01 - 0.02 mm. In the application we further assume that the concrete is linear-elastic until f_t is reached.

Fig. 5 shows a comparison between our assumptions with G_c/f_t = 0.01 mm, E/f_t = 10 000 and a tension test from /4/ with a gage length of 1" (25 mm). This corresponds to a theoretical average elongation over the gage length when σ reaches 0, i.e. $w = w_1$, of $2 \cdot 0.01/25 = 800 \cdot 10^{-6}$. The assumptions seem to agree reasonably with the test result. A lower value of E/f_t would have improved the agreement, but from the point of view of the energy balance approach the E-value corresponding to unloading is most important and this justifies the choice E/f_t = 10 000.

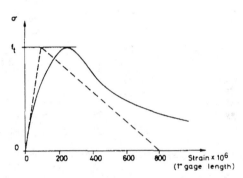

Fig. 5 A test result
from a tensile
test according
to Evans & Mara-
the /4/, compared
to a corresponding
assumed relation
by the analysis

A special feature of the proposed method is that it explains not only the growth of existing cracks, but also the formation of new cracks, as it is assumed that cracks start forming when the tensile stress reaches f_t, i.e., the same criterion is used for formation and propagation of cracks.

The analysis can be performed with a rather coarse mesh, as in the example below, because there are no stress singularities and the amount of absorbed energy is not very sensitive to the mesh size. The possibility of using a coarse mesh means that rather complicated problems can also be treated without using too many elements.

Application to an unreinforced beam in bending

In order to study the applicability of the method the following case has been analysed /2/.

An unreinforced concrete beam with a constant rectangular cross-section is loaded by a pure bending moment M according to Fig. 6. When the bending moment reaches a value M_0 the tensile stress in the bottom fibre reaches f_t. As we assume that the concrete cannot take higher tensile stresses than f_t, cracks will form and start opening when M is increased above M_0. We will now study how these cracks grow when the bending moment increases. In order to simplify the calculations we assume that only one crack opens, and that this happens at the section of symmetry.

The finite element mesh used for the calculation is shown in Fig. 6. The bending moment M is applied as a couple of forces at the

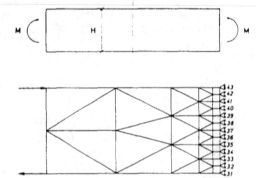

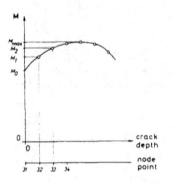

Fig. 6 Bent rectangu-
        lar beam and
        a corresponding
        FEM representa-
        tion

left end of the beam. The crack is assumed to open at the section to
the right, which is the section of symmetry.

M_0 is the moment which gives $\sigma_{31} = f_t$, where σ_{31} is the stress
at point 31. M_0 would be the failure moment if the material were elastic and perfectly brittle. When M is raised above M_0 the crack starts
opening at point 31. At that point we introduce a force corresponding
to the relation between stress σ and crack width w according to Fig.
4c. With this new finite element system we can calculate the stress
at point 32 and we can determine that value $M = M_1$, which gives a
stress $\sigma_{32} = f_t$. We can now introduce another force at point 32 and
calculate a moment $M = M_2$, giving $\sigma_{33} = f_t$ etc. By proceeding in the
same way we get a relation between crack depth and applied moment
according to Fig. 7.

Fig. 7 Calculated bending moment
        M versus crack depth

When the crack grows the corresponding bending moment reaches a
maximum value M_{max} whereupon it starts decreasing. As the maximum value
is reached the structure becomes unstable if M is kept constant, and
it fails suddenly as the crack propagates.

The relation M_{max}/M_0 is the same as the relation between bending strength and tensile strength, as M_0 is the moment which makes
the maximum bending stress in the uncracked section equal to the tensile strength.

It can be shown that the behaviour of the beam depends on the parameter H/l_c, where H is the beam depth and l_c is a critical length, defined by

$$l_c = EG/f_t^2 \qquad (3)$$

As the realtion

$$EG_c = K_c^2$$

holds for plain stress and approximately for plain strain, we may also write

$$l_c = (K_c/f_t)^2 \qquad (4)$$

Fig. 8 shows the results of the above analysis as well as of an analysis where shrinkage strains ε_s according to Fig. 9 have been taken into account.

Fig. 8 Theoretical variation of ratio between bending and tensile strength with beam depth H and $l_c = (K_c/f_t)^2 =$

$= EG_c/f_t^2$

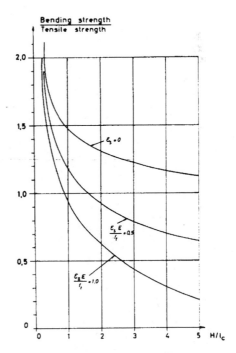

Fig. 9 Assumed distribution of shrinkage strains

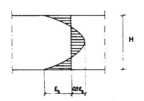

It must be remembered that the results in Fig. 8 correspond to a simple FEM model where only one crack is assumed to open, independent of the stresses in the other parts of the beam. A more realistic model with cracks opening in all places where f_t is exceeded will give somewhat different results with higher values of M_{max}/M_0, especially where shrinkage strains are present.

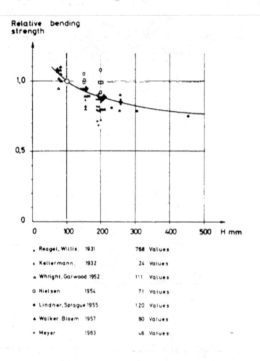

Fig. 10 Test results of bending strength versus beam depth, summarized by Meyer /3/, compared to theoretical curve for l_c = 100 mm

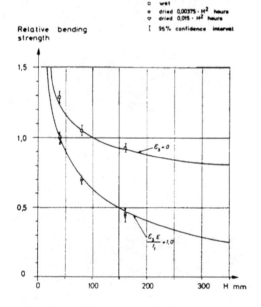

Fig. 11 Test results of bending strength versus beam depth for one quality of concrete, tested wet and dried in 45% RH, compared to theoretical curves for l_c = 100 mm

Fig. 10 shows a comparison between theoretical values according to Fig. 8 and test results summarized by Mayer /3/. The theoretical curve is shown for $l_c = EG_c/f_t^2 = 10\ 000 \cdot 0.01 = 100$ mm, corresponding to the values used in Fig. 5. It has been assumed that there is no shrinkage.

Fig. 11 shows a comparison between theoretical values according to Fig. 8 and our own test results. Regarding the influence of shrinkage it must be noticed that the test specimen had a square cross-section, drying in all directions, whereas the theoretical curve is valid for a specimen drying only upwards and downwards, and that creep was not taken into account in the calculations.

In spite of its simplification, the model seems to be able to explain the test results.

Conclusion

The proposed method of combining fracture mechanics and finite element analysis seems to yield realistic results regarding crack formation and propagation as well as regarding failure even if a coarse element mesh is used. This opens up the possibility of studying complicated problems with a limited amount of computer work.

References

/1/ Welch, G B and Haisman, B "Fracture toughness measurements of concrete," University of New South Wales, Sydney, Australia, Univiv. Report No R 42, January 1969.

/2/ Petersson, P-E and Modéer, M "Model based on fracture mechanics for the calculation of crack propagation in concrete," (in Swedish with English summary), Division of Building Technology, Lund Institute of Technology, Sweden, Report No 70, 1976.

/3/ Mayer, H "Die Berechnung von Durchbiegung von Stahlbetonbauteilen," Deutscher Ausschuss für Stahlbeton, H 194, W Ernst & Sohn, Berlin, 1967.

/4/ Evans, P H and Marathe, M S "Microcracking and stress-strain curves for concrete in tension," Materials and Structures (RILEM), No 1, pp 61 - 64, 1968.

/5/ Salah El-Din, A S and El-Adawy Nassef, M M "A modified approach for estimating the cracking moment of reinforced concrete beams," ACI Journal No 7, July 1975, pp 356 - 360.

A TRIBUTE TO
"Mechanics of Crack Arrest in Concrete"
by J.P. Roumaldi and G.B. Batson

Foreword by Surendra P. Shah

The pioneering paper by Romualdi and Batson (1963) made a strong contribution to the development of fiber reinforced concrete. Fibers have been used in inorganic binders for a long time. Mud reinforced with straw is often cited as an example of ancient use of fibers. Since the industrial revolution, the use of asbestos fibers in portland cement matrix for producing cement board represents perhaps the most prevalent use of fibers. The research to replace asbestos fibers with alkali-resistant glass fibers started in England and Russia (Majumdar and Ryder 1968). Today, fiber-reinforced thin sheets made with fibers such as cellulose and polymeric fibers continue to be produced in increasing quantities using manufacturing methods such as the hatschek process, the spraying process, and extrusion (ACI Committee 549 2004). For these products, the matrix is portland cement paste or mortar and not concrete. The use of short, randomly distributed fibers in ready mixed concrete (or shortcrete) was critically stimulated by Romualdi and Batson's paper and the subsequent patent that was issued based on that work. Their research provided the impetus for using steel fibers to control cracking in concrete. Several companies subsequently started producing steel fibers in different shapes and dimensions. The commercial success of steel fibers led to the development of synthetic fibers (for example polypropylene and PVA fibers). ACI Committee 544 has been in the forefront of these new developments. Today, fibers are used world-wide in increasing quantities, and the commercial success can be traced to the work of Romualdi and Batson, among others.

The original idea behind the work by Romualdi and Batson was that use of short fibers, which are randomly and finely distributed, can increase the tensile strength of concrete. They argued that fibers can be spaced much more closely than conventional reinforcement and they can arrest small cracks that are of the size of the spacing, the smaller the size of the flaw, the higher the tensile strength of brittle materials. This concept had some deficiencies. Shah and Rangan (1971) pointed out that concrete already has flaws of the size of the coarse aggregates and that the arresting mechanism of fibers is limited by the relatively weak bond between fibers and matrix. As a result, fibers do not increase tensile strength but they do

247

dramatically improve toughness (Shah and Rangan 1971). This improved toughness important in crack control. Today, measuring toughness of fiber reinforced concrete is one of the key tests specified by relevant ASTM Standards.

The paper by Romualdi and Batson stimulated my interest in both fiber reinforced concrete and fracture mechanics. I have coauthored a textbook on each of these subjects (Balaguru and Shah 1992; Shah et al. 1995). I wrote a discussion to their paper while I was a graduate student at Cornell University (Broms and Shah 1964). The pursuit to answer the question why fibers did not increase tensile strength but increased the toughness led me to study fracture mechanics. It turns o that the size of the flaw, the dimension of the fibers, the interfacial bond strength, and the size of the specimens interact in a complex manner. Our recent work shows that tensile strength of concrete can indeed be increased if fibers, which are of the micron-scale and exhibit sufficiently good bond, are used (Shah 1991; Akkaya et al. 2003). We are now extending this idea by using nanofibers with the hope of making cement paste itself super ductile.

REFERENCES

ACI Committee 549, (2004). "Report on Thin Reinforced Cementitious Products (ACI 549.2R-04)" 28 pp.

Akkaya Y., Shah S. P. and Ghandehari M., (2003). "Influence of Fiber Dispersion on the Performance of Microfiber Reinforced Cement Composites," *Innovations in Fiber-Reinforced Concrete for Value*, SP-216-1, V. 216, American Concrete Institute, Farmington Hills, MI, pp. 1-18.

Balaguru, P. and Shah, S. P., (1992). "Fiber Reinforced Cement Composites," McGraw Hill, New York.

Broms, B. B. and Shah, S. P., (1964). Discussion of "Mechanics of Crack Arrest in Concrete," by Romualdi, J. P. and Batson, G. B., Proceedings of ASCE J. of Engineerin Mechanics Division, V. 90, pp. 167-171.

Majumdar, A. J. and Ryder, J. F., (1968). "Glass Fiber Reinforcement of Cement Products," *Glass Technology*, V. 9, pp. 78-84.

Romualdi, J. P. and Batson, G. B., (1963). "Mechanics of Crack Arrest in Concrete," Proceedings of ASCE J. of Engineering Mechanics Division, V. 89, pp. 147-168.

Shah, S. P., (1991). "Do Fibers Increase the Tensile Strength of Cement-Based Matrixes?" *ACI Materials Journal*, V. 88, pp. 595-602.

Shah, S. P. and Rangan, V. B., (1971). "Fiber Reinforced Concrete Properties," ACI JOURNAL, *Proceedings* V. 68, pp. 126-135.

Shah, S. P., Swartz, S. E. and Ouyang, C., (1995). "Fracture Mechanics of Concrete," John Wiley & Sons, New York.

Surendra P. Shah *is the Walter P. Murphy Professor of Civil Engineering at Northwestern University. He is the Director of the NSF Science and Technology Center for Advanced Cement-Based Materials. His current research interests include fracture, fiber-reinforced composites, nondestructive evaluation, transport properties, processing, rheology, nanotechnology, and use of solid waste materials. He is an ACI Fellow, a member of NAE, and has won the ACI Arthur R. Anderson and Robert E. Philleo awards.*

Journal of the

ENGINEERING MECHANICS DIVISION

Proceedings of the American Society of Civil Engineers

MECHANICS OF CRACK ARREST IN CONCRETE

By James P. Romualdi[1] and Gordon B. Batson,[2] Assoc. Members, ASCE

SYNOPSIS

The application of linear-elastic fracture mechanics reveals that the strength of concrete in tension is limited by internal holes and micro-cracks. Fracture arrest can be achieved by reducing the spacing of reinforcement to a suitable scale. Reinforcement diameter decreases in proportion to reduction in spacing in order to maintain steel percentage. Theoretical results indicate that the tensile cracking strength of concrete increases in proportion to the inverse square root of the reinforcement spacing. Tests on closely spaced wire reinforced beams support the theoretical calculations.

INTRODUCTION

The relatively low tensile strength of concrete is normally considered an unavoidable deficiency of the material. One accepts this deficiency as inevitable and to compensate for the lack of tensile strength in a variety of ways. Thus, concrete tension is ignored in beams and the tensile force is assigned to the reinforcing steel, or prestressing is used, permitting dead load and live

Note.—Discussion open until November 1, 1963. To extend the closing date one month, a written request must be filed with the Executive Secretary, ASCE. This paper is part of the copyrighted Journal of the Engineering Mechanics Division, Proceedings of the American Society of Civil Engineerings, Vol. 89, No. EM3, June, 1963.

[1] Assoc. Prof., Carnegie Inst. of Tech., Pittsburgh, Pa.
[2] Asst. Prof., Clarkson College of Tech., Potsdam, N. Y.

load tensile stresses to cancel out initially predisposed compressive stresses. Throughout the development of reinforced concrete, however, the basic limitation of low tensile strength has not been avoided. Prestressing does not overcome this limitation but merely by-passes it with an alternate mechanism.

Furthermore, it should be noted that conventional reinforced concrete is not a two-phase material in the true sense of the word. That is, the existence of one phase (that is, steel or concrete) does not improve the basic strength properties of the other phase and, consequently, the over-all performance of the composite material is dictated by the individual performance of each phase. In comparison, the matrix in fiberglass prevents crack extension from one flaw sensitive glass fiber to another and provides load transfer along broken filaments. The result is a high tensile strength and toughness not inherent in either phase acting individually.[3]

The lack of beneficial interaction between the steel rods and concrete matrix in reinforced concrete, however, is not in fact unavoidable. Application of linear-elastic fracture mechanics analysis to this problem reveals that a true two-phase behavior can be attained if the distances between adjacent reinforcing elements is reduced to a suitable scale. The basis for the appropriate analysis is the crack extension force concept advanced by Irwin[4] as a measure of the influences that tend to extend a crack in a stressed medium. As a flaw in the concrete tends to enlarge to a crack, displacements develop in the material ahead of the crack as a result of the stress field singularity at the crack edge. The greater rigidity of steel reinforcement in the immediate vicinity of the crack, however, opposes these displacements, and forces are exerted by the reinforcement on the concrete matrix.

By means of equations describing compatibility between adjacent points on the reinforcement and in the concrete, it is possible to calculate these forces and, from suitable fracture mechanics applications, to interpret them in terms of a reduction in the crack extension force. Results of such calculations reveal that the stress required to extend a crack beyond the area enclosed by adjacent groups of reinforcing rods is inversely proportional to the square root of the rod spacing. The effect is not significant until the reinforcement spacing is less than approximately 0.5 in. At smaller spacings, the tensile strength increases markedly. A reduction in spacing is accomplished with a corresponding reduction in the diameter of the reinforcing elements in order to maintain a constant percentage of steel. At effective small spacings, the reinforcing elements are relatively fine wires and steel percentages are on the order of a few percent.

The material just described is not without parallel to fiberglass, with one significant exception. The filler material, or matrix, in fiberglass serves to prevent crack propagation from one glass filament to another, but it is the glass filaments, which occupy approximately 70% of the material by volume, that constitutes the tensile load carrying fraction. On the other hand, the steel fibers (wires) in closely spaced wire reinforced concrete, occupying only a few percent of the concrete by volume, prevent crack propagation in the concrete, and it is the concrete that is the tensile load carrying fraction.

A qualitative description of this mechanism in relation to earlier riveted stiffener fracture arrest concepts can be found in another paper by the au-

[3] "Two-Phase Materials," by G. Slayter, Scientific American, Vol. 206, No. 1 January, 1962, p. 124.

[4] "Fracture Mechanics," by G. R. Irwin, Proceedings, First Symposium on Naval Structural Mechanics, Pergamon Press, New York, N. Y., 1960.

thors.[5] The theoretical analysis for the mechanism of crack arrest by closely spaced wire reinforcement will be presented, and the experimental evidence to support the theory will be reviewed.

RELEVANT FRACTURE MECHANICS CONCEPTS

Linear-elastic fracture mechanics is gaining more widespread use, and a full treatment of the subject is available in the literature. In order to provide continuity with the development to follow, however, a brief outline of the basic theory will be presented.

A. A. Griffith[6] postulated an energy release concept in 1921 in order to explain the discrepancies in the then accepted rupture theory. If U is the reduction in stored elastic energy of a stressed medium because of the presence of a crack, V represents the energy of the crack surface, and a refers to the radius of an internal crack, the criterion for crack extension is

$$\frac{\partial}{\partial a} (U - V) = 0 \dots \dots \dots \dots \dots (1)$$

The work required to extend a crack in a brittle material is related to the surface free energy of the newly created crack surfaces. Thus, the energy of a crack surface in a two-dimensional plate element, on a per unit thickness basis, is

$$V = 4\,T\,a \dots \dots \dots \dots \dots \dots (2)$$

in which T is the surface tension. In estimating the reduction in strength of a brittle material in the presence of a crack, from Eq. 1, it is necessary only to have an analytical expression for U and a knowledge of the magnitude of T. For the plain stress situation of a crack of length 2a in a thin stressed plate that is subjected to tensile stress σ, as shown in Fig. 1, the reduction in stored elastic energy is

$$U = \frac{\pi\,\sigma^2\,a^2}{E} \dots \dots \dots \dots \dots (3)$$

in which E represents the modulus of elasticity. Introducing Figs. 2 and 3 into Eq. 1, the condition for crack initiation in a brittle material (for the situation depicted in Fig. 1) is

$$\frac{\pi\,\sigma^2\,a}{E} = 2\,T \dots \dots \dots \dots \dots (4)$$

[5] "The Behavior of Reinforced Concrete Beams with Closely Spaced Reinforcement," by J. P. Romualdi, and G. B. Batson, Journal of the American Concrete Institute (forthcoming).

[6] "The Phenomena of Rupture and Flow in Solids," by A. A. Griffith, Philosophical Transactions, Royal Society of London, A-221, 1921.

The Griffith approach was extended to ductile materials by E. Orowan[7] and G. R. Irwin[8] by considering the irrecoverable work associated with the plastic enclave at the crack tip. Thus, Eq. 4 becomes

$$\frac{\pi \sigma^2 a}{E} = 2\,T + \frac{\partial W}{\partial a} \quad \dots\dots\dots\dots\dots\dots (5)$$

in which W is the work caused by plastic distortion. The second quanity on the right-hand side of Eq. 5 is orders of magnitude larger than the term in-

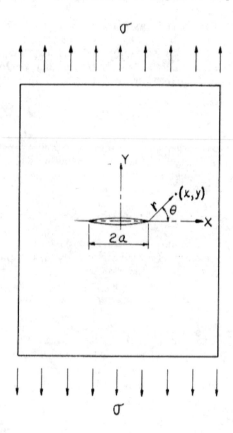

FIG. 1.—CENTRALLY NOTCHED FLAT PLATE IN TENSION

volving surface tension for most metals. As will be shown subsequently, however, the energy to extend a crack in concrete is on the order of that calculated from the term 2 T.

[7] "Fundamentals of Brittle Behavior in Metals," by E. Orowan, Symposium held at the Massachusetts Inst. of Tech., Cambridge, Mass., June, 1950.

[8] "Fracture Dynamics," by G. R. Irwin, Fracturing of Metals, Amer. Soc. of Metals, Cleveland, Ohio, 1948.

In abbreviated form, the elastic energy release rate is given the sumbol, G, and the work rate to extend the crack—right side of Eq. 5—is represented by G_c. The units of G are work per unit extension per unit thickness, and it is referred to as the crack extension force. The critical value of G for crack initiation, G_c is a material property, whereas G is primarily a function of loading and geometry.

In general, it is necessary to distinguish between three possible crack extension modes when examining G_c values. The first is an "opening" or cleavage mode and the other two are shear modes that are not important to this analysis. Herein, the symmetry of loading is assumed to be such that the component of shearing stress on the plane of expected crack extension is zero. This is equivalent to saying that only the first "opening" mode of fracture occurs.

In principle, it is possible to predict crack extension with a knowledge of the largest expected crack and an analytical expression for the appropriate crack extension force, G. Limitations in application, however, arise from the fact that convenient solutions for G are not available for a wide variety of situations. Nevertheless, substantial progress can be made in anticipating fracture behavior in complex arrangements of loading and crack geometry by synthesizing known solutions and using suitable approximations.

Application to problems involving a combination of loadings is greatly facilitated by describing the conditions leading to fracture in terms of a stress intensity factor in the immediate vicinity of the crack tip. Irwin[9] shows that the stresses perpendicular to the plane of the crack in the limit of relatively small distance r from the crack border, are given by

$$\sigma_y = K \frac{\cos \frac{\theta}{2}}{\sqrt{2\,r}} \left[1 + \sin \frac{\theta}{2} \sin \frac{3\theta}{2} \right] \quad \dots \dots \dots \quad (6)$$

in which r represents a radius from the crack tip to the point in question, and θ is the angle formed by the radius and the x-axis. The coordinates are as shown on Fig. 1.

The stress intensity factor K, in Eq. 6, is related only to the loading and geometry of the structural element. It is also shown[9] that the strain energy release rate is related to the stress intensity factor by

$$G = \frac{\pi K^2}{E} \quad \text{(for plane stress)} \quad \dots \dots \dots \dots \quad (7)$$

and

$$G = \frac{\pi K^2}{E} \left(1 - \mu^2 \right) \quad \text{(for plane strain)} \quad \dots \dots \dots \quad (8)$$

in which μ is Poisson's ratio.

Advantage in referring to K and K_c rather than G and G_c lies in the fact that the total K-value because of superimposed stress fields is a linear addi-

---

[9] "Analysis of Stress and Strains Near End of a Crack," by G. R. Irwin, Journal of Applied Mechanics, Vol. 24, No. 3, September, 1957, p. 361.

tion of K-values related to the individual stress fields. Thus, assuming body to be acted on by loading systems $Q_1, Q_2, \ldots \ldots Q_n$, the total stress intensity factor, which governs the behavior of a crack in the body, is

$$K_T = \pm K_1 \pm K_2 \cdots \cdots \pm K_n \cdots \cdots \cdots \cdots \cdots (9)$$

in which K_i is the K-value associated with loading Q_i, and a minus sign indicates that the loading system tends to close the crack. Eq. 9 also assumes the same crack extension mode for each loading system.

The viewpoint just outlined is the essence of fracture mechanics analysis in its broadest sense. With little elaboration, the theory offers an interesting insight into the apparently low tensile strength of concrete. Consider a disk-shaped crack in the interior of a solid and perpendicular to the principal tensile stress. I. N. Sneddon[10] has shown that the presence of such a crack, of radius a, lowers the potential energy of the medium by

$$U = \frac{8 \left(1 - \mu^2\right) \sigma^2 a^3}{3E} \cdots \cdots \cdots \cdots \cdots (10)$$

The crack extension force tendency is

$$G = \frac{\partial U}{\partial A} = \frac{\partial U}{\partial a} \frac{da}{dA} \cdots \cdots \cdots \cdots \cdots (11)$$

in which A is the area of newly created crack surface associated with crack extension. The term da/dA for a circular crack of radius a is $1/2\pi a$ and $\partial U/\partial a$ is obtained from Eq. 10, whence

$$G = \frac{4 \left(1 - \mu^2\right) \sigma^2 a}{\pi E} \cdots \cdots \cdots \cdots \cdots (12)$$

M. F. Kaplan[11] has observed values of G_c of approximately 0.1 in.-lbs per sq in. for several mixes of Portland cement. Tests that are to be described subsequently have indicated lower values on the order of 0.02 in.-lb per sq in. Using the lower value, and assuming μ equal to 0.3 and E equal to 3×10^6 psi, critical crack sizes can be calculated for selected stress levels by equating the right side of Eq. 12 to the selected G_c value. For a tensile stress of 500 psi, the corresponding crack radius is 0.21 in. and, for a stress of 1,000 psi, the critical crack radius is 0.05 in.

These crack radii are significant inasmuch as they are of the same order of magnitude as the holes and flaws normally found in concrete. Thus, the strength of concrete in tension is related to a largest flaw concept rather than a maximum "cohesion." It is possible to conclude from this that the tensile strength of concrete can be increased by eliminating internal holes or flaws. This is probably true. In fact, carefully prepared mixes of concrete compacted to a high density exhibit tensile stresses on the order of 1,000 psi. But

---

[10] "The Distribution of Stress in the Neighborhood of a Crack in an Elastic Solid," by I. N. Sneddon, Proceedings, Royal Society of London, Series A, Vol. 187, 1946, p. 229.

[11] "Crack Propagation and the Fracture of Concrete," by M. F. Kaplan, Journal of the American Concrete Institute, November, 1961.

it is not possible to rely on such tensile strengths for structural purposes when a small crack—caused, perhaps, by fatigue or thermal shock—propagate through the entire tension zone. On the contrary, an opposite viewpoint is expressed herein. The existence of internal flaws is recognized, but the desired situation is one in which each flaw is localized within a prescribed boundary and prevented from full crack extension. Again, the parallel with fiberglass is noted: In fiberglass a crack in any one filament is prevented from spreading to adjacent filaments and is thus localized in terms of damage.

FRACTURE ARREST MECHANISM

The following presentation assumes a mass of reinforced concrete that is subjected to a uniform remote tensile stress, σ. The reinforcement consists

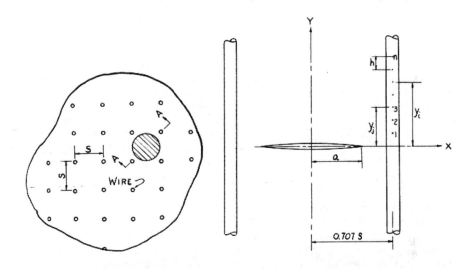

FIG. 2.—CROSS SECTION THROUGH WIRE REINFORCED CONCRETE AT LOCATION OF FLAW

FIG. 3.—SECTION THROUGH TWO WIRES AND CIRCULAR CRACK

of steel wires continuous through the mass of concrete, parallel to the tensile stress, and arranged in a rectangular array. A hole, or flaw, in the form of a circular crack is assumed in the concrete, as shown in Fig. 2. The crack is centrally located between four adjacent wires, and the diameter of the crack is equal to the rod spacing, S.

Fig. 3 is a section through two rods and the crack and is parallel to the stress (section A-A of Fig. 2). In the absence of a crack, the strain in the concrete due to remote tension is equal to the strain in the wires, and no shear forces exist at the interface between the two materials. In the presence of a crack, however, the additional concrete displacements caused by the extensional strains in the neighborhood of the crack are resisted by the wires, which are assumed infinitely stiff. This resistance causes a distribution of shear forces along those wires that act to close the crack. The resulting force distribution, $f(y)$, has the units force per unit length.

Solutions for the interaction force distribution are obtained for discrete points along the wire, as shown in Fig. 3. The points are spaced at a distance, h, and, assuming the distributed force along the wire at any point, y_j, to be constant over the interval h, the interaction force at any point, y_j, is P_j, equal to $f_j h$.

Let v_i be the y-directed displacement of a discrete point, y_i, because of the presence of the crack in an infinite homogeneous isotropic medium (the concrete mass neglecting the presence of the wires), and let d_{ij} be the displacement of point y_i in the concrete because of a unit force at the location of the wire at point y_j. Extensions of the wire are neglected by virtue of being much stiffer than the concrete. The condition for no relative displacement between the concrete and the wire at each of the n discrete points is

$$v_i - \sum_{j=1}^{n} d_{ij} P_j = 0 \quad \dots\dots\dots\dots\dots (13)$$

The set of simultaneous equations represented by Eq. 13 can be solved for the forces P_j. The stress intensity factor, K_p, caused by the forces P_j, can be computed and subtracted from the stress intensity factor because of the remote tensile stress, K_σ.

The expression for K_σ is obtained from Eqs. 8 and 12, whence

$$K_\sigma = \frac{2\sigma\sqrt{a}}{\pi} \quad \dots\dots\dots\dots\dots\dots (14)$$

The expedient (and approximation) used to evaluate the stress intensity factor because of the forces P_j is as follows. Neglect the presence of the crack and compute the average compressive stress caused (by the forces P_j along the four adjacent wires) over the area that is to be occupied by the crack. The existence of the crack (a traction free surface) is recognized by assuming an internal pressure of equal magnitude but opposite sign to that calculated over the crack area. This pressure, p, cancels the compressive stress and results in the required traction free area. The usefulness of this approach lies in the fact that the expression for K for an internal crack in the presence of remote stress σ is of the same form as that of a crack with internal pressure in a stress-free body. The letter symbol σ has been replaced by p in Eq. 14. The resulting total stress intensity factor, from Eq. 9, is then

$$K_T = K_\sigma - K_p = \frac{2\sqrt{a}}{\pi} (\sigma - p) \quad \dots\dots\dots\dots (15)$$

Exact solutions for displacements in the vicinity of circular cracks (ellipsoidal in the thickness direction) in a stress field are known, but the solutions are in a cumbersome form. A simpler mathematical model is obtained by assuming that a thick slice cut out parallel to the direction of applied stress and containing a flaw can be analyzed as a plate problem in plain strain.

The displacement v_i can be calculated with the aid of a stress function suggested by M. Westergaard.[12] Let the Airy stress function be

$$\phi = \text{Re } \bar{\bar{Z}} + y \text{ Im } \bar{Z} \quad\dots\dots\dots\dots\dots (16)$$

in which $\bar{\bar{Z}}$, $\bar{Z}$, and Z' are successive derivatives of a function $\bar{\bar{Z}}(z)$, and z is the complex variable $(x + iy)$. The appropriate stress function for the problem at hand is

$$Z(z) = \frac{\sigma z}{\sqrt{z^2 + a^2}} \quad\dots\dots\dots\dots\dots (17)$$

and the plain strain displacement is given by

$$v = \frac{(1 + \mu)}{E} \left[2(1 + \mu)\text{Im } \bar{Z} - y \text{ Re } Z \right] \quad\dots\dots\dots (18)$$

The terms involving $\text{Im } \bar{Z}$ and $\text{Re } Z$ can be found in terms of the coordinates shown in Fig. 4. The stress function Eq. 17 can be written in the form

$$Z(z) = \frac{\sigma z}{(z + a)^{\frac{1}{2}} (z - a)^{\frac{1}{2}}} \quad\dots\dots\dots\dots\dots (19)$$

and letting

$$z + a = \rho_2 \, e^{i\theta_2} \quad\dots\dots\dots\dots\dots (20a)$$

$$z = \rho \, e^{i\theta} \quad\dots\dots\dots\dots\dots (20b)$$

and

$$z - a = \rho_1 \, e^{i\theta_1} \quad\dots\dots\dots\dots\dots (20c)$$

the expressions for $\text{Im } \bar{Z}$ and $\text{Re } Z$ become

$$\text{Im } \bar{Z} = \sigma \, \rho_1^{\frac{1}{2}} \, \rho_2^{\frac{1}{2}} \, \sin\left(\frac{\theta_1 + \theta_2}{2}\right) \quad\dots\dots\dots (21)$$

---

[12] "Bearing Pressure and Cracks," by H. M. Westergaard, Journal of Applied Mechanics, June, 1939, pp. A 49–A 53.

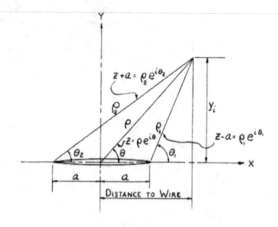

FIG. 4.—AUXILIARY COORDINATES FOR
EVALUATING STRESS FUNCTION

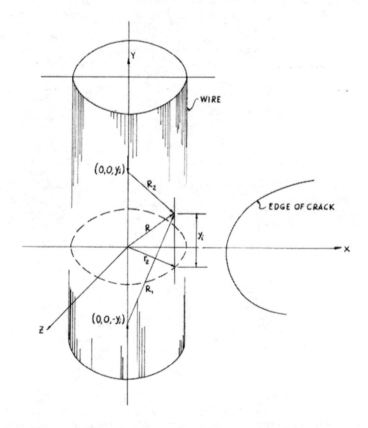

FIG. 5.—GEOMETRIC CONFIGURATION OF ROD AND FORCES

and

$$\mathrm{Re}\ Z = \frac{\sigma\,\rho\,\cos\left(\theta - \dfrac{\theta_1 + \theta_2}{2}\right)}{\rho_1^{\frac{1}{2}} \quad \rho_2^{\frac{1}{2}}} \quad \dots\dots\dots\dots \quad (22)$$

Substituting Eqs. 21 and 22 into Eq. 18, the displacement expression

$$v = \frac{\sigma\,\rho_1^{\frac{1}{2}}\,\rho_2^{\frac{1}{2}}\,(1 + \mu)}{E}\left[2\,(1 + \mu)\,\sin\left(\frac{\theta_1 + \theta_2}{2}\right)\right.$$

$$\left. - \frac{y\,\rho}{\rho_1\,\rho_2}\,\cos\left(\theta - \frac{\theta_1 + \theta_2}{2}\right)\right]\dots\dots\dots\dots \quad (23)$$

Eq. 23 consists of two parts, the displacement as a result of uniform stress, σ,

$$v = \frac{\sigma\,y}{E}\left(1 - \mu - 2\,\mu^2\right)\dots\dots\dots\dots \quad (24)$$

and the singularity condition. Only the displacement caused by the singularity is of interest, thus Eq. 24 must be subtracted from Eq. 23 in calculations for v_i.

The coefficient d_{ij} is the displacement of the concrete at y_i due to a unit load at y_j neglecting the restraining effect of the reinforcing wire. The solution for the displacement of a point in an infinite medium because of two equal and opposite forces is known. However, the medium in the present situation has a crack that tends to "soften" it, and a correction must be added to the displacement of the solid medium. A crack is actually two stress free surfaces in the solid. The correction or additional displacement can be computed by creating a crack in the solid and finding the displacement of any point due to the creation of the crack. This can be accomplished by applying the stress distribution from the unit load at point y_j in an equal and opposite sense over the region in which the crack is located. The additional displacement of any point because of this assumed internal (negative) pressure in the crack is the required correction.

W. R. Dean, H. W. Parsons, and D. W. Sneddon[13] present the solution for the displacement caused by two equal and opposite forces in an infinite solid medium, as shown in Fig. 5. It is assumed that the bond forces between the concrete and steel are uniform around the surface of the rod, and the resultant of the bond forces can be assumed to act along the center line of the rod. Therefore, the unit forces for computing the influence coefficient d_{ij} should also be

13 "A Type of Stress Distribution on the Surface of a Semi-Infinite Elastic Solid," by W. R. Dean, H. W. Parson, and D. W. Sneddon, Proceedings, Cambridge Philosophical Society, Vol. 40, 1944, p. 5.

applied at the center line of the rod and the displacement found at the surface of the rod. The coefficients are computed, neglecting the restraining effect of the rod, but the position of the rod establishes the geometric position of the forces for computing the influence coefficients. Referring to Fig. 5, r_2 represents the radius of the rod, the y-axis the center line of the rod, and D is a point on the surface of the rod. The unit loads (P = 1) are located at the positions $\pm y_j$ and D is the point (z = y_i) at which the displacement is sought.

The displacement for two opposite and equal forces[13] of magnitude $8 \pi G(Q + 2G)/(Q + G)$ is

$$v = \frac{\left(y_i + y_j\right)^2}{R_1^3} - \frac{\left(y_i - y_j\right)^2}{R_2^3} + \frac{Q + 3G}{Q + G}\left(\frac{1}{R_1} - \frac{1}{R_2}\right) \quad \ldots \ldots (25)$$

in which

$$R_1^2 = r_2^2 + \left(y_i + y_j\right)^2 , \; R_2^2 = r_2^2 + \left(y_i - y_j\right)^2 \quad \ldots \ldots \ldots (26)$$

and the symbols Q and G are Lame's constants and are defined for plane strain as

$$Q = \frac{E \mu}{(1 + \mu)(1 - 2\mu)} \quad \ldots \ldots \ldots \ldots \ldots (27a)$$

and

$$G = \frac{E}{2(1 + \mu)} \quad \ldots \ldots \ldots \ldots \ldots \ldots (27b)$$

Expressed in the symbols adopted for use in this paper, the displacement at y_i because of a unit load at y_j, without the correction for the existence of the crack, is

$$d'_{ij} = \frac{1}{B}\left[\frac{\left(y_i + y_j\right)^2}{R_1^3} - \frac{\left(y_i - y_j\right)^2}{R_2^3} + \frac{Q + 3G}{Q + G}\left(\frac{1}{R_1} + \frac{1}{R_2}\right)\right] \quad \ldots \ldots (28)$$

in which

$$B = \frac{8\pi G (Q + 2G)}{(Q + G)} \quad \ldots \ldots \ldots \ldots \ldots \ldots (29)$$

The unit forces create a stress distribution in the x-z plane given[13] by

$$\sigma y = \left[\frac{-12 G y_j^3}{\left(r^2 + y_j^2\right)^{\frac{5}{2}}} - \frac{4 G^2 y_j}{(Q + G)\left(r^2 + y_j^2\right)^{\frac{3}{2}}}\right]\frac{1}{B} \quad \ldots \ldots \ldots (30)$$

in which r is the radial distance to any point in the x-z plane. With the aid of Eq. 30 the average stress over the area occupied by the crack can be calculated. The particular procedure that is used is unimportant herein. The results presented herein were obtained by dividing the crack area into segments and obtaining the stress at the center of each segment. The sum of each stress multiplied by the area of the appropriate segment yielded the total force over the area and, dividing by the area of the crack, the average stress was calculated. It is necessary to multiply the calculated stress by four, to account for the four adjacent rods. The resulting average stress, $\bar{\sigma}$, is the stress to be superimposed over the crack area, with opposite sign, in order to provide the necessary displacement correction.

The displacement caused by the creation of the crack as a traction free surface is determined in a straightforward manner. Eq. 23 and 24, which yield displacements in the vicinity of a crack caused by remote tension σ, also apply for the case of a crack with internal pressure in a stress-free medium. The correction to be added to Eq. 28, is then

$$
d''_{ij} = \frac{\bar{\sigma}\rho_1^{\frac{1}{2}}\rho_2^{\frac{1}{2}}(1 + \mu)}{E} \left[2\,(1 + \mu)\,\sin\left(\frac{\theta_1 + \theta_2}{2}\right) \right.
$$
$$
\left. - \frac{y_i\,\rho}{\rho_1\rho_2} \cos\left(\theta - \frac{\theta_1 + \theta_2}{2}\right) \right] - \frac{\bar{\sigma}\,y_i}{E}\left(1 - \mu - 2\mu^2\right) \quad \ldots\ldots(31)
$$

The term d_{ij} is the sum of d'_{ij} and d''_{ij}.

With calculated values of v_i and d_{ij}, the forces P_j can be determined from Eq. 13 for any stress, σ. The pressure, p, over the area occupied by the crack (neglecting the existence of the crack) caused by all of the forces P_j along the four rods adjacent to the crack can then be determined and substituted into Eq. 15. A comparison of the resulting value of K_T with the critical value, K_C, indicates whether or not the crack is stable for the selected stress level, σ.

CRITICAL STRESS INTENSITY FACTOR FOR CONCRETE

Quantitative calculations for permissible stress levels below which internal flaws in concrete are stable, for a given reinforcement spacing, require a knowledge of the critical stress intensity factor K_C (or G_C). A procedure for obtaining such values from notched beams in bending has been examined by Kaplan.[11] His tests indicate a G_C value on the order of 0.1 in.-lb per sq in. Kaplan also calculates the theoretical value of G_C from values of the surface energy of tobermorite, the major constituent of portland cement, and of quartz. S. Brunauer[14] has found that the surface energy, T, of tobermorite is approximately 0.0022 in.lb- per sq in. Assuming a mix ratio of one part cement to three parts quartzite, and assuming a surface energy for quartzite of 0.0054 in.-lb per sq in., Kaplan computes a surface energy for the mix of 0.0046 in.-

[14] "The Surface Energy of Tobermorite," by S. Brunauer, D. L. Kantro, and C. H. Weise, Canadian Journal of Chemistry, Vol. 37, 1959.

lb per sq in. The resulting value of G_c, equal to 2T, is then on the order of 0.01 in.-lb per sq in. which is approximately one-tenth of the value experimentally determined by Kaplan.

Values of G_c used in this analysis were obtained by a procedure that is more commonly used in obtaining G_c values for metals. Concrete plates, similar in geometry to Fig. 1, were cast with centrally located slots and broken in tension. The plates were 2.5 in. thick, 24 in. wide, and 32 in. long. The

FIG. 6.—RUPTURED SPECIMEN AFTER TEST FOR G_c OF CONCRETE

central slots varied from 2 in. to 12 in. in length. Stress and crack length at failure were substituted into the plain strain expression

$$G_c = \frac{\pi \, \sigma^2 \, a}{E} \left(1 - \mu^2\right) \dots\dots\dots\dots\dots (32)$$

for determination of G_c.

A typical test arrangement is shown in Fig. 6, and test results are plotted in Fig. 7. The results show a scatter of values from about approximately 0.03 to 0.07 in.-lb per sq in. The values decrease generally with a decrease in crack size. The trend indicates a value of approximately 0.02 to 0.03 in.-lb per sq in. at very small crack sizes, and these values were selected for use in subsequent calculations. It should be emphasized, however, that no correction was made for possible slow crack growth prior to fracture, and the computed values of G_C, based on original crack length, are somewhat in error.

Slow crack extension with increasing load is observed in notched beam-bending fracture tests of concrete. This indicates that a large strain zone, similar to the plastic zone for a crack in a metal, is forming and growing.

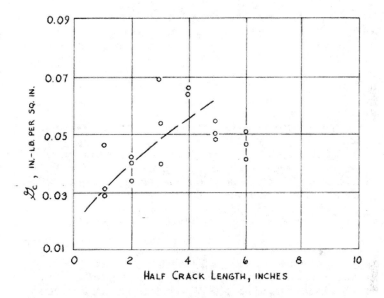

FIG. 7.—EXPERIMENTAL VALUES FOR G_c

In concrete, this zone is the locus of small cracks. In applications considered herein, the crack extension is too small to have acquired a characteristic size "large-strain" zone, and the resistance G_c is therefore small. The magnitude of G_c is expected to be an increasing function of crack size. This is verified by the trend of the data ploted in Fig. 7.

THEORETICAL RESULTS

The procedure for calculating the terms v_i and d_{ij}, for a variety of combinations of wire diameter and spacing, was programmed for repeated solution on an electronic digital computer. The values of v_i and d_{ij} were obtained from the equations previously examined, and the simultaneous equations, represented by Eq. 13, were solved for the forces P_j. The average compressive stress over the area occupied by the crack, because of all the forces P_j along the four rods adjacent to the crack, is the negative internal pressure, p, used in Eq. 15. It should be remembered that the existence of the crack is temporarily ignored in calculating the average compressive stress over the area occupied by the crack, and the superposition of this average stress, in an opposite sense (internal negative pressure), is the mechanical equivalent of creating the crack.

All calculations are performed for an assumed remote tension of 1,000 psi. The internal crack pressure, p, is computed, as previously noted, and the total stress intensity factor thus obtained, from Eq. 15, is compared to the value of K_c (derived from the known value of G_c). If K_T is less than K_c, the remote stress may be increased by the indicated ratio and, by the same token, the remote stress may have to be reduced if K_T is greater than K_c.

The results of twelve solutions for steel percentages (by volume) of 2.5%, 5.0%, and 7.0% are shown in Fig. 8. The ordinate is cracking stress (the stress at which the assumed disk-shaped crack propagates beyond the bounds of the four adjacent wires) and the abscissa is the center to center wire spacing.

As a step in calculating the cracking stresses of Fig. 8, the maximum value of the interaction force P_j is also obtained. Adjustment of the remote stress to achieve total K_T equal to K_c, as previously considered, also adjusts the forces P_j. Thus, for each point on Fig. 8, there is a corresponding maximum corrected force, P_j, which, when divided by the surface area of the wire over the interval h, yields the maximum bond stress, τ, along the wire. These values are plotted in Fig. 9 as a function of wire spacing.

Fig. 8 is significant in that it indicates true two-phase behavior at the smaller spacings. For any percentage of steel, the smaller the spacing, the higher is the cracking stress. For spacings on the order of 0.4 in., for 2.5% of steel, the cracking stress is approximately 600 psi, and for a spacing of 0.2 in., the cracking stress rises to over 800 psi. The curves show a steady decrease in cracking stress at larger spacings but it should be recognized that it is assumed that a crack exists with a diameter equal to the wire spacing. This is unrealistic at the larger spacings and conventional tensile stresses govern.

Because the allowable stress increases with a decrease in spacing, it is to be expected that the bond stress at cracking would increase with decreased spacing. This is indicated in Fig. 9. The higher stresses should be anticipated, because as the spacing decreases, the size of wire decreases, and its surface area per unit length decreases. However, it must be observed that the ratio between the bond stresses will not be the same as the ratio of the corresponding cracking stress. For instance, consider the two solutions listed in Table 1. The allowable stress for 7.0% steel is 14% greater than that for 2.5% steel, but the bond stress is 97% greater. It may be possible to develop the bond of 453 psi and not 890 psi for cases with 7% steel. In other words, the heavier reinforced specimen is stiffer or more brittle and could fail in bond long before the specimen with only a third of the steel for almost equal allowable stress. This is an important concept both structurally and economically. It is possible to have nearly the same allowable stress for two different designs, one with one-third the steel of the other. Over-reinforcing is not only more expensive, but actually produces a weaker structural unit.

Fig. 8 is based on an assumed G_c value of 0.02 in.-lb per sq in. The theoretical cracking strength as a function of wire spacing for a G_c value of 0.03 in.-lb per sq in. is shown in Fig. 10. The curves are similar in all respects to those of Fig. 8 except that the cracking stresses are uniformly higher.

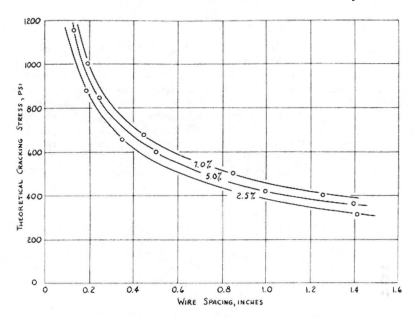

FIG. 8.—CRACKING STRESS AS A FUNCTION OF WIRE SPAC-
ING (G_c = 0.02 in.-lb per sq in.)

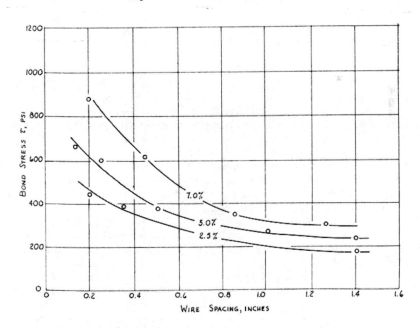

FIG. 9.—MAXIMUM BOND STRESS AS A FUNCTION OF SPAC-
ING (G_c = 0.02 in.-lb per sq in.)

EXPERIMENTAL EVIDENCE OF CRACK ARREST MECHANISM

The curves in Figs. 8 and 10 indicate that the tensile strength of concrete increases in proportion to the inverse square root of the reinforcement spacing. A suitable area of experimentation for verfication of these theoretical conclusions is the testing of reinforced concrete beams in bending. Results of such tests, performed in connection with this study, have been previously reported by the authors.[5] The test data are reviewed subsequently, however, and are evaluated in terms of the theoretical relationships previously noted.

A series of beams with closely spaced wire reinforcement were tested in bending. The beams were 3 in. wide, 5 in. deep, and 6 ft 6 in. long. The beams were supported over a span of 6 ft and loaded at their third points. The only aggregate used was sand. The water-cement ratio was 0.45, and the sand-cement ratio was 2.50.

The lower (tension) region of the beams were reinforced with continuous wires arranged as shown in Fig. 11. The percentage of steel was maintained at 1.47% but the spacing between wires was varied. Vertical and horizontal spacings were not always equal inasmuch as a limited variety of wire diameters were available, and it was sometimes necessary to adjust the ratio of vertical to horizontal spacing to satisfy the requirement of constant steel per-

TABLE 1

Steel percentage	Wire radius, in inches	Spacing, in inches	Cracking stress, in psi	Max., in psi
7.0	0.0312	0.20	1000	890
2.5	0.0174	0.20	878	453

centage. The effective spacing is calculated as the average of vertical and horizontal spacings.

It is argued that an increase in tensile cracking strength of the concrete will have a beneficial effect on the ultimate strength of the beams. This is despite the fact that the nominal extreme fiber tension stress at ultimate load will be greater than the cracking strength of the concrete. At extreme fiber post-cracking stages, the crack will not penetrate to the neutral axis, as is the case with conventionally reinforced beams, but it will be arrested at a lower stress region in the interior of the beam. The remaining tension zone in the interior of the beam will add slightly to the internal resisting couple, but over-all beneficial effect is expected to be greater than that offered by the added internal moment. Westergaard has pointed out[15] that tension cracks extending to the neutral axis of beams in bending have a detrimental effect on the adjacent compression region. Thus, crack retardation may be expected to enhance the performance of beams in bending to an extent not amenable to direct computation.

The results of the bending tests presented in Fig. 12 support this contention. The ultimate strengths are presented in terms of the dimensionless ratio

[15] "Stresses at a Crack, Size of Crack and Bending of Reinforced Concrete," by H. M. Westergaard, Journal of the American Concrete Institute, Vol. 5 November-December, 1933, p. 93.

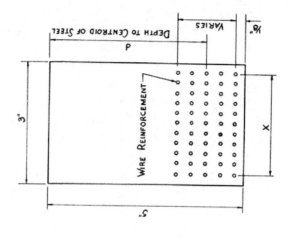

FIG. 11.—TYPICAL CROSS SECTION
OF BEAM

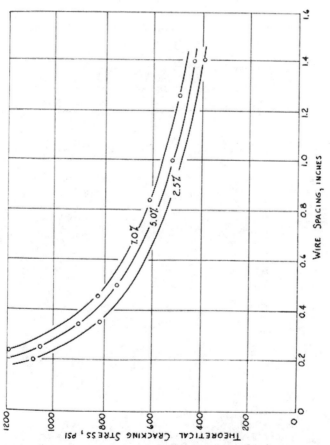

FIG. 10.—THEORETICAL CRACKING STRESS AS A FUNCTION
OF WIRE SPACING (G_c = 0.03 in.-lb per sq in.)

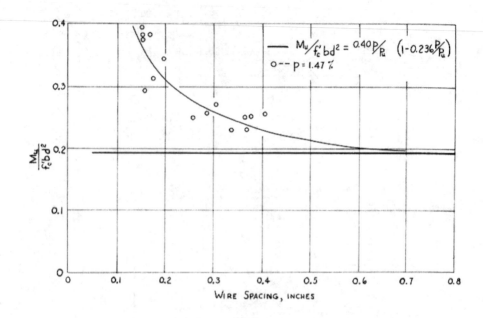

FIG. 12.—RELATIONSHIP BETWEEN ULTIMATE
STRENGTH AND WIRE SPACING

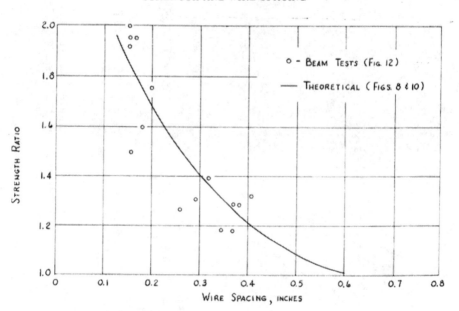

FIG. 13.—EXPERIMENTAL AND THEORETICAL
STRENGTH RATIOS AS A FUNCTION OF
WIRE SPACING

$M_u/f'_c \, bd^2$, in which M_u is the ultimate moment, f'_c denotes the compressive strength of concrete, b represents the beam width, and d refers to the depth to centroid of steel. The data exhibit a definite upward trend below spacings of 0.4 in. to 0.6 in. It should be observed that the only variable reflected in the data of Fig. 12 is the average spacing. As the spacing increases, the results approach the empirical ultimate strength formula for conventional beams. The formula appears in Fig. 12 and is obtained from the Report of the ASCE-ACI Joing Committee on Ultimate Strength Design.[16]

The data in Fig. 12 can be compared more directly with the theoretical curves by replotting, as in Fig. 13, in terms of a strength ratio defined as the ratio of strength at a particular spacing to the strength at large spacings. Thus, the ratio of $M_u/f'_c \, bd^2$ for any point of Fig. 12 to the value of $M_u/f'_c \, bd^2$ given by the solid horizontal line (approximately 0.195) is the strength ratio plotted in Fig. 13. The theoretical curves of Figs. 8 and 10 (extrapolated to a steel percentage of 1.47%) are also replotted in Fig. 13. Inasmuch as the theoretical curves continue to decrease at increasing spacing, however, it is necessary to establish a cut-off point. This point is selected as a spacing of 0.6 in. and is based on the fact that the curve through the data of Fig. 12 indicates no fracture arrest at spacings greater than 0.6 in. The curves for G_c values of 0.02 and 0.03 in.-lb per sq in. are almost identical because the strength ratio is a function of the shape of the curves rather than their absolute values.

The observed agreement between the experimental strength ratios from the beam tests is in good agreement with the theoretical ratios and provides experimental verification of the proposed mechanism.

CONCLUSIONS

Application of linear-elastic fracture mechanics to reinforced concrete indicates that the relatively low tensile strength of concrete is not inherent to the material but can be avoided with suitable reinforcement arrangements. At appropriate small spacings, incipient flaws are prevented from enlarging and propagating throughout the tension zone. The result is a true two-phase material that exhibits strength properties not restricted by the characteristics of each separate phase.

The engineering significance of these concepts, when reduced to practical application, is of importance to structures that are sensitive to crack formation. Of special importance in this respect are highways and airfields, and marine installations and liquid containers such as tanks and pipelines.

The existence of a crack arrest mechanism in closely spaced wire reinforced concrete also suggests that such a material could be expected to offer high fatigue and impact resistance.

ACKNOWLEDGMENTS

The results reported herein are abstracted from a study of fracture arrest mechanisms in reinforced concrete performed by Gordon B. Batson and pre-

---

[16] "Report of ASCE-ACI Joint Committee on Ultimate Strength Design," Proc. Sep. No. 809, ASCE, Vol. 81, October, 1955.

sented to the Carnegie Institute of Technology, Pittsburgh, Pa. in partial fulfilment of the requirements for the degree Doctor of Philosophy. Funds for this study were made available through a grant from the National Science Foundation.

The writers are grateful to George R. Irwin who reviewed the manuscript and offered many helpful comments and suggestions.

A TRIBUTE TO

"Studies of the Physical Properties of Hardened Portland Cement Paste"

by T.C. Powers and T.L. Brownyard

Foreword by H.J.H. Brouwers

In their pioneering work, Powers and Brownyard were the first to systematically investigate the reaction of cement and water and the formation of hydrated cement paste. In the late 1940s, in a series of landmark papers, they presented a model for the cement paste in which unreacted cement, free water (capillary porosity), and the hydration product (which is porous in itself, that is, the gel porosity) were distinguished. They introduced the concept of nonevaporable water (water retained in P-dried state) and gel water (additional water retained upon saturation): their specific volumes are lower than that of free water, causing chemical shrinkage and creating capillary space. Careful execution of experiments resulted in the quantity and specific volume of both nonevaporable water and gel water. Powers and Brownyard were among the first who employed new theories and techniques such as adsorption, B.E.T surface area, XRD, and calorimetry. Critical paste properties were measured by extensive and carefully executed experiments, including the amount of retained water and the chemical shrinkage associated with the hydration reaction. These properties were further related to the content of the four most important clinker phases, viz. alite, belite, aluminate, and ferrite. Additionally, the composition of the cement paste was related to engineering properties such as compressive strength, shrinkage, porosity, water permeability, and freezing/thawing resistance. The impact of this standard work is paramount and their concepts and the results are used in contemporary cement and concrete science (Taylor (1997), Neville (2000)). Czernin (1959), Locher (1975), Hansen (1986), Jensen and Hansen (2001), Brouwers (2004, 2005, 2007), and Livingston et al. (2007) presented more detailed discussions on the authors' work, validated and confirmed the key findings using contemporary techniques, and also extended the approach to new research areas.

Both Powers and Brownyard performed their research at the Portland Cement Association (PCA), at that time located in Chicago, Illinois. Information about the life and work of Dr. Treval Clifford Powers can be collected, but Dr. Theodore Lucius Brownyard seems somehow to have disappeared, no further records of him after 1948 can be found by this author.

Dr. Treval Clifford Powers;
February 8, 1900, Palouse (Washington),
June 30, 1997, Green Valley (Arizona).

Dr. Powers received a Bachelor of Arts degree from Willamette University in 1925, majoring in chemistry. He worked for PCA from 1930 until his retirement in 1965. For the next 7 years, he taught, lectured, and consulted internationally in the field of cementitious materials before moving to Arizona.

On the occasion of his retirement, a symposium was sponsored by the Highway Research Board, to which workers from all over the world contributed. In 1966, it was published as the monumental Special Report No. 90 by the Highway Research Board (1966).

Probably unknown to most people working in the field of cement and concrete is that after his retirement, Dr. Powers studied "The Phenomenon of Inflation." His unorthodox economic theory resulted in the book *Leakage: The Bleeding of the American Economy* (Benchmark, 1996), which has been hailed as a pivotal work in the field of macroeconomics. Besides his research on the structure of fresh and hardened cement paste, Dr. Powers is also known for his mortar and concrete research on consistency, workability, rheology, durability, unsoundness, shrinkage and swelling, abrasion resistance, sulfate resistance, frost resistance etc. and is author of the book *The Fresh Properties of Concrete* (1968). Dr. Powers won the ACI Wason Research Medal in 1933, 1940, and together with Dr. Brownyard in 1948. He became an Honorary Member of ACI in 1961 and received the ACI Arthur R. Anderson Award in 1976. He also received the Sanford E. Thompson Award of the American Society for Testing and Materials (ASTM) in 1957.

Dr. Brownyard was born in Ensley Township, Newaygo County, Michigan, on June 6, 1905. In 1930, he entered The Johns Hopkins University in Baltimore as Francis P. Garvan Fellow at Large, and obtained his Doctor of Philosophy degree in 1934. His PhD thesis is entitled "The Retention of Water Vapor by Alumina," and in this work advanced techniques (P-drying, water-vapor adsorption) were employed that were also used later in his work with Dr. Powers and reported in their paper series. Dr. Brownyard joined the research group of Dr. Powers at the PCA in 1937, where he stayed until 1943 when he was called up by the Navy as a Lieutenant U.S. Naval Reserve. He served in the United States Naval Air Transportation Service (Navigation) throughout the war years and remained with the Navy until at least May 1948. The results reported in their paper series from 1947-1948 therefore concern their work done at the PCA many years before.

What follows in this special volume is the last part (Part 9) of their series, p. 933-992, which comprises a comprehensive summary of the eight foregoing parts. The reader is, however, warmly encouraged to read all nine parts of this remarkable landmark publication.

References

Brouwers, H.J.H. (2004), The Work of Powers and Brownyard Revisted: Part 1, Cement and Concrete Research, Vol. 34, p. 1697-1716.

Brouwers, H.J.H. (2005), The Work of Powers and Brownyard Revisted: Part 2, Cement and Concrete Research, Vol. 35, p. 1922-1936.

Brouwers, H.J.H. (2007), The Work of Powers and Brownyard Revisted: Part 3, Proceedings 12th International Congress on the Chemistry of Cement, Montréal, 8-13th July 2007, W1-05.6, Eds. J.J. Beaudoin, J.M. Makar and L. Raki, National Research Council of Canada, Montreal, Canada.

Czernin, W. (1959), Die physikalische Beschaffenheit der Hydratationsprodukte, Zement und Beton, Vol. 16, p. 10-15 (in German).

Hansen, T.C. (1986), Physical Structure of Hardened Cement Paste, A Classical Approach, Materials and Structures, Vol. 19, p. 423-436.

Highway Research Board (1966), Symp. on Structure of Portland Cement Paste and Concrete, Highway Res. Board Spec. Rep. No. 90, Washington D.C., U.S..

Jensen, O.M., and Hansen, P.F. (2001), Water-Entrained Cement-Based Materials I. Principles and Theoretical Background, Cement and Concrete Research, Vol. 31, p. 647-654.

Livingston, R.A., Nemes, N.M., and Neumann, D.A. (2007), States of water in hydrated cement paste: Powers and Brownyard revisited, Proceedings 12th International Congress on the Chemistry of Cement, Montréal, 8-13th July 2007, T1-03.3, Eds. J.J. Beaudoin, J.M. Makar and L. Raki, National Research Council of Canada, Montreal, Canada.

Locher, F.W. (1975), Volumenänderungen bei der Zementerhärtung, Sonderheft aus Zement und Beton, Heft 85/86, p. 1-4 (in German).

Neville, A.M. (2000), Properties of Concrete (4th ed.), Prentice Hall/Pearson, Harlow, U.K..

Taylor, H.F.W. (1997), Cement chemistry (2nd ed.), Thomas Telford, London, U.K..

H.J.H. Brouwers, *Department of Civil Engineering, Faculty of Engineering Technology, University of Twente*

The author studied Mechanical Engineering at Eindhoven University of Technology (the Netherlands) from 1981 until 1986. After his study, he worked at Akzo Nobel Central Research in Arnhem (NL) on plastic production processes and products. He completed a PhD thesis on the heat and mass transfer in plastic heat exchangers and condensers in 1990. Since 1992, he has been appointed at the University of Twente. His research interests include sustainable building and construction materials. He was appointed a Guest Professor at Wuhan University of Technology (China) in 2007.

Title 43-5a —a part of PROCEEDINGS, AMERICAN CONCRETE INSTITUTE Vol. 43

JOURNAL
of the
AMERICAN CONCRETE INSTITUTE
(copyrighted)

Vol. 18 No. 2   7400 SECOND BOULEVARD, DETROIT 2, MICHIGAN   October 1946

Studies of the Physical Properties of Hardened Portland Cement Paste*

By T. C. POWERS†
Member American Concrete Institute

and T. L. BROWNYARD‡

IN NINE PARTS

Part 1. A Review of Methods That Have Been Used for Studying the Physical Properties of Hardened Portland Cement Paste
Part 2. Studies of Water Fixation
Appendix to Part 2
Part 3. Theoretical Interpretation of Adsorption Data
Part 4. The Thermodynamics of Adsorption
Appendix to Parts 3 and 4
Part 5. Studies of the Hardened Paste by Means of Specific-Volume Measurements
Part 6. Relation of Physical Characteristics of the Paste to Compressive Strength
Part 7. Permeability and Absorptivity
Part 8. The Freezing of Water in Hardened Portland Cement Paste
Part 9. General Summary of Findings on the Properties of Hardened Portland Cement Paste

SYNOPSIS

This paper deals mainly with data on water fixation in hardened portland cement paste, the properties of evaporable water, the density of the solid substance, and the porosity of the paste as a whole. The studies of the evaporable water include water-vapor-adsorption characteristics and the thermodynamics of adsorption. The discussions include the following topics:

1. Theoretical interpretation of adsorption data
2. The specific surface of hardened portland cement paste
3. Minimum porosity of hardened paste
4. Relative amounts of gel-water and capillary water
5. The thermodynamics of adsorption
6. The energy of binding of water in hardened paste
7. Swelling pressure

*Received by the Institute July 8, 1946—scheduled for publication in seven installments; October 1946 to April, 1947.
†Manager of Basic Research, Portland Cement Assn. Research Laboratory, Chicago 10, Ill.
‡Navy Dept., Washington, D. C., formerly Research Chemist, Portland Cement Assn. Research Laboratory, Chicago 10, Ill.

FOREWORD

This paper deals with the properties of hardened portland cement paste. The purpose of the experimental work on which it is based was to bring to light as much information as is possible by the methods of colloid chemistry and physics. Owing to the war, the original program, which included only a part of the field to be explored, was not completed. Moreover, the interpretation of the data is incomplete, partly because of the inability of the authors to comprehend their meaning, and partly because of the need of data from experiments yet to be made.

Although the work is incomplete, it represents a considerable amount of time and effort. Experimental work began in a small way in 1934 and continued until January 1943. Some additional work was done in 1945 during the preparation of this paper. The first three years was a period of intermittent work in which little of permanent value was accomplished beyond the development of apparatus and procedures. This phase of the work presented many problems, some of which have never been solved to our complete satisfaction.

The interpretation of the results of experiments also presented many difficulties. During the course of our experiments, important new developments in colloid science were coming to light through a series of papers from other laboratories. It was necessary to study these papers as they appeared and to seek their applications to our problems. The result is that the theory on which much of our present interpretation is based is one that did not exist when our work began and is one that is still in the process of development. The reader may note that many of the papers referred to in Part 3 were not published until 1940 or later.

The theory referred to is that of multimolecular adsorption by Brunauer, Emmett, and Teller as first given in 1938 and as amplified in the paper by Brunauer, Deming, Deming, and Teller in 1940. In justification for the use of such a recent and unfinished development, we may note in the first place that a remarkable number of papers by various authors have appeared since 1940 strongly supporting the kind of use that we have made of the theory, particularly the estimation of surface area. In the second place, the basic conclusions reached through the use of the theory might have been reached from a strictly empirical analysis of the data. However, it is difficult to imagine how a picture of the hardened paste as detailed as the one presented in this paper could have been drawn without adopting theoretically justified assumptions.

The paper is composed of nine parts. Part 1 contains a review of previous work done in this field and discusses various experimental methods. Part 2 elaborates on the principal method used in the present study, namely, the measurement of water-fixation. It also presents the empirical aspects of the data so that the reader may become familiar with facts to be dealt with.

Part 3 presents the theories upon which an interpretation of the data in Part 2 can be based. It gives also a partial analysis of most of the experimental data given in Part 2 in the light of the adopted basis of interpretation. Part 4 is a discussion of the thermodynamics of moisture-content changes in hardened paste and the phenomena accompanying those changes. It is thus an extension of the earlier discussion of theory.

In Part 5 data are presented pertaining to the volumes of different phases in the paste. The interpretation of these data involves the use of factors developed in the preceding parts of the paper. The final result is a group of diagrams illustrating five different phases, the relative proportions of each, and how those relative proportions change as hydration progresses.

The relationship between the physical characteristics of the hardened cement paste and compressive strength of mortars is discussed in Part 6. A similar discussion of permeability and absorptivity is given in Part 7.

A study of the freezing of water in hardened paste is presented in Part 8. The conditions under which ice can exist in the paste are described and empirical equations are given for the amounts of water that are freezable under designated conditions.

The properties of portland cement paste as they appear in the light of these studies are described in Part 9. This part amounts to a summary of the outcome of the study, at its present incomplete stage, without details of experimental procedures, or theoretical background.

As mentioned in the first paragraph, a particular point of view as to the meaning of the data has been adopted. Specifically, we have assumed, on the basis of evidence given in the paper, that the various phenomena discussed are predominantly of physical rather than chemical nature. The result of the study therefore constitutes a hypothesis, or series of hypotheses, rather than a rigorous presentation of established facts. Considering the present state of our knowledge, we believe this policy to be more fruitful than one of trying to maintain a strictly unbiased view as to the meaning of the data. As written, the paper represents the thinking of one group of workers (influenced, of course, by many others), and it implicitly invites independent investigations of the same field by any who may have good reason to adopt a different point of view. To this end, we have appended tabulations of the original data.

Though we thus concede the possibility of other interpretations, we nevertheless feel confident that a large part of the present interpretation will withstand logical criticism. However, it seems very likely that corrections and changes of emphasis will develop as experimental work continues, and as further advances are made in fundamental colloid science.

The paper is directed primarily toward all who are engaged in research on portland cement and concrete. However, it may be of considerable interest to many who seek only to understand concrete as they work with it in the field. Studied in connection with earlier papers on the characteristics of paste in the plastic state,* this paper affords a comprehensive, though incomplete, picture of the physical nature of portland cement paste. It, therefore, pertains to any phase of concrete technology that involves the physical properties of the cement paste. This means that the paper should find application to most phases of concrete technology.

For the most part, the reader will find few items of data that bear directly on specific questions or problems. Successful application of this study to research or practical technology requires some degree of comprehension of the work in its entirety. Consequently, it is not likely that a single, casual reading will reveal much that is of value to one not already familiar with the methods and background of this type of investigation.

ACKNOWLEDGMENTS

We are deeply indebted to Mark L. Dannis and Harold Tarkow, not only for their long and painstaking labor with the various experiments, but also for their contributions to an understanding of the results. Mark Dannis made most of the adsorption and specific-volume measurements and Harold Tarkow performed the freezing experiments reported in Part 8.

We are grateful to Gerald Pickett, whose constructive criticism was of great value throughout most of the period of study.

---

*Bull. 2, "The Bleeding of Portland Cement Paste, Mortar and Concrete," by T. C. Powers, P.C.A. Research Laboratory (1939); Bull. 3, "Rate of Sedimentation," by Harold H. Steinour, P.C.A. Research Laboratory (1944), reprinted from *Ind. Eng. Chem. 36*, 618; 840; 901 (1944); Bull. 4, "Further Studies of the Bleeding of Portland Cement Paste," by Harold H. Steinour, P.C.A. Research Laboratory (1945).

We are especially indebted to Harold H. Steinour, who took time from his own work to carry on the final volumenometer work described in Part 5. Also, he helped prepare the discussion of thermodynamics in Part 4 and gave much valuable criticism of various other parts of the paper. ·

To Virginia Atherton, who made many of the hundreds of computations, typed the manuscript, and corrected printer's proof we express our kindest thanks.

Part 1.   A Review of Methods That Have Been Used for Studying the Physical Properties of Hardened Portland Cement

CONTENTS

Starting as a suspension of cement particles in water, portland cement paste becomes a solid as the result of chemical and physical reactions between the constituents of the cement and water. A solidified paste of typical characteristics is capable of giving up or absorbing a volume of water equal to as much as 50 per cent of the apparent volume of the paste. These facts engender the idea that whatever the chemical constitution of the new material produced by chemical reaction, the new material is laid down in such a way as to enclose water-filled, interconnected spaces. That is, the hydration product appears to be not a continuous, homogeneous solid, but rather it appears to be composed of a large number of primary units bound together to form a porous structure. It seems self-evident that the manner in which the primary units are united, that is, the physical structure of the paste, is closely related to the quality of the paste and is therefore something about which we should be well informed.

Freyssinet[1]* discerned the need for knowledge of paste structure and devised a hypothesis about the setting and hardening process and about the structure of the hardened paste. Giertz-Hedström,[2] an active contributor to this subject, has given an excellent review of publications on this subject. This review, together with Bogue's[3] earlier one of a slightly different aspect of the subject, obviates the necessity of an extensive historical review at this time.

A program of studies of the properties of the hardened paste was begun in this laboratory in 1934. It has consisted mainly of studies of the fixation of water, but has also included measurements of the heat-effects accompanying the regain of water by the previously dried paste, measurements of the freezing of the water in the saturated paste, and various other related matters.

This work has yielded a considerable amount of information on the physical aspects of hardened paste. It contributes to the knowledge of the chemical constitution of the hydration products only in a negative way; that is, it shows that some of the current information on the constitution of the hydration products must be incorrect. Later parts of this paper will give an account of these studies.

METHODS FOR STUDYING THE PHYSICAL PROPERTIES OF THE HARDENED PASTE†

The question of structure can be broken down into three parts: first, the question as to the chemical constitution of the hydration products, which includes the question of structure of the ultimate parts; second, the question of the structure of the smallest primary aggregations of the ultimate parts; third, the question of how the primary aggregations are assembled and how they are held together. A review of some of the work done by earlier investigators follows.

Microscopic examinations

The light-microscope. The effectiveness of the microscope as a means of studying the structure of the hardened paste is limited because the

---

*See references end of Part 1.
†See also the review by Giertz-Hedström (Ref. 3).

units of the essential part of the structure are too small to be seen. The results obtained by Brown and Carlson[4] are typical. They, like others, observed that the hardened paste is predominantly "amorphous," so far as the microscope can reveal. Embedded in this amorphous mass are the remnants of unhydrated clinker grains, crystals of calcium hydroxide, and sometimes crystals of other compounds.

Kühl[5] reported that thin sections of hardened cement paste showed ". . . a residue of undecomposed cement particles, separated by a gray and only slightly differentiated mass which gives a feebly diffused luminescence in polarized light. Even under the highest magnification individual particles cannot be distinguished in this material, which is obviously almost entirely ultramicroscopic in structure." However, on examining the same specimens 20 years later he found that ". . . the passage of years had resulted in fundamental changes. No longer (was the material) uniform and only slightly differentiated under polarized light as was the case a few months after their preparation. They now showed a definitely increased (polarized-light) transmission and, most noteworthy of all, their properties were markedly different according to the percentages of water with which they had been gaged. The specimens gaged with the greatest amount of water showed the greatest changes while those mixed with the least water had undergone considerably less modification." The changes mentioned were such as to suggest that the originally colloidal material had gradually changed toward the microcrystalline state, the change being greater the higher the original water content.

Useful information has been obtained by microscopic observations of the hydration of cement in the presence of relatively large quantities of water. But it is unlikely that the structure developed under these conditions is the same as that developed in pastes; hence, conclusions about the normal structure drawn from observations of this kind are open to question.[6] For example, Le Chatelier[7] observed that when a large quantity of water was used, needlelike crystals of microscopic dimensions soon developed. He concluded from this that similar, though submicroscopic, crystals developed under all conditions.

Brownmiller[8] described the results of microscopic examinations of hardened paste by means of reflected light. The method is a modification of that described by Tavasci[9] and Insley[10] for studying the constitution of clinker. In addition to the use of etchants to bring different phases into contrast, Brownmiller treated the surface with a dye which was taken up by the so-called amorphous material and the microcrystalline phases. Although Brownmiller's primary object was to develop the experimental technique, some of his conclusions concerning the nature of hardened paste and the hydration process are of considerable interest. He found that there was ". . . no microscopic evidence of channeling of water into the interior of cement particles to selectively hydrate any single major constituent. Hydration seems to proceed by the gradual reduction in the size of the particles as a function of the surface exposed." This conclusion seemed to be based on the appearance of the coarser particles that remained unhydrated after the first day.

Brownmiller found that a Type III* cement having a specific surface of 2600 appeared to be almost completely hydrated after one day in a sealed vial and six days in water. A Type I cement having a specific surface of 1800 showed an unhydrated residue of about 15 per cent after one day in a sealed vial and 28 days in water. The water-cement ratio of the original paste was 0.4 by weight in both cases.

The only microcrystalline hydrate mentioned by Brownmiller was calcium hydroxide. This was found as clusters of fine crystals embedded in what Brownmiller called the hydrogel.

Brownmiller found that the etched surface of the 7-day-old paste made of Type I cement showed "an extremely complicated but interesting structure. A close examination . . . shows that the cement hydrogel is not a formless mass but has an intricate structure."

The electron microscope. Eitel[11] used the electron microscope for photographing the hydration products of some of the constituents of portland cement. The article consulted gives almost no details concerning the method of preparing the samples that were photographed. It appears that the samples were taken from dilute suspensions of the hydrated material. Presumably, samples of $Ca(OH)_2$ were taken from saturated or supersaturated "milk of lime" and hydration products of C_3S and C_3A from saturated solutions of water in isobutyl alcohol. The isobutyl alcohol was used to dilute the water and thus make possible a relatively high concentration of the solid with respect to water and at the same time a dilute suspension. Since the isobutyl alcohol was saturated with water, the chemical activity of the water was unaffected by the presence of the isobutyl alcohol.

Several photographs of these preparations (magnifications ranging from 7200 to 36000) were published. The $Ca(OH)_2$ taken from milk of lime as well as that formed from the hydrolysis of C_3S appeared as hemispheres ranging in size from about 0.1 to 0.5 micron. The calcium silicate hydrate appeared as thin crystalline needles about one-half

---

*See A.S.T.M. Designation C150-44 where five types of portland cement are defined as follows:
Type I   —For use in general concrete construction when the special properties specified for Types II, III, IV, and V are not required.
Type II —For use in general concrete construction exposed to moderate sulfate action, or where moderate heat of hydration is required.
Type III—For use when high early strength is required.
Type IV —For use when a low heat of hydration is required.
Type V —For use when high sulfate resistance is required.

micron long. The C_3A appeared mainly as rounded particles ("roses") about 0.1 micron in diameter. Referring to these and apparently to other observations, Eitel concluded that although the hydration products of portland cement are predominantly colloidal, they appear crystalline—not amorphous—to the electron microscope.

Sliepcevich, Gildart, and Katz,[12] reported the results of attempts to photograph the hydration products of portland cement and the major constituents hydrated separately. Most of the photographs published were of samples prepared as follows: 0.5 to 0.75 g of portland cement or a cement constituent was mixed with about 10 cc of purified water and allowed to stand. At the desired age the specimen for photographing was obtained by taking a drop of the supernatant liquid and allowing it to evaporate on a collodion film previously prepared. The material on this film was thus whatever dissolved or suspended material the drop contained.

In some respects the results were like those found by Eitel. Photographs of calcium hydroxide appeared like those of Eitel but whereas Eitel concluded that the particles were hemispheres, Sliepcevich, Gildart, and Katz concluded that they were spheres. From each material the latter investigators usually found material of several geometric forms. Some of the material appeared amorphous and some crystalline. As did Eitel, those investigators found the majority of crystals to be in the colloidal size range.

The significance of these results is open to question until it is known definitely just what relation the samples obtained in the manner described have to the hydration products making up the mass of a hardened cement paste.

X-ray examinations

The results of X-ray examinations were summarized by Giertz-Hedström[13] as follows: "X-ray examinations of hardened cement have so far given little beyond a confirmation of what has been shown by the microscope. The presence of clinker remains and crystallized calcium hydroxide is thus confirmed by Brandenburger.[14] The structure of the main mass, the "cement gel," is, however, such as to give, at least for the present, no clear guidance in the X-ray diagrams. This may be due to its lacking a crystalline structure or other regular fine structure or to the crystals being so small or deformed (for example bent needles) that no definite interferences are obtained."

Bogue and Lerch[15] mention the use of X-ray analysis in connection with microscopic examination. The X-ray confirms the microscopic indication that unaltered beta or gamma dicalcium silicate remained in pastes after 2 years of curing. X-ray diffraction patterns from both hydrated tricalcium silicate and hydrated dicalcium silicate showed at the end of 2 years no evidence of the development of a new crystalline structure such as would be expected if the hydrates were to change from the theoretically unstable gel state to the stable microcrystalline state. As mentioned above, evidence of the beginning of such a change within a period of 20 years was reported by Kühl.

Water fixation

Because direct observation fails to answer many questions concerning the structure, properties, and behavior of hardened portland cement paste, indirect methods of study have been used. The principal one is that of studying the manner in which water is held in the hardened paste.

Isotherms and isobars. The fixation of water by water-containing solids is usually measured in terms of the amounts of water held at various vapor pressures with temperature constant, or in terms of the amounts held at various temperatures with pressure constant. The curves obtained by the first method are called *isotherms.* Those obtained by the second method are called *isobars.* Both of these methods have been used in the study of hardened portland cement paste. The nature of the hydration or dehydration curve depends on the manner in which the water is combined and on other factors to be discussed.

Binding of water in hydroxides. In metallic hydroxides, which represent one class of compounds that may be included among hydrates, the elements of water are present as OH-groups that are strongly bound by the metallic ions. This is usually recognized in writing the formulas of metallic hydroxides; thus, calcium hydroxide is usually given the formula $Ca(OH)_2$ rather than $CaO.H_2O$.

Water bound by covalent bonds. In many hydrates, the water molecule retains its identity to a large degree, i.e., H_2O is a unit in the structure. An example is $MgCl_2.6H_2O$. In this hydrate the six molecules of water are bound to the magnesium ion by covalent bonds and are arranged around the magnesium ion in an octahedral grouping. To indicate this, the formula should be written $Mg(H_2O)_6Cl_2$, for this more nearly represents the structure.

Water bound by hydrogen bonds. There is another type of compound in which the water molecule remains intact and is bound to the compound by one or both of its hydrogen atoms. The molecules so held are said to be bound by hydrogen bonds. $CuSO_4.5H_2O$ and $NiSO_4.7H_2O$ are hydrates in which one of the water molecules is bound in this way.

* * * * *

Water held in a compound by any of the types of bond described above is properly regarded as being chemically bound. The removal of water from such hydrates necessarily gives rise to a new solid phase and hence the isotherms and isobars of these hydrates should show well marked steps in accordance with the phase rule. Fig. 1a gives, for example, the relationship between water content and vapor pressure for the hydrates of copper sulfate.

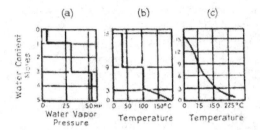

Fig. 1 – Univariant and bivariant dehydration curves

(a) Isothermal p-x curve for $CuSO_4.5H_2O$
(b) Isobaric T-x curve for $Cr_2(SO_4)_3.18H_2O$
    The first $15H_2O$ come off along a univariant curve, the remaining $3H_2O$ being zeolitic
(c) Zeolitic dehydration of green $Cr_2(SO_4)_3.15H_2O$

(Curves and caption from Emeleus & Anderson)

Zeolitic water. One type of microcrystalline hydrate, which comprises the zeolites and several basic salts and hydroxides of bivalent metals, gives smooth isotherms or isobars. Fig. 1c is an example of an isobar from $Cr_2(SO_4)_3.15H_2O$. Water held in this type of compound is called zeolitic water.

According to Emeleus and Anderson[16] zeolitic water is regarded as being packed between the layers of the crystal or in the interstices of the structure. A distinguishing characteristic of zeolitic water is that it may be removed without giving rise to a new solid phase. Its removal may, however, change the spacing between successive layers of the crystal.

Water held in such a way as to exhibit the behavior described above is sometimes referred to as being in a state of zeolitic solution or solid solution.[17]

Lattice water. Emeleus and Anderson[16] distinguish a type of hydrate in which there is water of crystallization "that cannot be supposed to be associated chemically with the principal constituents of the crystal lattice." As an example, they cite potassium alum, $KAl(SO_4)_2.12H_2O$. There is little question that six of the twelve molecules of water are linked to the aluminum ion by covalent bonds. The remaining six molecules are known to be arranged octahedrally around the potassium ion but at such a large distance from it as to suggest to Emeleus and Anderson that the interaction is very weak and hence that the water is not chemically bound to the potassium ion. This perhaps represents a borderline case between chemically bound water and zeolitic water, which is supposed not to be chemically bound. The fact that exactly six molecules of water are associated with the potassium ion is accounted for by the geometry of the crystal lattice. The removal of these six molecules of water presumably gives rise to a new crystalline phase, however, and hence the isobars and isotherms should be stepped. When more information on this type of hydrate becomes available, perhaps many of the examples cited will have to be placed in one of the classifications listed above.

Adsorbed water. In addition to any water held by the chemical forces mentioned above, a small amount per unit of surface is held by surface forces. These forces, physical rather than chemical, are known collectively as van der Waal's forces.[18] If the specific surface of the solid phase is small, the amount so held is usually undetectable. But if the specific surface is very large, as it is for colloidal material, then physically adsorbed water can be a large fraction of the total held under given conditions; indeed, anhydrous solids such as quartz powder can hold relatively large amounts of water by surface adsorption if the powder is extremely fine. Zeolitic water can be regarded as adsorbed water, the "surfaces" in this case being certain planes in the crystal, as described above. The subject of adsorption will be treated much more fully in later sections of this paper.

Interpretation of isobars

Influence of surface adsorption. From what was said above it might appear that by means of isobaric or isothermal dehydration data water held in microcrystalline hydrates could readily be distinguished from that held as zeolite water, in solid solution, or by adsorption. It will be developed below that such a distinction can be drawn under some circumstances but not under others. The complication can best be illustrated by describing the work of Hagiwara.[19] Theoretically, the vapor pressure of the water in a very small crystal of a hydrate should be greater than that of a larger crystal of the same substance at the same temperature. Consequently, a mixture containing various sized crystals should exhibit a range in vapor pressures according to the range in particle size. Practically, the effect is not noticeable unless the particle size range extends into the range of colloidal dimensions. Theoretically, very small natural crystals or very small fragments of large crystals should behave similarly, though not necessarily identically. Consequently, the results of experiments with preparations made by pulverizing macrocrystals should be indicative of the general effects of changing particle size and particle-size range.

Hagiwara pulverized crystalline hydrates and obtained the isobar for each preparation. In one series of experiments, he used $Al_2O_3.3H_2O$ prepared by the method of Bonsdorff.[20] The original crystals were of microscopic size. The preparation was dried to constant weight in a desiccator over concentrated H_2SO_4 to establish the initial water content, which was determined by igniting a portion of the material. Samples thus dried were then heated in an electric oven at 100C for 30 minutes after which they were cooled in a desiccator and weighed. Finally, the amount of residual water was found by ignition. This was repeated on other samples at temperatures ranging from 90 to 220C as indicated in Fig. 2. Heating at 170C and at higher temperatures was continued until further heating caused no more change in the dry weight. The total heating period at these higher temperatures was not less than 5 hours and at 210C was 20 hours.

Although the corners are somewhat rounded, there is a well defined step in the isobar* at approximately 205C, where the water content decreases from 3 molecules to one molecule. This is in good agreement with the result obtained by Weiser and Milligan.[21] The rounded corner is the usual result in such experiments; very sharply defined corners are the exception.

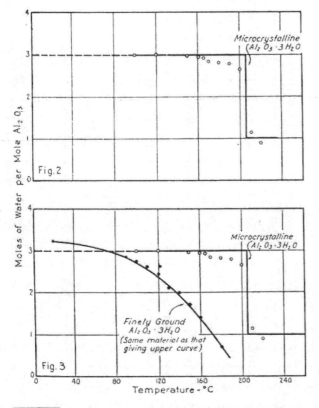

Fig. 2 & 3 – Isobars for
$Al_2O_3.3H_2O$
Data from T. Hagiwara
Alexander: Colloid Chemistry
Vol. I, pp. 647-658
The Chemical Catalog Co.
Inc. (N.Y.) 1926

*Although the curves in Fig. 2 and 3 are called isobars and the text indicates that isobaric conditions were intended, it seems probable that isobaric conditions were not actually maintained. If the heating of the sample was done in an oven in the presence of room air, the actual vapor pressure in the oven would vary with the humidity of the room air and would be different at different temperatures. However, over the temperature range used in the experiment the variations in pressure were probably small. At any rate it is not likely that had strictly isobaric conditions been maintained the outcome would have been significantly different.

Hagiwara then ground a portion of the dried preparation in an agate mortar for 1½ hours, using fine quartz powder as a grinding aid, thus greatly reducing the particle size. The experiments were repeated with this finely ground material with the results shown in Fig. 3, where the results shown in Fig. 2 are reproduced for comparison. A comparison of the curves in Fig. 3 shows three significant effects of reducing the size of the crystals:

(1) All semblance of a step is absent in the curve for the finely ground sample.

(2) The initial water content of the finely ground material is higher by 0.25 mole than that of the unground material. This additional water must have come from the atmosphere during the grinding. (The initial water content is that of the sample after it is dried to constant weight in a desiccator over conc. H_2SO_4.)

(3) The water is lost from the finely ground sample at a much lower temperature than from the unground material.

Hagiwara made a similar series of experiments with $Fe_2O_3.H_2O$ with the results shown in Fig. 4. The curve for the unground macrocrystalline material shows a well defined step. The curve for "Grind A," the shorter period of grinding, still shows a step though the corners are somewhat more rounded than for the unground hydrate and the step occurs at a lower temperature. When the grinding was more prolonged, "Grind B," the step disappeared and the initial water content increased to 1.54 molecules. Grinding had little effect on the temperature at which the final water content was reached.

It appears from Hagiwara's results that a hydrate in which the water is bound by chemical bonds may still yield a smooth isobar if the sample is made up of a mixture of particles of various sizes, the smallest particles being very small. This has a significant bearing on the interpretation of isobars in general. When a solid that has water for one of its con-

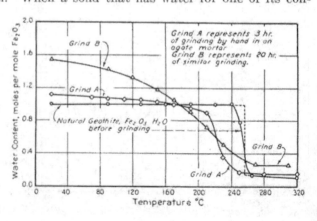

Fig. 4 – Effect of prolonged grinding on the isobars of $Fe_2O_3.H_2O$
Hagiwara, Colloid Chemistry Alexander Ed., Vol. I, pp. 647-58 (1926)

Grind A represents 3 hr. of grinding by hand in an agate mortar
Grind B represents 20 hr. of similar grinding.

Grind B

Grind A

Natural Geothite, $Fe_2O_3.H_2O$ before grinding

Grind B

Grind A

Water Content, moles per mole Fe_2O_3

Temperature °C

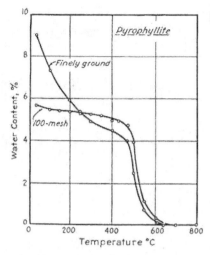

Fig. 5 – Isobar for pyrophyllite
Data from Kelley, Jenny and Brown
Soil Sci. v. 41, p. 260 (1936)

stituents yields a stepped isobar, it can usually* be concluded that the solid is a well crystallized hydrate. When, however, the isobar is a smooth curve without steps, it may represent a sample of the hydrate comprising particles of various sizes or it may represent a material in which the water is not bound by chemical bonds in the usual sense of this term. It appears also that a lack of steps in an isobar is not sufficient evidence that the hydrate has a zeolitic structure, for neither of the hydrates with which Hagiwara experimented was of that nature.

The other effect of fine grinding, namely, the increase in the initial water content brought about by grinding, is fully as significant as the one just mentioned. It must be assumed that the water in excess of that required by the formula is held by forces of a kind different from those that hold the hydrate water. The effect is clearly a surface effect, for the initial water content is much higher after the longer period of grinding than after the shorter period. (Compare "Grind B" with "Grind A" in Fig. 4.) It seems reasonable to suppose that this excess water is held by adsorption forces, i.e., forces which reside in the surface of the crystal and which came into prominence after the specific surface of the hydrate had been greatly increased by grinding.

This aspect of the effect of fine grinding is further emphasized by the results of experiments made by Kelley, Jenny, and Brown.[22] These authors studied the effect of grinding on the isobars of clay minerals. See Fig. 5. The isobar for the 100-mesh sample shows a well marked step near 500C and thus gives unmistakable evidence that the mineral is a microcrystalline hydrate. Comparing this with the isobar for the finely ground pyrophyllite, we see that the isobars are very nearly

---
*But not always. See remarks below on silicia gel.

identical above 400C. Each exhibits a well marked step; the steps occur at very nearly the same temperature; however, the height of the step is slightly less for the finely ground sample. Below 250C, the finely ground sample shows a larger water content than the 100-mesh sample. That is, just as with the materials Hagiwara used, after grinding there is initially a large amount of water in the finely ground sample in excess of the hydrate water represented by the nearly vertical portion of the isobar. This additional water must have been acquired from the atmosphere during grinding and must be held by some mechanism other than that which holds the hydrate water. It seems most unlikely that the excess water is zeolitic water, since fine grinding could hardly increase the total interplanar area of zeolite crystals.

Interpretation of isotherms

Isotherms of hydrates. The usual behavior of a hydrate when the water-vapor pressure around it is varied at constant temperature is illustrated in Fig. 6. This isotherm shows well defined steps with the corners slightly rounded, as indicated by the dotted lines. What the effect of pulverizing such material on the shape of the isotherm might be is not known directly from experiment, for apparently no experiments of this kind have been published. Presumably, a sufficient amount of grinding would produce a smooth isotherm, by virtue of the change in particle size and particle-size range. It might also be presumed that in a saturated condition the minute crystals would retain more water than corresponds to the highest hydrate. These presumptions follow from considerations given above in connection with the isobars.

Isotherms of gels. The appearance of a well defined step in the isotherm of a solid is not always positive proof of the existence of a hydrate of definite chemical composition. Fig. 7 illustrates this point.[23] As the arrow indicates, the isotherm was obtained by progressively lowering the water vapor pressure. Just below a pressure of 4 mm Hg, the isotherm becomes very steep, a fact which might be taken to indicate the existence of hydrates having the formulas $SiO_2.1\frac{1}{2}H_2O$ and $SiO_2.H_2O$. Fig. 8 shows the same isotherm as well as that obtained by progressively increasing the vapor pressure, the "rehydration isotherm" as it is sometimes called. Note that the latter gives no evidence of a hydrate. Weiser, Milligan, and Holmes investigated this matter fully by preparing silica gel from the same materials at various temperatures ranging from 0 to 100C and from other materials at various temperatures and under various conditions. Not all preparations exhibited the vertical section in the dehydration isotherm. Gels prepared at low temperatures exhibited a step at a higher water content than gels prepared at a high temperature. The samples prepared at 100C and aged at this temperature for a few hours, and hence under conditions favoring crystal

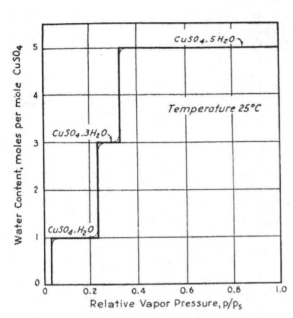

Fig. 6 – Water content vs. vapor pressure curve of $CuSO_4$

Collins and Menzies, J. Phys. Chem. v. 40, pp. 379-97 (1936)

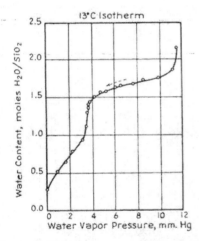

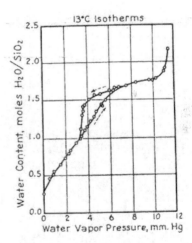

Fig. 7—(left) Dehydration isotherm for silica gel prepared from water glass at 25C

Weiser, Milligan and Holmes, J. Phys. Chem. v. 46, p. 586 (1942)

Fig. 8 (right)—Dehydration and rehydration isotherms for silica gel prepared from water glass at 25C

Weiser, Milligan and Holmes, J. Phys. Chem. v. 46, p. 586 (1942)

growth, gave no evidence of a step. No evidence of a step appeared in the rehydration isotherm of any preparation. No preparation gave evidence of crystallinity when examined by the electron diffraction method. These authors concluded that the step that occurs in the dehydration isotherm of some of the preparations is not evidence of the existence of a hydrate but is rather the result of a peculiarity of the physical structure of these gels. It follows from this conclusion that the structure of the gels prepared at low temperatures differs from that of the gels prepared at high temperatures, and there is evidence that this change in structure accompanying the increase in temperature of preparation is progressive.

Fig. 8 illustrates also the phenomenon called "sorption hysteresis." This will be discussed in another part of this paper.

* * * * *

The foregoing review shows that the interpretation of isobars and isotherms is not always a simple matter. Particularly, when the isotherm is smooth throughout, alternative interpretations must be considered carefully in the light of other pertinent information.

Water content vs. temperature curves (isobars) from hardened portland-cement paste

Review of published data. In this laboratory Wilson and Martin[24] obtained a group of isobars from hardened portland cement paste. The hardened paste was ground to pass the 28-mesh sieve and then was dried to constant weight at a constant temperature in a stream of air maintained at a low, constant water vapor pressure by bubbling the air through concentrated sulfuric acid.* The dry sample was then ignited at 1000C and the loss on ignition was taken as the water retained at the temperature of drying. Various drying temperatures were used, ranging from 50 to about 600C.† The resulting isobars are given in Fig. 9. Lea and Jones[25] obtained the isobars shown in Fig. 10. These authors plotted the loss in water rather than the amount retained.

In general those curves are not like those obtained from crystalline hydrates having definite amounts of water of crystallization. The nearly vertical rise in the curves between 400 and 450C, seen clearly in the curves of Lea and Jones, is attributed to the decomposition of $Ca(OH)_2$.

Krauss and Jörns[26] obtained isobars for the hardened paste at a constant vapor pressure of 7 mm Hg by using the instrument shown in Fig. 11. The sample is placed in A, which can be detached from the rest of the apparatus and which serves as a weighing bottle in following the changes in weight of the sample. With A in place as shown, the

---

*The air was freed of CO_2 by suitable means to prevent carbonation.
†The procedure used does not maintain strictly isobaric conditions, for the pressure would vary with temperature. However, the pressure is so small under all conditions that variations can usually be neglected.

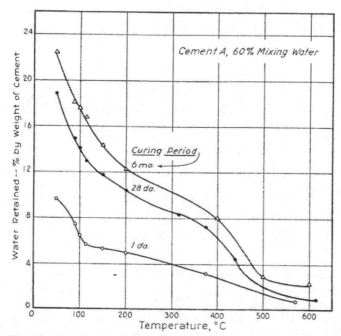

Fig. 9 – Effect of drying temperature on water retained, temperature range 50 to 600C
Wilson and Martin, J. Am. Concrete Inst. v. 31, p. 272 (1935)

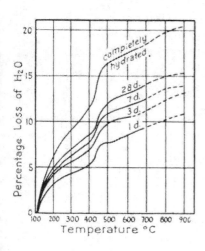

Fig. 10—Loss-on-heating curves for hardened neat cement, w/c = 0.22
Lea & Jones, J. Soc. Chem. Ind., v. 54, p. 63, 1935

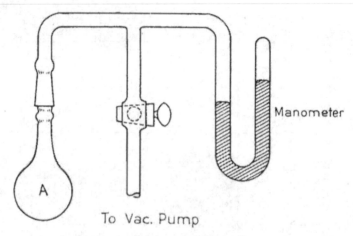

Manometer

To Vac. Pump

Fig. 11 – Krauss & Jorns' Apparatus

system is evacuated, thus removing water vapor as well as air. Periodically, the removal of water is interrupted by closing the stopcock and the water vapor pressure is observed. If the equilibrium pressure exceeds 7 mm Hg, the value chosen by Krauss and Jörns, the stopcock is opened and more water is removed by pumping. This process is repeated until at room temperature the equilibrium vapor pressure of the sample is less than 7 mm Hg. The temperature of the sample is then slowly raised until the pressure is exactly 7 mm. The loss of water to

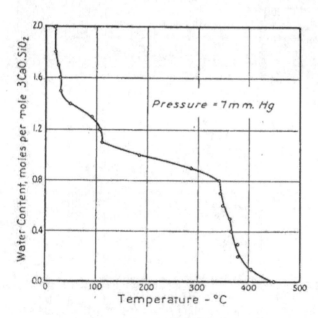

Pressure = 7 mm. Hg

Fig. 12 – Isobar for hardened $3CaO.SiO_2$*

*Probably a mixture of C_3S and $Ca(OH)_2$ (See text) Data from Krauss and Jorns, Zement v. 20, p. 317 (1931)

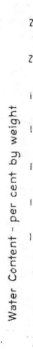
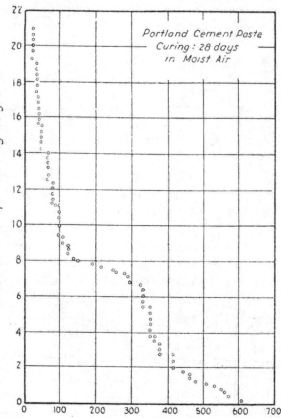

Fig. 13 — Isobar for portland cement paste obtained by Krauss and Jorns.

Zement v. 20, p. 343 (1931)

this point is determined by weighing A. Beyond this point, water is removed in small amounts by evacuation and after each decrement the temperature of the sample is raised until the pressure is exactly 7 mm Hg. Thus, the isobar is obtained. The results obtained by Krauss and Jörns are given in Fig. 12, 13, and 14.

Fig. 12 represents a sample described as tricalcium silicate (C_3S)* mixed with enough water to correspond with the formula $3CaO.SiO_2.-2H_2O$. The mixture was cured in saturated air 24 hours before the measurements were started. There is a *suggestion* of a step in the isobar

*Throughout this discussion the compositions of portland cements will be described in terms of the compound composition computed by the methods of L. A. Dahl, *Rock Products* v. 32 (23) p. 50, (1929) and R.H. Bogue, *Ind. Eng. Chem.* (Anal. Ed.) v. 1 (4) p. 192, (1929) or PCAF Paper No. 21 (1929). The following abbreviations will be used.

$C_3S = 3CaO.SiO_2$ $C_3A = 3CaO.Al_2O_3$
$C_2S = 2CaO.SiO_2$ $C_4AF = 4CaO.Al_2O_3.Fe_2O_3$

On this basis the composition is computed on the assumption that the iron and alumina compunds are C_4AF and C_3A. Swayze, *Am. J. Sci*, v. 244, pp. 1-30, 65-94, (1946) has recently shown that the iron oxide occurs in a phase having the general formula $C_6A_xF_{(3-x)}$ (in which x may vary from 0 to 2) which includes C_4AF as a special case. After it becomes possible to make allowance for this finding, discussions in later parts of this paper may need recasting in different terms. It seems unlikely, however, that any of the arguments or deductions would be greatly altered.

near 100C and a prominent step near 350C. The latter probably represents the decomposition of calcium hydroxide. A compound that might be represented by the break at 100C is not identified. Owing to the manner of its preparation (from a melt), the material thought to be tricalcium silicate was probably a mixture of dicalcium silicate and calcium hydroxide.

Fig. 13 represents a paste cured 28 days in moist air. There appear to be numerous closely spaced steps in this isobar. Krauss and Jörns believed that these steps were sufficiently distinct to indicate the presence of several hydrates having definite chemical formulas.

Fig. 14 represents a paste that had been cured several hours in boiling water* and then stored in the air of the laboratory for several years. As can be seen, the isobar has several well defined steps.

Endell[27] determined isobars for hardened paste, but he arbitrarily limited the heating period at any one temperature to one hour. There is evidence in his results that this was not always sufficient for the attainment of equilibrium. The isobars he obtained do not exhibit any features not exhibited by those reproduced in this paper.

Meyers[28] published isobars for hardened pastes and for hydrated samples of the pure compounds C_3S, C_2S, C_3A, C_4AF, and CaO hydrated separately (Fig. 15). The samples were heated in a vacuum in which the water vapor pressure was maintained at about 0.1 micron. Under these conditions the dissociation temperature of calcium hydroxide was found to be about 380-400F (193-204C). Neat hydrated cement heated under the same conditions showed a step at about 430F; presumably the step was due to the decomposition of calcium hydroxide. The conditions described for the experiments were such as to suggest that the difference between the dissociation temperature of the sample of $Ca(OH)_2$ and that of the $Ca(OH)_2$ in the hydrated cement was probably due to a difference in vapor pressure, the pressure being higher under the conditions that prevailed when the hydrated cement was tested.

The isobars for hydrated C_3S and C_2S show steps near 400F that may also be attributed to calcium hydroxide. The isobars for hydrate C_3A and C_4AF show a large step near 240F.

Discussion of isobars. The data of Krauss and Jörns seem to indicate that hydrated cement contains a series of hydrates besides $Ca(OH)_2$. However, the other curves, including those published recently by Meyers, indicate that the curves are smooth, except for one step in the neighborhood of 400F that is apparently due to microcrystalline $Ca(OH)_2$.

Since the structure of the hardened paste is predominantly of submicroscopic texture, a smooth isobar is to be expected whether the

---

*The specimen was a part used in the German Standard Test for Soundness.

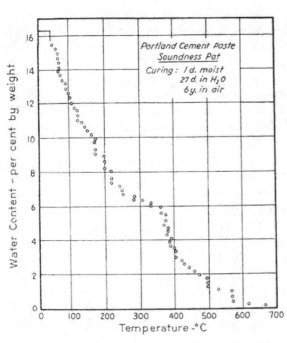

Fig. 14 — Isobar for portland cement paste obtained by Krauss and Jorns.
Zement v. 20, p. 343 (1931)

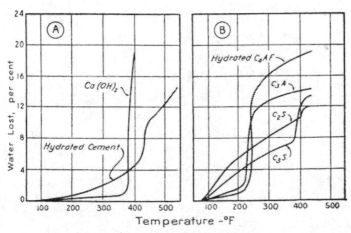

Fig. 15 — Isobars obtained by S. L. Meyers
Pit and Quarry (July, 1942)

hydration products are crystalline or not. As will be shown later, the specific surface of the hydrated material is so high that if the structure is of granular nature the granules must be of colloidal dimensions. If the particles were all of exactly the same size and constitution, a step in the isobar might be expected, despite the smallness of the particles. Without any a priori reason for assuming such uniformity in particle size, there is no basis for expecting anything but a smooth isobar except for the effect of calcium hydroxide already noted.

In general the isobars do not tell much about the hydration products. However, when the isobars are considered together with the information obtained with the microscope and X-ray, they may be considered to show that the hydration products are, for the most part, not in the microcrystalline state.*

Meyers' data on the four compounds C_3S, C_2S, C_3A, and C_4AF hydrated separately are of special interest. Note that both of the alumina-bearing compounds lost large amounts of water at about 250F. Since these two compounds usually constitute 20 per cent or more of the cement, a step on the curve for portland cement, or at least a sharp increase in slope, should occur at about 240F (116C) if those compounds are present in the hydrated cement. The fact that no such indication has been found can be taken as evidence that the hydration products of cement are not a simple mixture of the same hydration products that form when the compounds are hydrated separately; at least, they differ radically with respect to physical state, whether they do with respect to constitution or not.

Water content vs. vapor pressure curves at constant temperature (isotherms)

Jesser[30] was apparently the first to study the relationship between water content and vapor pressure for hardened paste at constant temperature. He used the method of van Bemmelen,[31] i.e., he left the specimens in a closed container over a solution of a salt or of H_2SO_4 at constant temperature, until they reached equilibrium with the vapor pressure of the solution. Starting with the saturated condition, he progressively subjected the samples to lower and lower humidities, finally drying them over concentrated H_2SO_4. He then subjected them to progressivly higher humidities, finally storing them over a solution having a relative vapor pressure of 0.98. After this he determined a second drying curve. His results are given in Fig. 16.

---

*Throughout this discussion a distinction will be made between the colloidal and microcrystalline states. The term "colloid" refers to any material, crystalline or not, having a specific surface of a higher order than particles visible with the light microscope. A colloidal material may exist as discrete particles or as gels, the latter being regarded as aggregations of once discrete colloidal particles. The term "microcrystalline" refers to ordered aggregations of molecules, atoms, or ions, at least large enough to be seen with a light microscope. The adjective "amorphous" is not used as the synonym of "colloidal" for such usage tends to obscure the fact that colloidal particles may themselves be crystalline, that is, of ordered structure. The possibility of crystalline colloids has long been recognized by colloid chemists. The actual existence of such colloids has been demonstrated by means of the electron microscope.[29]

Jesser used prisms about 1½x1½x4 in. made of neat paste having a water-cement ratio of 0.25 by weight. On the average, he left each prism at a given humidity about six weeks and assumed that this was sufficient time for equilibrium to be attained. Experiments in this laboratory, in which prisms of smaller cross section (1x1 in.) having a higher water-cement ratio (and consequently, a higher drying rate) were dried over dilute H_2SO_4 by much the same procedure, showed that 6 weeks was insufficient for the attainment of constant weight. Moreover, in specimens as large as those used by Jesser, hydration of the cement continues at an appreciable rate at the higher relative vapor pressures, especially in specimens cured only three days. These facts make the interpretation of his results difficult. The results are of interest none the less because they were the first to indicate the similarity between the behavior of the hardened paste and that of typically colloidal substances such as silica gel.

One striking fact in Jesser's results is that the first drying curve is not reversible. Work done in this laboratory confirms this.

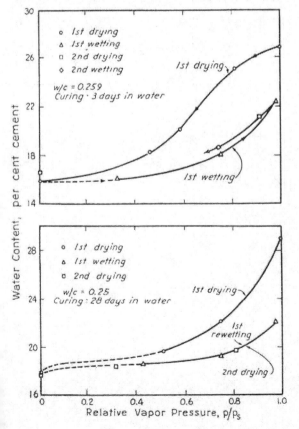

Fig. 16 – Water content versus relative vapor pressure.

Leopold Jesser, Zement v. 16, p. 741 (1927)

Fig. 17 – Diagram for apparatus used by Giertz-Hedstrom for determining isotherms for hardened cement paste

Zement v. 20, p. 672 (1931)

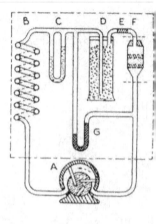

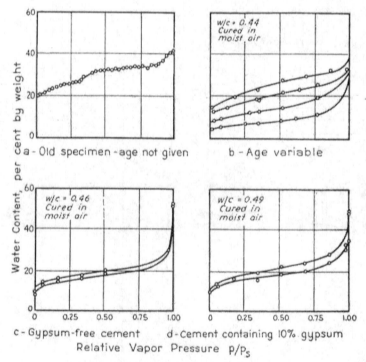

a - Old specimen - age not given

b - Age variable

w/c = 0.44
Cured in moist air

w/c = 0.46
Cured in moist air

w/c = 0.49
Cured in moist air

c - Gypsum-free cement   d - Cement containing 10% gypsum

Relative Vapor Pressure p/p_s

Water Content, per cent by weight

Fig. 18 – Isotherms for hydrated cement
Giertz-Hedstrom, Zement v. 20, p. 734 (1941)

Giertz-Hedström[32] published a number of isotherms for hardened paste. His procedure can be explained with the aid of Fig. 17. A pump, A, circulated air through a copper coil, B, a flow-meter, C, a wash bottle, D, and the sample-holder, F. The wash bottle, D, contained dilute H_2SO_4 and was partly filled with glass beads. The manometer, G, measured the pressure drop across D and F. The apparatus, except for the pump, was kept at a constant temperature in an air thermostat. A 1-g sample of pulverized, saturated paste was placed in F, which was detachable and served as a weighing bottle. Air was passed through the sample until periodic weighing showed that it had reached constant weight. When this point was reached, the H_2SO_4-solution first used in D, which was made very dilute to give a high relative vapor pressure, was replaced by a more concentrated solution and the sample was dried to constant weight at the lower relative vapor pressure. This procedure was repeated with progressively more concentrated H_2SO_4-solutions, and ended with concentrated H_2SO_4, so that several points were obtained along the isotherm. Giertz-Hedström's results are given in Fig. 18.

Berchem[33] has published isotherms for hardened cement and for hardened specimens of three of the principal compounds of portland cement. His method was essentially the method of Giertz-Hedström. As shown in Fig. 19 he obtained no experimental points at vapor pressures above $p = 0.63\ p_s$.

So far as the authors know, Jesser, Giertz-Hedström, and Berchem are the only investigators who have published isotherms for hardened portland cement pastes.*

Relationship between isotherms and isobars. In general, isotherms and isobars give information about the fixation of different portions of the water in the hardened paste. The isotherms give information about the fixation of that part of the water that is evaporable at a constant temperature, usually near room temperature; the isobars, on the other hand, give information about the fixation of the water that is not evaporable at room temperature. An exception is the work of Krauss and Jörns who, instead of determining isobars at a very low water vapor pressure as is commonly done, determined isobars at a vapor pressure of 7 mm Hg. This corresponds to a relative vapor pressure of approximately 0.3 at 25C. Thus, the range of their isobars overlaps the lower part of the isotherms given above as well as those determined in this laboratory.

Significance of isotherms. The isotherms, like the isobars, indicate that the hydration products are predominantly colloidal. They can be interpreted so as to give information about the volume and surface

---

*Gessner[34] has also studied the relationship between water content and relative vapor pressure of cement pastes. However, instead of determining a complete isotherm for a single sample, a different sample was used at each relative vapor pressure. Moreover, the procedure was such that the extent of chemical reaction and the water-cement ratio were different for each. Thus, many variables are involved and it is difficult to interpret the curves.

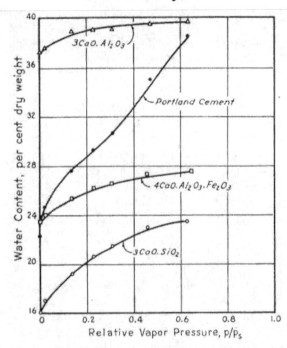

Fig. 19 — Water content vs. vapor pressure relationship

Berchem, Diss. Eidg. Techn. Hochschule, Zurich (1936)

area of the solid phase and other significant features of the properties and behavior of hardened paste. The presentation of such data and their interpretation are the main purpose of this paper.

Studies of water fixation by means of freezing tests

Studies of water fixation by means of freezing tests in various materials such as soils and plants have been reported by several investigators. Similar studies of hardened portland cement paste were reported by Giertz-Hedström[35] and by von Gronow[36]. With respect to this method Giertz-Hedström[37] says: "In all these tests the treatment is comparable with a reduction in water vapor pressure, that is to say, a form of drying out but with the addition of a different complication for each method."*

In a later paper the work done in this laboratory on the freezing of water in hardened portland cement pastes will be described.

SUMMARY OF PART 1

The material presented in Part 1 attempts to review the most significant information obtained by other investigators on the physical properties of hardened portland cement paste. It describes the experimental procedures and presents the test data of several important investigations.

*See also F. M. Lea, *Cement and Cement Manufacture*, v. 5, p. 395 (1932).

From reported microscopic studies it can be concluded that hardened cement paste is predominantly of submicroscopic texture. The only microcrystalline hydrate consistently reported is calcium hydroxide. Brownmiller found this to occur in clusters of very small crystals in the "cement gel." Although the gel state is theoretically unstable, Bogue and Lerch found no evidence of change toward the microcrystalline state over a period of 2 years. However, Kühl found evidence of such a change in pastes about 20 years old.

X-ray analyses do no more than confirm results of the microscopic method.

The relatively few reported observations made with the electron microscope indicate that the hydration products of portland cement may be colloidal but not amorphous. That is, they may be made up of submicroscopic crystals.

Several studies of physical properties of paste have been made by studying the fixation of water in hardened portland cement paste. Such studies are based on the fact that the characteristics of hydration or dehydration curves depend on both the physical and chemical characteristics of the materials involved. In hydroxides the water loses its chemical identity and appears in the structure as OH-groups. In many compounds it is bound molecularly by covalent bonds. In a third type of compound some of the water is bound by hydrogen bonds. In all the types of binding just mentioned the amount of water combined can usually be represented in a definite chemical formula and when the particles are of microscopic size or larger, such hydrates are stable through definite ranges of temperature and pressure.

In bodies of the zeolite type the water molecules are believed to be packed in the interstices of the solid structure and they are relatively loosely bound to the solid.

Any solid is capable of holding a small amount of water or other substance on its exposed surface by adsorption. The quantity held in this manner can be large when the specific surface of the solid is very high.

The amount of zeolitic water or adsorbed water held by a solid depends on the temperature and pressure of the water vapor surrounding the solid and the amount varies continuously with changes in either pressure or temperature.

A graph of the relationship between water content and temperature at constant vapor pressure is called an "isobar." The shape of the isobar of a hydrous solid depends on the specific surface of the solid and upon the nature of the combination between the solid and the water. Microcrystalline hydrates give stepped isobars having one or more steps.

The same hydrates reduced to submicroscopic particles of various sizes produce smooth isobars, showing more water in combination at the lower temperatures and less water at the higher temperatures than does the same material in the microcrystalline state. The isobar for zeolitic or for adsorbed water is a smooth curve under all conditions.

A graph of the relationship between water content and water vapor pressure at constant temperature is called an "isotherm." For microcrystalline hydrates the isotherm, like the isobar, is stepped. The material retains more water at low vapor pressures and less at high vapor pressures than does the same material in the microcrystalline state. This conclusion is based partly on experimental data and partly on inference from the isobaric relationships.

Under certain conditions isotherms from silica gel show a step similar to that of a microcrystalline hydrate. The resemblance is superficial, however, as other information shows that no definite hydrate exists over any given pressure range.

Isobars from portland cement paste have been obtained by several investigators. The findings of different investigators vary in some details. In general they show that the isobar is a smooth curve except for one step that is attributed to the decomposition of calcium hydroxide.

Isobars from the four principal compounds of portland cement, hydrated separately, show that the hydrates of C_3S and C_2S resemble that from portland cement, whereas the hydrates of C_3A and C_4AF show mainly the characteristics of microcrystalline hydrates, a step occurring at about 240F when vapor pressure is about 0.1 micron. The fact that Meyers found no step on the isobars for portland cement at 240F is evidence that the hydrates of C_3A and C_4AF that occur in portland cement are not the same, at least with respect to physical state, as those which form when these compounds are hydrated separately.

Isotherms from portland cement pastes have been obtained by a few investigators. The isotherms give information about the fixation of that part of the water that is evaporable at a constant temperature, usually near room temperature, whereas the isobars give the information about the fixation of that part of the water that is not evaporable at room temperature. The isotherms that have been obtained agree with the isobars in indicating that the water in hardened paste is *not* held as it is in microcrystalline compounds. Instead, the manner of binding is similar to that between water and silica gel.

Some studies of water fixation by a freezing-out procedure have been reported. The method is fundamentally similar to the drying-out procedure and the results obtained have about the same significance.

The data on the isothermal relationship between water content and vapor pressure obtained before the present investigation are too few to throw much light on the question of paste structure. Several of the earlier investigations were conducted under what are now known to be faulty test conditions.

REFERENCES

(1) E. Freyssinet, *Science et Industrie*, Jan., 1933.

(2) S. Giertz-Hedström, "Proc. Symposium on the Chemistry of Cements," p. 505 (Stockholm 1938).

(3) R. H. Bogue, "A Digest of the Literature on the Nature of the Setting and Hardening Processes in Portland Cement," Portland Cement Association Fellowship Paper No. 17 (Oct. 1928).

(4) L. S. Brown and R. W. Carlson, *Proc. A.S.T.M.* v. 36, Pt. II, 332 (1936).

(5) Hans Kühl, "Cement Chemistry and Theory and Practice," p. 34, Concrete Publications Ltd., London.

(6) Ref. 5, p. 36.

(7) Henri Le Chatelier, *Compt. rend.* v. 94, p. 13 (1882) "The Constitution of Hydraulic Mortars," (1887). Translated by J. L. Mack, McGraw-Hill, New York (1905).

(8) L. T. Brownmiller, ACI Journal, Jan. 1943; *Proceedings* v. 39, p. 193 (1943).

(9) B. Tavasci, Richerche sulla Constituzione del Clinker di Cemento Portland, *Giorn. chem. ind. applicata*, p. 583 (Nov. 1934).

(10) H. Insley, *J. Res. Natl. Bur. Stds.* v. 17, p. 353 (1936).

(11) W. Eitel, *Angewandte Chemie*, v. 54, p. 185-193 (1941).

(12) C. M. Sliepcevich, L. Gildart and D. L. Katz, *Ind. Eng. Chem.* v. 35, p. 1178 (1943).

(13) Stockholm Symposium, p. 513. (See Ref. 2)

(14) E. Brandenburger, *Schweizer Archiv*, p. 45, 1937.

(15) R. H. Bogue and Wm. Lerch, *Ind. Eng. Chem.* v. 26, p. 837 (1934), or Paper No. 27, Portland Cement Association Fellowship, National Bureau of Standards, Washington, D. C.

(16) H. J. Emeleus and J. S. Anderson, "Modern Aspects of Inorganic Chemistry," D. van Nostrand, Inc., p. 163, New York, 1942.

(17) R. M. Barrer, *Trans. Faraday Soc.* v. 40, p. 374 (1944).

(18) Stephen Brunauer, "The Adsorption of Gases and Vapors," Vol. I, Chapter 7, Princeton University Press, 1943.

(19) T. Hagiwara. In "Colloid Chemistry" by J. Alexander, Chapter 38, The Chemical Catalog Co., 1926.

(20) P. A. Bonsdorff, *Pogg. Ann.* v. 27, p. 275 (1833).

(21) H. B. Weiser and W. O. Milligan, *J. Phys. Chem.* v. 38, p. 1175 (1934).

(22) W. P. Kelley, Hans Jenny, and S. M. Brown, *Soil Sci.* v. 41, p. 260 (1936).

(23) H. B. Weiser, W. O. Milligan and J. Holmes, *J. Phys. Chem.* v. 46, p. 586 (1942).

(24) R. Wilson and F. Martin, ACI Journal, Jan.-Feb., 1935; *Proceedings* v. 31, p. 272.

(25) F. M. Lea and F. E. Jones, *J. Soc. Chem. Ind.* v. 54, p. 63 (1935).

(26) F. Krauss and G. Jörns, *Zement* v. 20, pp. 314, 341 (1931); also *ibid* v. 19, p. 1054 (1930).

(27) K. Endell, *Zement*, v. 15, p. 823 (1926).

(28) S. L. Meyers, *Pit and Quarry*, v. 35 p. 97, July, 1942.

(29) Thomas F. Anderson, "The Study of Colloids with the Electron Microscope," from "Recent Advances in Colloid Science," Interscience Pub. Co., New York, (1942).

(30) L. Jesser, *Zement* v. 16, p. 741 (1927); v. 18, p. 161 (1929).   Earlier reports in "Protokoll der Generalversammlungen des Vereines der Osterr." *Zementfabrikanten*, 1912, 1913, and 1914.

(31) J. M. van Bemmelen, "Die Absorption," Dresden, 1910.

(32) S. Giertz-Hedström, *Zement* v. 20, pp. 672, 734 (1941).

(33) Hans Berchem, Dissertation, Eidg. Tech. Hochschule, Zürich, 1936.

(34) H. Gessner, *Kolloid Zeitschrift* v. 46 (3) (1928); v. 47 (1-2) (1929).

(35) S. Giertz-Hedström, *Zement* v. 20, p. 672 (1931).

(36) H. E. von Gronow, *Zement* v. 25 (1936).

(37) Stockholm Symposium, p. 517.   (See Ref. 2)

Part 2—Studies of Water Fixation, is scheduled for the November 1946 Journal

Title 43-5b —a part of PROCEEDINGS, AMERICAN CONCRETE INSTITUTE Vol. 43

JOURNAL
of the
AMERICAN CONCRETE INSTITUTE
(copyrighted)

Vol. 18 No. 3   7400 SECOND BOULEVARD, DETROIT 2, MICHIGAN   November 1946

Studies of the Physical Properties of Hardened Portland Cement Paste*

By T. C. POWERS†
Member American Concrete Institute

and T. L. BROWNYARD‡

PART 2.   STUDIES OF WATER FIXATION

CONTENTS

*Received by the Institute July 8, 1946—scheduled for publication in seven installments; October 1946 to April, 1947. In nine parts: Part 1. "A Review of Methods That Have Been Used for Studying the Physical Properties of Hardened Portland Cement Paste"—ACI Journal, October, 1946. Part 2. "Studies of Water Fixation"—Appendix to Part 2. Part 3. "Theoretical Interpretation of Adsorption Data." Part 4. "The Thermodynamics of Adsorption"—Appendix to Parts 3 and 4. Part 5. "Studies of the Hardened Paste by Means of Specific-Volume Measurements." Part 6. "Relation of Physical Characteristics of the Paste to Compressive Strength." Part 7. "Permeability and Absorptivity." Part 8. "The Freezing of Water in Hardened Portland Cement Paste." Part 9. "General Summary of Findings on the Properties of Hardened Portland Cement Paste."
†Manager of Basic Research, Portland Cement Assn. Research Laboratory, Chicago 10, Ill.
‡Navy Dept., Washington, D. C., formerly Research Chemist, Portland Cement Assn. Research Laboratory. Chicago 10, Ill.

INTRODUCTION

In the preceding part of this paper some of the methods of studying hydrated portland cement paste were reviewed and the principal results obtained by previous investigators were presented. In this part of the paper the studies of water fixation carried out in this laboratory will be described.*

As shown in the first section, water fixation has claimed the interest of several investigators. The reason for such interest is not hard to find. Some of the water associated with hardened cement paste is obviously a constituent of the new solids produced by chemical reactions. If all such water is driven from the paste, the cohesion of the paste is destroyed. Another part of the water, amounting in saturated paste to as much as 50 percent of the volume of the paste, or even more, is free to leave the hardened paste without destroying the cementing value of the material. It does, however, have important effects on the hardened paste: the paste shrinks as water is lost and swells as it is gained; the strength and hardness of the hardened paste vary with its degree of saturation; some of this water is freezable and is thus a source of disruptive pressures that tend to disintegrate concrete exposed to weather. Furthermore, the amount of water that is free to come and go in response to changes in ambient conditions is an index to the degree of porosity of

---

*The characteristics of the cements mentioned in this part may be found in the Appendix to Part 2.

the hardened paste. The porosity is obviously an important property of the material related directly to its quality.

One incentive for studying the fixation of water in hardened paste was the possibility that suitable measurements of the manner in which the water is associated with the solids would provide the means of estimating the nature and size of the pores in the paste. It was hoped that such knowledge would simplify the problem of relating the chemical and physical characteristics of the cement to its quality. This hope arose rather directly from the hypothesis of Freyssinet[1]* which had a major influence on our choice of experimental procedure. The chosen procedure was intended to yield information on the porosity and pore-size distribution of the hardened paste and other information that might bear on the questions of volume change, durability, plastic flow, etc.

Porosity. To speak, as above, of the porosity of hardened paste is likely to be misleading unless the term is properly qualified. The word "porosity" can be interpreted differently according to past experience or to the chosen criterion as to what constitutes porosity. Certainly, the term is misleading here if it calls to mind such materials as felt or sponge.

Whether or not a material is considered to be porous depends in part on the means employed for detecting its porosity. If a material were judged by its perviousness alone, the decision would rest primarily on the choice of medium used for testing its perviousness. For example, vulcanized rubber would be found impervious, and hence, non-porous, if tested with mercury, but if tested with hydrogen it would be found highly porous. The perviousness of hardened cement paste to water and other fluids is direct evidence of the porosity of the paste.

Regardless of the size of the pore, a substance near enough to the boundary of the pore is attracted toward the boundary by one or more types of force known collectively as forces of adsorption. These forces are sufficiently intense to compress a fluid that comes within their range. If the fluid is a vapor, the degree of compression may be very great; the vapor may be liquefied or solidified; if the fluid is already a liquid, it may undergo further densification on making contact with the solid surface. Since the range of the forces causing such effects is very small— a few hundredths or thousandths of a micron—only a negligible part of the enclosed space in pores of microscopic or macroscopic dimensions is within the range of surface forces. However, when the pores are of the same order of magnitude as the range of surface-forces, it follows that a large portion, or all, of the enclosed space is within the range of surface forces. For this reason, substances containing a large volume of sub-

*See references, end of Part 2.

microscopic pores exhibit properties and behavior not noticeable in ordinary porous bodies. For example, porous bodies of submicroscopic (colloidal) texture shrink and swell markedly on changing the liquid content of the pores, the magnitude of the effect being controlled by the intensity of attraction between the solid and the liquid. Moreover, changes in liquid content alter such properties as strength, elasticity, heat content, and other properties that in non-colloidal solids are virtually constant at a given temperature. Some of these effects will be the subject of discussion farther on.

CLASSIFICATION OF WATER IN HARDENED PASTE

The present discussion aims to elucidate those features of a hardened paste that are revealed by the relative proportions of the total water content that fall in three different categories, as follows:

(1) *Water of constitution.*

As used here, this term refers to water of crystallization or water otherwise chemically combined; it refers to water that is a part of the solid matter in a hardened paste.

(2) *Water bound by surface-forces—adsorbed water.*

(3) *Capillary water.*

This is that water which occupies space beyond the range of the surface-forces of the solid phase.

The above classification is of little practical use, for as yet no way has been devised for actually separating the total water content into such divisions. On drying, water of category (2) and of category (3) are lost simultaneously. Furthermore, not all the water in these two categories can be removed without removing also some of the water of constitution (category (1)). Nevertheless, since evaporation or condensation is the most feasible means of manipulating it, the total water must be studied first with respect to the relative volatilities exhibited by different portions of it. From such data, means of estimating the amounts of water in the three categories given above have been developed, as will be shown.

The water in a saturated, hardened paste is classified in this paper according to its volatility as follows: The water that is retained by a sample of cement paste after it has been dried at 23 C to constant weight in an evacuated desiccator over the system $Mg(ClO_4)_2.2H_2O +$ $Mg(ClO_4)_2.4H_2O$ as a desiccant* is regarded, in this discussion, as "fixed" or "combined" water. To avoid any unintentional commitments as to the state of combination of this part of the water, it is called *non-evaporable water*. The rest of the water in a saturated specimen is called the *evapor-*

---

*The material is purchased as "Dehydrite"—$Mg(ClO_4)_2$. The two molecules of water are added at the time of use. See Drying of Samples.

able water. The non-evaporable water probably includes most of the water of constitution, but not all of it, for at least one of the hydrates, calcium sulfoaluminate, is partially decomposed when the evaporable water is removed. On the other hand, it is not certain that all the non-evaporable water is water of constitution, for it is possible that some of it can be removed (by slightly raising the temperature) without decomposing any compound present. (See Part 1, Isobars from Portland Cement Paste.)   In this connection, a reading of Lea's paper "Water in Set Cement" is recommended.[2]

MATERIALS AND EXPERIMENTAL PROCEDURES

The materials used for these studies were hardened neat cement pastes, pastes of cement and pulverized silica, or cement-sand mortars made with a wide variety of commercial and laboratory-prepared cements. The experimental procedures differed somewhat from time to time and with the type of specimen employed. The general features of the procedures will be described here, and certain other details will be given at appropriate points in other sections of this paper. A detailed description of the materials and methods of the various projects will be found in the Appendix to Part 2.

PREPARATION OF SPECIMENS

Neat cement cylinders

(Series 254-K4B and 254-MRB). Neat cement specimens were prepared, usually at a water-cement ratio of 0.5 by weight, by molding the mixed paste in cylindrical wax-impregnated paper molds $\frac{7}{8}$-in. by 6-in. long. In some investigations cylindrical molds of other types were used. The molds were stoppered and laid in water horizontally as soon as they were filled, and the stoppers were removed after about 24 hours so that the curing water might have ready access to the cement paste.

In mixing the pastes, 200 g of cement was mixed with the desired amount of water in a kitchen-type mixer. The mixer was operated at top speed for two minutes and then the paste was allowed to rest for three minutes, and finally mixed again for two minutes. This procedure was followed to avoid the effects of certain types of premature stiffening, whether or not the cements showed any such tendency.

Mortar specimens

The majority of the mortar specimens were made from the mixes shown in Table 1.

As indicated in the Table 1, the aggregate consisted of standard Ottawa sand (20-30 mesh) and pulverized silica, the latter being of about the same specific surface as the cement. The quantity of silica was

TABLE 1—MIXES FOR MORTAR SPECIMENS
(Series 254-8-9-10-11)

Mix	Proportion by weight			Batch quantities in grams		
	Cement	Pulverized silica	Standard sand	Cement	Pulverized silica	Standard sand
A	1.00	—	1.64	1400	—	2300
B	1.00	0.33	2.30	1000	330	2300
C	1.00	0.71	3.65	750	530	2300

such as to give all the mixes about the same total (absolute) volume of cement + silica + water.

The water-cement ratios were adjusted to give a 1½-2-in. slump (6-inch cone) and varied through a small range with the different cements used. The values (after bleeding) were about 0.33, 0.45, and 0.58 for mixes A, B, and C, respectively.

The batches were mixed in a small power-driven, open-tub mixer. Each batch was first mixed 30 seconds dry and then for 2 minutes after the water was added. Two operators working simultaneously then made duplicate slump tests and returned the slump samples to the mixing tub. After remixing the material for 30 seconds, 2x2-in. cubes and 2x2x9½-in. prisms were cast in watertight, three-gang molds which had been previously weighed.

Measurements were made from which the air contents and the loss of water due to bleeding could be computed. This procedure was as follows: Before each cube mold was filled, its outside surface was carefully cleaned and, after filling, the mold and contents were weighed. Then the mold was placed in saturated air. After two hours, water that had accumulated at the top through settlement was carefully removed with absorbent paper and the mold again was weighed. The molds were then immersed in water at 70 F where they remained for at least 12 hours. They were then removed from the water, dried with paper and again weighed. Following this the specimens were removed from the molds, weighed in air surface-dry, and then in water so as to obtain the weight and volume of the material. The cubes were then stored in a fresh supply of water at 70 F where they remained until test or until they were 28 days old. Those that were scheduled for tests beyond 28 days were then stored in the fog room at 70 F.

During the water storage the water was changed periodically to prevent the building up of high alkali concentration.

At the scheduled time of test the cubes were again weighed in the surface-dry condition and under water. Those that had had a period of storage in moist air were placed in water one day before the scheduled test date to allow them to absorb water if they could.

The data obtained in this manner made it possible to ascertain the average amount of original unhydrated cement, silica, sand, water, and air in each group of companion hardened specimens.

The prisms were treated in the same way as the cubes except that the measurements of settlement (bleeding) were not made.

Truncated cones

In one of the earlier investigations (Series 254-7) mortar specimens were cast in watertight, truncated cones of 4-in. base, 2-in. top diameter, and 6-in. height. Measurements similar to those made on the cubes were made on these cones before and after removing the molds. This gave accurate data on the settlement and the final proportions of the ingredients of the mixtures.

TESTING OF MORTAR SPECIMENS

At the scheduled test ages, which usually ranged from 7 days to 6 months, two cubes of a kind were tested for compressive strength. Throughout these procedures the cubes were carefully kept wet and, after being tested, cubes of a kind were placed immediately in airtight containers.

PREPARATION OF SAMPLES FOR STUDIES OF HARDENED PASTE

Mortar specimens

The tested mortar cubes in airtight containers, mentioned above, were taken from the containers as soon after the strength test as possible and passed quickly through a small jaw crusher. The crushed material was immediately transferred to a nest of sieves (No. 4-8-14-28-35-100-150) already cleaned, assembled, and sealed at the joints with wide rubber bands. The sieves were shaken on a sieving machine for 5 or 10 minutes and then, to prevent losses of water by evaporation, the nest of sieves was opened in the moist room and the material caught between the 35- and 100-mesh or, in some series, between the 48- and 100-mesh sieves, was transferred to a screw-top sample bottle. This material, which consisted of granules of hardened cement paste or hardened paste and pulverized silica, was used for the studies to be described.

Neat cement cylinders and mortar cones

The neat cement cylinders and mortar cones were weighed in air and in water by procedures somewhat like that described for the mortar cubes. Then, since no physical tests were made on these specimens, they were immediately passed through the jaw crusher and a granular sample was obtained by the procedure described above. In some of the earliest tests the crushing was done with mortar and pestle, but this procedure permitted too much drying and carbonation of the material.

Neat cement slabs

For the most recent project of this study (Series 254-18) the test samples were very thin, neat-cement slabs. These were prepared from cylinders by sawing off slices and then grinding the slices on a glass plate with carborundum dust and water. By this method the slabs were reduced to an average thickness of about 0.3 mm. When saturated, they were translucent.

DRYING OF SAMPLES

The granular samples described above, in quantities not exceeding 15 g, were placed in wide-mouthed weighing bottles and stored in vacuum desiccators with anhydrous magnesium perchlorate (Dehydrite). (The desiccators were exhausted with a Cenco Hyvac pump.) When an excess of the anhydrous desiccant was used, the effective drying agent was a mixture of $Mg(ClO_4)_2$ and $Mg(ClO_4)_2.2H_2O$. With the thought of avoiding the dehydration of the calcium hydroxide, we used a quantity of anhydrous magnesium perchlorate in each desiccator such that when the original compound had combined with all the water given up by the samples the desiccant had become a mixture of $Mg(ClO_4)_2.2H_2O$ and $Mg(ClO_4)_2.4H_2O$; that is, this was the mixture that determined the final water vapor pressure in the desiccator. (Although this was the intention, there is some evidence in the data that the desired result was not always realized. In some cases the final desiccant was probably the mixture $Mg(ClO_4)_2 + Mg(ClO_4)_2.2H_2O$. Some of these cases are mentioned in later discussions, but it was impossible to identify all cases with certainty.)

In some of the earlier projects other desiccants were used, namely, P_2O_5, H_2SO_4, and CaO. In some the drying was done in desiccators containing air instead of in vacuum desiccators. However, most of the data reported here were obtained by the procedure described above.

Reproducibility of results

To test the reproducibility of results obtained by the drying procedure used for the greater part of this investigation, four sets of samples, each comprising 11 companion portions, were prepared from a single neat paste specimen $3\frac{1}{2}$ months old. The results are given in Table 2.

The differences among the figures in any one column indicate the degree of variation among the samples in a given desiccator. The figures for the average loss for the different sets indicate the variations, if any, between conditions in different desiccators. The average losses for sets A and B are slightly higher than for sets C and D. Sets A and B were

TABLE 2—REPRODUCIBILITY OF DRYING LOSSES

Cement: Laboratory blend of 4 commercial brands, Lot 13495
Nominal w/c = 0.50 by wt.
Curing: $3\frac{1}{2}$ months in water

Sample No.	Loss of water—% by wt.			
	A	B	C	D
1	19.81	20.14	19.75	19.87
2	20.06	20.01	19.84	19.80
3	19.93	20.10	19.85	19.96
4	19.99	20.13	19.66	19.89
5	20.06	20.10	19.67	19.82
6	20.09	20.07	19.86	19.84
7	19.98	20.04	19.93	19.87
8	20.00	20.09	19.63	19.87
9	20.13	20.03	19.84	19.84
10	20.00	20.04	19.74	19.79
11	19.72	20.20	19.58	19.90
Average	19.98	20.09	19.76	19.86

dried immediately after they were prepared. Sets C and D were stored in screw-top sample bottles for about one week before they were dried. It seems, therefore, that the smaller loss from sets C and D was probably due to the additional hydration of these two sets during the one-week waiting period.

DETERMINATION OF NON-EVAPORABLE WATER

One-gram portions of the samples dried as described above were heated at about 1000 C for about 15 minutes. The samples were cooled and weighed and then given a 5-minute reheat to check the completeness of ignition. The amount of loss minus the ignition loss of the original cement is called the non-evaporable water content of the sample.

The computation involves the assumption that the weight of the non-evaporable water is exactly equal to the increase in ignition loss. . Such an assumption introduces some error. In the first place the original cement was not pre-dried as were the hydrated samples before determining loss on ignition. Hence, the ignition loss as reported for the original cement might be slightly above the value correct for this computation. A second, more serious, source of error arises from ignoring the increase in the amount of combined carbon dioxide. Although precautions against exposure of the granular samples of hardened paste to carbon dioxide were taken, some carbonation did occur. Tests made on 15 different samples showed that in 60 percent of the cases carbonation amounted to less than 0.5 percent of the weight of the original cement. However, carbonation as high as 1.9 percent was found. When carbonation has occurred, the loss on ignition of the carbonated sample will be greater than the non-evaporable water content before carbonation occurred. The increase is about 0.59 times the weight of CO_2 combined. For example, if the loss on ignition is 0.2 g per g of cement greater than the original loss on ignition, and if the CO_2 content has increased by 0.005 g per g of cement, the non-evaporable water would be 0.2 minus the quantity $(0.005 \times 0.59) = 0.197$. Thus, in this example, the assumption that the increase in loss on ignition is equal to the non-evaporable water results in an error of about 1.5 percent. At earlier stages of hydration, when the loss on ignition is smaller, the relative error would be considerably greater for the same amount of carbonation.

Since the necessary data are available on only a few of the samples and since also there is some question as to the accuracy of the figures for amount of carbonation, no attempt to correct loss on ignition for CO_2 was made in preparing the data for this report. Variations in the amount of carbonation among the various samples undoubtedly contributes to the random variations that will be noted.

Degree of desiccation of dried samples

The degree of desiccation obtained by the drying procedure described above is indicated by the data given in Table 3, which gives also the results obtained with other desiccants. For brevity, only one of the two components of the desiccating mixture is given. The samples tested were neat cement pastes (original w/c (by wt.) $= 0.5$), that had been cured 1 year in water. Each paste was made with a different cement, the group representing a wide range in chemical composition.

It will be noted that with any given desiccant, the percentages of non-evaporable water for the different pastes differ over a considerable range. However, it is significant that all the results obtained with one desiccant bear a virtually constant ratio to the results obtained with another. This is shown in Table 4, where the results are expressed as

TABLE 3
(Data from Series 254-K4B)

Paste No.	Water retained at equilibrium with the desiccant indicated, % by wt. of cement in specimen			
	P_2O_5	$Mg(ClO_4)_2$	$Mg(ClO_4)_2.2H_2O$	H_2SO_4 conc.
4S	18.3	21.4	22.8	22.3
5S	17.4	20.6	22.0	22.7
7Q	21.4	25.4	26.6	27.1
7P	21.1	25.2	26.5	27.1
7S	20.6	24.6	25.9	26.5
11S	17.6	20.9	22.2	22.5

TABLE 4

Paste No.	Amount of water retained relative to that retained by $Mg(ClO_4)_2.2H_2O$			
	P_2O_5	$Mg(ClO_4)_2$	$Mg(ClO_4)_2.2H_2O$	H_2SO_4, conc.
4S	0.80	0.94	1.00	0.98*
5S	0.79	0.94	1.00	1.03
7Q	0.80	0.95	1.00	1.02
7P	0.80	0.95	1.00	1.02
7S	0.79	0.95	1.00	1.02
11S	0.79	0.94	1.00	1.02

*This value is probably in error—too low. In another group of tests, the ratio for conc. H_2SO_4 was found to be 1.08. Possibly the sulfuric acid used in this second group had a slightly higher water vapor pressure than the acid represented in the table.

ratios to the quantity retained over a mixture of magnesium perchlorate dihydrate and magnesium perchlorate tetrahydrate.

The published information on the actual water vapor pressures maintained by these desiccants is not entirely satisfactory. The values given in Table 5, below, are the most reliable that can be found. Note that these values are upper limits; the actual water vapor pressures may be much lower.

TABLE 5

Drying agent	Residual water at 25 C		
	Mg. per liter	Relative vapor pressure, p/p_s*	Reference
P_2O_5	$<2.5 \times 10^{-5}$	$<1 \times 10^{-6}$	(1)
$Mg(ClO_4)_2$(anhyd.)	$<3 \times 10^{-3}$	$<130 \times 10^{-6}$	(3)
H_2SO_4	$<3 \times 10^{-3}$	$<130 \times 10^{-6}$	(2)
CaO	$<3 \times 10^{-3}$	$<130 \times 10^{-6}$	(3)

*p = existing water vapor pressure. p_s = water vapor pressure over a plane surface of pure water—the "saturation pressure" at a given temperature.
(1) Morley, *J. Am. Chem. Soc.* v. 26, p. 1171 (1904).
(2) Morley, *Am. J. Sci.* v. 30, p. 141 (1885).
(3) Bower, Bureau Stds. J. Research v. 12, p. 246 (1934).

The data for CaO are open to question. Evidence to be presented in Part 4 indicates that the equilibrium relative vapor pressure of water over CaO may be much less than the value given.

The data for P_2O_5 and H_2SO_4 are the result of very painstaking measurements and are probably close to the correct ones. The results in Table 4 bear this out. The amount of water retained by pastes dried over P_2O_5 is less than that retained over any other desiccant; that retained over H_2SO_4, conc., is more. With respect to $Mg(ClO_4)_2$(anhyd.), the water vapor pressure maintained by this desiccant is certainly far less than the upper limit given in Table 5. The data in Table 4, together with the data given on page 286, indicate that the relative vapor pressure is well below 24 x 10^{-6}, the vapor pressure of water at dry ice temperature (-78 C) relative to "saturation pressure" at 25 C.

Data on the vapor pressure over $Mg(ClO_4)_2.2H_2O$ are not available in the literature. However, the data on page 286, indicate that it is about 24 millionths of the "saturation pressure."

A method of drying more commonly used than the isothermal procedures just discussed is that of oven-drying at a temperature at or slightly above the normal boiling point of water. To compare the degree of desiccation obtained from such oven-drying with that obtained isothermally over $Mg(ClO_4)_2.2H_2O + Mg(ClO_4)_2.4H_2O$, four samples that had previously been dried by the latter procedure were placed in an oven at 105 C and allowed to come to constant weight. The results are shown in Table 6.*

TABLE 6

No. of Sample	Loss in weight in oven—% of non-evaporable water content as found by isothermal drying over $Mg(ClO_4)_2.2H_2O$ + $Mg(ClO_4)_2.4H_2O$
16213	10
16214	11
16198	10
15669	13

Stability of hydrates

The figures given in the foregoing paragraphs indicate the "degree of dryness" produced by the method adopted for this investigation in terms of the amount of water retained by the paste and the relative vapor pressure of this residual water, called non-evaporable water. An attempt will now be made to indicate the amount of water retained by the hydrated compounds of portland cement when dried by this procedure.

The microscope reveals that both microcrystalline and colloidal materials occur in hardened paste, the colloidal material appearing as an amorphous mass enclosing microcrystalline $Ca(OH)_2$ and unhydrated residues of the original cement grains. Any such microcrystalline hy-

---

*In this test no attempt was made to control the water vapor pressure in the oven. This is the incorrect procedure that has frequently been used in studies of this kind.

drate will remain unaltered during the process of drying if its dissociation pressure is lower than the vapor pressure maintained by the drying agent. If the dissociation pressure of the hydrate is higher than the vapor pressure maintained by the drying agent, dehydration is possible but not certain; only direct trial will tell whether it will occur under the conditions of the experiment. Under suitable experimental conditions, the hydrate will lose one or more gram-molecular weights of water per mole of hydrate without appreciable change in vapor pressure, the amount lost being determined by the nature of the hydrate.

As was shown in Part 1, the water content of *colloidal* hydrates bears no small-whole-number, molar ratio to the anhydrous material (except perhaps by chance) and none of it can be removed without a corresponding change in the equilibrium water vapor pressure. That is, the water content of a colloidal hydrate varies continuously with changes in ambient conditions. The colloidal material in hardened cement pastes predominates over non-colloidal constituents to such a degree that the dehydration process shows only the characteristics associated with colloidal material and therefore the dehydration curves do not indicate directly the extent to which the microcrystalline material becomes decomposed.

The extent to which the hydrates of the major compounds of portland cement are dehydrated under the drying conditions described can be estimated from the data given in Table 7. The data pertain to products obtained by hydrating the compounds separately. The first eight lines of data show the amounts of water retained by C_3S (under the drying conditions described) after various periods of hydration. They show that the amount is greater the longer the period of hydration. However, a maximum would be expected, though it is not clearly indicated by these data.

As brought out in Part 1, the figures given in Table 7 should be regarded as single points on smooth isobars and therefore have no unique significance. Had the temperature of drying been higher, the amount of water retained at any given age would have been less, and vice versa. On the other hand, if the hydration products were microcrystalline hydrates, each hydrate would probably be stable over a considerable temperature range, with pressure constant, or over a pressure range with temperature constant.

The alumina-bearing compounds that occur in portland cement clinker, *when hydrated separately*, produce microcrystalline hydrates having definite amounts of water of crystallization. A list of several compounds is given in Table 8, together with information as to their stability in the presence of $Mg(ClO_4)_2.2H_2O$, CaO, or P_2O_5.

TABLE 7—FIXED WATER IN HYDRATED C_2S AND C_3S AS REPORTED BY SEVERAL INVESTIGATORS

Compound	Nominal w/c by wt.	"Fixed water" at age indicated, grams per gram of original anhydrous material					
		3 days	7 days	28 days	6 mo.	1 year	3 years
C_3S^a	0.35	0.103	—	0.146	0.150	0.190	—
C_3S^b	0.40	0.198	—	—	—	0.213	—
C_3S^c	0.78	—	—	—	—	—	0.31
C_3S^d	0.33	—	0.103	0.143	0.207	—	—
"	0.45	—	0.102	0.147	0.224	—	—
"	0.60	—	0.104	0.150	0.238	—	—
"	1.00	—	0.110	0.161	0.254	—	—
C_2S^a	0.30	0.013	—	0.034	0.108	0.122	—
C_2S^b	0.40	0.019	—	0.043	—	0.138	—
C_2S^c	0.33	—	—	—	—	—	0.09
C_2S^d	0.33	—	0.020	0.036	0.134	—	—
"	0.45	—	0.020	0.032	0.142	—	—
"	0.60	—	0.016	0.025	0.120	—	—
"	1.00	—	0.017	0.026	0.130	—	—

a — R. H. Bogue and Wm. Lerch, PCAF Paper, No. 27.
   The specimens were cured in vials with excess water present. Material ground to pass 100 mesh, 90 percent to pass 200. "Fixed water" is the loss on heating at 1000 C from samples pulverized and dried in an oven at 105 C with no control of the water vapor pressure in the oven.
b — R. H. Bogue, Effects of Phase Composition on the Volume Stability of Portland Cement, PCAF (1940) (mimeographed)
   The specimens were cured in vials with no extra water. The material was "ground to approximately 2200 cm²/gm." "Fixed water" as in a.
c — This laboratory
   The specimens were molded and cured in extraction-thimbles surrounded with water. The silicates were each ground to give 85 percent passing the No. 200 sieve, but the trisilicate was nevertheless the finer, p/p_s at equilibrium was about 0.5 x 10⁻⁴. The amount of water was determined by heating at 1000 C.
d — F. P. Lasseter, Chemical Reactions in the Setting of Portland Cement—Dissertation, Columbia University, 1939.
   The specimens were cured in vials with extra water present. Samples of -100 mesh material were dried 3 hr. at 105 C in "dry CO_2-free air."

The first compound listed, the high-sulfate form of calcium sulfoaluminate, may occur in hardened paste to the extent that gypsum is present for its formation (assuming an excess of C_3A). The data indicate that all but 9 of the 32 molecules of water of crystallization may be lost. In an average cement containing 1.7 percent SO_3, all of which reacted to form the calcium sulfoaluminate, the amount of hydrated sulfoaluminate per gram of cement would be about 0.09 g. About 0.03 g of this would be lost on drying.

The second item in Table 8 refers to the low sulfate form of calcium sulfoaluminate, a compound which probably does not form under the conditions prevailing in the hardening of the pastes used here. If it did occur, the data indicate that 2 of the 12 molecules of water of crystallization might be lost on drying over $Mg(ClO_4)_2 \cdot 2H_2O$.

The hexahydrate of C_3A evidently would not be dehydrated by $Mg(ClO_4)_2 \cdot 2H_2O$. The 12-hydrate of C_3A is reduced to about the 8-hydrate on drying over $Mg(ClO_4)_2 \cdot 2H_2O$. $C_4A \cdot 12H_2O$ is not dehydrated by the conditions used for this study.

TABLE 8

Compound	Number of molecules of water retained in the presence of the desiccant indicated		
	$Mg(ClO_4)_2.2H_2O$	CaO	P_2O_5
$C_3A.3CaSO_4.32H_2O$	9[a]	8[b]	7.5[c,d]
$C_3A.CaSO_4.12H_2O$	10[a]	—	8[c,d]
$C_3A.6H_2O$ (cubic)	—	6[c]	—
$C_3A.12H_2O$ (hex)	—	8[c]	—
$C_4A.12H_2O$	—	—	12[f]

a — This laboratory.
b — Jones: Symposium on the Chemistry of Cements (Stockholm, 1938), p. 237.
c — Forsen: Zement v. 19, pp. 1130, 1255 (1930); v. 22, pp. 73, 87, 100 (1933).
d — Mylius: Acta Acad. Aboensis v. 7, p. 3 (1933); see b.
e — Thorvaldson, Grace & Vigfusson: Can. J. Res. v. 1, p. 201 (1929).
f — Assarsson: Symposium on the Chemistry of Cements (Stockholm, 1938), p. 213.

It thus appears that of the various microcrystalline hydrates that can be formed from the constituents of portland cement only the calcium sulfoaluminate would be decomposed to an appreciable extent; it would lose 72 percent of its water of crystallization. After a long period of hydration, the water held by the hydration products of C_3S and C_2S amounts to 20 to 30 percent and 10 to 14 percent of the weight of the original material, respectively.

Before this subject is closed it should be said that the occurrence of the microcrystalline hydrates of C_3A in hardened paste, particulary $C_3A.-6H_2O$, is very doubtful. Several observations indicate this. One is the fact that drying-shrinkage is greater for cements of high C_3A content. This cannot be explained on the basis that C_3A combines with water to form the hexahydrate $C_3A.6H_2O$, since that crystal does not lose water under the conditions of ordinary shrinkage tests.

DETERMINATION OF TOTAL EVAPORABLE WATER

The water that a sample is capable of holding in addition to the non-evaporable water is called the *evaporable water*, as defined before. The procedure for determining the evaporable water content of granulated samples is as follows: About 5 grams of the sample to be saturated is placed in a 50-ml Erlenmeyer flask fitted with a special stopper that permits either the introduction of water from a burette or a stream of dried air free from CO_2. At the start, water is slowly dropped onto the sample from the burette until the sample, upon being shaken, gathers into a lump and clings to the flask. Dry air is then passed over the sample while it is vigorously shaken by hand. After 2 minutes of this treatment, the flow of air is stopped and the shaking of the flask is continued. If the sample persists in gathering into a lump, the drying is continued for 2 more minutes. This procedure is continued until the particles just fail to cling to each other and to the flask. The total water

TABLE 9—DATA ON TOTAL WATER CONTENT OF SATURATED SAMPLES

Series 254-MRB

Cement No.	Age at test, days	$\dfrac{w_o}{c}$	Total water at test, w_t/c				$\dfrac{w_n}{c}$
			Original specimen	Granules			
				SSD 1	SSD 2	SSDO	
1	2	3	4	5	6	7	8
14900	126	0.45	0.526	0.508	0.515	0.527	0.227
14901	126	0.39	0.498	0.491	0.493	0.503	0.223
14902	133	0.39	0.515	0.501	0.495	0.511	0.227
14903	133	0.42	0.527	0.511	0.516	0.526	0.227
14904	162	0.42	0.489	0.490	0.481	0.499	0.228
14905	162	0.41	0.493	0.490	0.482	0.502	0.230
14906	173	0.48	0.551	0.550	0.541	0.567	0.236
14907	173	0.41	0.464	0.461	0.458	0.474	0.219
14908	200	0.39	0.487	0.479	0.475	0.492	0.225
14909	200	0.48	0.562	0.548	0.546	0.572	0.226
14910	204	0.46	0.521	0.513	0.510	0.535	0.228
14911	204	0.46	0.536	0.526	0.521	0.546	0.229
14912	212	0.49	0.551	0.547	0.541	0.568	0.225
14913	212	0.41	0.478	0.477	0.476	0.493	0.221
14914	222	0.42	0.495	0.487	0.499	—	0.225
14915	222	0.44	0.518	0.520	0.517	0.530	0.224
Average			0.513	0.506	0.504	0.523	0.226

SSD = Saturated, surface-dry.
SSD1 = Granulated sample (100-48 mesh) dried in vacuo over $(MgClO_4)_2.2H_2O$ and then resaturated in the presence of air
SSD2 = Granulated sample dried in the same way as SSD1, and resaturated in a vacuum.
SSDO = Granulated sample of original, undried material brought to the SSD condition by adding water in the presence of air
w_n/c = Non-evaporable water, g per g of cement.
w_o/c = Original water-cement ratio by wt., corrected for bleeding
w_t/c = Total water-cement ratio at time of test

held by the sample in this condition, minus the non-evaporable water, is the total evaporable water as defined above.

Data from 40 such determinations showed that the average difference in the values obtained in duplicate determinations by a given operator was 0.36 percent of the dry weight. In three cases out of 40, the difference in values was more than 1 percent. Other experiments showed that the results obtained by two operators working independently did not differ more than did duplicate determinations made by a given operator.

The procedure just described permits water to enter previously dried granules from all sides simultaneously. Since the dried grains are known to contain a considerable amount of adsorbed air, the question arises as to how completely the air is displaced by the water. To answer this question, some dried samples were evacuated, so as to remove most of the adsorbed air, and then the water for saturation was introduced in the absence of air. Companion samples were treated in the presence of air in the usual manner.

TABLE 10—DATA ON TOTAL WATER CONTENT OF SATURATED SAMPLES
Series 254-K4B

Ref. No.	Age at test, days	$\dfrac{w_o}{c}$	Total water at test, w_t/c			$\dfrac{w_n}{c}$
			Original specimen	Granules SSD	SSDO	
1	2	3	4	5	6	7
1-S	180	0.470	0.556	0.543	0.557	0.223
1-P	180	0.473	0.577	0.559	0.576	0.233
1-Q	*180	0.425	0.521	0.502	0.515	0.229
4-S	144	0.463	0.522	0.510	0.525	0.179
4-P	138	0.460	0.548	0.512	0.535	0.177
4-Q	138	0.450	0.518	0.495	0.515	0.177
5-S	150	0.427	0.502	0.498	0.510	0.165
5-P	146	0.453	0.542	0.509	0.519	0.159
5-Q	150	0.456	0.533	0.514	0.527	0.165
6-S	196	0.471	0.529	0.508	0.530	0.215
6-Q	191	0.447	0.532	0.512	0.536	0.222
7-P	164	0.473	0.570	0.556	0.575	0.240
7-Q	171	0.480	0.548	0.549	0.564	0.239
11-P	164	0.445	0.521	0.516	0.532	0.186
11-Q	172	0.440	0.515	0.509	0.516	0.190
15-S	202	0.485	0.558	0.536	0.561	0.217
15-Q	202	0.445	0.555	0.529	0.544	0.220
16-P	223	0.464	0.540	0.525	0.541	0.226
16-Q	223	0.456	0.516	0.502	0.520	0.225
20-S	170	0.472	0.549	0.543	0.554	0.231
20-P	167	0.462	0.551	0.542	0.555	0.233
20-Q	176	0.436	0.520	0.508	0.519	0.226
Average		0.455	0.537	0.520	0.540	0.208

SSD = Saturated, surface-dry.
$SSDO$ = Granulated sample of original, undried material brought to the SSD condition by adding water in the presence of air
w_n/c = Non-evaporable water, g per g of cement
w_o/c = Original water-cement ratio by wt., corrected for bleeding
w_t/c = Total water-cement ratio at time of test

Results are given in columns 5 and 6 of Table 9. (Table 9 gives also other data confirming those in Table 10. The averages 0.506 and 0.504 for the ordinary and vacuum procedures, respectively, show that the air has no appreciable influence on the results.

DISCUSSION OF GRANULAR SAMPLES

Since most of the experiments to be described were made with granular samples of the original specimens, it is necessary to consider the extent to which the granules differ from the original material.

Neat cement—effect of granulation on porosity

Table 10 gives water content data for a group of neat cement specimens and the granular samples prepared from them. The original specimens were 1x7-in. neat cement cylinders that had been stored under water for the periods shown in column 2. During the curing period, they gained in weight, the average gain being 0.082 gram per gram of cement (0.537-0.455).

From each specimen one granular sample (100-48 mesh) was prepared and then saturated by adding excess water to the granules. The excess was evaporated until the saturated surface-dry condition was reached. The results are given in column 6. A comparison of columns 4 and 6 will show that if the difference shown is significant, we may conclude that the saturated granules held slightly more water than the original specimen did at time of test. This indication is somewhat more definite in Table 9. Compare columns 4 and 7. This proves that in specimens of this kind the small granules have very nearly the same porosity as the original specimen, and it indicates that even though the original specimens were stored continuously under water, they did not remain fully saturated. This indication was supported by the dry appearance of the freshly crushed cylinders.

Neat cement—effect of drying on porosity of granules

Other samples of each specimen were dried over $Mg(ClO_4)_2.2H_2O$ and then brought to the saturated surface-dry condition. The results, given in column 5 of Table 9, should be compared with those in column 6. Also in Table 9 compare columns 5 and 6 with column 7. The average water content of the dried and resaturated granules is about 96 percent of that of the saturated granule that had not been dried.

This shows that the drying of the granules produced a permanent shrinkage that reduced the porosity of the granules below that of the paste in the original specimen. In samples of this kind (moderately low w/c, well cured) the effect is small. In specimens of higher w/c and lesser degree of hydration, the effect should be larger.

Mortar specimens—effect of granulation on porosity of paste

The mortar specimens used in these studies were made with non-absorptive, quartz sand. Consequently, all water originally in the specimen (after bleeding) as well as that absorbed during curing is held in the paste, and data showing differences between the total water contents of the original specimens and that of the granular samples represent differences in the degree of saturation, or in the porosity, of the hardened paste, just as they do with neat specimens.

Data of this kind were obtained from mortar cubes for specimens of different ages and different water-cement ratios. Typical results are given in Fig. 2-1, A and B.

The cement represented in A is a slow hardening type; that in B is normal.

In each diagram the circled dots represent the total water content of the original specimen; the crosses, the total water content of the dried-and-resaturated granules; and the triangles, the granules that were saturated without preliminary drying.

It is apparent that for specimens cured 28 days or more, the relationships are about as were found for the neat pastes described above. However, at earlier ages, especially for the slow hardening cement, the granules show less porosity than the pastes of the original specimens, the difference being greater, the higher the original water-cement ratio.

These results seem to indicate that during the early stages of hydration the paste contains voids nearly as large as the granules of the samples and that as hydration proceeds, these larger voids disappear.

On the whole, these results show that the porosity of a granular sample is about the same as that of the pastes in the original specimen except for specimens having pastes of very high porosity. A granular sample that has been dried has a smaller total pore volume than the original paste. From other data it is known that this effect, in well cured specimens, diminishes with decrease in the original water-cement ratio and probably becomes negligible at about $w_o/c = 0.3$ by weight.

METHODS OF STUDYING THE EVAPORABLE WATER

As shown by the earlier work reviewed in Part 1, when a specimen of hardened paste at room temperature is exposed to water vapor or to air containing water vapor, its water content spontaneously changes until equilibrium between the water held in the specimen and the outside water vapor is established. The establishment of equilibrium involves a change in moisture content of the sample, for the nature of the hardened paste is such that at a given temperature the relationship between vapor pressure of the water in the hardened specimen and the water content is represented by a smooth curve. Moreover, the nature of the paste is such that a specimen can remain saturated only when it is in contact with saturated water vapor or with liquid water.

Much of the work to be reported here consisted in determining the relationships between the evaporable water content and the vapor pressure for various samples of hardened cement paste. The taking up of moisture from the atmosphere will be referred to as *adsorption*, and the reverse will be called *desorption*, even though other processes might be involved. The plotted results will be called *adsorption* and *desorption* *isotherms*, respectively. When speaking of both processes collectively or of the processes in general without specifying the direction of moisture change, the term *sorption* will be used.

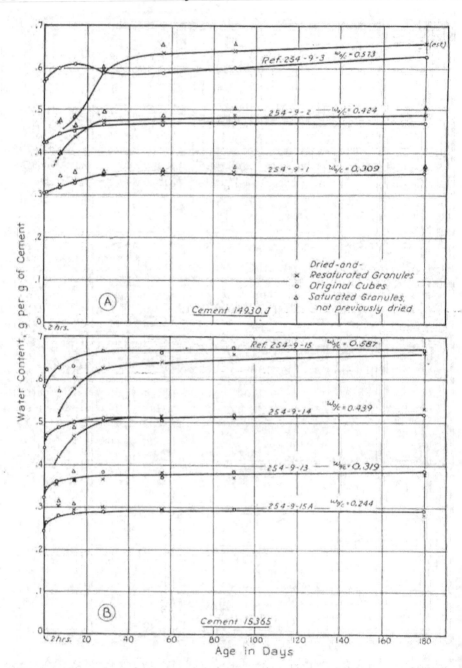

Fig. 2-1—Comparison of water content of intact cubes with that of granular samples from from the same cubes

THE APPARATUS FOR SORPTION MEASUREMENTS

Two types of apparatus were used for sorption measurements. In one the samples were exposed to water vapor only and in the other the samples were exposed to CO_2-free air containing controlled amounts of water vapor. The first is referred to as the *high-vacuum apparatus* and the second as the *air-stream apparatus*.

High-vacuum apparatus

The high-vacuum apparatus used for these studies is illustrated schematically in Fig. 2-2. As shown, two samples may be kept under test simultaneously. The samples may be either small granules or thin wafers. If granules, they are contained in small buckets made of platinum foil which are suspended on helical springs made of quartz in the two chambers marked C. If the samples are wafers, they are suspended from the springs by platinum hooks.

After the air has been pumped out, water vapor of known pressure is admitted to chamber C. The pressure of the vapor is indicated directly by the oil in manometer D. The arrangement is such that during the adsorption process the sample is never subjected to a higher vapor pressure than that with which it will finally be in equilibrium. This is an important feature of the method, for experience has shown that if the ambient vapor pressure is allowed to change as the samples approach equilibrium, the equilibrium-weight is different from what it would have been had the vapor pressure been maintained constant. This is due to the phenomenon of hysteresis, discussed later on.

The changes in weight of the sample are observed by measuring the changes in length of the quartz springs by means of a cathetometer. The spring-cathetometer combination has a sensitivity of about 0.2 mg. With a live load of about 400 mg this gives adequate accuracy.

The water vapor pressure is generated by the water (or ice) in bulb A or bulb B. Bulb B is used for the lowest pressure of the range employed which is that of water at the temperature of dry ice wetted with alcohol, -78 C. For all higher vapor pressures cock 2 is closed and 1 is open, thus utilizing bulb A. The temperature of the water (or ice) in A is controlled by a cryostat, which is maintained at any desired temperature down to -25 C within about ± 0.05 C.

For the highest pressure used, a small amount of water is distilled from A into the bottom of C and stopcock 1 is then closed. By maintaining the temperature of the tube outside the 25 C air-bath above 25 C, the water vapor pressure in C is, theoretically, maintained at 23.756 mm of *Hg*, the saturation pressure of water at 25 C. Accurate measurements at this vapor pressure, or at any vapor pressure above about 95 percent of the saturation pressure, cannot be obtained by this method because of condensation on the springs.

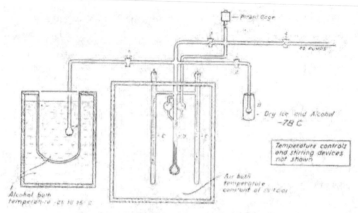

Fig. 2-2—High vacuum sorption apparatus

Fig. 2-3—General view of apparatus

Between cocks 3 and 4 a Pirani-type vacuum gage is attached so as to indicate the pressure on the "zero" side of the manometer. This is to make certain that the readings on the manometer are not vitiated by slow leaks on the zero side.

To check against leaks on the other "pressure" side of stopcock 3, the temperature of the bath surrounding A is measured by means of an eight-junction thermocouple and a type-K potentiometer. The vapor pressure of the ice or water in bulb A can then be ascertained from handbook data. Any discrepancies between the pressure shown at D and the pressure indicated by the temperature at A that are greater than the inaccuracy of measurement would be indicative of pressure from gas other than water vapor.

A general view of the apparatus is given in Fig. 2-3. The cabinet in the foreground contains the controlled bath for bulb A. The large cabinet in the middle background is the 25 C air-bath. This cabinet is the same as that used for the air-stream apparatus to be described below. It can be used for both methods simultaneously, although that has not been done as yet.

The cabinet in the foreground is the cryostat. It contains a cylindrical vessel of about 10-gallon capacity filled with alcohol. This is cooled by the refrigeration unit mounted under the cabinet. A one-gallon container is mounted, submerged to its upper rim, in this alcohol bath. The container is a double-walled glass vessel with air between the walls. It contains the alcohol in which bulb A, Fig. 2-2, is immersed. By means of an electrical heater and thermoregulator, the temperature of this one-gallon bath is maintained at whatever level is desired. The thermoregulator is a laboratory-made, toluene-mercury type. It operates through an electronic switch and Mercoid relay.

The air in the large cabinet is kept in rapid circulation by means of two electric fans and two air-driven windshield fans. The cabinet is cooled by continuously circulating cold alcohol through a copper coil inside the cabinet. The circulated alcohol is cooled by means of another coil dipping into the outer alcohol bath of the cryostat described in the foregoing paragraph.* The cabinet is heated by an electric heater (about 200 watts). The input to the electric heater is controlled by a laboratory-made, toluene-mercury thermoregulator that operates through an electronic switch and Mercoid relay. The sensitivity of the regulator is about 0.005 C. The variation in temperature at any given point does not exceed 0.01 C, and the average temperatures at different points do not differ more than 0.02 C.

Air-stream apparatus

The air-stream apparatus is built in and around the large cabinet just described. It was designed to deliver 11 streams of air simultaneously, each stream having a different water content and hence different water vapor pressure. The following description pertaining to one of the air streams is applicable also to the rest.

The air to be conditioned is taken from the compressed air supply of the laboratory. The air pressure is reduced to 3 lb. per sq. in. by means of two diaphragm-type pressure-reduction valves connected in series. The low-pressure air is then delivered to a train of one-gallon bottles such as is illustrated in the lower part of Fig. 2-4. The first bottle

---

*This arrangement is used at present. For most of the period covered by this paper cold tap water from the building supply was used, but this often failed its purpose during the summer.

Fig. 2-4—Schematic diagram of one of
the air conditioning trains for adsorption
tests

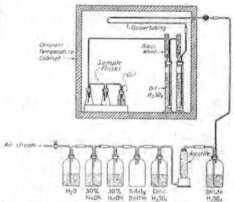

contains water, and the next two sodium hydroxide solutions. The
water bottle at the head of the train prevents the formation of sodium
carbonate in the inlet tube of the caustic-soda bottles. Next in line is
an empty bottle for safety and this is followed by a bottle of concentrated sulfuric acid (specific gravity 1.84) to dry the air. The dry air is
then delivered to a tower of Ascarite to remove any traces of carbon
dioxide that might have escaped the caustic-soda solutions. The air
stream then passes through a 3-gallon bottle containing dilute sulfuric
acid. The output of this bottle is divided into two streams, one of which
is shown in Fig. 2-4. The strength of the acid in the large bottle just
mentioned is so regulated that it gives the air passing through it a water
content somewhat below that desired for either of the two streams taken
from the bottle. This slightly-too-dry air then is piped into the constant
temperature cabinet where it circulates, first through a length of copper
tubing to permit the temperature to reach 25 C and then through two
towers of sulfuric acid connected in series as shown in the upper part of
Fig. 2-4. The second stream taken from the bottle is led similarly to
another pair of acid-towers, regulated to give a different vapor pressure.
The strength of the acid in the towers is carefully regulated to have
exactly the vapor pressure desired in the outgoing stream of air. To
insure equilibrium between the stream of air and the acid the air is
dispersed as fine bubbles by means of porous plugs fastened to the ends
of the inlet tubes. (These porous plugs were made in the laboratory by
sintering granulated glass in a crucible.) To remove entrained droplets
of acid, each tower is equipped with a glass-wool filter as shown.

The outgoing stream of air is led through rubber connections to an
Erlenmeyer flask containing the sample under test. As the air passes
the dry granules, they absorb some of the water vapor. This continues
until the vapor pressure of the water in the sample becomes equal to
that of the water vapor in the air stream.

Two samples are run simultaneously by connecting sample-flasks in tandem as shown. The outgoing stream of air from the second flask bubbles through a mineral oil contained in a 6-oz. bottle and then escapes to the interior of the cabinet. The mineral-oil trap prevents back-diffusion of moisture and carbon dioxide from the air in the cabinet to the sample.

Eleven such pairs of sample-bottles in the cabinet make it possible to obtain simultaneously 11 points on the adsorption curves for each of two materials.

Because the air delivered to the acid towers inside the cabinet is in each case slightly drier than the output from the towers, the level of the acid in the towers gradually subsides during the continuous flow of the air streams. About once a month it is necessary to replenish the towers by adding distilled water. This is done by means of glass tubes (not shown in sketch) leading from the stoppers in the tops of the acid towers through the top of the cabinet. Similarly, the acid in the large bottles outside (under) the cabinet and the caustic-soda solutions are renewed about once a month.

During the development period, the water content of each air stream was measured by passing a measured volume of the air through weighing tubes filled with P_2O_5. The relative vapor pressure of each stream was then computed from the law for perfect gases. A number of such measurements showed that the water vapor pressure in the air streams differed from that which could be computed from the strength of the acid by less than 0.025 mm of mercury or a difference in p/p_s* of less than 0.001. When this was learned, the air streams were considered always to be at equilibrium with the acids in the towers.

The sample flasks were removed from the cabinet once daily and weighed on a chemical balance, care being taken to minimize the exposure of the granules. A typical record of the results of such weighings is shown in Fig. 2-5. This diagram shows that for those samples exposed to water vapor of relatively low pressure the weights reached a maximum and thereafter declined. At vapor pressures of 0.8 p_s or higher the weight either remained constant after one or two days or else continued to increase steadily, though very slightly, with time, this tendency being more pronounced the higher the vapor pressure. The increase in weight just mentioned is believed to be due to hydration of fresh surfaces of clinker residues exposed on crushing the original sample.

The behavior of the specimens exposed to the drier atmospheres is not understood. The phenomenon was not observed when using the high-vacuum apparatus. From this it may be inferred that the presence of air

*p = vapor pressure of air steam
p_s = saturation vapor pressure of water

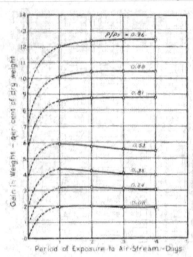

Fig. 2-5—Typical relationship between gain in weight and period of exposure

may have something to do with the result. However, as will be shown later, the major aspects of the results obtained in the presence of air are essentially the same as those obtained in the absence of air.

Inasmuch as the decrease in weight shown by the lower curves in Fig. 2-5 continued for as long as two weeks, it was decided to use maximum rather than final weights. There was some question as to whether the final weight was any more significant than the maximum weight; also, since the decline from the maximum represented but a small percentage of the total gain, it did not seem justifiable to retard the experimental work to the extent necessary to get final weights.

Reproducibility of results

The reproducibility of the data obtained in the manner just described is illustrated in Table 11. These are results from two sets of samples made from the same specimen, each set being tested independently. The corresponding figures are in very good agreement except at the two highest pressures. Such differences were commonly observed and were probably due to different degrees of proximity to equilibrium.

Comparisons such as those that are given in Table 11 were made at other times during the course of these experiments, with similar results. Nevertheless, there is reason to believe that in some groups of tests the variability was considerably greater than would be expected from such data as those presented above. Possibly such variations are due not so much to variations in the adsorption measurements themselves as to variations in auxiliary tests as when the samples contained pulverized silica and therefore required a chemical analysis for the estimation of cement content. The discrepancies that will be noted among the various

TABLE 11—REPRODUCIBILITY OF THE ISOTHERMS

Cement: 16189
Initial w/c: 0.50
Curing: 6 weeks in water

Relative vapor pressure p/p_s	Total water-content of sample indicated, % by weight of cement	
	A	B
0.0 (non-evap. H_2O)	15.47	15.42
0.08	17.98	18.03
0.16	18.87	18.94
0.32	20.10	20.28
0.39	20.82	20.98
0.46	21.44	21.65
0.53	22.02	22.09
0.60	22.82	22.90
0.70	24.82	24.76
0.81	27.52	27.53
0.88	30.43	29.69
0.96	35.31	34.60

data yet to be presented are often such as would result from errors in the determination of the cement content of the sample. The data obtained from samples of neat cement were less erratic.

Use of ordinary desiccators

In some auxiliary work, neither the air-stream nor high-vacuum apparatus was used. Instead, samples were placed in ordinary air-filled desiccators in the presence of a suitable desiccating agent. The samples were weighed from time to time until the results indicated equilibrium to have been reached.

Theoretically, the results obtained in this way should, in most respects, be the same as those obtained by the methods already described. Actually, the results from the samples dried in desiccators did not agree very well with the results obtained by the other two methods. The cause of the discrepancy is not known. It was observed, however, that the rate of absorption in an air-filled desiccator is very much less than that in vacuum or air stream. This suggests the possibility that the exposure of samples was terminated too soon, that is, that they did not approach equilibrium as closely in the air-filled desiccators as they did when tested by either of the other two methods. Another possibility is that, owing to the longer exposure and to the continued presence of air, samples tested in desiccators might have become carbonated sufficiently to influence the final results. At any rate this method is not recommended.

RESULTS OF THE SORPTION MEASUREMENTS—EMPIRICAL ASPECTS OF THE DATA

General features

Fig. 2-6 and Tables 12 to 17 record a run made with the high-vacuum apparatus illustrated in Fig. 2-2. In this case the sample was a very thin wafer of hardened neat cement paste described in Table 12, $w_o/c = 0.5$ by weight. In its initial, saturated state it weighed 380.5 mg, as indicated by the uppermost point in Fig. 2-6. After the sample was installed, the air was pumped out of the apparatus. The initial pumping period was made brief to avoid overdrying the sample. The object was to remove the air from the chamber without removing water from the sample, if possible. To maintain the water vapor pressure as high as possible during the pumping a small amount of water was introduced into the sample chamber before the pumping began. The desired result was not obtained; the pump removed the water vapor so rapidly that nearly half the evaporable water in the sample was removed during only 6 minutes of pumping.

As soon as the initial pumping was finished, the sample was subjected to a vapor pressure of 0.94 p_s. Owing to the losses suffered during the initial pumping, the sample gained in weight at this pressure until it reached equilibrium at a weight of 374.4 mg. Then the pressure was lowered step by step and the rest of the points appearing on the desorption curve were obtained. At the final weight, 309.8 mg, the sample was at equilibrium with the vapor pressure of the ice at -78 C, the temperature of dry ice.

As soon as the evaporable water had been removed, the vacuum pumps were operated for many hours so as to remove as much air from the system as possible. Then the vapor pressure was increased stepwise, thus establishing the adsorption curve shown.

As shown in Fig. 2-6, the adsorption and desorption curves coincided only at pressures below 0.1 p_s. (As a matter of fact, it is not certain that the curves coincided over this range, but it seems probable that they did so.) Studies of other materials[3] show that in the range of pressures where the curves form a loop, innumerable curves within the loop can be produced under suitable experimental conditions. If the process of adsorption or desorption is reversed at any point short of the horizontal extremes of the loop, the part of the curve that had previously been generated will not be retraced but instead the points will cut across the loop. If at any stage of adsorption in this range the process is reversed, the resulting downward curve will cross over from the adsorption to the desorption curve. If the desorption curve is reversed, then a new rising curve will cross over toward the adsorption curve, but instead of joining the adsorption curve the new curve will rise more or less parallel to the adsorption curve, the loop being closed only at the saturation point. Thus, it is possible to obtain points representing thermodynamic equilib-

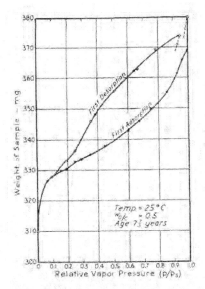

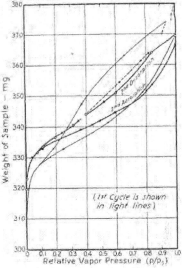

Fig. 2-6A (upper left)—Data from Tables 12 and 13

Fig. 2-6B (upper right)—Data from Tables 14 and 15

Fig. 2-6C (lower right)—Sorption isotherms for cement slab made from cement 13495

High vacuum apparatus. Data from Tables 16 and 17

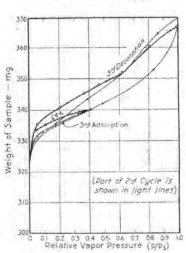

rium* between the evaporable water in the sample and the ambient water vapor anywhere between the desorption and adsorption curves.

*Chemists tend to question whether or not these should be called equilibrium points. They feel that, like points representing chemical equilibrium, a given point should be attainable from either side.

However, the requirement that a state of equilibrium must be approachable from either side with the same result does not properly apply to all physical equilibria. See for example the "ink bottle theory" of sorption hysteresis (Brunauer, p. 398). This theory shows that different amounts of water could be in equilibrium with the same vapor pressure. This is not to say that the conditions pictured in developing the ink bottle theory actually exist in hardened paste. It merely refutes the idea that equilibrium between water content and vapor pressure requires that only one water content can be associated with a given vapor pressure.

A paper by W. O. Smith (Sorption in an Ideal Soil, Soil Sci. v. 41, p. 209, (1936)) is especially pertinent. He showed by geometrical analysis that in an assemblage of spheres holding water by capillary condensation, different amounts of water can be in thermodynamic equilibrium with the same vapor pressure. Such equilibrium is reversible in the sense that the same *surface curvature* should be established at a given vapor pressure, regardless of the direction of approach. See Part 3, Capillary Condensation.

TABLE 12—FIRST DESORPTION CURVE FOR SLAB PREPARED FROM
CEMENT 13495

High-vacuum apparatus
Age 7 years, 116 days
Original w/c = 0.50 by wt.

p/p_s (p_s = 23.756 mm of Hg)	Wt. of sample, mg	Evaporable water in the sample	
		mg	Fraction of dry wt. of sample ($=w$)
1.000	380.5	70.7	.2485
?	346.8 (a)	37.0	.1194
0.942	374.4	64.6	.2085
0.780	369.3	59.5	.1921
0.663	363.1	53.3	.1720
0.509	355.8	46.0	.1485
0.351	346.1	36.3	.1139
0.250	336.5	26.7	.0862
0.193	333.4	23.6	.0762
0.099	328.0	18.2	.0587
0.000	309.8	00.0	.0000

(a) Weight after 6 minutes of pumping—vapor pressure unknown.

TABLE 13—FIRST ADSORPTION DATA FOR SLAB PREPARED FROM
CEMENT 13495

High-vacuum apparatus

p/p_s (p_s = 23.756 mm of Hg)	Wt. of sample, mg	Evaporable water in the sample	
		mg	Fraction of dry wt. of sample ($=w$)
0.000	309.8	00.0	.0000
0.064	326.7	16.9	.0545
0.155	329.8	20.0	.0646
0.193	330.7	20.9	.0675
0.249	332.1	22.3	.0720
0.350	335.1	25.3	.0817
0.446	338.0	28.2	.0910
0.598	343.0	33.2	.1072
0.745	351.0	41.2	.1330
0.855	356.6	46.8	.1511
0.959	366.4	56.6	.1827
0.995	369.6	59.8	.1930
1.000		67.0 (est.)	.2162 (est.)

TABLE 14—SECOND DESORPTION CURVE FOR SLAB PREPARED FROM
CEMENT 13495

High-vacuum apparatus

p/p_s ($p_s = 23.756$ mm of Hg)	Wt. of sample, mg	Evaporable water in the sample	
		mg	Fraction of dry wt. of sample ($= w$)
0.995	369.6	50.0	.1565
0.848	364.1	44.5	.1392
0.594	350.7	31.1	.0973
0.397	344.0	24.4	.0763
0.82*	364.3	44.7	.1399
0.314	340.5	20.9	.0654
0.194	336.7	17.1	.0535
0.128	334.2	14.6	.0457
0.078	331.7	12.1	.0379
0.004	323.4	3.8	.0119
0.000	319.6	0.0	.0000

*Temperature controls failed and caused unintentional rise in pressure.

TABLE 15—SECOND ADSORPTION CURVE FOR SLAB PREPARED FROM
CEMENT 13495

High-vacuum apparatus

p/p_s ($p_s = 23.756$ mm of Hg)	Wt. of sample, mg	Evaporable water in the sample	
		mg	Fraction of dry wt. of sample ($= w$)
0.000	319.6	0.0	.0000
0.042	330.4	10.8	.0338
0.112	333.2	13.6	.0426
0.220	335.7	16.1	.0504
0.364	339.0	19.4	.0607
0.450	340.7	21.1	.0660
0.596	344.7	25.1	.0785
0.806	351.4	31.8	.0995
1.00 (?)	366.8	47.2	.1477

TABLE 16—THIRD DESORPTION OF SLAB PREPARED FROM CEMENT 13495
High-vacuum apparatus

p/p_s ($p_s = 23.756$ mm of Hg)	Wt. of sample, mg	Evaporable water in the sample	
		mg	Fraction of dry wt. of sample ($=w$)
1.00 (?)	366.8	45.8	.1427
0.807	360.8	39.8	.1240
0.624	352.0	31.0	.0966
0.467	348.0	27.0	.0841
0.370	345.3	24.3	.0757
0.202	340.9	19.9	.0620
0.052	335.3	14.3	.0445
0.043	334.2	13.2	.0411
0.000	321.0	00.0	.0000

TABLE 17—THIRD PARTIAL ADSORPTION AND PARTIAL DESORPTION DATA
FROM SLAB PREPARED FROM CEMENT 13495
High-vacuum apparatus

p/p_s ($p_s = 23.756$ mm of Hg)	Wt. of sample, mg	Evaporable water in the sample	
		mg	Fraction of dry wt. of sample ($=w$)
0.000	321.0	0.0	.0000
0.052	332.3	11.3	.0352
0.094	333.2	12.2	.0380
0.178	335.4	14.4	.0448
0.321	338.7	17.7	.0552
0.405	340.1	19.1	.0595
0.326	339.2	18.2	.0567
0.146	336.5	15.5	.0483
0.049	333.6	12.6	.0392

The lack of reversibility as described above is shown by materials of various kinds.

Although the phenomenon has not been investigated extensively here, there is little reason to doubt that portland cement pastes all show essentially the behavior described above. This matter of hysteresis is significant and should be kept in mind in connection with the theoretical discussion that follows later in this paper. It is a principal reason for believing that ordinary laws of chemical reaction cannot be applied to the reactions involving the gain or loss of evaporable water.

Besides the effects common to many materials, portland cement paste exhibits certain irreversible phenomena not found among some other types of materials. This is shown in Fig. 2-6B, where the second desorption-and-adsorption curves of the sample are given.

A break in the second desorption curve at $p = 0.395\ p_s$ will be noted. After equilibrium at this pressure had been established, the cryostat was set to produce a lower pressure, but during the night the temperature controls failed, the pressure rose to $p = 0.82\ p_s$ and the sample-weight increased, giving the point indicated by the cross. (This point probably does not represent an equilibrium value, but is close to it.) When proper operation of the cryostat was restored, the point at $p = 0.315\ p_s$ was obtained.

The light-line curves in Fig. 2-6B are those of Fig. 2-6A, shown for comparison. The marked difference between the first and second cycles is believed to be due to two factors: One is the irreversible shrinkage (described in Part 1) that reduces the capacity of the sample for evaporable water. The other is the additional hydration of the cement in the sample that occurs while the sample is subjected to vapor pressures above about 0.8 p_s. Although these samples had been stored in water for several years they seem to have contained unhydrated clinker that was exposed when the thin wafers were prepared.

No explanation for one feature of the irreversibility has been found. Note that on the first desorption the minimum weight reached was 309.8 mg. On the second desorption the minimum weight was 319.6 mg. Continued hydration has the effect of increasing the minimum weight, but the increase shown here is much too great to be accounted for in this way. It is possible that the observed minimum weight for the first desorption was in error by several milligrams. However, the original data offer no clue as to the nature or cause of the error, if there was one.

Fig. 2-6C shows the third desorption and a partial third adsorption curve. The third *desorption* curve differs from both the first and second desorption curves, but the third *adsorption* is practically the same as the second adsorption. In fact, when the results are expressed as percentage of the minimum weight, the second and third adsorption curves are identical. Tests on other samples show that after the first cycle of drying and wetting the adsorption curves are reproducible. But the indications of a limited amount of data are that the desorption curves are greatly influenced by small variations in experimental conditions and are difficult to reproduce exactly.

On the third desorption, Fig. 2-6C, after the weight corresponding to 0.4 p_s had been established, the pressure was intentionally lowered stepwise with the result indicated by the graph. This illustrates what was said above about the irreversibility of this process in the range of pressures where the curves form a loop. Note that the points cut across the loop and join the desorption curve. This behavior is similar in character to that obtained with other materials[3]. It should be noted, however, that the vapor pressure at which the loop closes is much lower than that observed with other materials. Moreover, the loop closes at a much lower pressure than would be predicted from Cohan's hypothesis[4].

The size and shape of the hysteresis loop, and the course of the curve when the process is reversed within the limits of the loop, are probably characteristic of the physical structure of the hardened paste[4,5]. At any rate the whole phenomenon cannot be understood until these loops can be adequately interpreted. However, practically all the measurements reported in this paper were of adsorption only. Therefore, the interpretation of the adsorption curve is the only part of the problem that can be considered here.

Along with the measurements described above, measurements were made on the sample described in Table 18. This sample was prepared from a neat-cement cylinder that had been molded under high pressure with w/c only 0.12 by weight.

The results are given in Tables 18 to 23 and in Fig. 2-7, all three cycles being shown on the same graph. The features pointed out in Fig. 2-6 can be seen here also, and others besides. Note that the effect of the reversal in pressure that occurred during the second desorption was somewhat different from that on the other specimen. Note also that the lower parts of the second and third desorption cycles are identical. The indication is that with a specimen as dense as this, the paste becomes "stabilized" after the first drying so that desorption as well as adsorption curves are reproducible, provided that the specimen is always saturated at the start. The differences among the desorption curves in the upper range are believed to be due to slight differences in the degree of saturation at the beginning of the desorption part of the cycle.

Comparison of the results obtained with high-vacuum and air-stream apparatus

Fig. 2-8 and Tables 24 and 25 give adsorption data for two granulated pastes, the data being obtained first with the air-stream apparatus and then, about three years later, with the high-vacuum apparatus. The granules had been sealed in glass ampoules during the three-year interval. The later tests were made on samples from the same lot of granules as the earlier ones, but not on the same samples as used in the first test. Thus, the curves obtained by each method were first-adsorption curves.

The granules had originally been dried by the regular procedure used in connection with the air-stream method, that is, over Dehydrite in a

TABLE 18—FIRST DESORPTION CURVE ON SLAB PREPARED FROM
CEMENT 14675

High-vacuum apparatus
Age 4 years 29 days
Original w/c = 0.12 by weight
Molded under 24,000 lb/in² pressure

p/p_s (= x) (p_s = 23.756 mm of Hg)	Wt. of sample, mg	Evaporable water in sample		
		mg	Fraction of dry wt. of paste (= w)	
1.000	664.4	47.8	0.0775	Initial wt. sat'd
?	647.9	31.3	0.0508	Wt. after 6 min. pumping
1.000	742.8	126.2	0.2046	Droplets condensed on sample
0.942	656.4	39.8	0.0645	
0.780	653.3	36.7	0.0595	
0.663	652.0	35.4	0.0574	
0.509	649.7	33.1	0.0537	
0.351	647.4	30.8	0.0500	
0.250	643.4	26.8	0.0435	
0.193	641.5	24.9	0.0404	
0.099	638.1	21.5	0.0349	
0.000	616.6	00.0	0.0000	

TABLE 19—FIRST ADSORPTION CURVE ON SLAB PREPARED FROM
CEMENT 14675

High-vacuum apparatus

p/p_s (= x) (p_s = 23.756 mm of Hg)	Wt. of sample, mg	Evaporable water in sample	
		mg	Fraction of dry wt. of paste (= w)
0.000	616.6	00.0	0.0000
0.064	627.6	11.0	0.0178
0.155	629.9	13.3	0.0216
0.193	630.2	13.6	0.0221
0.249	631.5	14.9	0.0242
0.350	632.7	16.1	0.0261
0.446	634.0	17.4	0.0282
0.598	638.7	22.1	0.0358
0.745	642.5	25.9	0.0420
0.855	645.8	29.2	0.0474
0.959	653.8	37.2	0.0603
1.000	664.4*	47.8	0.0775

*Original weight.

TABLE 20—SECOND DESORPTION CURVE ON SLAB PREPARED FROM
CEMENT 14675

High-vacuum apparatus

p/p_s ($= x$) ($p_s = 23.756$ mm of Hg)	Wt. of sample, mg	Evaporable water in sample	
		mg	Fraction of dry wt. of paste ($= w$)
1.000 (a)	685.1	68.5	0.1111
0.957	656.4	39.8	0.0645
0.848	653.8	37.2	0.0603
0.594	648.7	32.1	0.0521
0.397	646.4	29.8	0.0483
0.82 (b)	650.7	34.1	0.0553
0.314	642.2	25.6	0.0415
0.194	639.4	22.8	0.0370
0.128	637.6	21.0	0.0341
0.078	635.8	19.2	0.0311
0.004	622.0	5.4	0.0088
0.000	616.6	0.0	0.0000

(a) Water visible on sample.
(b) Temperature controls failed and caused pressure to rise.

TABLE 21—SECOND ADSORPTION CURVE FOR SLAB PREPARED FROM
CEMENT 14675

High-vacuum apparatus

p/p_s ($= x$) ($p_s = 23.756$ mm of Hg)	Wt. of sample, mg	Evaporable water in sample	
		mg	Fraction of dry wt. of paste ($= w$)
0.000	616.6	0	0
0.042	626.1	9.5	0.0154
0.112	629.4	12.8	0.0208
0.220	631.0	14.4	0.0234
0.364	633.0	16.4	0.0266
0.450	634.5	17.9	0.0290
0.596	638.7	22.1	0.0358
0.806	644.3	27.7	0.0449
1.000	662 (est)	45.4 (est)	0.0736 (est)

TABLE 22—THIRD DESORPTION CURVE FOR SLAB PREPARED FROM CEMENT 14675

High-vacuum apparatus

p/p_s ($= x$) ($p_s = 23.756$ mm of Hg)	Wt. of sample, mg	Evaporable water in sample	
		mg	Fraction of dry wt. of paste ($= w$)
0.807	655.3	38.7	0.0628
0.624	647.9	31.3	0.0508
0.467	645.1	28.5	0.0462
0.370	643.3	26.7	0.0433
0.202	639.2	22.6	0.0367
0.052	634.8	18.2	0.0295
0.043	632.5	15.9	0.0258
0.000	616.6	00.0	0.0000

TABLE 23—THIRD PARTIAL ADSORPTION AND PARTIAL DESORPTION CURVES FOR SLAB PREPARED FROM CEMENT 14675

High-vacuum method

p/p_s ($= x$) ($p_s = 23.756$ mm of Hg)	Wt. of sample, mg	Evaporable water in sample	
		mg	Fraction of dry wt. of paste ($= w$)
0.00	616.6	0	0
0.052	627.6	11.0	0.0178
0.094	628.9	12.3	0.0199
0.178	631.1	14.5	0.0235
0.321	633.3	16.7	0.0271
0.405	634.2	17.6	0.0285
0.326	633.8	17.2	0.0279
0.146	631.6	15.0	0.0243
0.049	628.7	12.1	0.0196

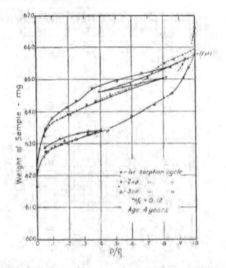

Fig. 2-7—Sorption isotherms for neat cement slab made from cement 14675
Data from Tables 18 to 23

vacuum desiccator. In the high-vacuum procedure these granules were exposed to the vapor pressure generated by ice at the temperature of dry ice, the lowest pressure used. After the final exposure to this low pressure in the high-vacuum apparatus, the samples were ignited. The final weights compared with those obtained after the earlier tests are given below:

	Sample No.	
	9-15A-6M	K4B-1Q
Loss on ignition as dried originally (g/g)...................	0.1428	0.1927
Loss on ignition as dried in high-vacuum apparatus (g/g)....	0.1506	0.1922

Note that the water content of K4B-1Q was the same (within the limits of probable error) under both drying conditions and that therefore the sample as received from the sealed ampoule was not changed by the exposure to the lowest vapor pressure used in the high-vacuum apparatus. As mentioned in connection with Table 5, above, this provides data for estimating the vapor pressure of the desiccant used in earlier tests. The vapor pressure over ice at dry ice temperature (-78 C) is given as 0.56 microns of mercury.[5] The pressure relative to the saturation pressure at 25 C is therefore about 24 x 10^{-6}.

The data for the other sample, 9-15A-6M, indicate that the two drying conditions were not exactly alike, the amount of water removed in the original drying being somewhat greater than that removed in the

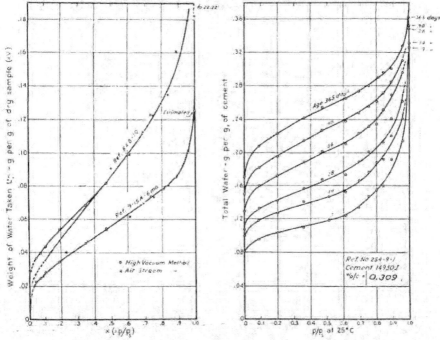

Fig. 2-8 (left)—Adsorption isotherms (25 C) for granular samples
Data from tables 24 and 25, Part 2, and from Tables A-8 and A-27 of Appendix to Part 2

Fig. 2-9 (right)—Adsorption isotherms showing effect of curing (air-stream apparatus)

TABLE 24—FIRST ADSORPTION CURVE FOR GRANULAR SAMPLE 9-15A-6M
High-vacuum method

p/p_s ($= x$)	Wt. of sample, mg	Evaporable water in the sample	
		mg	Fraction of dry wt. of sample ($= w$)
0.00	431.3	0.0	.0000
0.055	441.1	9.8	.0227
0.073	442.0	10.7	.0249
0.104	443.6	12.3	.0284
0.193	446.3	15.0	.0347
0.244	448.5	17.2	.0400
0.349	450.9	19.6	.0455
0.472	454.7	23.4	.0542
0.738	463.1	31.8	.0738
1.000			.1250*

*Observed value 0.1569, but known to be too high because of condensation in sample and spring. 0.1250 is based on the estimated water content of the sample in the saturated state.

TABLE 25—ADSORPTION CURVE FOR GRANULAR SAMPLE K4B-1Q
High-vacuum method

p/p_s ($= x$)	Wt. of sample, mg	Evaporable water in the sample	
		mg	Fraction of dry wt. of sample ($= w$)
0.00	542.2	0.0	.0000
0.055	562.2	20.0	.0369
0.073	563.7	21.5	.0395
0.104	566.3	24.1	.0442
0.193	571.4	29.2	.054)
0.244	574.0	31.8	.0587
0.349	579.4	37.2	.0686
0.472	586.6	44.4	.0819
0.738	608.9	66.7	.1230
1.000			.2295*

*Original water content after drying and resaturating.

high-vacuum apparatus. This would indicate that the vapor pressure over the magnesium perchlorate hydrate is somewhat less than that over ice at -78 C. However, there is some reason to believe, as pointed out before, that the drying agent in the original tests was sometimes inadvertently $Mg(ClO_4)_2 + Mg(ClO_4)_2.2H_2O$ instead of $Mg(ClO_4)_2.2H_2O + Mg(ClO_4)_2.4H_2O$. This could be one of those instances.

In regard to the course of the curves over the lower range of vapor pressures, we will show later that theoretically the presence of air should reduce the amount of adsorption in the manner shown by the plotted data for K4B-1Q. That is, the two series of points for this sample differ only as they theoretically should. It will be seen later that in other important respects the two series of points have the same significance and that the two methods give essentially the same result.

The two series of points for sample 9-15A-6M fall practically on the same line. Theoretically, the crosses should drop below the circles in the low-pressure range. The fact that they do not can be accounted for by the data given above showing that the sample used in the original tests (air-stream method) was dried to a lower water content than the sample used in the later tests (high-vacuum method). It will be seen later that the drier the sample the higher the "knee" of the adsorption curve. It therefore seems that by chance alone the effect of the difference in initial water content exactly offset the effect of the presence of air.

These data indicate that adsorption in the presence of air is essentially the same as that in the absence of air when the small effect of the air itself is taken into account. This is important, for it shows that the interpretations worked out by other investigators for adsorption from a pure gas phase can be applied with modifications to the adsorption of water vapor from a mixture of air and water vapor.

It should be noted that practically all the data given in this paper were obtained by the air-stream method. *Unless otherwise stated, it is correct to assume that all adsorption data were obtained by the air-stream method.*

Effect of extent of hydration on the position of the adsorption curve

Fig. 2-9 gives a group of adsorption curves for a given kind of paste at different stages of hydration. The paste was obtained from mortar prisms that had been cured continuously in water for periods ranging from 7 days to one year. The results shown are typical except that they represent a Type IV, rather than a Type I, cement. Since the plots of water contents are expressed in terms of the weight of the original cement in the sample, the ordinates at $p/p_s = 0$ give the amounts of non-evaporable water and those at $p/p_s = 1^*$ give the total water contents at saturation. The curves illustrate the following general conclusions that are applicable to all samples tested, regardless of original water-cement ratio, age, or type of cement.

(1) The total water held at saturation ($p/p_s = 1$) increases as the length of the curing period increases.

(2) The non-evaporable water content also increases.

(3) The amount of water held at any intermediate vapor pressure increases with the length of the curing period.

(4) The evaporable water content, which is the difference between the total and the non-evaporable water, *decreases* as the length of the curing period increases.

The changes that take place during the period of curing are illustrated in another way in Fig. 2-10. This, like Fig. 2-9, represents a group of samples that were similar except for the extent of hydration at the time of test; they were prepared from mortar cubes all made from the same mix. Here the bottom curve represents the non-evaporable water and the top the total water content. The intermediate curves represent the water content after the originally dry samples had reached equilibrium with the relative vapor pressures indicated on the curves.

Note that all curves originate at (0,0) except the upper one. This one begins at a point representing the original water-cement ratio (corrected for bleeding). That is, zero age represents the time before any hydration takes place. At that time all the water in the sample will

---

*The topmost point has been plotted at $p/p_s = 1$ despite the fact that consideration of the effect of dissolved alkalies shows that it should be plotted at a lower p/p_s. This point is discussed further in connection with the effect of dissolved alkalies in Part 3.

have a relative vapor pressure of 1.0* and not any of it would be held if exposed to an atmosphere having any lesser water vapor pressure. At any time after hydration begins, only a part of the water can be lost in an atmosphere having an appreciable vapor pressure.

The rise of the top curve is due to absorption of water by the specimen from the curing tank. The points represent dried-and-resaturated granules and therefore are probably slightly below the level representing the capacity of the paste before drying, as explained before.

The rise of the bottom curve indicates the progress of hydration and, as will be shown later, is proportional to the increase in volume of the solid phase of the paste. The heights of the next three curves above the bottom curve ($p/p_s = 0.09; 0.19;$ and 0.36) are believed to depend on the total surface area of the solid phase and hence to depend primarily on the quantity of gel present. It will be shown later that the positions of these lower curves are independent of the total porosity of the sample. Although this particular plotting does not make it apparent, it is a fact that the position of the points representing pressures greater than about $0.475 p_s$ depend on the total porosity of the sample as well as on the extent of hydration. The basis for these interpretations and the uses made of the information are subjects treated in later parts of this paper.

Fig. 2-11 gives some of the same data that appear in Fig. 2-9 in terms of a unit weight of dry paste rather than weight of original cement as before. It therefore shows the evaporable water only. Note that as the length of the period of wet curing increases, the total evaporable water decreases and the amount held at low vapor pressures increases. Since the total evaporable water may be taken as a measure of the total porosity of the hardened paste, this graph shows that the amount of water held at vapor pressures near the saturation pressure depends on the porosity of the sample. On the other hand, the amounts of water held at low pressures appear here to vary inversely with the porosity. However, it will be proved that the amount held at low pressure does not depend on porosity.

Influence of original water-cement ratio (w_o/c) on the shape of the adsorption curve

Fig. 2-12 to 2-15 present adsorption curves for samples having different water-cement ratios but the same degree of hydration as measured by the non-evaporable water content. The points for these curves were obtained by interpolations on plots such as that shown in Fig. 2-10. The four figures represent three different cements, two different degrees of hydration, and three (in one case, four) different water-cement ratios. Considered together, they show that differences in age and original water-cement ratio have no influence on the shape of the lower part of the ad-

---

*Again neglecting the effect of dissolved alkalies.

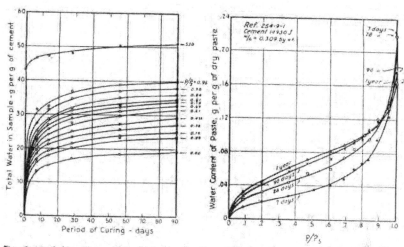

Fig. 2-10 (left)—Changes in amounts of water held at any given vapor pressure as influenced by the length of the curing period
Cement 15007J-Ref. 9-5 w₀/c = 0.433

Fig. 2-11 (right)—Adsorption isotherms showing evaporable water only

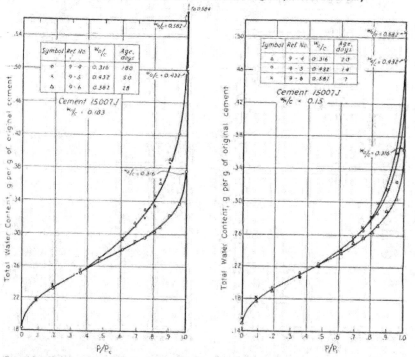

Fig. 2-12 (left)—Adsorption isotherms for samples of different w₀/c but equal non-evaporable water

Fig. 2-13 (right)—Adsorption isotherms for samples of different w₀/c but equal non-evaporable water

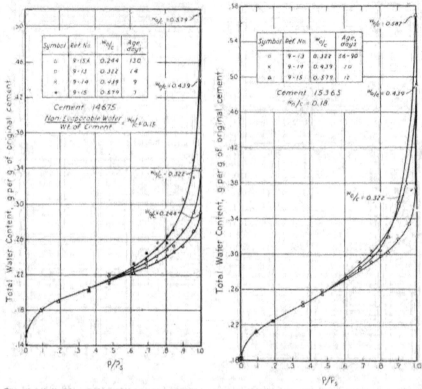

Fig. 2-14 (left)—Adsorption isotherms for samples of different w_o/c but equal non-evaporable water

Fig. 2-15 (right)—Adsorption isotherms for samples of different w_o/c but equal non-evaporable water

sorption curves apart from the effect on the level of the starting point: at a given degree of hydration the same curve holds for all ages and water ratios. In other words, the amount of water taken up in the lower third of the range of vapor pressures depends only on the extent of hydration and hence only on the increase in quantity of hydration-product in the sample. On the other hand, the total amount of evaporable water depends upon the porosity of the solid phase which *at a given degree of hydration* depends upon the original water-cement ratio.

The data just considered show that the lower third of the adsorption curve has the same shape for different ages and different porosities of samples made from the same cement. Fig. 2-16 and 2-17 are presented to show that the lower third of the curves have the same shape not only for these conditions but also for different cement compositions. These plots are like those of Fig. 2-12 to 2-15 except that the scale of ordinates is the ratio of the amount of water taken up at a given pressure to the

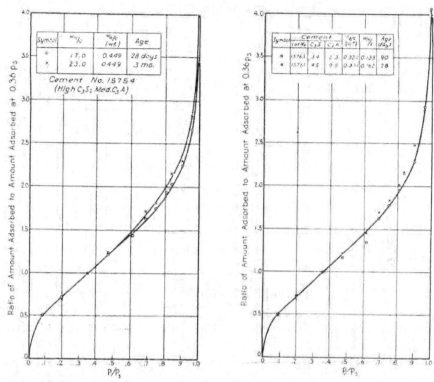

Fig. 2-16 (left)—Adsorption isotherms for which the amount adsorbed is expressed as a ratio to the amount adsorbed at p/p$_s$ = 0.36
Different degrees of hydration

Fig. 2-17 (right)—Adsorption isotherms for which the amount adsorbed is expressed as a ratio to the amount adsorbed at p/p$_s$ = 0.36
Different cements and different degrees of hydration

amount taken up at a pressure of 0.36 p_s. The coincidence in the lower range of pressures proves that the lower part of the curves can be represented by the same form of mathematical expression.

Empirical relationship between the amount of adsorption at low pressures and the non-evaporable water content

Fig. 2-18 shows typical relationships between the amount of water held at low vapor pressure and the non-evaporable water content for samples prepared from two different cements. Symbols of different shape for the same cement designate different original water-cement ratios, and different points of the same shape represent a mix of given water ratio at different stages of hydration.

Although these data were among the first obtained in this investigation and as a consequence show the influence of imperfect laboratory technique, they illustrate adequately the fact that with any given cement

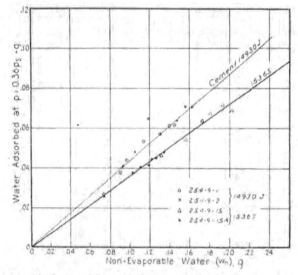

Fig. 2-18—Relationship between amount of water held at low pressure and the non-evaporable water content for two different cements

the adsorption at low vapor pressure (any pressure below about 0.4 p_s) is directly proportional to the extent of hydration as measured by the non-evaporable water content. A study of this relationship will be presented in another part of this paper.

General results from various cements

The results of some of the adsorption tests and measurements of non-evaporable water are shown in graphical form for various cements* in Fig. 2-19 to 2-23. In Fig. 2-19, for example, the total evaporable water is represented by the height of the column above the horizontal reference line and the non-evaporable water by the length of the column extending downward. The proportions of evaporable water held between various relative vapor pressures are shown by the relative lengths of the blocks making up the column. As will be shown later, the length of the first block above the zero line (up to line 0.35) is approximately proportional to the surface area of the cement gel. By assuming that the surface area is proportional to the amount of cement gel, the length of this block may also be taken to indicate the relative amount of cement gel in the sample.

The effect of differences in water-cement ratio for specimens of the same age is shown in Fig. 2-19 and 2-20. The effect of prolonging the period of curing for specimens of the same initial water-cement ratio can best be seen by reference to Fig. 2-21, 2-22, and 2-23. In reading these diagrams it is helpful to remember that at zero age there would be

---

*For characteristics of the cements, see Appendix to Part 2.

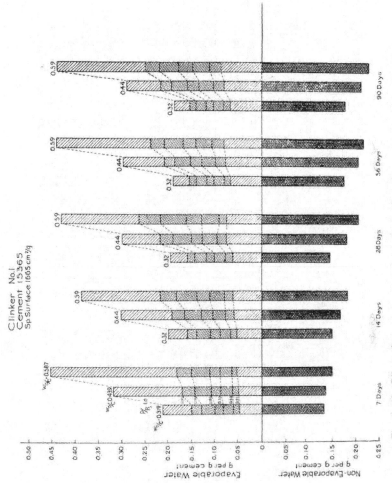

Fig. 2-19—Effect of water-cement ratio on the hardened paste at the ages indicated

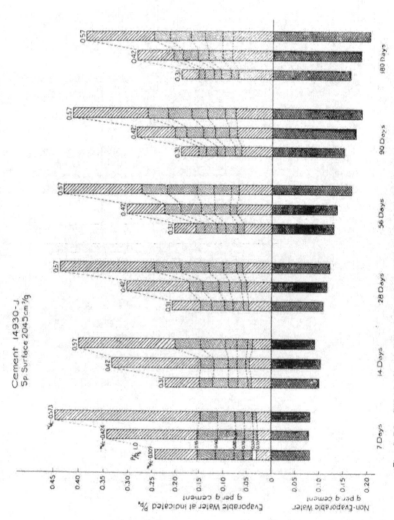

Fig. 2-90—Effect of water-cement ratio on the hardened paste at the ages indicated

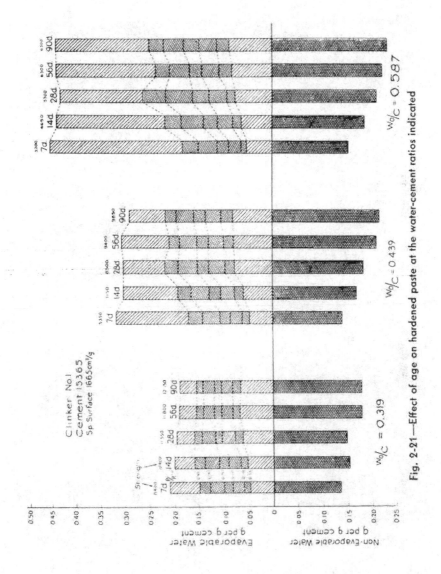

Fig. 2-21—Effect of age on hardened paste at the water-cement ratios indicated

Fig. 2-22—Effect of age on hardened paste at the water-cement ratios indicated

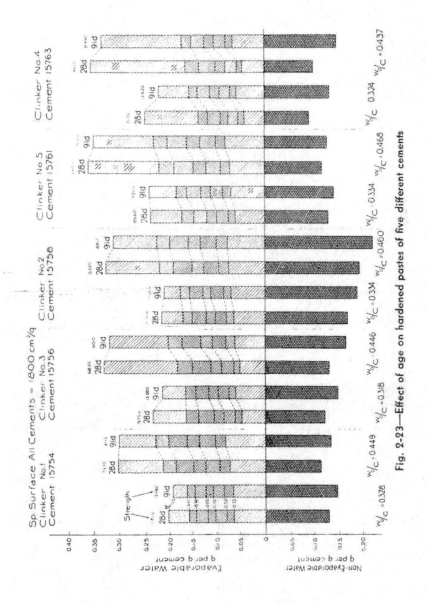

Fig. 2-23—Effect of age on hardened pastes of five different cements

no non-evaporable water and hence no column extending downward
and the column for evaporable water would have a height equal to the
original water-cement ratio, corrected for bleeding. Therefore, the difference between the height of the evaporable water column and the
original water ratio indicates the degree of reduction in porosity brought
about by the curing.

Some of the irregularities shown in these diagrams are believed to be
due to imperfections in experimental technique. It seems probable
that a given group of diagrams representing regular changes in w_o/c or
in age should show a regular pattern of change. In most of the interpretations built up in later parts of this paper, these irregularities are ignored.

EFFECT OF STEAM CURING

One test only of steam-cured material was made. The result was so
significant, however, that it will be given here. The procedure was as
follows: a paste of normal consistency was made, composed of 1 part
cement 15756, 0.71 part pulverized silica (Lot 15918), and 0.43 part water,
by weight. This was made into two prisms $1x1x11\frac{1}{4}$ in. The prisms
were cured over night in the molds and then were steamed at 420 F
in an autoclave for about 6 hours, after which they were immersed in
water over night. The bars were then crushed and a 48-80 mesh sample
taken for adsorption tests.

Two-inch cubes were made from the same cement-silica mixture,
but with slightly higher water-cement ratio—0.50 instead of 0.43. These
were cured continuously under water for 28 days. They were then
crushed, granular samples were taken, and adsorption characteristics
were determined in the usual way.

The results of these tests are given in Table 26 and Fig. 2-24. They
show that curing at high temperature radically alters the adsorption
characteristics. Note particularly that about 90 percent of all the
evaporable water was taken up at pressures above 0.8 p_s. The significance of this will be discussed more fully in the succeeding parts of
the paper.

SUMMARY OF PART 2

The water in saturated hardened cement paste is classified as evaporable and non-evaporable. This classification is based on the amount of
water retained by a specimen dried in a vacuum desiccator at 23 C over
the system $Mg(ClO_4)_2.2H_2O + Mg(ClO_4)_2.4H_2O$. The pores in a hardened
paste are defined as those spaces occupied by evaporable water.

This part of the paper deals with measurements of non-evaporable
water and the adsorption isotherms of the evaporable water in various
samples of hardened cement paste.

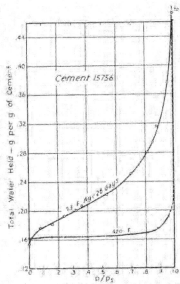

Fig. 2-24—Effect of steam curing on adsorption characteristics

TABLE 26—EFFECT OF STEAM CURING
Cement 15756

Relative vapor pressure	73 F for 28d $w_n/c = .478$	Autoclaved at 420 F $w_n/c = .43$
(w_n)*	(.1537)	(.1615)
0.08	.0220	.0015
0.16	.0329	.0017
0.24	.0390	.0028
0.32	.0478	.0025
0.36	.0530	.0026
0.53	.0689	.0038
0.70	.0969	.0052
0.81	.1283	.0081
0.85	.1408	.0090
0.88	.1623	.0131
0.96	.2230	.0300
1.00	.4367	.3009

*w_n = non-evaporable water.

A general description of materials and experimental apparatus and procedures is given, with reference to the Appendix to Part 2 for more complete information. Data are presented on the stability of the hydrates of the constituents of portland cement, in the presence of different desiccating agents. Indications are that of the microcrystalline hydrates that might occur in hardened cement paste, only the calcium sulfoaluminate would be decomposed to an appreciable extent by the desiccant used in these studies.

The experiments were for the most part made on granular samples prepared from the original cylinders or cubes. Data are presented indicating that the granular samples were representative of the original pastes, except for pastes of comparatively high porosity.

The empirical aspects of the experimental results are described and discussed. Adsorption and desorption curves from the same sample present a so-called hysteresis loop similar to those found for other materials. In addition, the curves show some features of irreversibility not commonly found among other materials. Most of the study pertains to adsorption isotherms only.

Adsorption of water vapor from humidified streams of air (air-stream apparatus) was found to be the same as adsorption from water vapor alone (high-vacuum apparatus), except at pressures below about 0.3 p_s, where the adsorption in the absence of air was expected to be greater than that in the presence of air. The curves obtained by the two methods are believed to have the same significance.

Graphs are presented from which the following conclusions are drawn:

(1) The total water held at saturation ($p/p_s = 1.0$) increases as the length of the curing period increases.

(2) The non-evaporable water content also increases.

(3) The amount of water held at any intermediate vapor pressure increases with the length of the curing period.

(4) The evaporable water content, which is the difference between the total and the non-evaporable water, decreases as the length of the curing period increases.

Curves are presented showing that differences in age and original water-cement ratio have no influence on the shape of the lower part of the adsorption curves. On the other hand, the position of the upper part of the curve and the total amount of evaporable water in a saturated specimen depend on both age and original water-cement ratio. These conclusions apply to all cements.

For a given cement the amount of *evaporable* water held at any pressure up to about 0.4 p_s is directly proportional to the *non*-evaporable water content. The proportionality constant is different for cements of different type.

An adsorption curve for cement paste cured for six hours in the autoclave at 420 F is compared with the curve obtained from a similar paste cured at 73 F for 28 days. Results show that curing at high temperature and pressure produces adsorption characteristics radically different from those observed in specimens cured in the ordinary way.

REFERENCES

1. E. Freyssinet, *Science et Industrie* (Jan. 1933).
2. F. M. Lea, *Cement & Cement Mfgr.* v. 5, p. 395 (1932).
3. K. S. Rao, "Hysteresis in Sorption," *J. Phys. Chem.* v. 45 (3) pp. 500-531 (1941).
4. L. H. Cohan, *J. Am. Chem. Soc.* v. 66, p. 98 (1944).
5. N. A. Lange, *Handbook of Chemistry*, 4th Edition, p. 1269.

Appendix to Part 2

CONTENTS

DESCRIPTIONS OF MATERIALS AND TABULATIONS OF ORIGINAL DATA

Information is given in this appendix concerning the materials used in each series and concerning the preparation of test specimens and samples. This information supplements that given in the text.

Also given are tabulations of the original data. The authors regard such a full presentation desirable because of the uniqueness of the data and because of the speculative nature of the interpretation offered in the text. That is, alternative interpretations may occur to other investigators in this field and we consider that they should have access to the original material.

Characteristics of cements

The cements used in any given series can be readily identified in Table A-1. Their chemical and physical properties are tabulated in order of lot numbers in Tables A-2 and A-3.

Description of specimens made in series 254-265

Mortar Specimens: Truncated cones: Base 4 in.; top 1½ in.; altitude 6 in.

Cement: Lot 14502 (see Tables A-2 and A-3 for characteristics).

Aggregate: A mixture of Elgin sand and Ottawa silica graded as follows:

Weight, per cent of size indicated					
Ottawa Silica		Elgin Sand			
200– 100	100– 48	48– 28	28– 14	14– 8	8– 4
2.4	4.9	23.6	29.9	16.3	22.9

TABLE A-1—SERIES INDEX TO CEMENTS

Series	Cement Nos.					
254-265	14502					
254-MRB	14898-39AQ 14904-45AQ 14910-52AQ	14899-40PC 14905-46PC 14911-51PC	14900-41SC 14906-47SC 14912-53SC	14901-42AQ 14907-48AQ 14913-54AQ	14902-43PC 14908-49PC 14914-55PC	14903-44SC 14909-50SC 14915-56SC
254-K4B	13721-1S 13733-5S 13740-7P 13765-15Q 13780-20Q	13722-1P 13734-5P 13741-7Q 13766-16S	13723-1Q 13735-5Q 13752-11P 13767-16P	13730-4S 13736-6S 13753-11Q 13768-16Q	13731-4P 13737-6P 13763-15S 13778-20S	13732-4Q 13738-6Q 13764-15P 13779-20P
254-7	14675					
254-8	14930J 15014J	15007J	15008J	15011J	15012J	15013J
254-9	14930J	15007J	15011J	15013J	15365	
254-11	15495 15761	15497 15763	15669 16198	15754 16213	15756 16214	15758
254-13	15367 15923* 15930*	15498 15924* 15932*	15623 15925* 15933*	15670 15926* 15934*	15699 15927* 15935*	15921* 15929*
254-16	15754 16189	15756	15758	15761	15763	16186
254-18	13495	14675	15365	13723-1Q		

*All cements marked * were ground in the laboratory. The rest were ground in commercial plants.

Mixes: Specimens represented the following mortar mixes, by weight: 1:0 (neat); 1:1½; 1:1, 1:2, 1:3, 1:5, 1:7.

Mixing: Each batch was mixed 30 sec. dry and 2 min. wet in a small power-driven, open-tub mixer.

Molding: Cones were cast in watertight molds of known capacity, the mortar being puddled with a light tamper.

Measurements: The weight of the filled calibrated mold was measured to 1 g immediately after filling, and again after 20-24 hr. in the fog-room. On stripping, the specimens were weighed in air and in water.

Curing: In molds in the fog-room for the first 20-24 hr.; in the fog-room thereafter. Temperature: 70 F.

Drying: The granular samples were dried in air-filled desiccators over concentrated sulfuric acid.

Composition of specimens: See Table A-4.

Analysis of granular samples: See Table A-5.

Adsorption data: See Table A-6.

TABLE A-2—CHEMICAL ANALYSES AND COMPUTED COMPOUND COMPOSITION

All computations are based on the weight of the cement unless otherwise indicated. The computed compositions are based on the oxide analyses corrected for free lime but not for other minor constituents.

Lot No.	Ref. No.	Major Constituents									Minor Constituents								Computed Compound Composition				
		SiO_2	Al_2O_3	Fe_2O_3	Total CaO	MgO	SO_3	Loss on Ign.	In-sol. Res.	Free CaO	FeO	TiO_2	P_2O_5	MnO_3	Na_2O	K_2O	$CHCl_3$ Soluble	CO_2	C_3S	C_2S	C_3A	C_4AF	$CaSO_4$
13405		20.79	6.02	3.11	63.57	3.16	1.65	1.00	0.14	1.11					0.22	0.52			51	21	11	10	2.8
13421†	1S	21.08	6.10	2.15	64.10	2.91	1.80	0.79	0.24	0.36	0.0				0.10	0.97			50.0	22.7	12.5	6.6	3.06
13422†	1P	20.93	6.18	2.17	63.48	2.94	1.80	0.87	0.23	1.18	0.0	0.31			0.10	1.38			44.8	26.3	12.7	6.6	3.06
13423†	1Q	21.13	5.85	2.17	64.18	2.99	1.80	0.79	0.18	1.49	0.36				0.10	1.11			47.0	25.2	11.8	6.6	3.06
13430†	4S	19.02	4.84	6.85	62.12	4.12	1.80	0.90	0.11	0.29	0.0				0.41	0.10			39.9	23.0	1.7	20.8	3.06
13431†	4P	19.13	4.92	6.70	61.63	4.09	1.80	0.97	0.37	3.80	0.16	0.37			0.33	0.20			42.3	23.0	1.7	20.4	3.06
13432†	4Q	18.79	5.08	7.17	61.72	4.21	1.80	0.78	0.20	1.55	1.27				0.37	0.12			32.6	14.2	1.3	21.8	3.06
13433†	5S	23.16	3.33	4.15	64.47	1.52	1.80	1.20	0.14	0.04	0.0				0.27	0.14			52.8	26.7	1.8	12.6	3.06
13434†	5P	22.61	3.81	4.31	64.23	1.52	1.80	2.40	0.10	0.32	0.0	0.16			0.35	0.46			49.5	27.6	3.1	13.1	3.06
13435†	5Q	22.97	3.27	4.40	63.53	1.50	1.80	1.81	0.10	0.41	0.0				0.37	0.42			49.0	26.0	1.2	13.4	3.06
13436†	6S	21.06	5.85	2.97	65.77	1.38	1.80	0.92	0.20	0.00	0.0				0.07	tr.			59.0	15.8	10.7	9.0	3.06
13437†	6P	20.97	5.99	3.08	65.30	1.39	1.80	0.84	0.17	0.33	0.0	0.26			0.10	0.11			56.0	17.8	10.7	9.3	3.06
13438†	6Q	20.99	5.90	3.03	65.57	1.43	1.80	0.83	0.22	0.45	0.03				0.08	0.08			56.4	17.6	10.5	9.2	3.06
13440†	7P	20.46	6.96	2.31	63.23	3.31	1.80	0.80	0.22	0.40	0.05	0.33			0.42	0.58			45.0	24.7	14.5	7.0	3.06
13441†	7Q	20.48	6.89	2.28	63.55	3.30	1.80	0.82	0.20	0.53	0.36				0.46	0.38			46.0	24.0	14.4	7.0	3.06
13452†	11P	21.18	4.70	4.89	65.10	0.78	1.80	0.94	0.19	0.15	0.0				0.60	0.16			59.6	13.7	4.2	14.9	3.06
13453†	11Q	21.57	4.48	4.48	65.61	0.79	1.80	0.86	0.16	0.33	0.33	0.34			0.51	0.06			61.5	15.4	3.7	13.6	3.06
13456†	15S	21.23	5.56	2.90	62.90	4.07	1.80	0.72*	**	0.11	0.0				0.23	0.41			47.4	25.2	9.9	8.8	3.06
13457†	15P	21.21	5.57	2.83	62.59	4.06	1.80	0.85	0.14	1.28	0.0	0.28			0.28	0.86			41.7	29.4	9.9	8.6	3.06
13458†	15Q	21.23	5.58	2.89	62.92	4.06	1.80	0.76*	**	1.39	0.32				0.26	0.40			42.4	28.9	9.9	8.8	3.06
13466†	16S	21.55	6.10	2.49	64.00	3.16	1.80	0.81*	**	1.39	0.0				0.23	0.15			47.0	26.5	12.0	7.0	3.06
13467†	16P	21.51	6.10	2.49	63.83	3.15	1.80	0.93*	0.23	0.39	0.33	0.32			0.28	0.38			45.0	27.2	12.0	7.0	3.06
13468†	16Q	21.53	6.10	2.49	63.95	3.16	1.80	0.81*	**	0.30	0.57				0.15	0.23			45.6	27.3	12.0	7.0	3.06
13778†	20S	19.37	7.35	3.77	65.31	0.98	1.80	0.68*	**	0.32	0.0				0.13	0.42			57.6	12.5	13.1	11.5	3.06
13779†	20P	19.35	7.34	3.77	65.08	0.97	1.80	0.91	0.15	1.24	0.0	0.45			0.18	0.76			53.6	15.2	13.1	11.5	3.06
13780†	20Q	19.34	7.34	3.77	65.28	0.98	1.80	0.73*	**	1.38	0.02				0.15	0.45			53.3	15.5	13.1	11.5	3.06

(Continued on next page)

TABLE A-2—(CONTINUED)

Lot No.	Ref. No.	SiO_2	Al_2O_3	Fe_2O_3	Total CaO	MgO	SO_3	Loss on Ign.	Insol. Res.	Free CaO	$Fe_2O_3(Tot.)$	P_2O_5	MnO	Na_2O	K_2O	$CHCl_3$ Soluble	CO_2	C_3S	C_2S	C_3A	C_4AF	$CaSO_4$
14502		21.02	6.07	2.75	63.49	2.94	1.76	1.00	0.14	0.96				0.28	0.60			45	26	11	8	3.0
14560		20.78	5.03	3.98	64.99	1.35	2.27	0.49	—	0.30				0.22	0.31			60	17	7	13	4.04
14575		20.76	5.07	2.55	63.83	3.02	1.71	0.55	0.11	1.19				0.26	0.56			48.1	23.2	11.8	7.8	2.90
14598‡	39AQ	20.72	6.45	3.25	63.89	2.6	0.58	0.99	—	0.67								49.4	22.2	11.6	9.9	0.98
14599‡	40PC	20.80	6.52	3.12	63.69	2.5	0.65	0.91	—	1.16								47.5	23.8	12.0	9.5	1.11
14600‡	41SC	20.78	6.64	3.18	64.19	2.5	0.32	0.87	—	0.09								49.2	22.1	12.2	9.7	0.88
14901‡	42AQ	20.68	6.82	3.16	63.78	2.7	0.58	1.04	—	0.67								46.8	24.0	12.7	9.6	0.98
14902‡	43PC	20.72	6.92	3.18	63.63	2.4	0.61	0.92	—	0.97								45.2	25.4	12.9	9.7	1.03
14903‡	44SC	20.78	6.86	3.12	63.78	2.4	0.60	0.99	—	0.13								45.5	25.6	12.9	9.5	1.02
14904‡	45AQ	20.70	6.73	3.35	64.03	2.4	0.52	0.81	—	0.58								48.4	22.0	9.1	10.2	0.88
14905‡	46PC	20.48	6.82	3.12	63.88	2.6	0.57	1.02	—	0.81								48.8	22.0	12.2	9.5	0.96
14906‡	47SC	20.40	6.98	3.14	63.98	2.7	0.36	0.76	—	0.05								49.4	21.3	13.2	9.6	0.60
14907‡	48AQ	20.70	6.95	3.31	63.07	2.7	0.59	0.87	—	0.04								42.7	27.1	12.8	10.2	1.00
14908‡	49PC	20.94	6.79	3.39	63.12	2.7	0.61	1.02	—	0.24								42.0	28.4	12.0	10.3	1.03
14909‡	50SC	21.16	6.72	3.38	63.14	2.7	0.52	0.75	—	0.07								41.3	29.6	12.0	10.3	0.88
14910‡	52AQ	20.92	6.87	3.47	63.30	2.7	0.52	0.18	—	0.10								42.5	28.0	12.3	10.6	0.88
14911‡	51PC	20.88	7.23	3.51	63.09	2.6	0.48	0.23	—	0.04								39.6	30.1	13.0	10.6	0.82
14912‡	53SC	21.04	7.09	3.41	63.40	2.6	0.48	0.30	—	0.06								40.8	29.1	13.0	10.4	0.82
14913‡	54AQ	21.18	7.13	3.39	62.89	2.6	0.75	0.28	—	0.96								36.6	33.7	13.1	10.3	1.28
14914‡	55PC	21.08	7.09	3.49	62.84	—	0.76	0.37	—	0.63								37.3	32.4	13.2	10.6	1.29
14915‡	56SC	21.06	6.59	3.37	62.43	2.5	0.78	0.35	—	0.46								39.3	30.3	11.7	10.2	1.32
15007J		23.42	4.36	3.21	62.46	1.65	1.35	0.81	0.09	tr.				0.22	0.41		0.24	22.7	55.5	6.1	9.8	2.64
15008J		22.78	4.77	3.46	64.92	1.32	1.30	0.84	0.07	0.62				0.23	0.51	0.025d	0.49	18.0	32.2	6.1	10.3	2.22
		22.69	4.87	4.10	64.51	1.27	1.26	0.78	0.09	0.08								17.7	29.1	6	12.5	2.14
15011J		23.09	4.73	3.45	64.62	1.19	1.43	0.67	0.12	0.40				a	b	0.014	0.66	43.1	29.1	6.7	10.5	2.43
15012J		23.65	4.39	3.43	64.53	1.09	1.34	0.74	0.07	0.37				b	0.49	0.054		43.0	33.4	6.1	10.4	2.28
15013J		20.98	6.85	2.43	62.75	3.52	1.71	0.74	0.07	0.64				c	—	***		39.0	29.3	14.0	7.3	3.00
15014J		21.18	6.42	2.40	62.96	3.61	1.61	0.70	0.08	0.59				0.32	0.40	0.041		41.7	29.3	13.0	7.3	2.73
15365		20.78	6.42	2.20	63.86	2.48	2.48	0.96	0.19	0.93	0.60 0.28	0.03	0.31	0.17	0.16	0.039	0.32	45.5	28.0	13.3	6.7	4.22
15367K		21.87	6.83	2.23	65.30	2.63	0.41	0.15	0.33	0.98				0.17	0.16			53.5	28.4	13.3	6.7	0.70
15495		20.04	5.52	2.50	66.42	1.28	1.82	1.71	0.26	3.14	0.03 0.25	0.08	0.06	0.30	0.40	0.065	0.16	59.4	13.0	10.3	7.7	3.10
15497		19.98	5.55	2.59	66.55	1.33	1.82	1.52	0.15	3.14				0.30	0.40			60	13.9	10.3	7.9	3.10
15498K		20.92	5.82	2.53	67.71	1.36	0.19	0.85	0.25	2.71				—	—			62.5	13.0	11.2	7.7	0.32

(Concluded on next page)

† Minor constituents on clinker basis.
‡ These analyses were made in the plants furnishing the clinker, except for *SO₃* and free *CaO* which were determined in this laboratory. The values are based on clinker weights instead of cement weights.
§ Ground in laboratory.
K Clinker
* The loss on ignition for the clinker was not determined. The values shown here represent the loss on ignition from the gypsum and that from the clinker.
** Not determined.
*** 0.008% tallow; 0.005% Vinsol resin.
a. Alkali analyses made on 15693J.
b.   "   "   "   " 15912J.
c.   "   "   "   " 15911J.
d Tallow.

TABLE A-3—DENSITY, SPECIFIC VOLUME,

| Lot No. | Density and Specific Volume, as Computed from Displacement in | | | | Specific Surface cm²/g A.S.T.M. |
| | Kerosene | | Water | | |
	Density g/cm³	Sp. Vol. cm³/g	Density g/cm³	Sp. Vol. cm³/g	
13495	3.161	0.316			1868
13721	3.130	0.320			1645
13722	3.110	0.322			1745
13723	3.109	0.322			1535
13730					1735
13731					1800
13732					1705
13733					1790
13734					1715
13735					1665
13736	3.163	0.316			1685
13737	3.152	0.317			1815
13738	3.139	0.319			1715
13740					1655
13741					1655
13752					1740
13753					1610
13763	3.165	0.316			1780
13764	3.143	0.318			1630
13765	3.104	0.322			1800
13766					1845
13767					1735
13768					1745
13778	3.145	0.318			1705
13779	3.135	0.319			1730
13780	3.128	0.320			1695
14502	3.145	0.318			1820*
14560	3.154	0.317	3.184	0.314	1085
14560	3.150	0.318	3.170	0.316	1540
14560	3.155	0.317	3.192	0.314	2045
14560	3.156	0.317	3.206	0.312	2550
14675	3.143	0.318			1865
14898	3.140	0.318			1620
14899					1610
14900					1620
14901	3.150	0.318	3.197	0.313	1640
14902					1590
14903	3.167	0.316	3.225	0.310	1630
14904					1580
14905					1610
14906					1620
14907					1660
14908					1630

a. All those cements marked a were ground in the laboratory. The rest were ground in commercial plants.
b. This includes +325 material.
c. Densities of these cements were not determined. The values given are for cements of similar fineness made from the same clinker, but no allowance was made for differences in gypsum content.
* 1560 cm²/g by the permeability method.

AND SPECIFIC SURFACE OF CEMENTS

Lot No.	Density and Specific Volume, as Computed from Displacement in				Specific Surface, cm²/g	
	Kerosene		Water		A.S.T.M.	Permeability Method
	Density g/cm³	Sp. Vol. cm³/g	Density g/cm³	Sp. Vol. cm³/g		
14909					1630	
14910	3.165	0.316	3.207	0.312	1610	
14911					1620	
14912	3.181	0.314	3.228	0.310	1640	
14913					1640	
14914	3.144	0.318			1610	
14915					1650	
14930J	3.218	0.311	3.290	0.304	2045	
15007J	3.189	0.314	3.260	0.307	2015	
15008J	3.201	0.312	3.239	0.309	1825	
15011J	3.204	0.312	3.263	0.306	1835	
15012J	3.191	0.314			1740	
15013J	3.162	0.316	3.247	0.308	1810	
15014J	3.174	0.315			2010	
15365	3.135	0.319	3.187	0.314	1640	3120
15495	3.101	0.322	3.136	0.319	1440	2780
15497	3.109	0.322	3.178	0.315	2500	5150
15669	3.215	0.311	3.257	0.307	2290	3810
15754	3.135	0.319	3.174	0.315	1800	3420
15756	3.174	0.315	3.209	0.312	1800	3060
15758	3.107	0.322	3.158	0.317	1800	3570
15761	3.155	0.317	3.210	-0.312	1800	2950
15763	3.215	0.311	3.252	0.308	1800	2760
15921 a	3.135 c	0.319	3.190 c	0.314	1820	2870
15922 a	"	"	"	"	1890	3350
15923 a	"	"	"	"	2070	4850
15924 a	3.107 c	0.322	3.16 c	0.316	1815	2930
15925 a	"	"	"	"	1870	3360
15926 a	"	"	"	"	2020	4580
15927 a	3.176 c	0.315	3.22 c	0.310	1800	2860
15929 a	"	"	"	"	2080	4770
15930 a	3.215 c	0.311	3.25 c	0.308	1795	2630
15932 a	"	"	"	"	2050	4280
15933 a	3.155 c	0.317	3.21 c	0.312	1820	2960
15934 a	"	"	"	"	1855	3480
15935 a	"	"	"	"	2080	4480
16186	3.135	0.319	3.188	0.314	1702 b	3200
16189	3.174	0.315	3.214	0.312	1849 b	3200
16198	3.215	0.311	3.254	0.308	2014 b	3200
16213	3.135	0.319	3.179	0.315	1263	2430
16214	3.135	0.319	3.184	0.314	1528	2920

TABLE A-4—UNIT ABSOLUTE VOLUME COMPOSITION OF THE MORTARS USED IN SERIES 254-265

Ref. No.	Unit Absolute Volume Composition				Water-Cement Ratio		
	Cement	Sand	Water	Air	Volume Basis	Wt. Basis	Gal/Sk.
323	0.5601	—	0.4169	0.0192	0.744	0.236	2.66
506	0.4046	0.2438	0.3331	0.0189	0.823	0.262	2.95
509	0.3195	0.3850	0.2826	0.0129	0.884	0.268	3.17
512	0.2221	0.5353	0.2264	0.0162	1.019	0.323	3.65
515	0.1666	0.6022	0.2075	0.0237	1.245	0.395	4.46
518	0.1062	0.6399	0.2250	0.0289	2.118	0.670	7.59
521	0.0787	0.6638	0.2216	0.0359	2.816	0.893	10.09

TABLE A-5—ANALYSES OF GRANULAR SAMPLES USED FOR ADSORPTION AND NON-EVAPORABLE WATER MEASUREMENTS IN SERIES 254-265

Ref. No.	Cement Cont. Sol. SiO_2 Meth. % dry weight	Cement Cont. SO_3 Meth. % dry weight	Ignition Loss, % dry weight	CO_2(1) Loss % dry weight	Non-Evap. Water(2) % dry weight	Non-Evap. Water, % cement content		Sand Content (by difference)	
						Sol. SiO_3	SO_3 Meth.	Sol. SiO_3	SO_3 Meth.
323	85.6(3)	—	14.42	0.67	13.7	16	—	0.7	
506	66	70	17.50	4.99	12.5	19	18	21.0	17.8
509	57	62	19.01	7.58	11.4	20	18	23.1	26.3
512	47	52	20.45	9.91	10.5	22	20	42.4	37.0
515	41	47	22.63	11.86	10.8	26	23	48.0	42.5
518	39	42	21.92	12.40	9.5	24	23	51.8	48.6
521	34	36	21.26	13.22	8.0	23	22	57.7	55.5

(1) CO_2 comes chiefly from calcareous sand (Elgin).
(2) Non-evaporable water obtained by correcting loss on ignition for CO_2-loss.
(3) Ignited weight taken as cement content since this is a neat paste.

TABLE A-6—ADSORPTION DATA FOR SERIES 254-265
Age: 110 days

p/p_s	Total Water Retained at Relative Vapor Pressure Indicated, g/g dry weight						
	Ref. 323	Ref. 506	Ref. 509	Ref. 512	Ref. 515	Ref. 518	Ref. 521
w_n	.137	.125	.114	.105	.108	.095	.080
0.11	.1474	.1384	.1237	.1121	.1141	.1008	.0836
0.20	.1552	.1448	.1310	.1183	.1199	.1060	.0884
0.36	.1649	.1544	.1396	.1254	.1274	.1128	.0945
0.50	.1752	.1626	.1472	.1331	.1353	.1206	.1009
0.61	.1811	.1683	.1526	.1382	.1400	.1264	.1052
0.75	.1947	.1800	.1634	.1491	.1532	.1443	.1224
0.80	.1962	.1826	.1649	.1510	.1558	.1453	.1252
0.826	.2013	.1862	.1703	.1569	.1636	.1560	.1327
0.888	.2085	.1941	.1776	.1629	.1731	.1651	.1431
0.93	.2201	.2022	.1868	.1730	.1850	.1865	.1592
0.98	.2225	.2053	.1887	.1767	.1888	.1991	.1718
SSD	.250	.220	.210	.197	.227	.267	.259

w_n = non-evaporable water, p/p_s = about 24×10^{-5}.
SSD = Water content of granular sample, saturated, surface-dry for sample that had been dried and resaturated.

Description of specimens made in series 254-MRB

Neat Specimens: Cylinders, 1x7 in.

Cements: See Tables A-1 to A-3.

Burning Conditions: Lot Nos. 14910, 14911, 14912: hard burned; Lot Nos. 14913, 14914, 14915; soft-burned; others: normal plant burning. Changes in burning condition were brought about by changing length of burning zone.

Cooling Condition: The symbol PC signifies cooling by regular plant method; SC signifies slow cooling by storage in an insulated box where temperatures at or above red-heat were maintained for about 24 hours; AQ signifies cooling to temperatures below dull-red within 10 seconds by use of an air-blast.

Grinding: In the laboratory mill with enough added gypsum for 1.8 percent total SO_3.

Mixing: The cement was placed with water in a kitchen-type mixer and mixed for 2 minutes, allowed to rest for 1 minute, and then mixed for 1 minute. $w/c = 0.5$ by weight at mixing.

Casting: The pastes were poured into 1x7-in. waxed-paper cylinders.

Curing: In the molds under water. Molds stored horizontally.

Drying: The granular samples were dried in a vacuum desiccator over $Mg(ClO_4)_2 \cdot 2H_2O$.

Adsorption Data: See Table A-7.

TABLE A-7—ADSORPTION DATA FOR SERIES 254-MRB
Water-cement ratio corrected for bleeding

p/p_s	Total Water Retained at Relative Vapor Pressure Indicated, g/g cement								
	14898-1AQ $w_o/c =$ .382 Age 120d	14899-1PC $w_o/c =$ .388 Age 120d	14900-1SC $w_o/c =$ .446 Age 126d	14901-2AQ $w_o/c =$ .391 Age 126d	14902-2PC $w_o/c =$ .393 Age 133d	14903-2SC $w_o/c =$ .424 Age 133d	14904-3AQ $w_o/c =$ .425 Age 162d	14905-3PC $w_o/c =$ .411 Age 162d	14906-3SC $w_o/c =$ .476 Age 173d
w_n	.2171	.2225	.2274	.2228	.2273	.2271	.2284	.2299	.2355
.088	.2615	.2614	.2684	.2629	.2665	.2664	.2723	.2757	.2794
.20	.2737	.2781	.2848	.2755	.2825	.2823	.2891	.2924	.2966
.355	.2977	.3034	.3111	.2992	.3092	.3091	.3143	.3184	.3271
.51	.3179	.3209	.3245	.3116	.3285	.3277	.3333	.3393	.2510
.61	.3298	.3355	.3534	.3332	.3422	.3448	.3485	.3529	.3702
.69	.3461	.3511	.3656	.3437	.3578	.3602	.3578	.3631	.3831
.75	.3610	.3666	.3852	.3649	.3743	.3797	.3749	.3811	.4048
.80	.3675	.3724	.3918	.3700	.3807	.3842	.3824	.3879	.4107
.84	.3782	.3813	.4000	.3803	.3883	.3926	.3941	.3982	.4217
.89	.3971	.3983	.4100	.3908	.3981	.3996	.4168	.4176	.4438
.96	.4318	.4225	.4459	.4491	.4475	.4401	.4553	.4469	.4737
SSD	.4604	.4581	.5082	.4911	.5013	.5106	.4897	.4898	.5496
SSDO	----		.5267	.5031	.5108	.5261	.4993	.5021	.5673

p/p_s	Total Water Retained at Relative Vapor Pressure Indicated, g/g cement								
	14907-4AQ $w_o/c =$ .406 Age 173d	14908-4PC $w_o/c =$ .394 Age 200d	14909-4SC $w_o/c =$ .483 Age 200d	14910-5AQ $w_o/c =$ .460 Age 204d	14911-5PC $w_o/c =$ .464 Age 204d	14912-5SC $w_o/c =$ .489 Age 212d	14913-6AQ $w_o/c =$ .410 Age 212d	14914-6PC $w_o/c =$ .423 Age 222d	14915-6SC $w_o/c =$ .437 Age 222d
w_n	.2191	.2250	.2255	.2282	.2294	.2252	.2206	.2253	.2240
.088	.2605	.2673	.2669	.2704	.2723	.2703	.2665	.2675	.2667
.20	.2789	.2853	.2846	.2865	.2940	.2883	.2839	.2847	.2830
.355	.3037	.3108	.3119	.3142	.3166	.3167	.3075	.3101	.3097
.51	.3231	.3327	.3346	.3365	.3383	.3416	.3275	.3293	.3299
.61	.3354	.3463	.3496	.3470	.3558	.3558	.3389	.3443	.3441
.69	.3459	.3573	.3639	.3533	.3571	.3698	.3514	.3537	.3562
.75	.3629	.3764	.3871	.3793	.3832	.3907	.3678	.3736	.3759
.80	.3683	.3835	.3948	.3844	.3905	.3956	.3704	.3771	.3787
.84	.3766	.3920	.4061	.3952	.4017	.4048	.3771	.3847	.3869
.89	.4027	.4136	.4333	.4280	.4365	.4300	.4061	.4137	.4149
.96	.4279	.4394	.4659	.4706	.4801	.4547	.4314	.4347	.4327
SSD	.4606	.4771	.5477	.5131	.5259	.5473	.4767	.4870	.5203
SSDO	.4741	.4922	.5725	.5348	.5458	.5675	.4932		.5296

Key: SSD = Water content of granular sample, saturated, surface-dry for sample that had been dried and resaturated.

SSDO = Water content of granular sample that was brought to saturated condition without preliminary drying.

AQ = Air quenched.
PC = Plant cooled.
SC = Slow cooled.
w_n = Non-evaporable water; p/p_s = about 24×10^{-6}.

Description of specimens made in series 254-K4B

Neat Specimens: Cylinders, 1x7½ in.

Cements: See Tables A-1 to A-3.

Cooling: Symbol P signifies regular plant cooling; S signifies slow cooling after reheating clinker; Q signifies quick cooling after reheating clinker.

Grinding: In the laboratory mill with enough added gypsum for 1.8 percent total SO_3.

Mixing: The cement was placed with water in a kitchen-type mixer and mixed for 2 minutes, allowed to rest for 2 minutes, and then mixed for 2 minutes. $w/c = 0.5$ by weight at mixing.

Casting: The pastes were poured into 1x7½-in. cylindrical molds.

Curing: In the molds stored horizontally under water for 20-24 hrs.; under water thereafter. Temperature: 70 F.

Drying: The granular samples (48-100 mesh) were dried in a vacuum desiccator over $Mg(ClO_4)_2.2H_2O$.

Adsorption Data: See Table A-8.

Description of specimens made in series 254-7

Mortar Specimens: Truncated cones: base, 4 in.; top, 2 in.; altitude, 6 in.

Cement: Lot 14675. See Tables A-2 and A-3 for characteristics.

Batches: The batches were made up as follows:

Ref. No.	Mix by Wt.	Weights, gms. per batch						Cement g	Water, ml
		Ottawa Silica			Cow Bay Sand				
		200-100	100-48	48-28	28-14	14-8	8-4		
7-1	1-0	—	—	—	—	—	—	4000	1010
7-2	1-½	36	73	125	579	301	386	3000	830
7-3	1-1	54	110	187	868	453	578	2250	675
7-4	1-2	77	157	266	1234	644	822	1600	570
7-5	1-3	86	177	299	1389	724	925	1200	545
7-6	1-4	90	184	311	1447	654	1064	938	590
7-7	1-5	90	184	311	1447	654	1064	750	570

Mixing: Each batch was mixed 30 sec. dry and 2 min. wet, in a small power-driven, open-tub mixer.

Molding: From each batch 3 watertight molds of known capacity were filled. The mortar was puddled with a light tamper.

Measurements: The weight of the filled calibrated mold was measured to 1 g immediately after filling, and again after 20-24 hr. in the fog-room. On stripping, the weights of the specimen in air and in water were obtained.

Curing: In molds in the fog-room for the first 20-24 hr.; under water thereafter. Temperature: 70 F. Some of the molds were not stripped until the specimens were 48 hr. old, but the specimens were nevertheless immersed after the first 24 hr.

Drying: The granular samples were dried in a vacuum desiccator over $Mg(ClO_4)_2.2H_2O$.

Cement-Silica Specimens: Cylinders cast in test tubes (⅞ x 6 in.)

Cement: Lot 14675. See Tables A-2 and A-3 for characteristics.

Silica: Lot 13239. 95 percent passing No. 200-mesh sieve.

Proportions:

Ref. No.	Proportions by Wt.			c/SiO_2	Nominal w/c	
	Cement c	Silica SiO_2	Water w		wt.	gal/sk
1	0.736	0	0.264	100/0	0.36	4.06
2	0.590	0.148	0.262	80/20	0.444	5.00
3	0.483	0.260	0.257	65/35	0.530	5.97
4	0.411	0.336	0.253	55/45	0.618	6.96
5	0.376	0.376	0.248	50/50	0.660	7.43

Mixing: Cement and silica were premixed by tumbling them together in a large glass bottle. The dry material was placed with water in a kitchen-type mixer, and mixed for 2 minutes, allowed to rest for 3 minutes, and then mixed for 2 minutes.

Casting: The pastes were poured into $\frac{7}{8}$ x 6 in. test tubes which had previously been calibrated by filling them with water from a burette.

Curing: The level-full test tubes were stored under water until the third day after casting, at which time the glass molds were broken off and the specimens were reimmersed in water where they remained until tested.

Drying: The granular samples were dried in a vacuum desiccator over $Mg(ClO_4)_2 \cdot 2H_2O$.

Test Results: All test results are given in Part 5.

Description of specimens made in series 254-8

Mortar Specimens: Cubes, 2 in.

Cements: See Tables A-1 to A-3.

Pulverized Silica: About same fineness, volume basis, as cement.

Proportions:

Mix	Relative Proportions			w/c by weight (approx.)
	Cement	Pulverized Silica	Std. Ottawa Sand	
A	1	0	1.64	0.33
B	1	0.330	2.30	0.46
C	1	0.707	3.07	0.61

Mixing: Each batch was mixed 30 sec. dry and 2 min. wet, in a small power-driven, open-tub mixer before making slump test. Slump-sample returned to tub and batch mixed additional 30 sec. before casting.

Slump Test: Made in duplicate on 6-in. cone. Water adjusted to give $1\frac{1}{2}$-2-in. slump.

Molding: From each batch 3 cubes were cast in previously weighed, 3-gang, steel molds.

Measurements: The weight of the filled molds was measured to 1 g immediately after filling, and again 2-$2\frac{1}{4}$ hr. later after carefully removing any accumulated water with a suitable absorbent. The molds were dried and weighed again just prior to stripping. After stripping, the cubes were weighed in air and in water.

Curing: In molds in the fog-room for the first 20-24 hr.; then under water for 27 days; thereafter in the fog-room.

Drying: The granular samples were dried in a vacuum desiccator over $Mg(ClO_4)_2 \cdot 2H_2O$.

Composition of Specimens: The composition of the hardened cubes, derived from the measurements mentioned above, are given in Table A-9.

TABLE A-8—ADSORPTION DATA FOR SERIES 254-K4B

Water-cement ratios corrected for bleeding

Total Water Retained at Relative Vapor Pressure Indicated, g/g cement

p/p_s	13721-1S $w_0/c=.470$ Age 174d	13722-1P $w_0/c=.473$ Age 180d	13723-1Q $w_0/c=.425$ Age 180d	13730-4S $w_0/c=.463$ Age 144d	13731-4P $w_0/c=.460$ Age 138d	13732-4Q $w_0/c=.450$ Age 138d	13733-5S $w_0/c=.427$ Age 150d	13734-5P $w_0/c=.453$ Age 146d	13735-5Q $w_0/c=.456$ Age 150d	13736-6S $w_0/c=.471$ Age 196d	13737-6P $w_0/c=$ Age 191d	13738-6Q $w_0/c=.447$ Age 191d
w_0												
.09	.2231	.2332	.2290	.1786	.1772	.1773	.1650	.1589	.1650	.2148	.2297	.2220
.20	.2666	.2769	.2709	.2128	.2072	.2087	.1994	.1936	.1983	.2568	.2729	.2612
.355	.2830	.2934	.2863	.2268	.2173	.2211	.2136	.2071	.2140	.2723	.2904	.2764
.50	.3123	.3208	.3143	.2464	.2363	.2396	.2337	.2253	.2311	.2978	.3181	.3011
.61	.3910	.3478	.3405	.2646	.2316	.2554	.2502	.2404	.2491	.3266	.3487	.3277
.69	.3561	.3395	.3508	.2772	.2647	.2689	.2608	.2517	.2610	.3397	.3634	.3368
.75a	.3746	.3783	.3673	.2717	.2783	.2777	.2770	.2667	.2756	.3574	.3818	.3535
.80b	.3890	.3894	.3799	.2159	.3056	.2999	.2975	.2889	.2968	.3675	.3940	.3667
.84	.3962	.3999	.3878	.3180	.3121	.3037	.2999	.2923	.2996	.3761	.4029	.3734
.89	.4029	.4079	.3943	.3259	.3215	.3112	.3091	.3010	.3088	.3824	.4095	.3801
.96	.4294	.4457	.4269	.3718	.3698	.3528	.3482	.3446	.3513	.4099	.4337	.4145
SSD	.4477	.4727	.4497	.4116	.4036	.3916	.3839	.3842	.3890	.4318	.4554	.4478
SSDO	.5433	.5590	.5022	.5098	.5122	.4949	.4976	.5093	.5139	.5085	.5189	.5125
	.5572	.5755	.5149	.5249	.5349	.5148	.5102	.5193	.5268	.5295	.5462	.5361

(Concluded on next page)

Total Water Retained at Relative Vapor Pressure Indicated, g/g cement

p/p_4	13740-7P $w_0/c = .473$ Age 164d	13741-7Q $w_0/c = .480$ Age 171d	13752-11P $w_0/c = .483$ Age 164d	13753-11Q $w_0/c = .440$ Age 172d	13763-15S $w_0/c = .485$ Age 202d	13764-15P $w_0/c =$ Age 196d	13765-15Q $w_0/c = .415$ Age 202d	13766-16S $w_0/c =$ Age 322d	13767-16P $w_0/c = .404$ Age 223d	13768-16Q $w_0/c = .436$ Age 223d	13778-20S $w_0/c = .472$ Age 170d	13779-20P $w_0/c = .463$ Age 167d	13780-20Q $w_0/c = .436$ Age 176d
w_s	.2395	.2390	.1864	.1896	.2173	.2109	.2201	.2096	.2236	.2250	.2308	.2329	.2262
09		.2810	—	.2267	.2589	.2494	.2591	.2501	.2700	.2689	.2736	.2730	.2664
20	.3051	.2988	.2380	.2403	.2735	.2653	.2735	.2695	.2869	.2854	.2914	.2894	.2816
355	.3372	.3236	.2611	.2631	.3017	.2874	.2973	.3033	.3163	.3131	.3183	.3130	.3073
50 e	.3653	.3556	.2782	.2826	.3224	.3133	.3030	.3094	.3379	.3324	.3443	.3383	.3326
61	.3812	.3660	.3074	.2944	.3343	.3238	.3234	.3323	.3592	.3427	.3507	.3531	.3447
69	.4003	.3840	.3188	.3125	.3665	.3387	.3583	.3441	.3749	.3673	.3766	.3636	.3624
747 d	.4098	.3960	.3310	.3240	.3794	.3514	.3596	.3595	.3869	.3778	.3888	.3821	.3740
802 e	.4215	.4048	.3378	.3346	.3738	.3588	.3604	.3693	.3987	.3927	.3974	.3908	.3811
84	.4284	.4110		.3401	.3906	.3634	.3740	.3844	.4048	.3925	.4035	.3077	.3870
89	.4518	.4450	.3767	.3770	.4202	.3979	.4174	.4114	.4331	.4255	.4301	.4245	.4157
96	.4671	.4671	.4098	.4148	.4391	.4244	.4542	.4376	.4500	.4426	.4499	.4440	.4366
SSD	.5564	.5489	.5162	.5087	.5362	.5008	.5290	.5450	.5253	.5021	.5426	.5424	.5080
SSDO	.5751	.5639	.5323	.5158	.5613	.5167	.5445	.5641	.5413	.5196	.5344	.5548	.5194

a-p/p_4 = 0.747 for Refs. 6-S, 6-P, and 6-Q.
b- " = 0.802 for Refs.
c- " = 0.476 for Refs. 15-S, 15-P, and 15-Q; p/p_4 = 0.47 for Refs. 16-S, 16-P, and 16-Q.
d- " = 0.75 for 16-S, 16-P, and 16-Q.
e- " = 0.805 for " ", ", and 16-Q.

Key:
SSD = Water content of granular sample, saturated, surface-dry for sample that had been dried and resaturated.
SSDQ = Water content of granular sample that was brought to saturated condition without preliminary drying.
S = Slow cooled after reheating clinker.
P = "Plant cooled."
Q = Quick-cooled after reheating clinker.
w_n = Non-evaporable water; p/p_4 = about 24×10^{-4}.

TABLE A-9—UNIT ABSOLUTE VOLUME COMPOSITION OF THE MORTARS USED IN SERIES 254-8

Cement No.	Ref. No.	Unit Absolute Volume Composition at End of the 2nd Hour				w/c at 2 hours	Cement Content of Paste
		Cement	Water	Air	Silica		
14930J	8-1	.2375	.2431	.035	.4843	.311	.494
	8-2	.1692	.2466	.032	.5521	.443	.407
	8-3	.1271	.2492	.029	.5953	.595	.338
15007J	8-28	.2363	.2649	.021	.4776	.344	.471
	8-29	.1698	.2567	.025	.5491	.464	.398
	8-30	.1288	.2500	.024	.5978	.595	.340
15008J	8-32	.1647	.2477	.055	.5322	.462	.399
	8-33	.1251	.2405	.055	.5796	.590	.342
15011J	8-40	.2407	.2508	.022	.4870	.319	.490
	8-41	.1730	.2494	.018	.5598	.442	.410
	8-42	.1208	.2522	.015	.6029	.595	.340
15012J	8-44	.1606	.2419	.077	.5207	.461	.399
	8-45	.1202	.2472	.068	.5636	.624	.329
15013J	8-46	.2345	.2532	.040	.4721	.332	.481
	8-47	.1713	.2520	.025	.5516	.453	.405
	8-48	.1260	.2455	.046	.5825	.599	.339
15014J	8-50	.1566	.2595	.079	.5045	.510	.376
	8-51	.1201	.2511	.074	.5548	.644	.324

Adsorption Data: See Table A-10.

TABLE A-10—ADSORPTION DATA FOR SERIES 254-8
Water-cement ratio corrected for bleeding

Total Water Retained at Relative Vapor Pressure Indicated, g/g cement

p/p_s	14930J-8-1 w_o/c = .311 Age 447d	14930J-8-2 w_o/c = .443 Age 362d	14930J-8-3 w_o/c = .595 Age 362d	15007J-8-28 w_o/c = .344 Age 479d	15007J-8-29 w_o/c = .464 Age 440d	15007J-8-30 w_o/c = .595 Age 479d	15008J-8-32 w_o/c = .462 Age 463d	15008J-8-33 w_o/c = .590 Age 463d	15011J-8-40 w_o/c = .319 Age 478d
w_n	.1808	.2006	.2101	.1980	.2169	.2323	.2105	.2208	.1843
.09	.2199	—	.2616	.2370	.2578	.2760	.2472	.2604	.2210
.20	.2360	.2641	.2765	.2538	.2759	.2939	.2641	.2798	.2375
.36	.2566	.2889	.3048	.2765	.2997	.3183	.2863	.3022	.2565
.47	.2681	.3042	.3224	.2918	.3191	.3367	.3024	.3237	.2699
.61	.2798	.3205	.3444	.3100	.3411	.3574	.3221	.3480	.2836
.69	.2858	.3346	.3624	.3179	.3591	.3752	.3361	.3690	.2912
.75	.2994	.3495	.3842	.3249	.3739	.3972	.3471	.3828	.2979
.81	.3057	.3626	.3975	.3350	.3832	.4126	.3673	.4084	.3080
.84	.3132	.3732	.4082	.3401	.3919	.4298	.3789	.4278	.3107
.89	.3290	.4024	.4674	.3489	.4221	.4831	.3933	.4461	.3218
.96	.3479	.4234	.4909	.3762	.4477	.5266	.4442	.5206	.3460
SSD	.3934	.5314	.6852	.4248	.5267	.6711	.5383	.6763	.2892
SSDO	.4132	.5431	.7060	.6228	.5600	.7178			

Total Water Retained at Relative Vapor Pressure Indicated, g/g cement

p/p_s	15011J-8-41 w_o/c = .442 Age 368d	15011J-8-42 w_o/c = .595 Age 368d	15012J-8-44 w_o/c = .461 Age 464d	15012J-8-45 w_o/c = .624 Age 464d	15013J-8-46 w_o/c = .332 Age 339d	15013J-8-47 w_o/c = .453 Age 333d	15013J-8-48 w_o/c = .599 Age 333d	15014J-8-50 w_o/c = .510 Age 487d	15014J-8-51 w_o/c = .644 Age 487d
w_n	.2102	.2218	.2109	.2227	.2185	.2407	.2527	.2472	.2527
.09	.2503	.2640	.2519	.2657	.2567	.2829	.2932	.2885	.2961
.20	.2667	.2817	.2694	.2835	.2737	.2991	.3103	.3079	.3152
.36	.2921	.3073	.2922	.3080	.2934	.3252	.3348	.3373	.3439
.47	.3149	.3329	.3137	.3315	.3076	.3446	.3546	.3587	.3685
.61	.3345	.3548	.3336	.3586	.3163	.3643	.3793	.3834	.3951
.69	.3463	.3745	.3504	.3761	.3333	.3746	.3942	.4050	.4205
.75	.3581	.3931	.3613	.3892	.3424	.3931	.4148	.4199	.4422
.81	.3657	.4003	.3794	.4145	.3468	.4002	.4281	.4359	.4627
.84	.3828	.4232	.3906	.4320	.3514	.4089	.4387	.4436	.4732
.89	.4131	.4659	.4066	.4546	.3673	.4375	.4820	.4656	.5065
.96	.4338	.4975	.4608	.5295	.3826	.4619	.5203	.5116	.5701
SSD	.5246	.6426	.5738	.6978	.4245	.5587	.6886	.6355	.7769
SSDO	.5306	.6756			.4461				

Key: *SSD* = Water content of granular sample, saturated, surface-dry for sample that had been dried and resaturated.
SSDO = Water content of granular sample that was brought to saturated condition without preliminary drying.
w_n = Non-evaporable water; p/p_s = about 24x10⁻⁶.

Description of specimens made in series 254-9

Mortar Specimens: Cubes, 2-in.; Prism, $2 \times 2 \times 9\frac{1}{2}$ in.

Cements: See Tables A-1 to A-3.

Pulverized Silica: Lot 15282. Specific surface, volume basis, about the same as that of cement.

Batches: The batches were made up as follows:

Mix	Cement	Pulverized Silica	Std. Ottawa Sand	Water (approx.)	Nominal w/c by Weight
A	1900	—	3100	620	0.326
B	1350	450	3100	610	0.452
C	1000	730	3100	600	0.600

Weights, gms. per batch

Mixing: As in Series 254-8.

Slump Test: As in Series 254-8.

Molding: From each batch 12 cubes and 1 prism were cast in previously weighed steel molds.

Measurements: Cubes: as in Series 254-8. Prism: the prism was weighed in air and in water at 28 days.

Curing: As in Series 254-8.

Drying: As in Series 254-8.

Test results for series 254-9

Composition of Hardened Specimens: The composition of the mortars in the hardened cubes, derived as in Series 254-8, is given in Table A-11.

TABLE A-11—UNIT ABSOLUTE VOLUME COMPOSITION OF THE MORTARS USED IN SERIES 254-9

Cement No.	Ref. No.	Mix	Unit Absolute Volume Composition at the End of the 2nd Hour				w/c at 2 hrs. (wt. basis)
			Cement	Water	Air	Silica	
14930J	9–1	A	.2401	.2437	.0308	.4863	.309
	9–2	B	.1718	.2397	.0284	.5610	.424
	9–3	C	.1268	.2380	.0292	.6072	.573
15007J	9–4	A	.2402	.2474	.0312	.4821	.316
	9–5	B	.1721	.2422	.0289	.5568	.433
	9–6	C	.1292	.2434	.0211	.6062	.570
15011J	9–7	A	.2415	.2493	.0245	.4852	.316
	9–8	B	.1727	.2445	.0240	.5593	.432
	9–9	C	.1288	.2394	.0251	.6073	.582
15013J	9–10	A	.2407	.2538	.0248	.4813	.324
	9–11	B	.1709	.2457	.0341	.5504	.443
	9–12	C	.1260	.2500	.0337	.5912	.611
15365	9–13	A	.2366	.2462	.0439	.4752	.319
	9–14	B	.1711	.2453	.0313	.5536	.439
	9–15	C	.1295	.2388	.0224	.6101	.587
	9–15A	Neat	.5316	.4220	.0487	—	.244

Adsorption Data: See Tables A-12 to A-27.

Chemical Analyses of Dried Granular Samples: See Table A-28.

Compressive Strength: Cubes were tested in compression, two at each age. See Tables 6-2 to 6-6, Part 6 for results. Samples for adsorption measurements were prepared from the broken cubes.

Modulus of Elasticity: The modulus of elasticity was determined from sonic measurements on the prism. See Table A-29 for results.

TABLE A-12—ADSORPTION DATA FOR REF. 254-9-1, CEMENT 14930J

w/c (by wt.):   Original 0.316; after bleeding 0.309
w_n = non-evaporable water; p/p_s = about 24x10⁻⁶
w_t = total water
(w_e = evaporable water can be obtained from the relationship $w_e = w_t - w_n$)

p/p_s	Total Water, w_t, Retained at Relative Vapor Pressure and Age Indicated, g/g cement						
	7 days	14 days	28 days	56 days	90 days	180 days	365 days
w_n	.0804	.0994	.1071	.1292	.1497	.1620	.1704
.088	.0957	.1183					
.089			.1327	.1598	.1812	.2000	
.090							.2080
.20	.1018	.1273	.1421	.1725	.1963	.2160	.2232
.355	.1097	.1407					
.36			.1557	.1893	.2155	.2335	.2422
.47			.1680	.2024	.2271	.2482	.2547
.51	.1185	.1473					
.61	.1247	.1533	.1738	.2109	.2338	.2598	.2654
.69	.1341	.1661	.1898	.2240	.2477	.2678	.2743
.75	.1477	.1763	.2007	.2323	.2558	.2754	.2800
.80	.1547	.1879	.1905	.2347	.2608	.2811	
.81							.2904
.84	.1599	.1925	.2136	.2521	.2715	.2915	.2963
.89	.1863	.2201	.2408	.2697	.2851	.3054	.3012
.96	.2152	.2421	.2623	.2974	.3105	.3184	.3282
SSD	.3258	.3324	.3493	.3473	.3522	.3576	.3627
SSDO	.3457	.3520	.3516	.3605	.3667	.3703	

Key: SSD = Water content of granular sample in saturated, surface-dry condition for sample that had been dried and resaturated.
SSDO = Water content of granular sample that was brought to saturated condition without preliminary drying.

TABLE A-13—ADSORPTION DATA FOR REF. 254-9-2, CEMENT 14930J

w/c (by wt.):   Original 0.441; after bleeding 0.424
w_n = non-evaporable water; p/p_s = about 24x10⁻⁶
w_t = total water
(w_e = evaporable water can be obtained from the relationship $w_e = w_t - w_n$)

p/p_s	Total Water, w_t, Retained at Relative Vapor Pressure and Age Indicated, g/g cement						
	7 days	14 days	28 days	56 days	90 days	180 days	365 days
w_n	.0798	.1029	.1165	.1352	.1735	.1853	.1953
.088	.0957	.1227					
.089			.1444	.1697	.2093	.2268	
.090							.2396
.20	.1020	.1315	.1542	.1889	.2254	.2473	.2569
.355	.1075	.1487					
.36			.1700	.2089	.2485	.2693	.2791
.47			.1819	.2194	.2643	.2873	.2987
.51	.1160	.1511					
.61	.1214	.1551	.1892	.2388	.2751	.3075	.3154
.69	.1335	.1722	.2076	.2516	.2939	.3184	.3286
.75	.1446	.1797	.2142	.2666	.3065	.3295	.3358
.80	.1517	.1928	.2051	.2671	.3133	.3347	
.81							.3507
.84	.1573	.1976	.2359	.2955	.3246	.3520	.3614
.89	.1879	.2426	.2784	.3238	.3496	.3720	.3735
.96	.2189	.2693	.3103	.3684	.3797	.3894	.4114
SSD	.3981	.4426	.4769	.4738	.4879	.4852	.5109
SSDO	.3995	.4626	.4936	.4864	.5017	.5024	

Key: SSD = Water content of granular sample in saturated, surface-dry condition for sample that had been dried and resaturated.
SSDO = Water content of granular sample that was brought to saturated condition without preliminary drying.

TABLE A-14—ADSORPTION DATA FOR REF. 254-9-3, CEMENT 14930J

w/c (by wt.):   Original 0.600; after bleeding 0.573
w_n = non-evaporable water; p/p_s = about 24×10^{-6}
w_t = total water
(w_e = evaporable water can be obtained from the relationship $w_e = w_t - w_n$)

p/p_s	Total Water, w_t, Retained at Relative Vapor Pressure and Age Indicated, g/g cement						
	7 days	14 days	28 days	56 days	90 days	180 days	365 days
w_n	.0822	.0896	.1214	.1638	.1850	.2008	.2142
.089	.1022	.1118	.1521	.1979	.2238	.2422	.2625
.20	.1054	.1180	.1635	.2130	.2409	.2601	.2842
.36	.1125	.1289	.1814	.2343	.2637	.2841	.3125
.47	.1192	.1337	.1848	.2484	.2814	.3032	.3327
.61	.1271	.1464	.2086	.2634	.3068	.3251	.3508
.69	.1385	.1626	.2173	.2882	.3207	.3398	.3700
.75	.1411	.1712	.2371	.3043	.3372	.3573	.3838
.80	.1553	.1721	.2354	.3182	.3470	.3700	
.81	—	—	—	—	—	—	.4012
.84	.1673	.2026	.2713	.3380	.3647	.3835	.4176
.89	.1955	.2318	.3099	.3761	.4114	.4261	.4450
.96	.2207	.2807	.3642	.4385	.4485	.4515	.5062
SSD	.4822	.4599	.5944	.6344	.6393	.5640	.6971
SSDO	.4732	.4851	.6021	.6579	.6562	.6028	—

Key: SSD = Water content of granular sample in saturated, surface-dry condition for sample that had been dried and resaturated.
SSDO = Water content of granular sample that was brought to saturated condition without preliminary drying.

TABLE A-15—ADSORPTION DATA FOR REF. 254-9-4, CEMENT 15007J

w/c (by wt.): Original 0.338; after bleeding 0.316
w_n = non-evaporable water; p/p_s = about 24×10^{-4}
w_t = total water
(w_e = evaporable water can be obtained from the relationship $w_e = w_t - w_n$)

p/p_s	Total Water, w_t, Retained at Relative Vapor Pressure and Age Indicated, g/g cement					
	7 days	14 days	28 days	56 days	90 days	180 days
w_n	.1259	.1404	.1538	.1681	.1729	.1835
.080	.1503	.1687	.1824	.2147	.2105	
.09	—	—	—	—	—	.2170
.20	.1612	.1816	.1950	.2167	.2234	.2311
.36	.1750	.1982	.2126	.2353	.2419	.2513
.47	.1848	.2111	.2270	.2496	.2574	.2672
.61	.1940	.2243	.2449	.2651	.2752	.2814
.69	.2082	.2378	.2587	.2752	.2821	.2907
.75	.2185	.2440	.2657	.2810	.2891	.2962
.80	.2215	—	.2715	.2856	.2941	
.81	—	—	—	—	—	.3026
.84	.2319	.2584	.2781	.3004	.3030	.3092
.89	.2520	.2810	.2979	.3077	.3146	.3235
.96	.2856	.2921	.3131	.3269	.3276	.3378
SSD	.3541	.3643	.3654	.3794	.3712	.3773
SSDO	.3716	—	.3747	.3853		.3921

Key: SSD = Water content of granular sample in saturated, surface-dry condition for sample that had been dried and resaturated.
SSDO = Water content of granular sample that was brought to saturated condition without preliminary drying.

TABLE A-16—ADSORPTION DATA FOR REF. 254-9-5, CEMENT 15007J

w/c (by wt.): Original 0.467; after bleeding 0.433
w_n = non-evaporable water; p/p_s = about 24x10⁻⁶ (about 24×10^{-6})
w_t = total water
(w_e = evaporable water can be obtained from the relationship $w_e = w_t - w_n$)

p/p_s	Total Water, w_t, Retained at Relative Vapor Pressure and Age Indicated, g/g cement					
	7 days	14 days	28 days	56 days	90 days	180 days
w_n	.1334	.1498	.1714	.1847	.1924	.2018
.089	.1585	.1801	.2026	.2336	.2341	—
.09	—	—	—	—	—	.2396
.20	.1698	.1942	.2169	.2399	.2500	.2555
.36	.1843	.2128	.2357	.2593	.2714	.2778
.47	.1972	.2243	.2522	.2751	.2917	.2979
.61	.2085	.2415	.2763	.2975	.3158	.3152
.69	.2232	.2570	.2906	.3128	.3284	.3315
.75	.2312	.2657	.3020	.3249	.3394	.3411
.80	.2364	—	.3132	.3302	.3460	—
.81	—	—	—	—	—	.3520
.84	.2517	.2867	.3191	.3527	.3607	.3614
.89	.2774	.3158	.3432	.3713	.3802	.3994
.96	.3157	.3254	.3695	.3899	.3980	.4111
SSD	.4667	.4764	.4913	.5002	.5092	.5502
SSDO	.5000	.4971	.5106	.5156	—	.5605

Key: SSD = Water content of granular sample in saturated, surface-dry condition for sample that had been dried and resaturated.
   SSDO = Water content of granular sample that was brought to saturated condition without preliminary drying.

TABLE A-17—ADSORPTION DATA FOR REF. 254-9-6, CEMENT 15007J

w/c (by wt.): Original 0.610; after bleeding 0.570
w_n = non-evaporable water; p/p_s = about 24x10⁻⁶ (about 24×10^{-6})
w_t = total water
(w_e = evaporable water can be obtained from the relationship $w_e = w_t - w_n$)

p/p_s	Total Water, w_t, Retained at Relative Vapor Pressure and Age Indicated, g/g cement					
	7 days	14 days	28 days	56 days	90 days	180 days
w_n	.1560	.1634	.1839	.2035	.2049	.2132
.089	.1824	.1921	.2191	—	—	—
.09	—	—	—	.2398	.2428	—
.20	.1918	.2066	.2341	.2561	.2603	.2758
.36	.2078	.2210	.2536	.2781	.2811	.3006
.47	.2209	.2342	.2668	.2975	.3038	.3218
.61	.2423	.2523	.2843	.3240	.3266	.3460
.69	.2545	.2694	.3136	.3405	.3407	.3589
.75	.2705	.2864	.3297	.3524	.3578	.3810
.80	.2816	.2870	.3347	.3585	—	—
.81	—	—	—	—	.3656	.3918
.84	.2998	.3140	.3634	.3836	.3818	.4151
.89	.3240	.3409	.3921	.4132	.4155	.4430
.96	.3597	.3774	.4244	.4456	.4413	.4780
SSD	.5084	.5300	.5845	.5900	.6019	.6676
SSDO	.5630	.5846	.6219	.6347	.6186	—

Key: SSD = Water content of granular sample in saturated, surface-dry condition for sample that had been dried and resaturated.
   SSDO = Water content of granular sample that was brought to saturated condition without preliminary drying.

TABLE A-18—ADSORPTION DATA FOR REF. 254-9-7, CEMENT 15011J

w/c (by wt.): Original 0.353; after bleeding 0.316
w_n = non-evaporable water, p/p_s = about 24×10^{-6}
w_t = total water
(w_e = evaporable water can be obtained from the relationship $w_e = w_t - w_n$)

p/p_s	Total Water, w_t, Retained at Relative Vapor Pressure and Age Indicated, g/g cement						
	7 days	14 days	28 days	56 days	90 days	180 days	365 days
w_n	.1137	.1333	.1430	.1557	.1643	.1705	.1760
.089	.1415	.1584	.1785	.1892	.1961	.2039	—
.09	—	—	—	—	—	—	.2111
.20	.1484	.1686	.1953	.2035	.2098	.2191	.2276
.36	.1617	.1838	.2069	.2211	.2268	.2359	.2468
.47	.1703	.1960	.2193	.2295	.2410	.2509	.2573
.61	.1808	.2038	.2312	.2401	.2531	.2632	.2685
.69	.1935	.2197	.2448	.2535	.2622	.2716	.2764
.75	.1942	.2289	.2534	.2627	.2704	.2817	.2861
.80	.2112	.2319	.2548	.2684	.2746	.2873	—
.81	—	—	—	—	—	—	.2931
.84	.2209	.2535	.2738	.2767	.2812	.2951	.3002
.89	.2480	.2787	.2955	.2905	.3015	.3125	.3109
.96	.2697	.3059	.3186	.3140	.3138	.3216	.3341
SSD	.3487	.3575	.3619	.3591	.3617	.3646	.3721
SSDO	.3587	.3710	.3696	.3713	.3685	.3794	

Key: SSD = Water content of granular sample in saturated, surface-dry condition for sample that had been dried and resaturated.
   SSDO = Water content of granular sample that was brought to saturated condition without preliminary drying.

TABLE A-19—ADSORPTION DATA FOR REF. 254-9-8, CEMENT 15011J

w/c (by wt.): Original 0.459; after bleeding 0.432
w_n = non-evaporable water; p/p_s = about 24×10^{-6}
w_t = total water
(w_e = evaporable water can be obtained from the relationship $w_e = w_t - w_n$)

p/p_s	Total Water, w_t, Retained at Relative Vapor Pressure and Age Indicated, g/g cement					
	7 days	14 days	28 days	56 days	90 days	180 days
w_n	.1228	.1527	.1654	.1781	.1913	.1986
.089	.1514	.1824	.2054	.2154	.2278	—
.09	—	—	—	—	—	.2359
.20	.1618	.1940	.2116	.2269	.2444	.2521
.36	.1762	.2064	.2300	.2464	.2647	.2751
.47	.1828	.2205	.2444	.2656	.2798	.2956
.61	.2005	.2357	.2562	.2858	.3023	.3126
.69	.2140	.2470	.2764	.3000	.3165	.3250
.75	.2254	.2634	.2890	.3119	.3289	.3364
.80	—	.2718	.2993	.3226	.3380	—
.81	—	—	—	—	—	.3437
.84	.2517	.2875	.3108	.3313	.3591	.3587
.89	.2829	.3249	.3251	.3618	.3816	.3827
.96	.3310	.3579	.3778	.3864	.4055	.4108
SSD	.4661	.4932	.4843	.4922	.4952	.4975
SSDO		.5155	.5045	.5075	.5165	.5119

Key: SSD = Water content of granular sample in saturated, surface-dry condition for sample that had been dried and resaturated.
   SSDO = Water content of granular sample that was brought to saturated condition without preliminary drying.

TABLE A-20—ADSORPTION DATA FOR REF. 9-9, CEMENT 15011J

w/c (by wt.): Original 0.610; after bleeding 0.582
w_n = non-evaporable water; p/p_s = about 24×10^{-6}
w_t = total water
(w_e = evaporable water can be obtained from the relationship $w_e = w_t - w_n$)

p/p_s	Total Water, w_t, Retained at Relative Vapor Pressure and Age Indicated, g/g cement					
	7 days	14 days	28 days	56 days	90 days	180 days
w_n	.1314	.1567	.1756	.1953	.2046	.2136
.089	.1573	.1871	.2176	.2332	.2427	—
.09	—	—	—	—	—	.2523
.20	.1693	.1994	.2231	.2484	.2600	.2693
.36	.1804	.2132	.2418	.2688	.2831	.2914
.47	.1901	.2244	.2562	.2897	.2977	.3139
.61	.2037	.2385	.2695	.3121	.3212	.3364
.69	.2160	.2520	.2948	.3294	.3408	.3526
.75	.2290	.2679	.3065	.3413	.3566	.3684
.80	—	.2804	.3179	.3590	.3692	—
.81	—	—	—	—	—	.3756
.84	.2574	.2999	.3344	.3684	.3939	.3990
.89	.2946	.3381	.3527	.4134	.4291	.4344
.96	.3453	.3931	.4233	.4469	.4588	.4670
SSD	.5576	.5258	.5793	.6471	.6212	.5800
SSDO	—	.5657	.6146	.6726	.6306	.6156

Key: SSD = Water content of granular sample in saturated, surface-dry condition for sample that had been dried and resaturated.
SSDO = Water content of granular sample that was brought to saturated condition without preliminary drying.

TABLE A-21—ADSORPTION DATA FOR REF. 9-10, CEMENT 15013J

w/c (by wt.): Original 0.326; after bleeding 0.324
w_n = non-evaporable water; p/p_s = about 24×10^{-6}
w_t = total water
(w_e = evaporable water can be obtained from the relationship $w_e = w_t - w_n$)

p/p_s	Total Water, w_t, Retained at Relative Vapor Pressure and Age Indicated, g/g cement					
	7 days	14 days	28 days	56 days	90 days	180 days
w_n	.1488	.1639	.1711	.1802	.1913	.1877
.089	.1748	.1909	.2028	.2147	—	—
.09	—	—	—	—	.2260	.2299
.20	.1859	.2042	.2161	.2277	.2409	.2426
.36	.2001	.2186	.2324	.2452	.2586	.2615
.47	.2110	.2304	.2472	.2602	.2760	.2763
.61	.2287	.2465	.2634	.2790	.2912	.2907
.69	.2386	.2604	.2761	.2899	.3015	.2917
.75	.2509	.2705	.2843	.2952	.3100	.3058
.80	.2541	.2680	.2857	.2979	—	—
.81	—	—	—	—	.3135	.3103
.84	.2653	.2863	.3004	.3104	.3212	.3151
.89	.2729	.2997	.3114	.3218	.3342	.3307
.96	.3019	.3110	.3228	.3335	.3417	.3418
SSD	.3745	.3831	.3781	.3852	.3873	.3784
SSDO	.3745	.3831	.3914	.3995	.4018	—

Key: SSD = Water content of granular sample in saturated, surface-dry condition for sample that had been dried and resaturated.
SSDO = Water content of granular sample that was brought to saturated condition without preliminary drying.

TABLE A-22—ADSORPTION DATA FOR REF. 9-11, CEMENT 15013J

w/c (by wt.): Original 0.459; after bleeding 0.443
w_n = non-evaporable water; p/p_s = about 24×10^{-6}
w_t = total water
(w_e = evaporable water can be obtained from the relationship $w_e = w_t - w_n$)

p/p_s	Total Water, w_t, Retained at Relative Vapor Pressure and Age Indicated, g/g cement					
	7 days	14 days	28 days	56 days	90 days	180 days
w_n	.1556	.1828	.1770	.2085	.2152	.2356
.089	.1830	.2143	.2131	—	—	—
.09	—	—	—	.2460	.2530	.2761
.20	.1932	.2269	.2272	.2604	.2695	.2933
.36	.2079	.2434	.2455	.2843	.2940	.3179
.47	.2190	.2572	.2626	.3017	.3124	.3372
.61	.2369	.2814	.2822	.3212	.3306	.3572
.69	.2447	.2911	.2985	.3363	.3426	.3660
.75	.2578	.3026	.3129	.3518	.3555	.3797
.80	.2614	.3051	—	—	—	—
.81	—	—	—	.3557	.3649	.3008
.84	.2788	.3228	.3316	.3690	.3763	.3958
.89	.2991	.3481	.3690	.3927	.4034	.4127
.96	.3247	.3698	.3933	.4115	.4265	.4547
SSD	.4435	.4831	.5248	.5298	.5643	.5705
SSDO	.4793	.5137	.5419	—	—	—

Key: SSD = Water content of granular sample in saturated, surface-dry condition for sample that hap been dried and resaturated.
SSDO = Water content of granular sample that was brought to saturated condition without preliminary drying.

TABLE A-23—ADSORPTION DATA FOR REF. 9-12, CEMENT 15013J

w/c (by wt.): Original 0.635; after bleeding 0.611
w_n = non-evaporable water; p/p_s = about 24×10^{-6}
w_t = total water
(w_e = evaporable water can be obtained from the relationship $w_e = w_t - w_n$)

p/p_s	Total Water, w_t, Retained at Relative Vapor Pressure and Age Indicated, g/g cement					
	7 days	14 days	28 days	56 days	90 days	180 days
w_n	.1583	.1828	.2028	.2208	.2357	.2447
.089	.1841	.2129	.2368	—	—	—
.09	—	—	—	.2582	.2778	.2856
.20	.1941	.2238	.2502	.2737	.2937	.3029
.36	.2063	.2395	.2663	.2971	.3173	.3272
.47	.2176	.2532	.2850	.3151	.3372	.3460
.61	.2345	.2747	.3075	.3396	.3579	.3690
.69	.2432	.2848	.3232	.3578	.3747	.3841
.75	.2584	.3003	.3395	.3731	.3946	.3983
.80	—	.3034	—	—	—	—
.81	—	—	—	.3796	.4029	.4166
.84	.2792	.3229	.3576	.3974	.4191	.4221
.89	.3018	.3507	.3995	.4296	.4557	.4468
.96	.3244	.3763	.4244	.4563	.4930	.5102
SSD	.5148	.5497	.5798	.6136	.7162	.6707
SSDO	.5743	.6200	.6438	—	—	—

Key: SSD = Water content of granular sample in saturated, surface-dry condition for sample that had been dried and resaturated.
SSDO = Water content of granular sample that was brought to saturated condition without preliminary drying.

TABLE A-24—ADSORPTION DATA FOR REF. 9-13, CEMENT 15365

w/c (by wt.): Original 0.326; after bleeding 0.319
w_n = non-evaporable water; p/p_s = about 24×10^{-6}
w_t = total water
(w_e = evaporable water can be obtained from the relationship $w_e = w_t - w_n$)

p/p_s	Total Water, w_t, Retained at Relative Vapor Pressure and Age Indicated, g/g cement					
	7 days	14 days	28 days	56 days	90 days	180 days
w_n	.1326	.1515	.1488	.1786	.1789	.1815
.09	.1596	.1803	.1803	.2133	.2133	.2168
.20	.1681	.1903	.1933	.2275	.2269	.2311
.36	.1809	.2043	.2106	.2461	.2460	.2495
.47	.1925	.2181	.2242	.2574	.2591	.2608
.61	.2052	.2313	.2414	.2725	.2734	.2740
.69	.2134	.2434	.2489	.2796	.2824	.2870
.75	.2244	.2541	.2571	.2898	.2926	.2922
.81	.2319	.2625	.2649	.2962	.2973	.2992
.84	.2391	.2688	.2783	.3017	.3026	.3078
.89	.2662	.2907	.2938	.3190	.3184	.3173
.96	.2906	.3123	.3036	.3367	.3341	.3344
SSD	.3570	.3669	.3639	.3847	.3702	.3791
SSDO	—	.3842	—	—	—	—

Key: SSD = Water content of granular sample in saturated, surface-dry condition for sample that had been dried and resaturated.
SSDO = Water content of granular sample that was brought to saturated condition without preliminary drying.

TABLE A-25—ADSORPTION DATA FOR REF. 254-9-14, CEMENT 15365

w/c (by wt.): Original 0.450; after bleeding 0.439
w_n = non-evaporable water; p/p_s = about 24×10^{-6}
w_t = total water
(w_e = evaporable water can be obtained from the relationship $w_e = w_t - w_n$)

p/p_s	Total Water, w_t, Retained at Relative Vapor Pressure and Age Indicated, g/g cement					
	7 days	14 days	28 days	56 days	90 days	180 days
w_n	.1394	.1711	.1841	.2105	.2150	.2224
.09	.1665	.2031	.2230	.2502	.2571	.2651
.20	.1758	.2142	.2377	.2655	.2730	.2819
.36	.1893	.2315	.2599	.2889	.2962	.3088
.47	.2009	.2470	.2757	.3062	.3165	.3250
.61	.2138	.2619	.2961	.3257	.3346	.3460
.69	.2237	.2767	.3102	.3366	.3512	.3626
.75	.2343	.2894	.3256	.3518	.3638	.3699
.81	.2419	.3008	.3322	.3621	.3717	.3830
.84	.2512	.3104	.3476	.3681	.3791	.3925
.89	.2828	.3399	.3761	.3968	.4044	.4094
.96	.3098	.3646	.3966	.4188	.4288	.4429
SSD	.4182	.4724	.5034	.5133	.5113	.5344
SSDO	—	.4877	—	—	—	—

Key: SSD = Water content of granular sample in saturated, surface-dry condition for sample that had been dried and resaturated.
SSDO = Water content of granular sample that was brought to saturated condition without preliminary drying.

388   Powers and Brownyard

TABLE A-26—ADSORPTION DATA FOR REF. 254-9-15, CEMENT 15365

w/c (by wt.): Original 0.610; after bleeding 0.587
w_n = non-evaporable water; p/p_s = about 24x10[-6]
w_t = total water
(w_e = evaporable water can be obtained from the relationship $w_e = w_t - w_n$)

p/p_s	Total Water, w_t, Retained at Relative Vapor Pressure and Age Indicated, g/g cement					
	7 days	14 days	28 days	56 days	90 days	180 days
w_n	.1530	.1855	.2102	.2213	.2296	.2546
.09	.1820	.2194	.2495	.2653	.2741	.2967
.20	.1922	.2321	.2646	.2820	.2918	.3139
.36	.2063	.2496	.2872	.3032	.3176	.3406
.47	.2162	.2636	.3030	.3249	.3357	.3609
.61	.2298	.2819	.3262	.3484	.3611	.3821
.69	.2395	.2937	.3382	.3641	.3783	.4056
.75	.2531	.3108	.3541	.3767	.3910	.4175
.81	.2578	.3139	.3637	.3898	.4074	.4347
.84	.2716	.3306	.3773	----	.4177	.4456
.89	.3060	.3706	.4197	.4228	.4461	.4681
.96	.3489	.4139	.4587	.4809	.5104	.5318
SSD	.5157	.5804	.6272	.6400	.6614	.6637
SSDO	.5707	.6031	----	----	----	----

Key: SSD = Water content of granular sample in saturated, surface-dry condition for sample that had been dried and resaturated.
SSDO = Water content of granular sample that was brought to saturated condition without preliminary drying.

TABLE A-27—ADSORPTION DATA FOR REF. 254-9-15A, CEMENT 15365

w/c (by wt.): Original 0.246; after bleeding 0.244
w_n = non-evaporable water; p/p_s = about 24x10[-6]
w_t = total waer
(w_e = evaporable water can be obtained from the relationship $w_e = w_t - w_n$)

p/p_s	Total Water, w_t, Retained at Relative Vapor Pressure and Age Indicated, g/g cement						270 days	
	7 days	14 days	28 days	56 days	90 days	180 days	A	B
w_n	.1152	.1259	.1358	.1396	.1452	.1554	.1691	.1722
.081	----	----	----	----	----	----	.1910	.1918
.09	.1380	.1501	.1611	.1684	.1741	.1856		
.161							.2000	.1999
.20	.1465	.1591	.1709	.1785	.1837	.1956		
.238							.2053	.2063
.322							.2111	.2116
.36	.1572	.1713	.1830	.1901	.1967	.2090	.2159	.2152
.47	.1658	.1811	.1933	.2002	.2061	.2177		
.53							.2275	.2277
.61	.1763	.1918	.2034	.2123	.2182	.2266		
.69	.1846	.1993	.2116	.2211	.2240	.2355		
.70							.2397	.2402
.75	.1988	.2133	.2217	.2256	.2306	.2399		
.81	.2021	.2146	.2259	.2324	.2389	.2459	.2509	.2504
.84	.2116	.2254	.2305	----	.2412	.2489		
.85							.2582	.2588
.88							.2634	.2619
.89	.2317	.2414	.2487	.2426	.2509	.2536		
.96	.2508	.2599	.2613	.2594	.2698	.2724	.2775	.2771
SSD	.3064	.2948	.3028	.2960	.2969	.2836	.2906	.3024
SSDO	.3128	.3076	----	----	----	----		

Key: SSD = Water content of granular sample in saturated, surface-dry condition for sample that had been dried and resaturated.
SSDO = Water content of granular sample that was brought to saturated condition without preliminary drying.
A and B refer to separate rounds.

TABLE A-28—ANALYSES OF GRANULAR SAMPLES USED FOR ADSORPTION AND NON-EVAPORABLE WATER MEASUREMENTS IN SERIES 254-9

Composition of Dry Samples at Age Indicated, percent dry weight

w/c at 2 hr. (wt. basis)	7 days Cmt.	7 days SiO₂	7 days H₂O	14 days Cmt.	14 days SiO₂	14 days H₂O	28 days Cmt.	28 days SiO₂	28 days H₂O	56 days Cmt.	56 days SiO₂	56 days H₂O	90 days Cmt.	90 days SiO₂	90 days H₂O	180 days Cmt.	180 days SiO₂	180 days H₂O	365 days Cmt.	365 days SiO₂	365 days H₂O
								Cement 14930J													
0.399	84.7	7.9	7.5	80.4	11.7	8.0	70.0	22.0	7.6	73.9	10.6	9.6	69.9	19.6	10.5	76.9	10.6	12.5	70.1	18.0	11.9
0.424	86.1	27.9	5.3	62.5	30.2	6.4	52.0	42.0	6.1	48.5	45.0	9.6	55.1	35.4	9.6	69.4	28.4	11.2	54.4	35.0	10.6
0.573	46.5	49.8	3.8	33.8	63.6	3.0	40.4	54.7	4.9	46.0	46.5	7.5	46.8	44.5	8.7	49.7	40.3	10.0	46.4	43.6	9.9
								Cement 15007J													
0.316	76.3	14.1	9.6	74.3	15.3	10.4	74.2	14.4	11.4	77.5	9.5	13.0	77.6	9.0	13.4	75.8	10.3	13.9			
0.433	60.5	31.5	8.1	58.1	33.1	8.7	57.4	32.8	9.8	60.8	27.9	11.2	60.6	27.7	11.7	47.9	42.5	9.7			
0.570	48.1	44.4	7.5	48.1	44.0	7.9	48.4	42.8	8.9	47.9	42.4	9.7	47.5	42.3	10.2	32.6	60.5	7.0			
								Cement 15011J													
0.316	79.0	12.1	9.0	71.7	18.9	9.6	75.5	13.7	10.8	72.8	15.7	11.3	73.7	14.2	12.1	78.6	8.0	13.4	78.8	7.3	13.9
0.432	51.0	42.8	6.3	58.9	32.1	9.0	58.5	31.8	9.7	58.1	31.5	10.4	61.0	27.3	11.7	57.9	30.6	11.5			
0.582	47.5	46.2	6.2	47.3	45.3	7.4	45.9	46.0	8.1	44.6	46.7	8.7	48.0	42.3	9.8	45.7	44.5	9.8			
								Cement 15013J													
0.324	80.3	7.7	12.0	80.2	6.7	13.1	79.1	7.3	13.5	70.1	6.7	14.2	78.0	7.1	14.9	62.5	25.8	11.7			
0.443	62.7	27.5	9.8	59.4	29.8	10.8	25.1	70.5	4.4	58.1	29.7	12.1	51.0	37.0	11.0	53.4	34.1	12.6			
0.611	46.1	46.6	7.3	47.7	43.6	8.7	45.4	45.4	9.2	45.0	45.1	9.9	35.2	56.5	8.3	40.4	49.8	9.9			
								Cement 15365													
0.319	82.2	7.0	10.9	78.3	9.8	11.4	50.1	42.4	7.5	76.8	9.4	13.7	76.6	9.7	13.7	72.5	14.3	13.2			
0.439	62.2	29.2	8.7	60.6	29.0	10.4	51.9	38.6	9.6	60.0	27.4	12.6	58.6	28.6	12.8	56.1	31.3	12.5			
0.587	45.4	47.6	7.0	48.5	42.5	9.0	44.8	45.8	9.4	46.6	43.0	10.3	46.5	42.9	10.7	47.7	40.2	12.1			

Cement content estimated from CaO determination. Water content estimated from ignition loss corrected for ignition loss of cement. Silica content found by difference.

TABLE A-29—YOUNG'S MODULUS OF MORTARS USED IN SERIES 254-9

Cement No.	w/c at 2 hrs. (wt. basis)	Young's Modulus at Age Indicated* millions of lb/in²					
		7 days	14 days	28 days	56 days	90 days	180 days
14930J	.309	4.47	4.98	5.45	5.50	5.75	6.00
	.424	3.67	4.30	4.85	5.14	5.36	5.66
	.573	2.57	3.34	4.13	4.71	4.87	5.20
15007J	.316	5.18	5.35	5.58	5.54	5.48	5.73
	.433	4.65	4.85	5.08	5.14	5.35	5.32
	.570	4.23	4.50	4.92	5.03	5.08	(a)
15011J	.316	5.10	5.45	5.62	5.76	5.88	6.00
	.432	4.55	4.85	5.20	5.30	5.42	5.48
	.582	4.13	4.48	4.83	4.89	5.00	5.00
15013J	.324	5.05	5.17	5.30	5.40	5.47	5.65
	.443	4.37	4.68	4.85	(a)	(a)	(a)
	.611	3.78	3.97	4.36	4.45	4.50	4.65
15365	.319	5.30	5.42	5.58	5.78	5.78	—
	.439	4.64	5.27	5.03	5.18	5.40	—
	.587	4.40	4.81	4.96	5.03	5.03	—

*Values are for a single prism.
(a) Prism broken.

TABLE A-30—UNIT ABSOLUTE VOLUME COMPOSITION OF THE MORTARS USED IN SERIES 254-11

Cement No.	Ref. No.	(See page 317)	Unit Absolute Volume Composition at 2 hours				w/c at 2 hours, (wt. basis)
			Cement	Silica	Air	Water	
15758	11–1	A	.2305	.4660	.0437	.2526	.334
	11–2	B	.1721	.5398	.0382	.2506	.460
15756	11–3	A	.2443	.4828	.0233	.2551	.318
	11–4	B	.1781	.5604	.0087	.2525	.446
15763	11–5	A	.2434	.4827	.0237	.2508	.324
	11–6	B	.1741	.5562	.0245	.2458	.437
15761	11–7	A	Note 1	—	—	—	.334
	11–8	B	—	—	—	—	.468
15754	11–9	A	.2409	.4746	.0315	.2540	.328
	11–10	B	.1727	.5484	.0271	.2526	.449
16213	11–11	B	.1775	.5592	.0135	.2497	.443
16214	11–12	B	.1766	.5580	.0131	.2522	.448
16198	11–13	B	.1745	.5621	.0121	.2512	.443
15669	11–14	B	.1725	.5579	.0157	.2538	.451
15495	11–15	B	.1764	.5488	.0302	.2445	.442
15497	11–16	B	.1731	.5453	.0266	.2549	.464

Note 1:   The specimens with Cement 15761, expanded in the molds and hence it was impossible to obtain satisfactory data for calculating the composition.
See p. 333 for description of specimens.

TABLE A-31—ANALYSES OF GRANULAR SAMPLES USED FOR ADSORPTION AND NON-EVAPORABLE WATER MEASUREMENTS IN SERIES 254-11

Cement No.	w/c at 2 hrs. (wt. basis)	Cement-, Silica-, and Non-Evaporable Water-Content of 35-100-Mesh Samples at Age Indicated, g/g dry weight					
		28 days			90 days		
		Cement	Silica	Non-Evap. Water	Cement	Silica	Non-Evap. Water
15758	.334	.783	.084	.134	.773	.079	.148
	.460	.598	.284	.117	.607	.258	.135
15756	.318	.788	.115	.097	.776	.108	.116
	.446	.616	.302	.082	.617	.279	.104
15763	.324	.834	.089	.077	.788	.107	.105
	.437	.647	.288	.065	.169	.289	.092
15761	.334	.802	.068	.130	.798	.059	.144
	.468	.630	.253	.117	.611	.260	.130
15754	.328	.767	.102	.131	.760	.091	.148
	.449	.591	.293	.116	.588	.277	.135
16213	.443	.5834	.3082	.1084			
16214	.448	.5864	.3130	.1006			
16198	.443	.6160	.3165	.0675			
15669	.451	.6287	.2976	.0736			
15495 (1)	.442	.5422	.3873	.0705			
15497 (1)	.464	.5560	.3424	.1016			

(1) Age 6 days.
See p. 333 for description of specimens.

TABLE A-32—FLEXURAL STRENGTH AND YOUNG'S MODULUS OF ELASTICITY OF MORTARS MADE WITH SPECIAL CEMENTS FOR THE BASIC-RESEARCH PROGRAM—SERIES 254-11

Cement No.	w/c at 2 hrs. (wt. basis)	Flexural Strength at Age Indicated lb/in²		Young's Modulus at Age Indicated millions of lb/in²	
		28 days	90 days	28 days	90 days
15758	.334	1395	1275	6.0	6.1
	.460	1090	970	5.5	5.4
15756	.318	1170	1295	5.8	6.4
	.446	915	1010	5.1	5.6
15763	.324	1035	1345	5.4	6.0
	.437	765	1115	4.7	5.5
15761	.334	1145	980	5.6	5.7
	.468	1015	790	5.2	5.3
15754	.328	1275	1210	6.0	6.5
	.449	1035	945	5.4	5.7

Flexural strength is the average of results for two prisms.
Young's modulus was calculated from the resonance frequency of vibration found by the electrodynamic method. The values for 28 days are the average of results for 12 prisms; those at 90 days, the average for 2 prisms.
See p. 333 for description of specimens.

TABLE A-33—ADSORPTION DATA FOR SERIES 254-11

Total Water Retained at Relative Vapor Pressure Indicated, g/g cement
Water-cement ratios corrected for bleeding

p/p₀	Cement 15758 Ref. No. 11-1 w₀/c = 0.334		Cement 15758 Ref. No. 11-2 w₀/c = 0.490		Cement 15756 Ref. No. 11-3 w₀/c = 0.318		Cement 15756 Ref. No. 11-4 w₀/c = 0.446		Cement 15763 Ref. No. 11-5 w₀/c = 0.324		Cement 15763 Ref. No. 11-6 w₀/c = 0.437		Cement 15761 Ref. No. 11-7 w₀/c = 0.334	
	28 days	90 days	28 days	90 days	28 days	90 days	28 days	90 days	28 days	90 days	28 days	90 days	28 days	90 days
.00	.1707	.1912	.1962	.2227	.1229	.1492	.1325	.1684	.0922	.1335	.1013	.1487	.1621	.1798
.08	.2019	.2255	.2326	.2601	.1472	.1802	.1578	.1997	.1128	.1624	.1231	.1802	.1908	.2141
.20	.2153	.2401	.2472	.2767	.1581	.1931	.1690	.2141	.1216	.1750	.1330	.1952	.2037	.2287
.36	.2331	.2596	.2680	.2993	.1725	.2105	.1839	.2313	.1328	.1909	.1447	.2118	.2211	.2476
.47	.2448	.2730	.2844	.3179	.1813	.2217	.1940	.2457	.1414	.2005	.1535	.2246	.2339	.2615
.61	.2695	.2879	.3045	.3375	.1931	.2445	.2055	.2598	.1530	.2112	.1651	.2343	.2483	.2755
.69	.2741	.3008	.3212	.3571	.2071	.2507	.2204	.2791	.1653	.2273	.1803	.2548	.2621	.2911
.75	.2817	.3060	.3300	.3637	.2170	.2566	.2323	.2867	.1737	.2355	.1903	.2630	.2796	.3003
.81	.2931	.3176	.3452	.3798	.2293	.2706	.2469	.3065	.1833	.2458	.2012	.2782	.2808	.3137
.84	.3004	.3266	.3548	.3918	.2373	.2754	.2556	.3128	.1910	.2544	.2097	.2910	.2899	.3206
.89	.3186	.3430	.3772	.4144	.2520	.2908	.2746	.3298	.2042	.2653	.2267	.3055	.3079	.3355
.96	.3504	.3752	.4273	.4605	.2973	.3213	.3310	.3924	.2416	.3015	.2777	.3651	.3490	.3733
SSD	.3975	.4162	.5247	.5082	.3751	.3764	.4721	.5127	.3354	.3674	.4287	.3030	.3978	.4144

Total Water Retained at Relative Vapor Pressure Indicated, g/g cement

p/pₛ	Cement 15761 Ref. No. 11-8 w₀/c = 0.408 28 days	90 days	Cement 15754 Ref. No. 11-9 w₀/c = 0.328 28 days	90 days	Cement 15754 Ref. No. 11-10 w₀/c = 0.449 28 days	90 days
w_n	.1852	.2120	.1703	.1961	.1967	.2301
.09	.2192	.2501	.2020	.2294	.2336	.2704
.20	.2346	.2673	.2150	.2418	.2480	.2866
.36	.2555	.2899	.2337	.2615	.2693	.3114
.47	.2722	.3071	.2475	.2766	.2869	.3308
.61	.2882	.3256	.2617	.2904	.2959	.3488
.69	.3056	.3454	.2737	.3059	.3223	.3699
.75	.3166	.3545	.2806	.3125	.3338	.3788
.81	.3304	.3734	.2926	.3227	.3482	.3842
.84	.3415	.3827	.2986	.3297	.3562	.4063
.89	.3666	.4001	.3118	.3387	.3758	.4187
.96	.4221	.4562	.3381	.3578	.4161	.4616
SSD	.5330	.5626	.3887	.3991	.5289	.5560

p/pₛ	Cement 16213 Ref. No. 11-11 w₀/c = 0.443 28 days	Cement 16214 Ref. No. 11-12 w₀/c = 0.448 28 days	Cement 16198 Ref. No. 11-13 w₀/c = 0.443 28 days	Cement 15669 Ref. No. 11-14 w₀/c = 0.451 28 days
w_n	.1720	.1854	.1098	.1084
.081	.2043	.2188	.1322	.1283
.161	.2152	.2302	.1400	.1385
.238	.2229	.2380	.1454	.1472
.322	.2338	.2491	.1537	.1545
.36	.2394	.2552	.1569	.1582
.53	.2579	.2778	.1692	.1726
.70	.2826	.3080	.1944	.1951
.81	.3144	.3288	.2174	.2226
.85	.3288	.3401	.2262	.2334
.88	.3356	.3550	.2484	.2528
.96	.3691	.3906	.2903	.3090
SSD	.4880	.5084	.4748	.4784

Total Water Retained at Relative Vapor Pressure Indicated, g/g cement

p/pₛ	Cement 15495 Ref. No. 11-15 w₀/c = 0.442 Age 6 days	Cement 15407 Ref. No. 11-16 w₀/c = 0.464 Age 6 days
w_n	.1300	.1825
.081	.1525	.2125
.161	.1604	.2237
.238	.1659	.2309
.322	.1728	.2402
.36	.1810	.2456
.53	.1873	.2765
.70	.2100	.2990
.81	.2306	.3228
.85	.2435	.3386
.88	.2625	.3539
.96	.3151	.4028
SSD	.4515	.5100

SSD = Water content of granular sample, saturated, surface-dry for sample that had been dried and resaturated.

w_n = Non-evaporable water;

p/p_s = about 24×10⁻⁶

TABLE A-34—UNIT ABSOLUTE VOLUME COMPOSITION OF THE MORTARS USED IN SERIES 254-13

Clinker No.	Ref. No.	Unit Absolute Volume Composition at 2 hours				w/c at 2 hours (wt. basis)
		Cement	Silica	Air	Water	
15367*	13-1	.2853	.2444	.0201	.4506	.494
	13-2	.2870	.2458	.0147	.4528	.493
	13-3	.2909	.2492	.0045	.4553	.489
	13-4	.2879	.2466	.0133	.4523	.491
15367**	13-1B	.2828	.2422	.0362	.4400	.486
	13-2B	.2828	.2422	.0297	.4458	.488
	13-3B	.2822	.2417	.0358	.4414	.488
	13-4B	.2840	.2441	.0240	.4476	.492
15623	13-5	.2931	.2529	.0053	.4489	.470
	13-6	.2919	.2519	.0058	.4504	.474
	13-7	.2920	.2520	.0063	.4497	.473
	13-8	.2898	.2501	.0073	.4528	.480
15699	13-9	.2827	.2436	.0204	.4537	.498
	13-10	.2824	.2433	.0219	.4530	.499
	13-11	.2816	.2427	.0232	.4529	.499
	13-12	.2796	.2410	.0297	.4503	.498
15498	13-13	.2888	.2444	.0200	.4472	.488
	13-14	.2909	.2462	.0154	.4480	.487
	13-15	.2905	.2458	.0114	.4524	.493
	13-16	.2909	.2462	.0124	.4509	.491

*First round of measurements.
**Second round of measurements.

TABLE A-35—ANALYSES OF THE GRANULAR SAMPLES USED FOR ADSORPTION AND NON-EVAPORABLE WATER MEASUREMENTS IN SERIES 254-13

Clinker No.	Ref. No.	Wt. % SO_3	w/c at 2 hrs. (wt. basis)	Composition of 35-100-Mesh Samples, g/g dry weight		
				Cement	Silica	Water
15367*	13-1	1.5	0.493	.518	.370	.111
	13-2	1.9	0.493	.519	.371	.110
	13-3	2.4	0.489	.520	.372	.108
	13-4	3.5	0.491	.524	.374	.102
15367**	13-1B	1.5	0.486	.519	.371	.110
	13-2B	1.9	0.488	.518	.370	.112
	13-3B	2.4	0.488	.518	.370	.112
	13-4B	3.5	0.492	.521	.372	.106
15623	13-5	1.5	0.470	.536	.383	.081
	13-6	2.0	0.474	.536	.383	.081
	13-7	2.5	0.473	.536	.383	.081
	13-8	3.5	0.480	.538	.384	.078
15699	13-9	1.5	0.498	.523	.373	.104
	13-10	2.0	0.499	.524	.374	.102
	13-11	2.5	0.499	.525	.374	.101
	13-12	3.5	0.498	.527	.376	.097
15498	13-13	1.5	0.488	.521	.371	.108
	13-14	2.0	0.487	.523	.373	.104
	13-15	2.5	0.493	.523	.372	.105
	13-16	3.5	0.491	.525	.375	.100

*First round of measurements.
**Second round of measurements.

Description of specimens made in series 254-11

Mortar Specimens: Cubes, 2 in.

Cements: See Tables A-1 to A-3.

Pulverized Silica: Lot 15918. Specific surface (Wagner), 6000 cm²/cm³.

Batches: Same as Mixes A and B of Series 254-9.

Mixing: Each batch was mixed 30 sec. dry, 1½ min. wet, allowed to rest 3 min., and then mixed 2 min. more in a small, power-driven, open-tub mixer. Batches remixed 30 sec. after slump test.

Slump Test: As in Series 254-8.

Molding: As for cubes in Series 254-9, except 15 per batch.

Measurements: As in Series 254-8.

Drying: As in Series 254-8.

Composition of Hardened Specimens: Computed as in Series 254-8. See Table A-30.

Chemical Analyses of Dried Granular Samples: See Table A-31. Determinations by same procedure as in Series 254-9.

Compressive Strength: See Table 6-1, Part 6.

Flexural Strength and Modulus of Elasticity: From prisms made from same materials in same proportions as in Series 290. See Table A-32.

Adsorption Data: See Table A-33.

Description of specimens made in series 254-13

Specimens: 2-in. cubes made of cement-silica pastes.

Cements: See Tables A-1 to A-3. Cements were prepared in the laboratory mill from plant-made clinkers. Three grinds of each clinker were made, one with no added gypsum, one with enough added gypsum to give a total SO_3 content of about 2.4 percent, and one with enough to give about 5 percent SO_3. Blends were made to give cements having 1.5, 2.0, 2.5, and 3.5 percent SO_3 and specific surface area (Wagner) of 1800 cm²/g.

Pulverized Silica: Lot 15918. Specific surface area (Wagner), 6000 cm²/cm³.

Weight Proportions: Cement: pulverized silica: water = 1.0 : 0.714 : 0.5.

Mixing: Each batch was mixed with a kitchen-type mixer 2 min., allowed to rest 3 min., and then mixed 2 min. more. Mixing water was cooled before use to give batch temperature of 73 ± 2 F after mixing.

Molding: Three cubes were molded from each batch.

Measurements: As in Series 254-8.

Curing: In water at 73 F. Curing water replaced with fresh water after first 24 hr., twice weekly thereafter.

Drying: As in Series 254-8.

Composition of Hardened Specimens: See Table A-34.

Analyses of Granular Samples: See Table A-35.

Compressive Strengths: See Table 6-7, Part 6.

Adsorption Data: See Table A-36.

Series 254-16

The specimens of this series were prepared for the heat of adsorption studies described in Part 4.

Cements: The cements used were 16186 and 16189, which were prepared from two of the groups of cements described in Series 254-11. No. 16186 was a blend of two cements prepared from clinker 15367, the blend having a specific surface area of 3200 cm²/g by the permeability method. No. 16189 had the same specific surface area, being a blend of cements prepared from clinker 15623. The clinkers were of Type I and Type II compositions, respectively.

TABLE A-36—ADSORPTION DATA FOR SERIES 254-13

Water-cement ratios corrected for bleeding

Age 28 days

Total Water Retained at Relative Vapor Pressure Indicated, g/g cement

p/p_1	Clinker 15367 Ref. No. 13-1 $w_0/c = 0.493$	Clinker 15367 Ref. No. 13-2 $w_0/c = 0.493$	Clinker 15367 Ref. No. 13-3 $w_0/c = 0.489$	Clinker 15367 Ref. No. 13-4 $w_0/c = 0.491$	p/p_1	Clinker 15367 Ref. No. 13-1B $w_0/c = 0.486$	Clinker 15367 Ref. No. 13-2B $w_0/c = 0.488$	Clinker 15367 Ref. No. 13-3B $w_0/c = 0.488$
.09	2147	2108	2083	1938	.081	2115	2158	2151
.20	2542	2504	2462	2295	.161	2500	2530	2527
.36	2732	2660	2619	2438	.238	2631	2681	2653
.47	2989	2903	2864	2631	.322	2737	2779	2749
.61	3181	3101	3027	2774	.36	2893	2920	2861
.69	3403	3317	3238	2961	.53	2957	2990	2957
.75	3605	3540	3439	3159	.70	3563	3274	3245
.81	3683	3610	3510	3224	.81	3621	3611	3563
.84	3854	3765	3681	3396	.85	3821	3862	3847
.89	3931	3833	3779	3495	.88	3987	4034	3995
	4091	4046	3987	3730		4131	4157	4174
.96	4502	4466	4435	4313	.96	4515	4543	4591
SSD	6229	5781*	6223	6176	SSD	6279	6199	6206

Total Water Retained at Relative Vapor Pressure Indicated, g/g cement

p/p_1	Clinker 15367 Ref. No. 13-4B $w_0/c = 0.492$	Clinker 15623 Ref. No. 13-5 $w_0/c = 0.470$	Clinker 15623 Ref. No. 13-6 $w_0/c = 0.474$	Clinker 15623 Ref. No. 13-7 $w_0/c = 0.473$	Clinker 15623 Ref. No. 13-8 $w_0/c = 0.480$	p/p_1	Clinker 15699 Ref. No. 13-9 $w_0/c = 0.498$	Clinker 15699 Ref. No. 13-10 $w_0/c = 0.499$
.081	2035	1518	1509	1515	1444	.081	1992	1937
.161	2407	1779	1744	1737	1671	.161	2346	2290
.238	2518	1833	1843	1838	1773	.238	2478	2423
.322	2807	1923	1910	1919	1846	.322	2568	2504
.36	2706	2018	2009	2004	1931	.36	2704	2618
.53	2783	2072	2054	2056	1989	.53	2771	2693
.70	3602	2261	2238	2230	2162	.70	3090	2891
.81	3310	2330	2396	2380	2565	.81	3322	3215
.85	3569	2783	2816	2931	2920	.85	3680	3519
.88	3732	2988	3003	3112	3115	.88	3739	3603
	4024	3224	3169	3312	3292		4113	3900
.96	4495	3858	3699	3861	3634	.96	4614	4490
SSD	6308	5772	5959	5965	6054	SSD	6210	6110

(Concluded on next page)

Total Water Retained at Relative Vapor Pressure Indicated, g/g cement

p/p_s	Clinker 15600 Ref. No. 13-11 $w_0/c = 0.499$	Clinker 15699 Ref. No. 13-12 $w_0/c = 0.498$	Clinker 15498 Ref. No. 13-13 $w_0/c = 0.488$	Clinker 15498 Ref. No. 13-14 $w_0/c = 0.487$	Clinker 15498 Ref. No. 13-15 $w_0/c = 0.493$	Clinker 15498 Ref. No. 13-16 $w_0/c = 0.491$
w_n	.1917	.1859	.2083	.1992	.2004	.1805
.081	.2247	.2156	.2468	.2355	.2352	.2232
.161	.2273	.2183	.2500	.2474	.2472	.2352
.238	.2462	.2346	.2688	.2534	.2658	.2430
.322	.2561	.2439	.2796	.2659	.2677	.2548
.36	.2643	.2507	.2902	.2747	.2717	.2581
.53	.2838	.2667	.3151	.2957	.2945	.2781
.70	.3144	.3082	.3487	.3273	.3243	.3162
.81	.3301	.3411	.3758	.3523	.3507	.3478
.85	.3587	.3511	.3901	.3661	.3675	.3662
.88	.3920	.3762	.4130	.3848	.3927	.3857
.96	.4526	.4390	.4485	.4374	.444	.4407
SSD	.6308	.6087	.5485	.5478	.5600	.5742

SSD = Water content of granular sample, saturated, surface-dry for sample that had been dried and resaturated.
* This figure is probably incorrect. By comparison with others, it should be about 0.617.
w_n = Non-evaporable water; p/p_s = about 24×10⁻⁴.

Specimens: The specimens were 1½x3-in. neat cement cylinders, nominal $w/c = 0.50$ by weight. The pastes were mixed with a kitchen-type mixer, following the 2-3-2 schedule described for earlier series. The specimens were cured continuously in water until they were used.

Results of Experiments: Experimental procedures and the results are given in Part 4 of the text.

Series 254-18

This series comprises several experiments using the high-vacuum adsorption apparatus.

Cements: The cements used were 13495, 13723-1Q, 14675, and 15365. These are cements of about average Type I composition.

Specimens: The original specimens were neat-cement pastes. As explained in the text, the samples made with cements 15365 and 13723-1Q were granules prepared previously for Series 254-9 (Ref. 15A, age 180 days) and 254-K4B (Ref. 1Q), respectively. The original specimens from which granular samples were taken were 2-in. cubes.

The specimen made with cement 13495 was a slab, cast on edge, about 0.25 cm thick and 10 cm square. The paste was mixed with a kitchen-type mixer, 2 min. mixing, 3 min. rest, followed by 2 more min. of mixing, $w/c = 0.5$ by weight. The mold was stored under water immediately after casting. When the paste was 1 day old, the square was cut into 1x10x0.25 cm slabs and these were stored in sealed bottles containing water-saturated cotton. After 7 years and 116 days of such storage, one of the 1x10x0.25 slabs was ground on a plate-glass surface with water and powdered emery until the thickness was reduced to an average of about 0.3 mm. This thin slab was used for adsorption measurements.

The specimen made with cement 14675 was a cylinder about 3 cm in diameter by 4 cm high. The original water-cement ratio was 0.12 by weight. The cement was mixed with the water by kneading with a stiff spatula on a steel plate. The moist mix was then loosely packed into a steel mold. By means of a close-fitting plunger and hydraulic press, the sample was compacted. The applied pressure was 24,000 lb/in², which was just enough to bring water to the surface of the specimen. A cross-section of the specimen at time of test was free of visible voids.

The cylinder was removed from the mold immediately after casting and then cured continuously under water in a covered can. It was 4 years 29 days old when used for these experiments.

The sample for adsorption measurements was obtained by sawing out a thin slab parallel to the vertical axis of the cylinder and grinding it to a thickness of about 0.3 mm as described above. The sample used actually comprised two such slabs, each about 1.2 x 3.8 x 0.03 cm.

Test Results. All the experimental data are given in the text.

Title 43-5c —a part of PROCEEDINGS, AMERICAN CONCRETE INSTITUTE Vol. 43

JOURNAL
of the
AMERICAN CONCRETE INSTITUTE
(copyrighted)

Vol. 18 No. 4   7400 SECOND BOULEVARD, DETROIT 2, MICHIGAN   December 1946

Studies of the Physical Properties of Hardened Portland Cement Paste*

By T. C. POWERS†
Member American Concrete Institute

and T. L. BROWNYARD‡

Part 3. Theoretical Interpretation of Adsorption Data§

CONTENTS

*Received by the Institute July 8, 1946—scheduled for publication in seven installments; October 1946 to April, 1947. In nine parts:

Part 1. "A Review of Methods That Have Been Used for Studying the Physical Properties of Hardened Portland Cement Paste". ACI Journal, October, 1946.
Part 2. "Studies of Water Fixation"—Appendix to Part 2. ACI Journal, November, 1946.
Part 3. "Theoretical Interpretation of Adsorption Data."
Part 4. "The Thermodynamics of Adsorption"—Appendix to Parts 3 and 4.
Part 5. "Studies of the Hardened Paste by Means of Specific-Volume Measurements."
Part 6. "Relation of Physical Characteristics of the Paste to Compressive Strength."
Part 7. "Permeability and Absorptivity."
Part 8. "The Freezing of Water in Hardened Portland Cement Paste."
Part 9. "General Summary of Findings on the Properties of Hardened Portland Cement Paste."
†Manager of Basic Research, Portland Cement Assn. Research Laboratory, Chicago 10, Ill.
‡Navy Dept., Washington, D. C., formerly Research Chemist, Portland Cement Assn. Research Laboratory, Chicago 10, Ill.
§The characteristics of the cements mentioned in this section may be found in the Appendix to Part 2.

The adsorption isotherms obtained from hardened cement paste are identical in several respects with those obtained from other materials that are very different in chemical and physical properties. For example when glass spheres[1]* or oxide-coated cathodes of radio tubes[2] are exposed to nitrogen vapor (at the temperature of liquid air), or when a plane mercury surface is exposed to CCl_4 vapor (11 C),[3] the adsorption curves obtained are of the same type as those for water vapor on cement paste. Also, the same type of curve is obtained when crystalline solids such as titanic oxide, stannic oxide, zinc oxide or pulverized quartz are exposed to water vapor at room temperature[4]. Moreover, curves of the same type may be obtained with different vapors on the same solid[5].

The similarities just mentioned exist not only among materials that are not porous, that is, materials on which adsorption is confined to the visible surfaces, but also among many porous solids having negligible superficial surface areas. With suitable vapors the following materials, some porous, some not, all give the same type of isotherm: building stone[6]; cotton[7, 8]; asbestos fibre[9]; wood[10]; wood pulp[11]; carbon black[12]; titania gel, ferric oxide gel, rice grains[13]; cellophane[14]; bone-char[15]; cellulose[16]; silica gel[17]; proteins[18]; soils[19]; wool[20].

It appears therefore that the curves found for portland cement paste are not characteristic of the particular substances composing the paste but represent some factor common to many dissimilar substances. We will see in what follows that this common factor is probably nothing other than a solid surface that has an attraction for the adsorbed substance.

B.E.T. THEORY

Various theories have been advanced to explain the taking up of gases and vapors by solid materials[5]. Among the most recent, and at present the most useful, is the theory of Brunauer, Emmett and Teller, [21, 22] known as the multimolecular-adsorption theory, or the B.E.T. theory for brevity. It is beyond the scope of this paper to discuss the B.E.T. theory in full; reference should be made to Brunauer's book[5] or to the original papers for an adequate treatment. However, it is necessary to review here the main features of the theory.

The theory rests on a concept advanced earlier by Langmuir. The taking up of a gas by a solid is considered to be the result of a physical attraction between the molecules of the gas and the surface molecules of the solid.† This field of force is believed to arise from three different

---
*See references end of Part 3.
†Chemical reaction with the solid is not excluded by the theory but it will not be considered here.

causes, or to be made up of three different forces that are known collectively as *van der Waal's forces*. Hence, the process under discussion is called *van der Waal's adsorption*. These forces are of a lesser order of intensity than those involved in most chemical reactions, but they may be effective over greater distances.

A solid surface exposed to a continuous bombardment of gas molecules catches and holds some of the gas molecules, at least momentarily. Moreover, when the gas is also a vapor such as water, the molecules caught on the surface are in a condensed state and may be considered as a separate phase. Hence, when they are adsorbed, the molecules must give up their latent heat of vaporization. Besides this, adsorption usually is accompanied by a further evolution of heat which may be said to represent the energy of interaction between the solid and the condensed substance; this is called the *net heat of adsorption*.

Some of the adsorbed molecules acquire enough kinetic energy to escape from the force field of the solid surface. The over-all result is a continuous interchange between the surface region and the interior of the vapor phase, but the average molecular concentration at the solid surface remains higher than that of the interior of the vapor phase by virtue of the surface attraction.

The derivation of the mathematical statement of the theory starts with the assumption that the rate of condensation is directly proportional to the frequency of impact between the solid and the vapor molecules, which frequency is proportional to the vapor pressure when temperature is constant. The rate of evaporation is expressed as a function of the amount of energy a condensed molecule must acquire to escape from a particular situation in the condensed phase. In the derivation of the mathematical expressions that have found use, only two situations of a molecule in the condensed phase are recognized: (1) a molecule may be condensed on bare surface; (2) a molecule may be condensed on a layer of previously condensed molecules. It is assumed that a molecule in the second situation can escape when it acquires energy exactly equal to its heat of vaporization; a molecule in the first situation must acquire a different (usually greater) amount of energy to escape. In other words, the net heat of adsorption is assumed to be zero for all molecules not in the first layer.*

The theory requires that at any given vapor pressure the amount adsorbed is directly proportional to the surface area of the solid.

A logical extension of the assumptions made in the derivation is that at the saturation pressure there is no limit to the number of layers that might be condensed on an open surface.

---

*Brunauer, Emmett, and Teller have published an equation representing the assumption that the net heat of adsorption from the second layer also differs from zero. This equation includes also the assumption that the packing of molecules is different in the first from that in the succeeding layers. This equation does not appear to have found use (See Ref. 21, p. 313).

The most widely used mathematical statement of the theory is the following expression:

$$\frac{w}{V_m} = \frac{C(p/p_s)}{(1 - p/p_s)(1 - p/p_s + C(p/p_s))} \quad\dots\dots\dots\dots\dots\dots(A)$$

in which

w = quantity of vapor adsorbed at vapor pressure p

V_m = quantity of adsorbate required for a complete condensed layer on the solid, the layer being 1 molecule deep

p = existing vapor pressure

p_s = pressure of saturated vapor

C is a constant related to the heat of adsorption as follows:

$$C = k\,e^{\frac{Q_1 - Q_L}{RT}}$$

where

k is a constant assumed to be 1.0 in computations.

Q_L = normal heat of condensation of the vapor per mole of vapor

Q_1 = total heat of adsorption per mole of vapor

$(Q_1 - Q_L)$ = net heat of adsorption per mole of vapor

R = the gas constant

T = absolute temperature

e = base of natural logarithms

Owing to the assumptions made in the derivation, eq. (A) would be expected to hold only for adsorption on exterior surfaces. It could hardly be expected to hold for surfaces on the interior of a porous solid where unlimited adsorption would obviously be impossible. Brunauer, Emmett, and Teller recognized this and introduced another constant n which was intended to be the maximum number of layers adsorbed. The resulting four-constant equation does not fit any known data from a porous adsorbent over the whole pressure range. However, Pickett[23] discovered a way to improve the derivation of the B.E.T. four-constant equation and supplied a better expression. This equation has the same four constants as the original. It fits many adsorption curves over about 90 percent of pressure range. In some cases it conforms to the extremes, but in the middle range the theoretical curve is above the experimental. There are also many curves that this equation does not fit in the high-pressure range. One reason for this will be explained in connection with the theory of capillary condensation, discussed below.

In general, the four-constant equations did not prove to be very useful in this study; hence, they are not given here. However, the three-constant eq. (A) can be used to represent the low-pressure part of the curve precisely. Of the three constants, p_s is the same for all curves and C is the same for most of them. Consequently, in most cases adsorption characteristics can be represented by V_m alone.

THE THEORY OF CAPILLARY CONDENSATION

Condensation of vapor in a porous cement paste seems to be most adequately explained by a combination of a theory based on the energy available at the solid surface, such as the B.E.T. theory discussed above, and a theory based on energy available at the surface of a liquid, the capillary-condensation theory.

The capillary-condensation theory rests on the fact that the surface of a liquid is the seat of available energy. The molecules at the surface of a liquid not being completely surrounded by other molecules of like kind are under an inwardly directed intermolecular force. When a given body of water is changed in shape so as to increase its surface area, work must be done against the forces tending to draw the molecules out of the surface. Consequently, when left to itself, a small body of liquid tends to become spherical, since that is the form giving a minimum of surface.

This phenomenon has an effect on the vapor pressure of the liquid. How this comes about can be seen by considering the behavior of water in a small glass cylinder, as shown in Fig. 3-1. The solid curve at the top

Fig. 3-1

represents the meniscus of the water surface. Owing to the surface tension, which strives to straighten the meniscus, that is, to reduce its curvature and thus reduce the surface area, the water in the vessel is under tension. Consequently, the vapor pressure of the water in the tube will be less than normal for the existing temperature. The greater the curvature of the meniscus, the greater the tension in the water and hence the lower the vapor pressure. The relationship between surface-curvature and vapor pressure was worked out by Lord Kelvin. It may be written

$$\ln p/p_s = -\frac{2\sigma M}{d_f R T r} \dots \dots (1)$$

where

p_s = vapor pressure over plane surface at temperature T, the saturated vapor pressure

p = the existing vapor pressure over a concave surface

σ = surface tension of liquid

d_f = density of liquid

M = molecular weight of liquid

R = the gas constant

T = absolute temperature

r = radius of curvature of the circular meniscus

Under the conditions pictured in Fig. 3-1 the greatest curvature that the liquid can have is limited by the radius of the container. When the liquid surface has this curvature, the liquid can be in equilibrium with only one vapor pressure, p, corresponding to the radius of curvature r, as given in eq. (1). If the pressure of the vapor is kept below p, all the liquid in the vessel will evaporate. If the pressure is maintained above p, some vapor will condense, increasing the amount of water in the vessel. But under the conditions pictured, condensation would lessen the curvature of the liquid as indicated by the dotted line and there would be a corresponding rise in the equilibrium vapor pressure. If the vapor pressure is kept equal to the saturation pressure, that is, the maximum possible over a plane surface at the existing temperature, condensation will proceed until the tube fills and the surface curvature disappears ($r = \infty$).

The minimum relative vapor pressure at which the liquid in the vessel can retain its meniscus depends on the maximum possible curvature of the meniscus. This in turn depends on the bore of the cylinder. Table 3-1 gives an idea of the curvature required to produce a given effect on vapor pressure.

The main point to note in Table 3-1 is that the surface must have a high degree of curvature to produce an appreciable effect on the vapor pressure of the liquid. For example, if the radius of curvature is 0.1 micron, the vapor pressure is 99 percent of the normal value, p_s. A radius of curvature of 0.0015 micron would reduce the pressure to 50 percent of p_s. The figures given should not be taken too literally; they are undoubtedly in error through the low-pressure range, for the equation takes no account of the fact that the physical properties of the liquid are affected by capillary and adsorption forces. The table serves only to indicate what the order of magnitude of the curvatures must be when capillary condensation occurs.

An "adsorption curve" of almost any shape could easily be accounted for by the capillary condensation theory. The simplest approach is to imagine first that the voids in a porous solid are cylindrical pores of

TABLE 3-1—RELATIONSHIP BETWEEN AQUEOUS
RELATIVE VAPOR PRESSURE AND RADIUS OF CURVATURE
Calculated from Kelvin's Equation—Temperature = 25 C

Relative vapor pressure, p/p_s	Radius of curvature of meniscus	
	cm	microns
0.10	4.6 x 10⁻⁸	.0005
0.20	6.6 x 10⁻⁸	.0007
0.30	8.8 x 10⁻⁸	.0009
0.40	11.5 x 10⁻⁸	.0012
0.50	15.2 x 10⁻⁸	.0015
0.60	20.8 x 10⁻⁸	.0021
0.70	29.5 x 10⁻⁸	.0030
0.80	47.2 x 10⁻⁸	.0047
0.90	100.0 x 10⁻⁸	.0100
0.95	204.0 x 10⁻⁸	.0204
0.98	532.0 x 10⁻⁸	.0532
0.99	1052.0 x 10⁻⁸	.1052
1.00	∞	∞

various sizes and that when a cylinder is partly filled, the radius of curvature of the liquid meniscus equals the radius of the cylinder. At a given pressure p, all cylinders smaller than the corresponding r (see eq. 1) would become or remain full and all larger than r would become or remain empty. The shape of the curve would therefore depend on the range of sizes present and the total capacity of each size.

This simple analogy led Freyssinet [24] and others before him to consider an adsorption curve to be a means of ascertaining pore-size distribution in systems of submicroscopic pores. However, a naturally formed porous solid so constituted is hardly conceivable. It is much more likely that the pore spaces resemble those in an aggregation of particles. The shapes of the particles may be spherical, fibrous, or between these extremes. Capillary condensation could occur in the interstices in the manner illustrated in Fig. 3-2. At the point of contact between two spheres there is a space of wedge-shaped cross section. Condensation in this space would form a circular lens around the point of contact and the liquid would present a curved surface. Similarly, where two prismatic bodies make contact, water condensed in the region of contact would present a curved surface, somewhat as shown.

In the circumstances pictured, the water surface would have two curvatures. Hence, in this case Kelvin's equation would take the general form

$$ ln \ p/p_s = - \frac{\sigma M}{d_l RT} \left(\frac{1}{r_1} + \frac{1}{r_2} \right) \quad \dots \dots \dots (2) $$

where

r_1 and r_2 are the principal radii of curvature.

For the conditions shown in Fig. 3-2 one of the r's would be negative.

Since the structure of paste is probably granular, fibrous, or perhaps plate-like, it is evident that Kelvin's equation provides no simple way of computing the size of the pores; it only gives the *effective* curvature of the water surface. It can, however, explain the condensation of vapor in a porous solid, and we will see evidence in the data indicating that a part of what is here called adsorbed water in cement pastes is taken up by capillary condensation.

COMBINING THE B.E.T. AND CAPILLARY CONDENSATION THEORIES

When adsorption of a vapor occurs in a porous solid of granular or fibrous structure, the liquid surfaces are certain not to be plane. They will be concave, at least in some regions. Therefore, the free surface energy of the solid and the free surface energy of the condensed liquid must both be causes of condensation.*

Brunauer, Emmett, and Teller tried to take this factor into account by adding a fifth constant representing the release of the surface energy of the liquid when two adsorbed layers merge[26]. This five-constant equation is very unwieldy and it embodies the assumption questioned by Pickett[23]. Also, it rests on the oversimplifying assumption that adsorption is occurring only between plane parallel surfaces.

By the B.E.T. theory, vapor would be expected to condense uniformly over all the available surface. But in a porous body, the surface tension

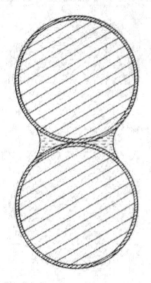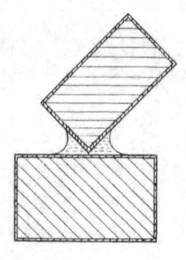

Fig. 3-2

*See Part 4.

of the liquid must influence the distribution of the condensed water, whether it is primarily responsible for the condensation or not. Thus, in Fig. 3-2, B.E.T. adsorption could lead only to a uniform layer of condensate around each sphere, but surface tension would require the liquid to collect as shown, for the condition pictured is the most stable one possible under the circumstances. This follows at once from the fact that if the liquid shown in the lens were spread evenly over the two spheres, the total surface area of the liquid would be increased and the work done would be equal to the product of the increase in area and the surface tension of the liquid.

If, as assumed in the B.E.T. equation, only the molecules in the first layer lose more than their heat of condensation, then all but the first layer should tend to collect in the lens. However, Harkins and Jura[27] have shown that the adsorption forces probably affect more than the first layer. Therefore, the net heat of adsorption probably represents the heat from several layers. This being true we can expect the adsorbed layer to vary in average thickness with the curvature of the liquid meniscus, the greater the curvature the greater the tendency for adsorbed molecules to collect in the lens.

On account of the effect of liquid surface tension the relationship between water content and vapor pressure depends on the characteristics of the pore system. Since the characteristics of the pore system are not predictable from any adsorption theory, it follows that no general equation can be expected to apply to all porous bodies over the whole pressure range. Since, however, no appreciable capillary condensation is to be expected below about $0.4p_s$, general theories may be expected to apply in this low range of vapor pressures.

As will be seen, little quantitative use is made of these theories, except the B. E. T. eq. (A) applied to the range $p = 0.05 \ p_s$ to $0.40 \ p_s$. However, many features of the interpretations given rest on the theories described above. That is, it was possible to use the theories qualitatively even where the mathematical expressions intended as expressions of the theoretical concepts were found to be inadequate.

Effect of soluble salts on adsorption curves

The foregoing discussion is based on the assumption that the adsorbed liquid is pure water. However, in hardened portland cement paste the water will contain dissolved salts, principally $Ca(OH)_2$, $NaOH$ and KOH.* At any given water content the observed reduction in vapor pressure is due not only to the capillary and surface effects described above, but also to the dissolved salts. The magnitude of the effect of the dissolved salts can be estimated from the vapor-pressure isotherms of the salt

---

*Because of its low solubility, $Ca(OH)_2$ can be ignored.

solutions and the amount of dissolved alkali in the sample of hardened paste.

Vapor-pressure data [28] for aqueous solutions of $NaOH$ and KOH are given in Fig. 3-3. The lowering of vapor pressure due to the alkalies can be determined from these curves, for any given concentration of the alkalies.

The amount of dissolved alkali in hardened paste probably varies considerably among the different samples. Sample No. 254-11-2 is considered to be representative of the average. The original mortar was prepared from cement 15758 (w_a/c = 0.46) and was cured 28 days in water. The cement originally contained 0.3 percent Na_2O and 0.4 percent K_2O which, in g/g of cement, corresponds to 0.0019 and 0.0024 of $NaOH$ and KOH, respectively. An unknown portion of these alkalies undoubtedly remained in the unhydrated cement and can be considered insoluble for the present purpose. Some of the soluble alkali was leached from the sample during the 28-day period of water curing. There is also reason to believe that some of it was adsorbed by the solid phase and thus effectively kept from the solution. Hence, the sample as tested must have contained considerably less than 0.004 g of soluble alkali (total of $NaOH$ and KOH) per g of cement. The adsorption isotherm from this sample is given in Fig. 3-4, upper curve. This curve presumably represents the combined effect of surface adsorption, capillary condensation, and dissolved alkali. The lower curve in Fig. 3-4 shows the amount of water that could have been held by 0.004 g of sodium hydroxide at any given relative vapor pressure above about 0.07 p_s, the vapor pressure of a saturated solution of sodium hydroxide at 25 C. (See Fig. 3-3.) Since the actual amount of alkali must have been less than 0.004 g, the amount of water that could have been held by the alkali alone would be represented somewhere below the curve as drawn.

It thus becomes apparent that at pressures below about 0.8 p_s only a very small part of the total water taken up by this cement paste could be accounted for by the dissolved alkalies. In the range of higher pressures, the possible effect of the alkali is greater. As p/p_s approaches 1.0, the amount of water that could be held by the alkali approaches infinity. Since, however, the topmost point of the curve is established by saturating the granular sample with liquid water, its position is determined by the capacity of the sample and the assumption that, at saturation, p/p_s = 1.0. In this case the capacity of the sample was 0.33 g of water per gram of original cement. With 0.004 g of alkali in 0.33 g of evaporable water the relative vapor pressure would be slightly below 1.0.

Since the effect of the alkali is small, no correction for its effect has been attempted; the topmost point is always plotted at p/p_s = 1.0, and

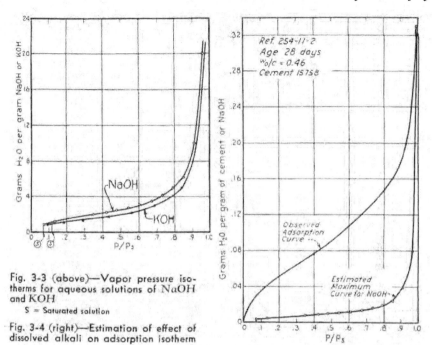

Fig. 3-3 (above)—Vapor pressure isotherms for aqueous solutions of $NaOH$
and KOH
    S = Saturated solution

Fig. 3-4 (right)—Estimation of effect of
dissolved alkali on adsorption isotherm

all other points are treated as if their positions were determined by
surface adsorption and capillary condensation only.

Differences in the amount of soluble alkali among various samples,
within the range that might reasonably be expected, probably have little
effect on the lower part of the curve, the part that is used in the analyses
presented below. However, such differences probably produce considerable effects on the shapes of the upper parts of the curves and hence
contribute to the difficulty of interpreting the upper parts.

To minimize the effect of dissolved alkali, most of the specimens were
stored in water for the first 28 days of their curing period to leach some
of the alkali from the specimens. Longer periods of water storage were
avoided because of undesirable leaching of $Ca(OH)_2$.

APPLICATION OF THE B.E.T. EQUATION (A)

Method of evaluating C and V_m

The constants C and V_m were evaluated in the manner recommended
by Brunauer, Emmett, and Teller. Eq. (A), written in the form

$$\frac{1}{w}\frac{x}{1-x} = \frac{1}{V_mC} + \frac{C-1}{V_mC}x, \quad (x = p/p_s)$$

shows that a plot of experimental values for $\dfrac{1}{w}\dfrac{x}{1-x}$ against x should

give a straight line. The slope of the line will be $\dfrac{C-1}{V_mC}$ and the inter-
cept on the y-axis will be $1/V_mC$. The application of this method to data from cement pastes is illustrated in Fig. 3-5 and in Tables 3-2 and 3-3. Two of the four diagrams represent data obtained by the air-stream method, and the others represent data obtained by the high-vacuum method.

TABLE 3-2—TYPICAL DATA FOR COMPUTING V_m AND C
Data obtained by air-stream method

p/p_s $(=x)$	w g/g of dry paste	$\dfrac{x}{1-x}$	$\dfrac{1}{w}\dfrac{x}{1-x}$
	Ref. 254-11-11—Cement 16213		
0.081	0.0189	0.088	4.65
0.161	0.0253	0.192	7.60
0.238	0.0298	0.312	10.45
0.322	0.0362	0.475	13.1
0.360	0.0395	0.562	14.2
0.530	0.0503	1.128	22.4
	Ref. 254-9-15A-180—Cement 15365		
0.09	0.0267	0.099	3.79
0.20	0.0348	0.250	7.18
0.36	0.0464	0.562	12.1
0.47	0.0539	0.887	16.5
	Ref. 254-9-15A-270A—Cement 15365		
0.081	0.0187	0.0873	4.68
0.161	0.0264	0.192	7.27
0.238	0.0310	0.312	10.0
0.322	0.0359	0.475	13.2
0.360	0.0400	0.563	14.1
0.530	0.0500	1.127	22.6

C and V_m can be computed conveniently from the intercept on the x-axis and from the ordinate at $x = 0.5$. Thus, when $\dfrac{1}{w}\dfrac{x}{1-x} = 0$,

$C = 1 - \dfrac{1}{x}$; and when $x = 0.5$, $V_m = \dfrac{1+C}{2C}w$. In Fig. 3-5A we see that

when $\dfrac{1}{w}\dfrac{x}{1-x} = 0$, $x = -0.053$ and when $x = 0.5$, $1/w = 19.3$.

Therefore,

$$C = 1 + \dfrac{1}{0.053} = 19.8, \text{ and } V_m = \dfrac{1+19.8}{2 \times 19.8} \times \dfrac{1}{19.3} = 0.027$$

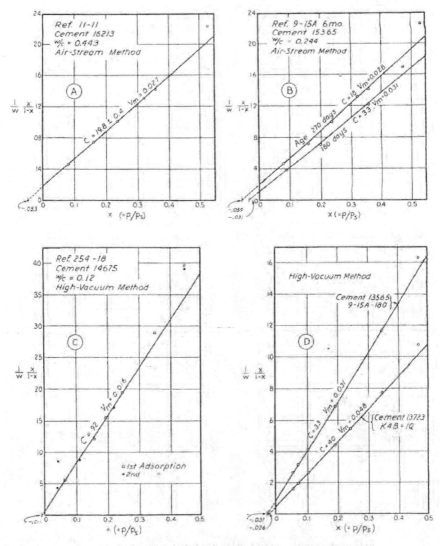

Fig. 3-5—Typical plots of the kind used for evaluating C and V_m
Data from Tables 3-2 & 3-3.

The nomenclature used here is the same as that used by Brunauer et al. except that they used V for the *volume* of gas adsorbed, whereas here w is used for *weight* adsorbed. w is expressed either in grams per gram of dry hardened paste (evaporable water removed) or as grams per gram of original cement. Having become accustomed to thinking of V_m as a factor proportional to surface area, we have somewhat illogically retained this symbol, but express it in grams instead of cc.

TABLE 3-3—TYPICAL DATA FOR COMPUTING V_m AND C

Data obtained by high-vacuum method

p/p_s $(= x)$	w g/g of dry paste	$\dfrac{x}{1-x}$	$\dfrac{1}{w}\dfrac{x}{1-x}$
	Ref. 254-18-9-15A-180—Cement 15365		
0.055	0.0227	0.0598	2.63
0.073	0.0249	0.0790	3.17
0.104	0.0284	0.117	4.13
0.193	0.0347	0.240	6.91
0.244	0.0400	0.322	8.06
0.349	0.0455	0.534	11.7
0.472	0.0542	0.885	16.3
	Ref. 254-K4B-IQ—Cement 13723		
0.055	0.0369	0.0598	1.62
0.073	0.0397	0.0790	1.99
0.104	0.0435	0.117	2.69
0.193	0.0540	0.240	4.40
0.244	0.0587	0.322	5.49
0.349	0.0686	0.534	7.78
0.472	0.0819	0.885	10.8
	Ref. 254-18—Cement 14675		
0.064	0.0552	0.0684	1.24
0.155	0.0646	0.1835	2.84
0.193	0.0675	0.2395	3.55
0.249	0.0720	0.3310	4.60
0.350	0.0817	0.5380	6.58
0.446	0.0910	0.8040	8.84

THE RELATIONSHIP BETWEEN V_m AND NON-EVAPORABLE WATER (w_n) FOR SAMPLES CURED AT 70-75 F

The quantity V_m is considered to be proportional to the internal surface area of the sample. Since the specific surface of microcrystalline material is negligible compared with that of colloidal material, V_m is also considered to be proportional to the amount of colloidal material in the sample. The quantity w_n represents the amount of non-evaporable water in both colloidal and non-colloidal material. Therefore, if a given cement produces the same kind of hydration products at all stages of its hydration, the ratio V_m/w_n should be constant for any given cement under fixed curing conditions. However, the ratio of colloidal to non-colloidal hydration products should be expected to differ among cements of different chemical composition. Hence, the ratio V_m/w_n should be different for different cements.

V_m and w_n are plotted for several different cements and different mixes and ages, in Fig. 3-6 and 3-7. The points in most of the diagrams show a considerable amount of scatter. Some of this is due to random experimental vagaries and some of it is apparently due to variations in drying conditions discussed earlier.

In view of the fact that the variations show no consistent influence of the original water-cement ratio or of the age of the sample, the relationships indicate that for any given cement the ratio V_m/w_n is independent of age or water-cement ratio.

If the points fell on a straight line through the origin, that would indicate that the ratio of colloidal to non-colloidal products is precisely the same at all stages of hydration. The data are not sufficiently concordant to indicate definitely whether this is so or not. There is some reason to believe that the reactions during the first few hours cannot produce exactly the same products as those that occur later. Particularly, the gypsum is usually depleted within the first 24 hours and thus the reactions involving gypsum cannot occur at later periods.

If calcium sulfoaluminate as produced in paste is non-colloidal, the ratio of colloidal to non-colloidal material should be lower during the first 24 hours than it is at any later time. The effect on the graph would be that of causing the proportionality line that holds for the later ages to cut the w_n-axis to the right of the origin. As said before, the plotted data do not indicate definitely where the intercept should be. They do indicate, however, that if the intercept is to the right of the origin, it is nevertheless near the origin, as indeed it should be in view of the relatively small amount of calcium sulfoaluminate that is formed. To simplify the handling of the data, we have assumed that the line passes through the origin and thus have considered the ratio of colloidal to non-colloidal material to be the same at all ages for a given cement.

Fig. 3-6 represents the data from Series 254-8 and 254-9. It represents 5 different commercial cements that had been used in experimental highways. The data on this series are the least concordant of all obtained in the investigation.

Fig. 3-7 represents cements prepared from 5 other commercial clinkers. Different plant grinds of each clinker were blended to give each cement a specific surface of 1800 sq. cm. per g (Wagner).

The ratios determined for the cements in each of these two groups were averaged. The results are shown in Table 3-4.

The figures in the third column give the mean values and those in the fourth give the probable error of the mean. Those in the last column give the probable error of a single test value and thus reflect the degree of scatter of the data.

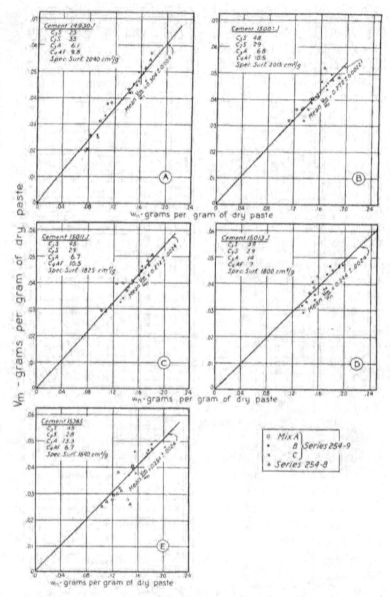

Fig. 3-6—Relationship between V_m and w_n for pastes of Series 254-9

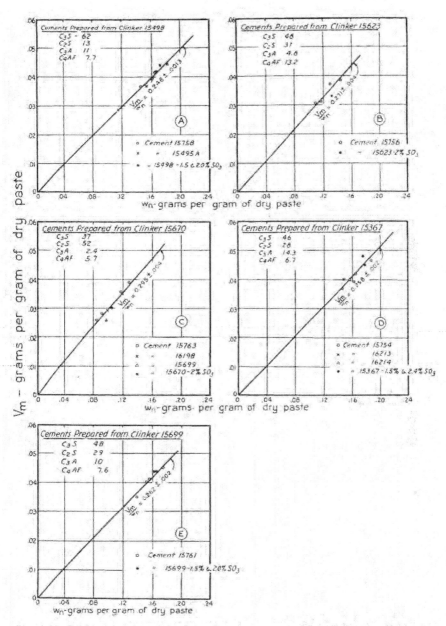

Fig. 3-7—Relationship between V_m and w_n for pastes of Series 254-11 and 254-13

TABLE 3-4—MEAN VALUES OF V_m/w_n FOR
TWO GROUPS OF CEMENTS

Cement No.	ASTM classification*	Mean value of V_m/w_a	Probable error of mean	Probable error of single value
		Series 254-9		
14930J	IV	.304	.00392	.0176
15007J	II	.272	.00216	.0089
15011J	II	.272	.00242	.0102
15013J	I	.244	.00259	.0107
15365	I	.254	.00239	.0115
		Series 254-11		
15498	III	.248	.00131	.003
15623	II	.271	.00405	.008
15670	IV	.295	.00411	.010
15367	I	.258	.00244	.006
15699	I	.262	.00203	.004

*ASTM designation C-150-40T. The classification here is based only on the computed quantities of the four major compounds. The surface area requirements are not met in all cases.

To evaluate the effect of composition, the assumption was made that the form of the relationship would be

$$\frac{V_m}{w_n} = A(\% \, C_3S) + B(\% \, C_2S) + C(\% \, C_3A) + D(\% \, C_4AF)$$

The values of the coefficients were determined first from 200 items of data representing about 50 different cements. Then, owing to the fact that 100 of these items represented only 5 cements (Series 254-9), a second analysis was made excluding the data from Series 254-9. The results of the two analyses were as follows:*

For 200 items of data:

Eq. (3): $\dfrac{V_m}{w_n} = \Bigg[$ .00208(%C_3S) +   .00326(%C_2S)+   .00251(%C_3A)
$\pm .00006$ $\pm .00004$ $\pm .00016$

+   .00549(%C_4AF)$\Bigg]$
$\pm .00030$

For 100 items of data:

Eq. (4): $\dfrac{V_m}{w_n} = \Bigg[$ .00230(%C_3S) +   .00320(%C_2S) +   .00317(%C_3A)
$\pm .00012$ $\pm .00006$ $\pm .00016$

+   .00368(%C_4AF)$\Bigg]$
$\pm .00046$

The two equations give similar coefficients for C_2S and C_3S but considerably different coefficients for C_3A and C_4AF. However, applied to the same cements, the computed results are not far different, except for

*See footnote, Part 1, page 121.

certain compositions. This is shown by the data given in Table 3-5. Here the observed mean values of V_m/w_n for the cements appearing in Fig. 3-6 and 3-7 are compared with values computed from composition. It appears that the value of V_m/w_n can be computed from composition with fairly satisfactory accuracy by means of either equation. However, eq. (4) probably gives the more correct evaluation of the effect of variations in composition, since individual cements appear in the analysis with approximately equal weights.

The influence of composition as given by eq. (4) is illustrated in Table 3-6.

The results given in the last column of the table show that the influence of composition on this ratio is not very large. The variation occurs mainly among those cements whose compositions differ from the average chiefly in C_3S, C_4AF or both.

TABLE 3-5—COMPARISON OF OBSERVED AND
COMPUTED VALUES OF V_m/w_n

Cement No.	ASTM type	Mean V_m/w_n observed	V_m/w_n computed from compound composition	
			Eq. (3)	Eq. (4)
15013J	I	0.244 ± 0.003	0.253	0.256
15365	I	0.254 ± 0.002	0.255	0.260
15367*	I	0.258 ± 0.002	0.253	0.258
15699	I	0.262 ± 0.002	0.254	0.255
Average		0.254	0.254	0.256
15007J	II	0.272 ± 0.002	0.269	0.264
15011J	II	0.272 ± 0.002	0.263	0.257
15623*	II	0.271 ± 0.004	0.284	0.272
Average		0.272	0.272	0.264
14930J	IV	0.304 ± 0.004	0.298	0.286
15670*	IV	0.295 ± 0.004	0.284	0.281
Average		0.300	0.291	0.284
15498*	III	0.248 ± 0.001	0.243	0.249

*This item represents all cements made from this clinker.

The theoretical significance of the coefficients of eq. (3) or (4) found by the method described is not certain, mainly because of the lack of definite knowledge concerning the chemical composition of the hydration products. The data support arguments given elsewhere to the effect that the hydration products of the alumina-bearing compounds are not microcrystalline as they are when these compounds are hydrated alone in an abundance of water; instead, the coefficients for C_3A and C_4AF,

TABLE 3-6—INFLUENCE OF CHEMICAL COMPOSITION ON V_m/w_n

Type of composition		Computed compound composition percent by wt.				Computed $\dfrac{V_m}{w_n}$ Eq. (4)
		C_3S	C_2S	C_3A	C_4AF	
Type I	Normal C_3A	45	29	9.7	7.5	0.255
	High C_3A	45	28	14.0	5.0	0.256
Type II	High iron	41	29	5.4	14.8	0.259
	High silica	40	41	6.4	9.7	0.279
Type III	Normal C_3A	59	13	10.4	7.6	0.238
	High C_3A	59	13	14.0	5.0	0.240
Type IV	High iron	25	48	6.2	13.8	0.282
	High silica	33	54	2.3	5.8	0.277

taken literally, indicate that, per gram of compound, these compounds contribute to the total surface area of the hydration products, that is, to V_m, as much as or more than do the two silicates, which are known to produce colloidal hydrates. In any event, the analysis shows that however the Al_2O_3 and Fe_2O_3 enter into combination in the hydration products, they must appear in solids having a high specific surface.

The coefficient of C_3S is less than that of C_2S. This result is compatible with the data of Bogue and Lerch[29] showing that both compounds produce a colloidal hydrous silicate, but only C_3S produces microcrystalline $Ca(OH)_2$. The indications are that $Ca(OH)_2$ does not decompose under the drying conditions of these experiments. Hence, the occurrence of $Ca(OH)_2$ contributes to w_n but contributes very little to V_m.

THE SPECIFIC SURFACE OF HARDENED PASTE

Computation of surface area

From the derivation of the B.E.T. equation it follows that the surface area of the adsorbent should be equal to the product of the number of adsorbed molecules in the first layer and the area covered by a single molecule. Hence, when V_m is expressed in grams per gram of adsorbent (dry paste),

$$S = a_1 \frac{V_m N}{M} \qquad \qquad (5)$$

where

S = the surface area of the adsorbent, sq. cm. per g

a_1 = the surface area covered by a single adsorbed molecule

$N = 6.06 \times 10^{23}$, the number of molecules in a gram-molecular wt. (Avagadro's number)*

M = molecular weight of the adsorbed gas.

The value of a_1 has been estimated in several ways. Livingston[30] found a value for water of 10.6×10^{-16} sq. cm. per molecule. Gans, Brooks, and Boyd[4] used the same figure. Emmett[31] gave a formula for computing a_1 from the molecular weight and density of the condensed vapor which gives nearly the same result if the normal density of water is used. As will be shown, values for molecular area obtained in this way when introduced into eq. (5) actually give surface areas S that are in close agreement with the results obtained by other procedures. Hence, for water we may write,

$$S = \frac{10.6 \times 10^{-16} \times 6.06 \times 10^{23} V_m}{18}$$

$$= (35.7 \times 10^6) V_m \text{ sq. cm. per g} \quad \ldots\ldots\ldots\ldots\ldots\ldots\ldots\ldots (6)$$

Verification of surface areas as computed from V_m

Gaudin and Bowdish[1] used pyrex-glass spheres calibrated by microscope measurements. Low temperature adsorption of nitrogen gave almost exactly the same specific surface as that computed from the mean size of the spheres. Harkins and Jura[32] developed a method of measuring surface area by first covering particles with a complete film of adsorbed water and then measuring the heat evolved when the particles were immersed in water. The results obtained by this method were compared with those from the B.E.T. method for 60 different solids. For 58 of the 60 solids the areas by the Harkins and Jura method differed from those obtained by the B.E.T. method by no more than 9 percent. Emmett[25, 31, 33] presented an extensive array of data showing that wherever particle size can be checked directly, as with the electron microscope, the results of the B.E.T. method look reasonable, to say the least. Because of such evidence as this, the B.E.T. method has been put to use by many investigators during the past few years.

The examples cited above were chosen from experiments made on solids that are non-porous. It is believed that V_m also gives the internal surface area of porous solids, provided that the molecules of the adsorbate are small enough to penetrate the pores and reach all parts of the surface. The fact that V_m is evaluated from data in the low pressure range only, and hence where capillary condensation in the pores is not a factor, supports this belief. With respect to cement paste, the pores are considered to be the spaces vacated by evaporable water when the sample is dried. The drying may be accompanied by irreversible shrinkage so that the

---

*6.023 x 10²³ is now the accepted value for Avagadro's number. This did not come to our attention until all the computations were completed. Since other factors are uncertain, it did not seem worth while to make the slight corrections indicated.

dried sample may not faithfully represent the original paste. The extent of the irreversible alteration is not known but it is considered to be small. Evidence of this is found in the fact that the total pore space, as measured by the total evaporable water, is not greatly altered by the drying; in fact the data indicate that it is increased. (See Table 9, Part 2.) Hence, V_m is considered to give the internal surface area of the solid phase in the dried samples. If drying affects the measured surface area, it would probably be in the direction of making it smaller.

In the remainder of this discussion it is assumed that V_m as determined in this investigation is proportional to the surface area of the solid phase. It will be seen that this assumption leads to highly significant results. Thus the assumption seems justifiable.

Results from hardened paste

The magnitudes of the surface areas and the rates at which surface develops during hydration as computed from eq. (6) are indicated by Table 3-7.

The figures pertain to the whole solid phase; that is, they are based on the combined weights of the hydration products and residue of original clinker. Therefore, the specific surface of the hydration products is higher than the highest figure given except any that might represent completely hydrated cement.

Specific surface in terms of w_n

Since $V_m = kw_n$, the specific surface of a paste can be computed if w_n is known, and if k for the particular cement is known. That is,

$$\frac{S}{c} = 35.7 \times 10^6 \, k \, \frac{w_n}{c} \dots \dots \dots (7)$$

$$\frac{S}{w_n} = 35.7 \times 10^6 \, k \dots \dots \dots (8)$$

Also

$$\frac{S}{c + w_n} = \frac{35.7 \times 10^6 \, k \, w_n}{c + w_n} = \frac{35.7 \times 10^6 \, k \, w_n/c}{1 + w_n/c} \dots \dots \dots (9)$$

Eq. (7) gives the surface area per unit of original cement, and eq. (9) gives it per unit of dry paste.

For the types of cement given in Table 3-6 the surface area per unit weight of non-evaporable water is as given in Table 3-8.

The non-evaporable water content may lie anywhere between zero and about 0.25 g per g of cement. Hence, according to these equations the specific surface may lie between zero and about 2.1 to 2.5 million sq. cm. per g of original cement.

TABLE 3-7—TYPICAL FIGURES FOR SPECIFIC
SURFACE OF HARDENED PASTE

Period of hydra- tion, days	Specific surface of paste for cements indicated; $w_o/c = 0.45$ (approx.)							
	14930J C_3S 23% C_3A 6%		15761 C_3S 45% C_3A 10%		15365 C_3S 45% C_3A 13%		15013J C_3S 40% C_3A 14%	
	Millions of sq. cm. per g of:							
	cement	dry paste	cement	dry paste	cement	dry paste	cement	dry paste
7	0.76	0.71	—	—	1.21	1.06	1.32	1.13
14	1.02	0.92	—	—	1.55	1.32	1.50	1.28
28	1.33	1.19	1.75	1.48	1.94	1.64	1.71	1.46
56	1.75	1.54	—	—	1.96	1.62	1.89	1.57
90	1.89	1.62	1.96	1.62	2.02	1.66	2.04	1.67
180	2.10	1.78	—	—	2.14	1.75	2.07	1.69
365	2.10	1.76	—	—	—	—	—	—

TABLE 3-8—SPECIFIC SURFACE OF
HARDENED PASTE IN TERMS OF NON-EVAPORABLE WATER CONTENT

Type of cement		V_m/w_n (= k)	S/w_n
Type I	Normal C_3A	0.261	9.3×10^6
	High C_3A	0.256	9.2×10^6
Type II	High iron	0.259	9.3×10^6
	High silica	0.279	10.0×10^6
Type III	Normal C_3A	0.238	8.6×10^6
Type IV	High iron	0.282	10.1×10^6
	High silica	0.277	9.9×10^6

Of course it cannot be literally true that $S = 0$ when $w_n = 0$, since
the initial surface area is that of the original cement. As measured
by adsorption, the specific surface of unhydrated cement is much higher
than that measured by methods previously used. Using a cement having
a specific surface of 1890 sq. cm. per g (Wagner), Emmett and DeWitt[34]
found a surface area of 10,800 sq. cm. per g by the nitrogen-adsorption
method. By the air-permeability method, this cement would show
about 3500 sq. cm. per g, which is probably close to the true *macroscopic*
surface area. The difference between the macroscopic surface area and
that as measured by adsorption might be due to microscopic, or submicroscopic, cracks in the clinker grains. Surfaces of such cracks would
be measured by the adsorption method, but not by the other. Since such

cracks have not been commonly reported, it seems more likely that the difference is due to a slight coating of hydration products on the grain surfaces. As shown above, an average cement shows about 9.3 x 10⁶ sq. cm. per g of non-evaporable water. Hence, to account for the 7400 sq. cm. difference between the two results, it is only necessary to assume that the cement had hydrated to the extent of

$$\frac{7400}{9.3 \times 10^6} = 800 \times 10^{-6} \text{ g of non-evaporable water per g of cement,}$$

or 0.08 percent of the weight of the cement. Such a small amount of hydration could easily occur during the normal handling of a sample during humid weather.

Whether the true surface area of the cement is of the order of 3000 or 10,000, it is clear that the initial surface area is negligible compared with that which finally develops.

THE SPECIFIC SURFACE OF STEAM-CURED PASTE

The effects of high-temperature steam-curing on the adsorption characteristics of cement paste were shown in Part 2, p. 300. In terms of the B.E.T. theory, the effects are as follows:

	Ref. 14-4 Normal curing	Ref. 14-6 Steam curing
C	15.4	20
V_m, g/g of cement	0.037	0.0020
V_m, g/g dry paste	0.032	0.0018
Sp. surface, sq. cm. per g of cement, millions	1.32	0.071
Sp. surface, sq. cm. per g of dry paste, millions	1.15	0.062
V_m/w_n	0.241	0.012
w_n, g/g of cement	0.1537	0.1615

The figures for V_m and specific surface of the steam-cured specimen are probably not very accurate because of the extreme smallness of the amounts of water taken up in the low-pressure range. The order of magnitude relative to the normally cured material is probably correct, however. The result indicates that all but about 5 percent of the colloidal material was converted to the microcrystalline state by high-temperature steam curing.

w/V_m CURVES

The samples of hardened paste used in these studies contained undetermined quantities of unhydrated material. Consequently, the weight of the adsorbent material could not be ascertained directly, a circumstance that increases the difficulty of interpreting the adsorption data. The problem was simplified by expressing the amount of adsorption, w, in terms of the surface area of the solid phase. Since the surface area is proportional to V_m, the ratio w/V_m could be used without computing the surface area.

Typical w/V_m curves are shown in Fig. 3-8. The uppermost curve represents the paste in a mortar specimen having $w/c = 0.587$, cured six months; the middle curve represents the paste from a richer mortar specimen of the same age, $w/c = 0.439$. The lowest curve represents the data given in the first group of Table 3-9. These data include water-cement ratios ranging from 0.12* to 0.32 by weight. The table shows that after long periods of curing and for w/c within this range, w/V_m is virtually the same for all samples at all vapor pressures. (In the lower range of pressures, w/V_m is always the same for all samples except for the effect of differences in C.†) The triangular points plotted in Fig. 3-8 represent the average values from this group.

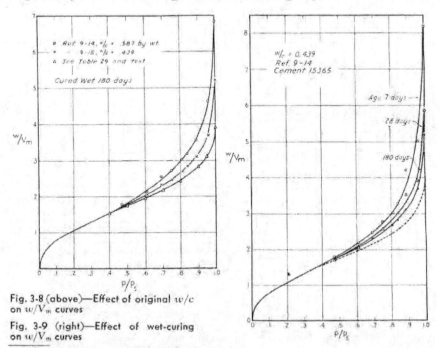

Fig. 3-8 (above)—Effect of original w/c on w/V_m curves

Fig. 3-9 (right)—Effect of wet-curing on w/V_m curves

*This very dry paste was molded by means of a press.
†See discussion in Part 4: "Significance of C of the B.E.T. Equation."

TABLE 3-9—TYPICAL w/V_m DATA

Data obtained by air-stream method, except as noted, and taken from plotted curves.

Ref. No. 254	Cement No.	Net w/c	Age, days	C	V_m, g/g dry paste	w/V_m at value of p/p_s indicated								v_t‡	w_n/c
						0.4	0.5	0.6	0.7	0.8	0.9	0.95	SSD†		
						Samples for which V_{maz} = about $4V_m$									
8-1	14930J	—	447	21	.045	1.56	1.66	1.82	2.05	2.32	2.82	3.07	3.99	.88	.1807
9-1	14930J	.309	365	21	.043	1.52	1.72	1.90	2.12	2.40	2.82	3.10	3.89	.86	.1704
9-1	14930J	.309	180	21	.042	1.52	1.72	1.90	2.12	2.40	2.85	3.10	3.88	.86	.1620
9-4	15007J	.316	180	16	.041	1.48	1.72	1.96	2.23	2.42	2.88	3.15	3.99	.87	.1835
9-10	15013J	.324	180	29	.043	1.55	1.80	2.00	2.17	2.40	2.75	2.95	3.73	.86	.1877
9-13	15365	.319	180	25	.039	1.52	1.77	1.98	2.25	2.52	2.92	3.20	4.25	.87	.1815
9-13	15365	.319	90	20	.041	1.55	1.75	1.98	2.20	2.47	2.92	3.20	4.02	.87	.1789
9-15A*	15365	.244	180	33	.031	1.57	1.80	2.00	2.25	2.50	2.75	3.18	3.58	—	—
9-15A*	15365	.244	180	33	.031	1.55	1.77	2.02	2.25	2.50	2.90	3.20	—	—	.1554
254-18*	14675	.12	4 yr.	92	.019	1.40	1.60	1.80	2.05	2.30	2.75	3.10	3.9	—	—
Avg.						1.53	1.74	1.94	2.17	2.43	2.84	3.12	3.91	.867	
						Samples for which $V_{maz} > 4V_m$									
9-14	15365	.439	180	19	.049	1.50	1.75	2.04	2.30	2.65	3.17	3.60	5.22	.89	.2221
9-14	15365	.439	28	19	.046	1.52	1.80	2.08	2.35	2.75	3.40	3.90	5.85	.90	.1841
9-14	15365	.439	7	26	.030	1.55	1.85	2.15	2.55	3.05	4.00	5.25	8.20	.91	.1400
9-15	15365	.587	180	19	.048	1.55	1.80	2.04	2.34	3.16	3.20	3.65	5.23	—	—
254-18	13495	.44§	7 yr.		.055	1.55	1.75	1.95	2.20	2.50	2.90	3.25	4.20	—	—

*Data obtained by high-vacuum method (not included in averages)
†Evaporable water content of saturated, surface-dry samples
‡See Part 5.
§Estimated.

In Fig. 3-9 the effect of prolonging the period of wet-curing on a given paste is shown together with the lowest curve of Fig. 3-8 for comparison.

Minimum porosity and the cement-gel isotherm

Considering Fig. 3-8 and 3-9 together we may conclude that the densest paste possible contains a pore-volume equal to the volume of the quantity of adsorbed water represented by about $4V_m$.

The shape of the lowest curve in Fig. 3-8 also seems to represent a limit that is approached as the pastes are made denser. Hence, for brevity we will call the lower curve of Fig. 3-8 the *cement-gel isotherm* or just gel-curve, when the meaning is clear. The part of the total evaporable water equal to $4V_m$ will be called *gel-water*.

When a paste is such that at saturation it contains a quantity of evaporable water equal to $4V_m$, we may infer that all the originally water-filled space· has become filled with porous hydration products. Thus, in such a paste the space outside the unhydrated clinker residue has only the porosity of the cement-gel itself.

When a paste is such that at saturation it contains a quantity of water exceeding $4V_m$, the excess over $4V_m$ is believed to occupy residual space outside the cement-gel. Water occupying this space is called *capillary water* in this discussion. It should be understood that this distinction between capillary water and gel-water is arbitrary, for some of the gel-water may be taken up by capillary condensation and is thus not different from the rest of the capillary water so far as the mechanism of adsorption is concerned. The distinction is justified by the fact that, in a saturated paste, the quantity of gel-water always bears the same ratio to the amount of gel, whereas the water called capillary water can be present in any amount according to the porosity of the paste as a whole.

Fig. 3-8 and 3-9, which are typical of all other w/V_m curves obtained, show that among various samples any increase in pressure up to about $0.45\ p_s$ is always accompanied by approximately the same increment of adsorption, regardless of differences in porosity.[*] From this we may infer that the capillaries (the spaces outside the gel) do not begin to fill at pressures below about $0.45\ p_s$. At higher pressures, however, a given increment in pressure will be accompanied by an increment of adsorption that is larger the greater the porosity of the sample. This may be taken as direct evidence of capillary condensation. The amount of water held by capillary condensation at any given pressure is represented by the vertical distance of the point in question above the gel-curve.

These ideas can be represented by a model such as is illustrated in Fig. 3-10. In A the shaded areas represent cross sections of spherical

---

[*]Such differences as there may be are due to differences in C of eq. (A), as is explained in Part 4.

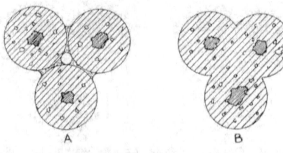

A   B

Fig. 3-10

bodies of cement gel with non-colloidal particles (microcrystalline hydrates and unreacted cement) embedded in them. Between the bodies is interstitial space containing capillary-condensed water, here pictured as lenses around the sphere-to-sphere contacts. The water content of the system is assumed to be below saturation, as indicated by the curvature of the lenses. At saturation, the interstitial space would be filled with capillary water, making the total water content equal to $4V_m$ plus the volume of capillary water.

Thus, if we consider the system pictured in Fig. 3-10A to be the sample represented by the upper curve of Fig. 3-8, at equilibrium with the pressure $p = 0.8\ p_s$, the water content of the spheres (the gel-water) would be 2.44 V_m, the capillary water would be 0.56 V_m, making a total of 3.00 V_m. At saturation the gel-water would be $4V_m$ and the capillary water 2.83 V_m, making a total of 6.83 V_m.

Fig. 3-10B represents a paste at the same stage of hydration as that represented in 3-10A but with a lower original w/c. Here the spheres of gel have merged into one body, eliminating all capillary water. The lowest w/V_m curve in Fig. 3-8, the cement-gel isotherm, would correspond to this case.

Estimation of pore- and particle-size

With data obtained from specimens containing no capillary space (as defined above) we can estimate the order of size of the elements of the solid phase and of its characteristic pores. Pore-size can be estimated from the hydraulic radius

$$\text{Hydraulic radius} = m = \frac{\text{volume of pores}}{\text{area of pore-walls}}$$

Pore volume is the space occupied by evaporable water and, in a paste without capillary space, this is equal to the volume of the gel water, i.e., the volume of $4V_m$. The area of the pore-walls is given by eq. (6).

$$S = 35.7 \times 10^6\ V_m$$

Hence,

$$m = \frac{4V_m v_g}{35.7 \times 10^6 V_m}$$

where

v_g = specific volume of the gel-water.

It will be shown later than the specific volume of the gel-water is about 0.90. Hence,

$$m = \frac{4 \times 0.90}{35.7 \times 10^6} = 10.01 \times 10^{-8} \text{ cm}$$

or approximately 10Å.*

The average size of a pore in the gel having a given hydraulic radius can be estimated by assuming that the cross section of the pore resembles a rectangular slit. Let b, h, and L be the width, thickness, and length, respectively, of the slit. Then

$$m = \frac{hbL}{(2h + 2b)L} = \frac{hb}{2(h + b)}$$

Solutions of this equation for various values of h and b are given below:

$$h = b \quad ; \quad m = 1/4 \, b$$
$$h = 2b \quad ; \quad m = 1/3 \, b$$
$$h = 4b \quad ; \quad m = 4/10 \, b$$
$$h = 10b \quad ; \quad m = 10/22 \, b$$
$$h = 100b \quad ; \quad m = 100/202 \, b$$

Thus, as h/b is made larger, m approaches ½ b as a limit. This means that the width of the pores is at least twice and at most four times the hydraulic radius. Since m was given as about 10Å, it follows that the average pore is from 20 to 40Å across, probably closer to 40Å than to 20Å if the particles are other than spherical.

The order of size of the colloidal particles cannot be computed directly because there is no way to correct for the volume of non-colloidal material, i.e., microcrystalline hydrates and unhydrated clinker. However, it is of interest to estimate the size without such correction since the volume of non-colloidal hydrates is relatively small and data are available for samples containing very little unhydrated clinker. The estimate is made by finding the size of spheres in an aggregation of spheres that would have the same total volume and surface area as dry hardened paste. The size of sphere is given by the relationship

$$r = \frac{3}{S'}$$

---

*Å = Ångstrom unit = 10^{-8} cm

where

> r = radius of sphere in cm
> S' = surface area in sq. cm per cu. cm

$$S' = d_p S$$

where

> d_p = density of dry paste, g per cu. cm

and S = surface area of dry paste, sq. cm per g.

For a typical paste cured at least 6 mo.,

> d_p = 2.44 g per cu. cm.
> S = 1.8 x 10⁶ sq. cm. per g

$$r = \frac{3}{2.44 \times 1.8 \times 10^6} = 68 \times 10^{-8} \text{ cm,}$$

say 70Å.

This indicates that if the solid phase were an assemblage of equal spheres, each sphere would have a diameter of about 140Å. The units of colloid material are probably smaller than this, but not very much smaller since most of the hydration product is colloidal and since there was probably little unhydrated material in the specimen on which this estimate is based.

These figures give a picture of a material made up of solid units averaging about 140Å in diameter, with interstices averaging say 20 to 40Å across. This should, of course, be taken only as an indication of the order of size of the elements of the fine structure. It indicates, for example, the necessary resolving power of a microscope capable of differentiating these features of hardened paste.

* * * * *

It is hardly necessary to add that the authors hold no belief that the gel develops as spheres or that the pores are rectangular slits of uniform cross section. Those assumptions were made only for convenience of illustration and computation. The bodies of hardened gel could be in the form of submicroscopic plates, filaments, prisms, or of no regular form at all. However, as developed above, the evidence points to the conclusion that the gel is a solid having a characteristic porosity.

Data on relative amounts of gel-water and capillary water

The relative amounts of gel-water and capillary water in saturated samples at various stages of hydration are shown in Fig. 3-11 and 3-12, for the materials of Series 254-9. The shaded portion of each column represents gel-water and the open portion capillary water. These charts bring out again the fact that for specimens of sufficiently low water-cement ratio, prolonged curing eliminates all capillary water.

In several instances there is an indication that the ratio of capillary to gel-water *increases* after a minimum is reached. Whether this is real or the result of experimental vagaries cannot be told without further experiment. If it is real, it might be due to the leaching of soluble material from the paste during the curing period. Such leaching would be expected to increase the porosity of the paste. It might also be due to a coarsening of the gel-texture by the formation of microcrystals at the expense of colloids. If so, the change is of considerable significance. Present data warrant no conclusions on this point.

There is a rather definite indication that the gel is able to fill but a limited amount of space, regardless of the length of the curing period. This is brought out in Fig. 3-13, where w_e/V_m (w_e = evaporable water) at saturation is plotted against w/c for all specimens cured 180 days or longer. This shows again that the minimum possible evaporable water content is about $4V_m$ and further that all samples having original water-cement ratios greater than about 0.32 by weight will contain some capillary water. The empirical relationship illustrated can be represented approximately by the equation

$$\frac{w_c}{V_m} = 12.2 \ (w/c - 0.32) \ \Bigg] \quad w/c \geq 0.32$$

where

w_c is the capillary-water content of specimens cured 6 months or more.

SUMMARY OF PART 3

Adsorption isotherms for water on hardened portland cement pastes show the same characteristics as those for vapors on many different organic and inorganic materials.

The process of adsorption and the conditions for equilibrium are explained in terms of the Brunauer-Emmett-Teller (B.E.T.) theory and the capillary condensation theory.

The B.E.T. eq. (A) is used for representing data over the range $p = 0.05 \ p_s$ to $0.45 \ p_s$. The equation is

$$\frac{w}{V_m} = \frac{cx}{(1 - x) \ (1 - x - cx)} \quad \dots\dots\dots\dots\dots\dots\dots \ (A)$$

where

w = weight of evaporable water held at equilibrium with pressure p,

V_m = quantity of water required for a complete condensed layer on the solid, the layer being 1 molecule deep on the average,

C = a constant related to the heat of adsorption,

$x = p/p_s$ where p_s = saturation pressure and p the existing pressure.

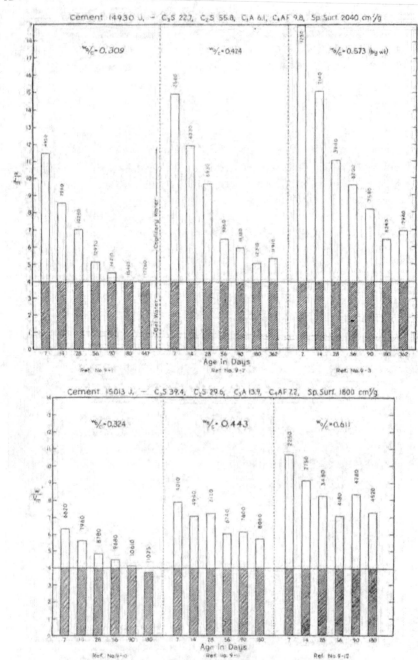

Fig. 3-11—Effect of hydration on w/V_m

Note: Figures over columns are compressive strengths of 2-in. cubes, psi.

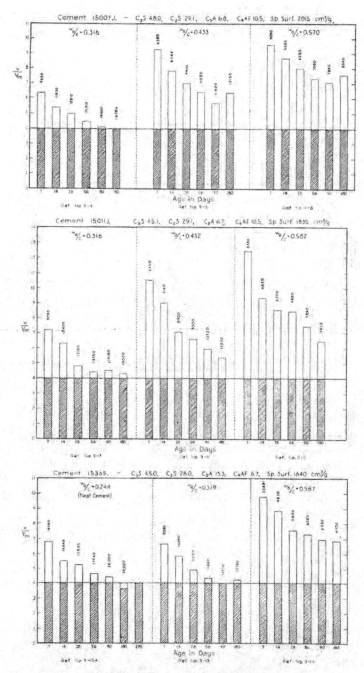

Fig. 3-12—Effect of hydration on w/V_m

Note: Figures over columns are compressive strengths of 2-in. cubes, psi.

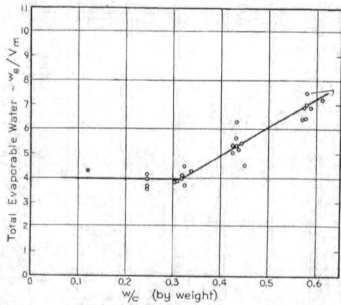

Fig. 3-13—Empirical relationship between total evaporable water per
unit V_m and original water-cement ratio for samples cured 180 days
or longer

V_m and C can be readily evaluated from experimental data and p_s
is a constant depending on temperature. C is about the same for all
pastes. Hence differences in adsorption characteristics are indicated by
differences in V_m.

The non-evaporable water content, w_n, is regarded as proportional
to the total amount of hydration products. Since V_m is porportional to
surface area and since practically all the surface is that of the colloids,
V_m is considered to be proportional to the colloidal material (gel) only.

The ratio V_m/w_n is considered to be a constant for any given cement.
It is influenced by compound composition about as follows:

$$\frac{V_m}{w_n} = 0.00230\ (\%C_3S) + 0.00320\ (\%C_2S) + 0.00317\ (\%C_3A) +$$

$$0.00368\ (\%C_4AF)$$

Among the different types of cement V_m/w_n varies from about 0.24 to
0.28.

The above equation implies that the hydrate of each compound is
colloidal or at least that all compounds occur as constituents of a complex colloidal hydrate.

The specific surface of hardened paste can be computed from the
relationship $S = 35.7 \times 10^6\ V_m$. It increases with the period of curing
and reaches about 2 million sq. cm per g of original cement.

The specific surface of the hardened paste is related to w_n as follows:

$$\frac{S}{w_n} = 35.7 \times 10^6 \, k,$$

where k is a constant for a given cement. Among the different types of cements, S/w_n ranges from about 8.6×10^6 to 10×10^6.

None of the relationships given above apply to paste cured at high temperature. Under steam pressure a sample cured 6 hours at 420 F showed only 0.07×10^6 sq. cm. of surface per g of cement, as compared with 1.3×10^6 for a paste cured 28 days, or about 2.0×10^6 for long curing, at room temperature.

When adsorption data are expressed in terms of w/V_m and p/p_s, the result is an isotherm based on the relative amount of gel. Such curves are virtually identical for all cement pastes over the pressure range $p = 0.05 \, p_s$ to $0.45 \, p_s$.

For pastes in which the total evaporable water content is about $4V_m$, the curves are identical for the whole pressure range.

For pastes having capacity for evaporable water exceeding $4V_m$, the excess is taken up over the pressure range $p = 0.45 \, p_s$ to $p = p_s$.

The evaporable-water capacity is smaller the lower the original water-cement ratio and the longer the period of curing, but it cannot be reduced below about $4V_m$.

Evaporable water in excess of $4V_m$ is believed to occupy interstitial space not filled by gel or other hydration products. The water in this space is called *capillary water*. The rest of the evaporable water is held within the characteristic voids of the gel and is called *gel-water* even though some of it might have been taken up by capillary condensation.

When the total evaporable-water capacity $= 4V_m$, the specimen contains no space for capillary water.

From the surface area of the solid phase, and its characteristic porosity, the average pore in the densest possible hardened paste is estimated to be from 20 to 40Å across.

From the volume of the solid phase and its surface area, the order of particle size, expressed as sphere diameter, is estimated at 140Å.

Data on the relative amounts of gel-water and capillary water in various samples are given graphically.

REFERENCES

(1) A. M. Gaudin and F. W. Bowdish, *Mining Technology*, v. 8 (3) pp. 1-6 (1944).

(2) L. A. Wooten and Callaway Brown, *J. Am. Chem. Soc.* v. 65, p. 113 (1943).

(3) H. Cassel, *Trans. Faraday Soc.* v. 28, p. 177 (1932). Quoted by Brunauer in Ref. 5, p. 289.

(4) D. M. Gans, M. S. Brooks, and G. E. Boyd, *Ind. Eng. Chem.* (Anal. Ed.) v. 14 p. 396 (1942).

(5) Stephen Brunauer, *The Adsorption of Gases and Vapors.* Vol. 1, Princeton University Press (1943).

(6) J. W. McBain and John Ferguson, *J. Phys. Chem.* v. 31, p. 564 (1927).

(7) Urquhart and Williams, *J. Textile Inst.* v. 40, p. T439 (1924).

(8) S. E. Shephard and P. T. Newsome, *Ind. Eng. Chem.* v. 26, p. 285 (1943).

(9) L. M. Pidgeon and A. Van Winsen, *Can. J. Res.* v. 9, p. 153 (1933).

(10) E. Filby and O. Maass, *Can J. Res.* v. 13, Sec. B., p. 5 (1935).

(11) C. O. Seborg, F. A. Simmonds, and P. K. Baird, *Ind. Eng. Chem.* v. 28, p. 1245 (1936).

(12) W. R. Smith, F. S. Thornhill, and R. I. Bray, *Ind. Eng. Chem.* v. 33, p. 1303 (1941).

(13) K. S. Rao, *J. Phys. Chem.*, v. 45, p. 500 (1941).

(14) V. L. Simril and Sherman Smith, *Ind. Eng. Chem.* v. 34, p. 226 (1942).

(15) V. R. Dietz and L. F. Gleysteen, *J. Res.*, Natl. Bur. of Stds. v. 29, p. 191 (1942).

(16) J. D. Babbitt, *Can. J. Res.* v. 20, p. 143 (1942).

(17) L. A. Reyerson and Cyrus Bemmels, *J. Phys. Chem.* v. 46, p. 31 (1942).

(18) Henry B. Hull, *J. Am. Chem. Soc.* v. 66, p. 1499 (1944).

(19) Lyle T. Alexander and M. M. Haring, *J. Phys. Chem.* v. 40, p. 195 (1936).

(20) J. B. Speakman, *Trans. Faraday Soc.* v. 40, p. 6 (1944).

(21) S. Brunauer, P. H. Emmett, and E. Teller, *J. Am. Chem. Soc.* v. 60, p. 309 (1938).

(22) S. Brunauer, L. S. Deming, W. E. Deming, and E. Teller, *J. Am. Chem. Soc.* v. 62, p. 1723 (1940).

(23) Gerald Pickett, *J. Am. Chem. Soc.* v. 67, p. 1958 (1945).

(24) E. Freyssinet, *Science et Industrie* (Jan. 1933).

(25) P. H. Emmett, *Ind. Eng. Chem.* v. 37, p. 639 (1945).

(26) Ref. 5, p. 168.

(27) W. D. Harkins and G. Jura, *J. Chem. Phys.* v. 11, p. 560 (1943) and *J. Am. Chem. Soc.* v. 66, p. 919 (1944).

(28) International Critical Tables, Vol. III. For *NaOH*, pp. 296 and 369. For *KOH*, pp. 298 and 373.

(29) R. H. Bogue and Wm. Lerch, *Ind. Eng. Chem.* v. 26, p. 837 (1934), or Paper No. 27, Portland Cement Association Fellowship, National Bureau of Standards, Washington, D. C.

(30) H. K. Livingston, *J. Am. Chem. Soc.* v. 66, p. 569-73 (1944).

(31) P. H. Emmett, *Advances in Colloid Science*, Interscience Publishers, Inc., New York, 1942, p. 6.

(32) Wm. D. Harkins and Geo. Jura, *J. Chem. Phys.* v. 11, p. 431 (1943).

(33) P. H. Emmett, Symposium on New Methods for Particle-Size Determination in the Subsieve Range, p. 95, A.S.T.M. Publication, 1941.

(34) P. H. Emmett and T. DeWitt, *Ind. Eng. Chem.* (Anal. Ed.) v. 13, p. 28 (1941).

Title 43-5d —a part of PROCEEDINGS, AMERICAN CONCRETE INSTITUTE Vol. 43

JOURNAL
of the
AMERICAN CONCRETE INSTITUTE
(copyrighted)

Vol. 18 No. 5   7400 SECOND BOULEVARD, DETROIT 2, MICHIGAN   January 1947

Studies of the Physical Properties of Hardened Portland Cement Paste*

By T. C. POWERS†
Member American Concrete Institute

and T. L. BROWNYARD‡

Part 4. The Thermodynamics of Adsorption of Water on Hardened Paste

CONTENTS

*Received by the Institute July 8, 1946—scheduled for publication in seven installments; October 1946 to April, 1947. In nine parts:

Part 1. "A Review of Methods That Have Been Used for Studying the Physical Properties of Hardened Portland Cement Paste". ACI JOURNAL, October, 1946.
Part 2. "Studies of Water Fixation"—Appendix to Part 2. ACI JOURNAL, November, 1946.
Part 3. "Theoretical Interpretation of Adsorption Data." ACI JOURNAL, December, 1946.
Part 4. "The Thermodynamics of Adsorption"—Appendix to Parts 3 and 4.
Part 5. "Studies of the Hardened Paste by Means of Specific-Volume Measurements."
Part 6. "Relation of Physical Characteristics of the Paste to Compressive Strength."
Part 7. "Permeability and Absorptivity."
Part 8. "The Freezing of Water in Hardened Portland Cement Paste."
Part 9. "General Summary of Findings on the Properties of Hardened Portland Cement Paste."

†Manager of Basic Research, Portland Cement Assn. Research Laboratory, Chicago 10, Ill.
‡Navy Dept., Washington, D. C., formerly Research Chemist, Portland Cement Assn. Research Laboratory, Chicago 10, Ill.

This discussion pertains to the energy changes that take place when water is adsorbed by hardened cement paste. The relationship of these changes to such physical effects as shrinking and swelling, capillary flow, and moisture diffusion will be considered briefly. Comparisons are made of the energy of binding of evaporable and non-evaporable water. Analysis of the energy changes into the two main forms of energy and consideration of the relative amounts of each are of interest in connection with the question of the extent to which water is modified when it is adsorbed on the solid.

THE HEAT OF ADSORPTION

As pointed out in Part 3, the adsorption of a vapor by a solid can be likened to the process of condensation both with respect to the kinetics of the process and the nature of the forces involved. Therefore, it might be expected that the heat liberated when the vapor is adsorbed would be comparable to the heat of liquefaction of the vapor. When the comparison is made, it is usually found that the heat of adsorption exceeds the heat of liquefaction. In the adsorption of water vapor on hardened cement paste, the heat of adsorption for the first increments of water added exceeds the heat of liquefaction by about 65 percent of the latter. This excess can be attributed, directly or indirectly, to interaction of the adsorbed molecules with the surface of the solid.

THE NET HEAT OF ADSORPTION

Definitions

The excess of the heat of adsorption over the heat of liquefaction is called the *net heat of adsorption.* If Q represents the heat of adsorption and Q_L the heat of liquefaction, then Q_a, the net heat of adsorption, is defined by,

$$Q_a = Q - Q_L \dots \dots \dots \dots \dots \dots \dots (1)$$

The definition just given amounts to regarding the adsorption of the vapor as a two-step process, as follows:

(1) Vapor at the saturation pressure, p_s, condenses to liquid, thereby liberating the heat of liquefaction, Q_L.

(2) The liquid water is then adsorbed, liberating the net heat of adsorption, Q_a. In this step, the water comes to equilibrium with vapor at a lower pressure, p.

As pointed out before (Part 3), the free surface energy of the solid and the free surface energy of the condensed liquid must both be causes of adsorption in a porous solid such as hardened paste. Hence, the net heat of adsorption must have its origin in at least two sources. At low vapor pressures, the net heat of adsorption has its origin in the interaction of the adsorbed molecules with the solid surface. When the pressure is increased above $0.45\ p_s$, where capillary condensation becomes a factor, the surface of the water film formed at lower pressures diminishes and becomes zero, or nearly zero, at saturation. The destruction of the water surface is accompanied by the liberation of the heat of water-surface formation. Thus, the net heat of adsorption is the sum of two terms, *the net heat of surface adsorption* and the *net heat of capillary condensation.* That is,

$$Q_a = Q_s + Q_c \dots \dots \dots \dots \dots \dots \dots (2)$$

where

Q_a = net heat of adsorption,
Q_s = net heat of surface adsorption, and
Q_c = net heat of capillary condensation.

Evaluation of total net heat of capillary condensation

The total amount of heat arising from the destruction of water surface, i.e., the total net heat of capillary condensation, when the paste goes from the dry to the saturated condition can be evaluated by means of the following considerations.

It may be assumed that the maximum extent of water surface is the area of the solid surface. It would seem, however, that this maximum could not exist at any vapor pressure. At low vapor pressure, the film would be incomplete, even when V_m g. are present, because of the chance distribution of molecules among the layers described in the B.E.T. theory. At higher pressure, the water film would be partly destroyed by capillary condensation. At saturation the water surface would disappear completely except for a negligible area about equal to the superficial area of the granules composing the sample. Nevertheless, each unit of solid surface was covered by a water film at some stage prior to the elimination of the film surface, and the total net heat of capillary condensation should be the same as if the formation of the water surface and its disappearance occurred consecutively.

In accordance with the assumption just stated, the total net heat of capillary condensation, Q_{ct}, is

$$Q_{ct} = Sh_c \quad \dots\dots\dots\dots\dots\dots\dots\dots\dots\dots\dots\dots (3)$$

where S = internal surface area of paste, sq. cm., and
$\quad h_c$ = heat of water-surface formation, cal per sq. cm.

According to Harkins and Jura,[1] h_c = 118.5 ergs per sq. cm. at 25 C, or $118.5 \times 2.39 \times 10^{-8}$ = 2.83×10^{-6} cal per sq. cm. Also by eq. (6) of Part 3,

$$S = 35.7 \times 10^6 V_m \text{ sq. cm.}$$

Therefore,

$$Q_{ct} = 2.83 \times 10^{-6} \times 35.7 \times 10^6 \times V_m$$
$$= 101 V_m, \text{ say } 100 V_m \text{ cal.} \dots\dots\dots\dots\dots\dots\dots (4)$$

Evaluation of total net heat of surface adsorption

The total amount of heat arising from the interaction of the adsorbed molecules with the solid surface, i.e., the total net heat of surface adsorption is given by

$$Q_{st} = Sh_s \quad \dots\dots\dots\dots\dots\dots\dots\dots\dots\dots\dots\dots (5)$$

where Q_{st} = total net heat of surface adsorption, cal per g. of paste,
$\quad S$ = internal surface area of paste, sq. cm. per g, of paste, and
$\quad h_s$ = total net heat of surface adsorption, cal. per cm. of paste.

Hence,

$$Q_{st} = 35.7 \times 10^6 V_m h_s \dots\dots\dots\dots\dots\dots\dots\dots (6)$$

If it can be assumed that h_s is the same for all pastes, and this is a reasonable assumption that will be used, then

$$\frac{Q_{st}}{V_m} = \text{const.} = k. \quad \dots\dots\dots\dots\dots\dots\dots\dots\dots\dots (7)$$

The total net heat of adsorption

The total net heat of adsorption will be the sum of the total net heat of surface adsorption and the total net heat of capillary condensation.

Thus,

$$Q_{at} = Q_{st} + Q_{ct} \dots\dots\dots\dots\dots\dots\dots\dots\dots\dots\dots\dots\dots\dots\dots(8)$$
$$= kV_m + 100V_m = (k + 100)V_m$$

* * * * * * *

At low vapor pressures, only the net heat of surface adsorption appears. At higher pressures the net heat of capillary condensation also appears. There is at present no basis for evaluating either term at any stage short of saturation.

* * * * * * *

Net heat of adsorption and heat of wetting

When adsorption is considered to be the two-step process mentioned above, step (2) immediately suggests a comparison of the net heat of adsorption with the heat of wetting.

Distinction must be made between the heat evolved when a solid surface is immersed in a body of liquid and the heat evolved when the surface is wetted by causing a film to spread over the surface. The heat of immersion exceeds the heat of spreading-wetting by the heat of formation of water surface.

The total net heat of adsorption, Q_{at}, must be very nearly if not actually, equal to the heat of immersion of the hardened paste. This follows because the water surface at saturation is virtually zero, as pointed out above. This means that if a sample of hardened paste is brought to saturation by adsorption of vapor no measurable amount of heat will be evolved if it is immersed in water.

The net heat of surface adsorption is comparable to the heat of spreading-wetting. If the thickness of the film is not a factor, i.e., if the interaction of the adsorbed molecules with the solid surface affects only the first layer of molecules adsorbed, the net heat of surface adsorption is strictly comparable to the heat of spreading-wetting, except for the possible effect of narrow crevices. (In cement gel, some water may be held in crevices so narrow that a water surface cannot form.) If the thickness of the film is a factor, the net heat of surface adsorption differs from the heat of spreading-wetting but the amount of the difference cannot be evaluated. However, the total net heat of surface adsorption should be equal to the heat of spreading-wetting of what may be called a complete film, i.e., a film so thick that the effect of interaction at the solid surface is no longer evident.

MEASUREMENT OF NET HEAT OF ADSORPTION

Materials and procedure

The net heat of adsorption was measured, using two different hardened pastes. From each paste twelve granular samples were prepared by

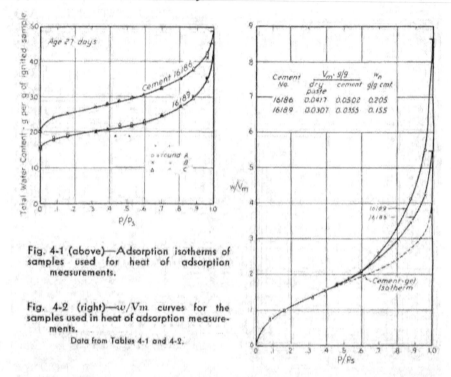

Fig. 4-1 (above)—Adsorption isotherms of samples used for heat of adsorption measurements.

Fig. 4-2 (right)—w/Vm curves for the samples used in heat of adsorption measurements.

Data from Tables 4-1 and 4-2.

first removing the evaporable water and then exposing the samples to different humidified air streams according to the method already described (Part 2).

When the samples had reached equilibrium, each was sealed in a separate glass ampoule, each of the twelve samples from a given paste being at equilibrium with a different vapor pressure. Such samples were prepared in triplicate.

The adsorption isotherms are shown in Fig. 4-1. The total water contents are plotted in order to show also the non-evaporable water contents. The values for $p/p_s = 1.0$, which ordinarily represent the water contents at saturation, were not measured for these samples; the points shown for this pressure represent the water contents before the samples were dried the first time.

w/V_m curves are given in Fig. 4-2. The broken line is the curve for cement-gel, as discussed in Part 3. Both pastes evidently contained space for capillary water.

The heat of adsorption was measured by the same heat-of-solution procedure that is used for measuring the heat of hydration of cement.* The procedure is first to dissolve the dry paste, measuring the heat

*Federal Specification SSC-158a-Sec. 31.

evolved, and then to dissolve a similar sample of paste containing adsorbed water. The indicated reactions are

$Paste$ + acid-solution + nH_2O → solution of paste

Heat evolved = Q_o cal per g of dry paste..........(9)

$Paste$ + nH_2O → $Paste.nH_2O$

Heat evolved = Q_a cal per g of dry paste..........(10)

$Paste.nH_2O$ + acid-solution → solution of paste

Heat evolved = Q_p cal per g of dry paste..........(11)

where

$Paste$ = dried paste

Q_o = heat of solution of dry paste

Q_p = heat of solution of paste containing n grams of evaporable water

Q_a = net heat of adsorption.

By Hess's law,

$$Q_a = Q_o - Q_p. \dots\dots(12)$$

This process, in effect, transfers the adsorbed water from the sample to the solution. Hence, the heat of vaporization does not appear and, on the assumption that the heat of solution of the adsorbed water in the acid is zero, the method may be regarded as giving the net heat of adsorption directly.*

The heat-of-solution method was adopted mainly because at the time the project was planned the heat-of-solution calorimeter was already set up. The results obtained are not altogether satisfactory, for in several cases the variation in the observed net heat of adsorption among companion samples was as great as or greater than the difference in heat content due to differences in adsorbed-water content. This results in some uncertainty as to whether certain observed differences are significant or not.

It should be noted that eq. (12) does not take into account the fact that Q_o and Q_p may represent the heats of solution of samples containing different amounts of adsorbed air. This inaccuracy must be accepted, for we have no knowledge of the change in adsorbed air content, or of its heat of desorption. However, the inaccuracy is probably small, owing to the relative smallness of the amount of air adsorbed at room temperature under a pressure of 1 atmosphere.

Experimental results

The experimental results are recorded in Tables 4-1 and 4-2. In Fig. 4-3 the net heats of adsorption are plotted against the equilibrium vapor pressures of the respective samples of each of the two cement pastes. They are plotted in this way to facilitate estimating the total net heats

---

*The small heat effect of charging n moles of water vapor from pressure p_1 to p is considered negligible.

TABLE 4-1—ADSORPTION AND HEAT OF ADSORPTION DATA FOR PASTE MADE WITH CEMENT 16186

Original w/c = 0.50 (not corrected for bleeding). Ref. 16-01A, B, and C. V_m = 0.0502 g/g ignited wt., average of A, B, and C. Heat of solution of orig. cement = 623 cal/g ignited wt. Age at test—27 to 29 days.

Sample No.	p/p_s	Total water, g/g of: dry paste	Total water, g/g of: ign. wt.	Evap. water g/g ign. wt.	Water adsorbed g/g of: dry paste	Water adsorbed g/g of: ign. wt.	w/V_m	Heat of solution cal/g ign. wt	Net heat of adsorption Q_a cal/g of: dry paste	Net heat of adsorption Q_a cal/g of: ign. wt.	$\frac{Q_a}{V_m}$
A-12.2a		.1688	.2031		0	0		537.5	0	0	
B-24.2a		.1702	.2051		0	0		539.0	0	0	
C†		.1696	.2042		0	0		538.0	0	0	
Avg.	0	.1695*	.2041*	0	0	0	0	538.2	0	0	——
A-11A		.2010	.2418		.0322	.0387		525.4	9.6	12.2	
B-23a		.2014	.2427		.0312	.0376		527.1	9.5	11.8	
Avg.	.081	.2012	.2422	.0381	.0317	.0381	0.76	526.2	9.6	12.0	239
A-7a		.2092	.2517		.0404	.0486		523.2	11.4	14.3	
B-19a		.2091	.2520		.0389	.0469		525.2	11.0	13.8	
Avg.	.161	.2092	.2518	.0477	.0396	.0478	0.95	524.2	11.2	14.0	279
A-9a		.2258	.2717		.0570	.0686		520.6	13.3	16.9	
B-21a		.2254	.2716		.0552	.0665		521.3	13.8	17.6	
Avg.	.322	.2256	.2716	.0675	.0561	.0676	1.37	521.0	13.5	17.2	342
A-10a		.2336	.2810		.0648	.0779		520.0	13.7	17.5	
B-22a		.2334	.2813		.0632	.0762		518.9	15.7	20.1	
C-10g		.2352	.2832		.0656	.0790		518.9	15.0	19.2	
Avg.	.39	.2340	.2818	.0777	.0645	.0777	1.55	519.3	14.7	18.9	376
A-8a		.2399	.2886		.0711	.0855		519.5	14.0	18.0	
B-20a		.2397	.2889		.0695	.0838		520.8	14.1	18.2	
C-8g		.2428	.2924		.0732	.0882		519.3	14.5	18.8	
Avg.	.46	.2408	.2900	.0850	.0713	.0858	1.71	519.9	14.2	18.3	364
A-1a		.2483	.2987		.0795	.0956		519.1	14.2	18.4	
B-13a		.2473	.2980		.0771	.0929		520.1	14.6	18.9	
C-1g		.2496	.3005		.0800	.0963		516.9	16.3	21.2	
Avg.	.53	.2484	.2991	.0950	.0789	.0949	1.89	518.7	15.0	19.5	388
A-5a		.2530	.3068		.0862	.1037		517.5	15.3	20.0	
B-17a		.2541	.3062		.0839	.1011		519.1	15.2	19.9	
Avg.	.60	.2546	.3065	.1024	.0850	.1024	2.04	518.3	15.3	20.0	398
A-4a		.2726	.3280		.1038	.1249		517.9	14.8	19.6	
B-16a		.2714	.3271		.1012	.1220		516.5	17.0	22.5	
C-4g		.2740	.3300		.1044	.1258		515.7	16.8	22.3	
Avg.	.70	.2727	.3284	.1243	.1031	.1242	2.48	516.7	16.2	21.5	428
A-2a		.2954	.3554		.1266	.1523		515.6	16.2	21.9	
B-14a		.2938	.3541		.1236	.1490		516.6	16.5	22.4	
Avg.	.81	.2946	.3548	.1507	.1251	.1506	3.00	516.1	16.4	22.2	442
A-3a		.3175	.3820		.1487	.1789		513.9	17.1	23.7	
B-15a		.3121	.3761		.1419	.1710		515.0	17.5	24.0	
Avg.	.88	.3148	.3790	.1749	.1453	.1750	3.48	514.4	17.3	23.8	474
A-6a		.3477	.4183		.1789	.2152		510.0	19.4	27.5	
B-18a		.3431	.4135		.1729	.2084		514.3	17.5	24.7	
C-6g		.3522	.4241		.1826	.2199		509.8	19.8	28.2	
Avg.	.96	.3477	.4186	.2145	.1781	.2145	4.28	511.4	18.9	26.8	534
A		.3997									
B†		.4002									
C		.3976									
Avg.	1.0	.3992	.481	.277	——	.277	5.5	509.5‡	——	28.7‡	572‡

*Non-evaporable water. †Estimated graphically from ignition loss; no dry sample available. ‡Estimated

TABLE 4-2—ADSORPTION AND HEAT OF ADSORPTION DATA FOR PASTE MADE WITH CEMENT 16189

Original $w/c = 0.5$ (not corrected for bleeding). Ref. 16-02A, B, and C. $V_m = 0.0355$ g/g ignited wt., average of A, B, and C. Heat of solution of orig. cement = 606 cal/g ignited wt. Age at test—42 to 44 days.

Sample No.	p/p_s	Total water, g/g of: dry paste	Total water, g/g of: ign. wt.	Evap. water, g/g ign. wt.	Water adsorbed, g/g of: dry paste	Water adsorbed, g/g of: ign. wt.	w/V_m	Heat of solution cal/g ign. wt.	Net heat of adsorption Q_a, cal/g of: dry paste	Net heat of adsorption Q_a, cal/g of: ign. wt.	$\frac{Q_a}{V_m}$
A-24.2g		.1375	.1594		0	0		542.2	0	0	
B-12.2c		.1340	.1547		0	0		546.2	0	0	
Cf		.1336	.1542		0	0		546.6	0	0	
Avg.	0	.1350*	.1561*	0	0	0	0	545.0	0	0	—
A-23g		.1602	:1847		.0227	.0253		536.1	5.1	6.1	
B-11c		.1557	.1798		.0217	.0251		539.1	5.9	7.0	
C-23c		.1562	.1803		.0226	.0261		540.6	5.1	6.0	
Avg.	.081	.1574	.1816	.0255	.0223	.0255	0.72	538.6	5.4	6.4	180
A-19g		.1682	.1950		.0294	.0356		534.8	6.3	7.5	
B-7c		.1634	.1887		.0305	.0340		534.6	9.7	11.5	
C-19c		.1641	.1894		.0307	.0348		537.0	8.1	9.6	
Avg.	.161	.1652	.1910	.0349	.0302	.0348	0.98	535.5	8.0	9.5	268
B-9c		.1741	.2010		.0401	.0463		534.0	10.2	12.2	
C-21c		.1757	.2028		.0421	.0486		535.4	9.0	11.1	
Avg.	.322	.1749	.2019	.0458	.0411	.0474	1.34	534.7	9.6	11.6	327
B-10c		.1803	.2082		.0463	.0535		532.9	10.9	13.1	
C-22c		.1818	.2098		.0482	.0556		534.1	10.3	12.5	
Avg.	.39	.1810	.2090	.0539	.0472	.0546	1.54	533.5	10.6	12.8	360
A-20g		.1905	.2209		.0530	.0615		529.2	10.6	13.0	
B-8c		.1857	.2144		.0517	.0597		533.2	10.7	13.0	
C-20c		.1876	.2165		.0540	.0623		532.6	11.4	13.9	
Avg.	.46	.1879	.2173	.0612	.0529	.0612	1.72	531.7	10.9	13.3	375
A-13g		.1943	.2253		.0568	.0659		528.7	11.0	13.5	
B-1c		.1907	.2202		.0567	.0655		532.2	11.4	14.0	
C-13c		.1914	.2209		.0578	.0667		533.6	10.6	13.0	
Avg.	.53	.1921	.2221	.0660	.0571	.0660	1.86	531.5	11.0	13.5	380
A-17g		.2011	.2331		.0636	.0737		527.7	11.8	14.5	
B-5c		.1976	.2282		.0636	.0735		—	—	—	
C-17c		.1984	.2290		.0648	.0748		532.4	11.6	14.2	
Avg.	.60	.1990	.2301	.0740	.0640	.0740	2.08	530.0	11.7	14.4	406
A-16g		.2153	.2496		.0778	.0902		526.6	12.5	15.6	
B-4c		.2149	.2482		.0809	.0935		529.0	13.7	17.1	
C-16c		.2145	.2476		.0816	.0934		530.7	12.7	15.8	
Avg.	.70	.2149	.2485	.0924	.0799	.0924	2.60	528.8	13.0	16.2	456
B-2c		.2383	.2752		.1043	.1205		528.2	14.0	17.9	
C-14c		.2385	.2753		.1049	.1211		528.8	14.0	17.8	
Avg.	.81	.2384	.2752	.1191	.1046	.1208	3.40	528.5	14.0	17.8	501
B-3c		.2635	.3043		.1295	.1496		526.7	14.9	19.4	
C-15c		.2572	.2969		.1246	.1447		(537.8)	14.4	18.7	
Avg.	.88	.2604	.3006	.1445	.1270	.1472	4.15	526.7	14.6	19.0	535
A-18g		.3062	.3550		.1697	.1966		(518.9)	(17.2)	(23.3)	
B-6c		.3058	.3531		.1718	.1984		526.8	14.3	19.4	
C-18c		.3003	.3466		.1660	.1924		523.3	14.7	19.8	
Avg.	.96	.3041	.3516	.1965	.1695	.1958	5.50	525.0	14.5	19.6	552
A		.3991	.4627								
Bf		.3872	.4489								
C		.3894	.4515								
Avg.	1.0	.3919	.4544	.2983	—	.298	8.65	—	—	20.3‡	572‡

*Non-evaporable water. †Estimated graphically from ignition loss; no dry sample available. ‡Estimated

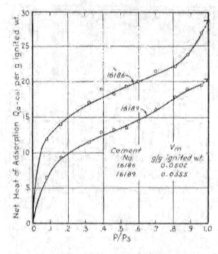

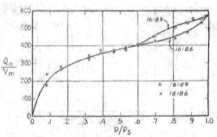

Fig. 4-3 (left)—Heat of adsorption vs. relative vapor pressure.

Data from Tables 4-1 and 4-2.

Fig. 4-4 (above)—$\dfrac{Q_a}{V_m}$ vs. p/p_s

of adsorption for the saturated samples, which were not measured. The terminus of the lower curve was estimated to be at 20.3 cal per g of ignited weight. Then, in accordance with eq. (8) the total net heat of adsorption was assumed to be proportional to V_m and the terminus of the upper curve estimated on this basis. That is,

$$\frac{(Q_{at})_1}{(V_m)_1} = \frac{(Q_{at})_2}{(V_m)_2}$$

From the data given in Fig. 4-3 and from the estimated value of $(Q_{at})_1$ we have the following:

$(Q_{at})_1 = 20.3$ cal per g ign. wt.
$(V_m)_1 = 0.0355$ g per g ign. wt.
$(V_m)_2 = 0.0502$ g per g ign. wt.

Hence,

$(Q_{at})_1/(V_m)_1 = 20.3/0.0355 = 572$ cal per g

and

$(Q_{at})_2 = 572 \times 0.0502 = 28.7$ cal per g

Reference to the upper curve of Fig. 4-3 will show that this estimate results in a reasonable terminus for that curve.

According to the discussion leading up to eq. (8) the amount of heat evolved by adsorption at a given pressure should be proportional, or nearly so, to the amount of surface covered at that pressure. According to the B.E.T. theory, the fraction of the total surface that is covered at a given relative vapor pressure is the same for all adsorbents having the same value for the constant C. This could be strictly true only in the absence of capillary condensation, unless the various adsorbents had pores of exactly the same size and shape. Thus, at least for the low pressure range, we could predict from theory that the relationship between Q_a/V_m and p/p_s should be the same for both samples, at least up to $p = 0.45$ p_s.

The relationship found between Q_a/V_m and p/p_s for the two cement pastes is shown in Fig. 4-4. If plotted separately the two series of points would be judged to describe different curves. However, in view of the possibility of considerable experimental error, it is doubtful whether the differences are significant, at least in the lower range of pressures. At any rate, differences in the lower range cannot be accounted for on the basis of current theory. In the upper range the separation of the curves might be due to a difference in size and shape of the pores and hence to a difference in the rate of change of water surface with change in pressure. The curves as drawn indicate that only those pores, or those parts of the pores, that fill at pressures above 0.6 p_s differ in size and shape.

Comparison of net heat of adsorption of water by cement paste with that of water on other solids

The total net heat of adsorption, Q_{at}, was estimated above to be 572 V_m.

Since $V_m = \dfrac{S}{35.7 \times 10^6}$, the heat per unit of surface $= \dfrac{572}{35.7 \times 10^6}$

$= 16 \times 10^{-6}$ cal per sq. cm. of solid surface or $16 \times 10^{-6} \times 4.18 \times 10^7 = 670$ ergs per sq. cm. of solid surface. Harkins and Boyd[2] measured the heats of immersion in liquid water of several different solids. The results were as follows:

$BaSO_4$	490 ergs per sq. cm. of solid surface
TiO_2	520
Si	580
SiO_2	600
ZrO_2	600
SnO_2	680
$ZrSiO_4$	850
Graphite	265

It is evident that the total net heat of adsorption for water in hardened cement paste is about the same as the heat of immersion of various non-porous minerals. As brought out before, the heat of immersion per sq. cm. of surface of these minerals should be about equal to their total net heats of adsorption per unit of surface if they were porous adsorbents.

Comparison of heat of hydration with net heat of adsorption

In another project, W. C. Hansen* measured the non-evaporable water contents and the heats of hydration on a group of 27 commercial cements comprising all types. The samples were neat pastes, $w/c = 0.40$ by

*Formerly of PCA laboratory. At present, Manager, Research Laboratories, Universal Atlas Cement Co.

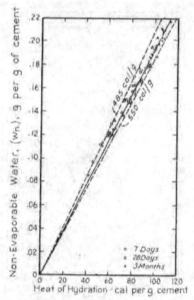

Fig. 4-5—Relationship between heat of hydration and non-evaporable water.

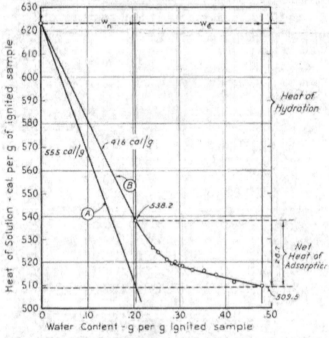

Fig. 4-6—Heat of solution data for pastes made with cement 16186.

Data from Table 4-1.

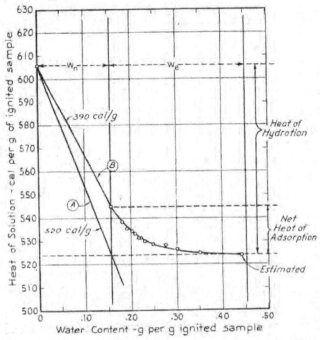

Fig. 4-7—Heat of solution data for pastes made with cement 16189.

Data from Table 4-2.

weight (not corrected for bleeding). They were cured in sealed vials at 70 F for periods ranging from 7 days to 1 year. The heat of hydration at each age was determined by the same heat-of-solution method described above. The non-evaporable water content was determined by the method already described. (Part 2)

The results are shown in Fig. 4-5. This graph indicates that the heat of hydration is directly proportional to the non-evaporable water content, and that the proportionality constants for the different cements differ, but do not differ widely.

Fig. 4-6 and 4-7 bring out the relationship between heat of hydration and heat of adsorption for the two samples used for the present study. In each diagram the point plotted for zero water content represents the heat of solution of the original cement. All the other points represent the hardened paste after 27 days of wet curing. In Fig. 4-6, for example, we see that the heat of solution of the original cement was 623 cal per g and that after hydration the heat of solution was 509.5 cal per g.† The difference, 113.5 cal, is the heat of hydration. When the evaporable water was removed before determining the heat of solution of the hy-

---

†This particular point was not obtained directly but was estimated from Fig. 4-1 in the manner already described. The same is true of the lowest point in Fig. 4-7.

drated cement, the heat of solution was 538.2 cal per g. The difference between 538.2 and 509.5, or 28.7 cal per g ignited weight, is the total net heat of adsorption, Q_{at}. The other points on the curve represent samples containing intermediate amounts of evaporable water.

The heat of hydration per g of non-evaporable water is about 555 cal for 16186 and 520 cal for 16189, which values agree fairly well with the data given in Fig. 4-5. These values are computed from the slopes of the lines marked A in Fig. 4-6 and 4-7.

The heat of reaction of the non-evaporable water alone is 416 cal per g of non-evaporable water for 16186 and 390 cal per g for 16189. These figures (based on lines B) indicate that the heat of reaction of the non-evaporable water is different for cements of different chemical composition.

From these results we may picture the heat of hydration as developing in the following way:

(1) Chemical reactions between the cement and water in the fresh paste produce new solid phases in which the non-evaporable water is an integral part. These reactions release a definite amount of heat for each unit of water combined, but the amount is different for cements of different chemical composition. (For cement 16186 the amount is 416 cal per g of non-evaporable water, or $416 \times 0.204 = 84.8$ cal per g of cement.)

(2) As the new solid phases (the reaction products) form, they adsorb water and the net heat of adsorption is released. This, according to the above estimates, is $572 V_m$ cal per g for all cements, and is equal to the heat of immersion of the dried paste. (For the paste made from cement 16186 this amounts to $572 \times 0.0502 = 28.7$ cal per g of cement.)

(3) The total heat of hydration is the sum of the heat of combination of the non-evaporable water and the net heat of adsorption $(84.8 + 28.7 = 113.5$ cal per g for 16186).

The amount of heat that adsorption generally contributes to the total heat of hydration can be estimated from the data given above. Let

Q_r = heat of reaction of the non-evaporable water, cal per g.

Then

$$Q_r = k_1 w_n \, ,$$

where

k_1 = a constant for a given cement. Also, as assumed before,

$$Q_{at} = 572 \, V_m \text{ cal per g }.$$

Since

$$w_n = k_2 V_m \, ,$$

where
k_2 = a constant for a given cement (see Part 3),

$$\frac{Q_{at}}{Q_r} = \frac{572\,V_m}{k_1 w_n} = \frac{572}{k_1 k_2} ;$$

or

$$\frac{Q_{at}}{Q_r + Q_{at}} = \frac{572}{k_1 k_2 + 572}$$

The data for the two cements discussed above are:

Cement No.	k_1	k_2	$\dfrac{Q_{at}}{Q_r + Q_{at}}$
16186	416	4.07	0.25
16189	392	4.39	0.24

This shows that for the cements cited the total net heat of adsorption of the evaporable water is about $\frac{1}{4}$ of the total heat of hydration.

The results from these two cements suggest that the ratio of the heat of adsorption to the heat of combination of the non-evaporable water is a constant, or nearly so. However, the close similarity in this case is evidently fortuitous. Q_r is the heat of combination of the water that is a part of the solid phase and Q_{at} depends on the surface area of the solid phase. Hence, only Q_r is appreciably influenced by chemical composition and the two quantities therefore should not always bear the same ratio to each other. However, for most portland cements cured under the same conditions, the ratios probably do not differ widely from those found for these two cements.

THE FREE-ENERGY AND ENTROPY CHANGES OF ADSORPTION

Underlying concepts

It will be shown that the net heat of adsorption represents a change in the internal energy of the system in which the reaction takes place. As expressed by Glasstone,[3] the internal energy content of a substance "is made up of the translational kinetic energy of the moving molecules . . . . . of the energies of rotation and vibration within the molecule, of the internal potential energy determined by the arrangements of the atoms and electrons and other forms of energy involved in the structure of matter. From the standpoint of thermodynamics, however, it is not necessary to know anything about the structure of the atom or molecule, and so it is sufficient to divide the internal energy into two parts only: these are (a) the kinetic energy of translation or, in brief, the kinetic energy, and (b) all other forms of energy." For the present purpose this statement can be amplified by adding that it is not necessary to distinguish energy resident at the surface of a phase from energy within the phase. It can all be regarded as internal energy.

Although the principles of thermodynamics can be applied without knowledge of the mechanism of the change from the initial to final conditions, it seems helpful to picture what is believed to occur.

In the introduction to this section, adsorption was likened to the wetting of a solid by immersion in a liquid or by the spreading of a liquid film. Although in the following discussion this analogy is not explicitly used, the treatment is not in conflict with the concept set forth earlier. In the earlier discussion, emphasis was placed on the change from the completely dry to the completely water-covered or saturated state. In the following discussion attention is centered on changes from one intermediate state to another.

As indicated in Part 3, a field of force exists over the surface of the solid matter of the hardened paste. When molecules, in this case water molecules, enter this force field, they are attracted to the surface. In the direction normal to the surface the force field of the surface supplements the normal cohesive forces between water molecules. The result is that the proportion of molecules having enough energy to escape from the adsorbed liquid during a given time interval is less than normal for the existing temperature. The vapor pressure is correspondingly below that of free water at the same temperature.

The mean specific volume of adsorbed water is *less* than that of free water (see Part 5). The adsorbed water thus appears to be in compression. This observation has led to the belief that adsorbed water is in the same state as would be produced by an external compressive force of sufficient magnitude to reduce the specific volume of free water to that of adsorbed water. This conclusion was reached by Lamb and Coolidge[4] from their experiments showing that for the adsorption of the vapors of eleven different liquids, the net heats of adsorption were roughly proportional to the compressibilities of the respective liquids. However, for several reasons this is regarded as an oversimplified interpretation of the data. We may note in the first place that increasing the external pressure on a liquid densifies it and *raises* its vapor pressure. Although adsorption densifies the liquid, it *decreases* the vapor pressure. In the second place we may note (as will appear later) that the change in entropy caused by applying an external force is very much smaller than that caused by adsorption, unless the applied force causes a change of state. An external pressure produces a uniform compression throughout the liquid. The force of adsorption acts, like gravitation, on the water molecules individually and the effect therefore must vary with the distance from the surface, or from the centers of greatest attraction, according to the gradients in intensity of the force-field.

It seems reasonable to regard the net heat of adsorption as representing the result of changes in the internal structure of the water (changes in the association and orientation of the molecules) and in the potential energy of the water molecules caused by the mutual attraction between the water molecules and the surface. The surface of the solid probably remains structurally unchanged.

Internal energy

A system in a given state is regarded as possessing a definite quantity of internal energy. The system may undergo a gain or a loss of internal energy by a gain or a loss of energy in the form of heat, by doing mechanical work, or by having mechanical work done on it. In thermodynamics, heat gained by the system and work done by the system are conventionally regarded as positive quantities.

According to the first law of thermodynamics the increase in internal energy is equal to the difference between the energy gained as heat and the energy lost by the system if it does mechanical work on its surroundings during the process. That is,

$$\Delta U = Q - w , \dots\dots\dots\dots\dots\dots\dots\dots\dots\dots\dots(13)$$

where

ΔU = increase in internal energy,
Q = heat gained, and
w = work done by the system.

When the external pressure is constant, the work term is proportional to the increase in volume. That is,

$$w = P\Delta v , \dots\dots\dots\dots\dots\dots\dots\dots\dots\dots\dots\dots(14)$$

in which

P = the constant external pressure, and
Δv = the increase in volume of the system.

It is conventional to subtract the initial value from the final to obtain the increment. For example, $\Delta U = U_2 - U_1$ and $\Delta v = v_2 - v_1$. The increment is called an increase whether in any given case it is positive or not. In the case of adsorption the final energy content and the final volume are less than the corresponding initial values. Hence, it is advantageous to write in terms of decreases, that is, in terms of $-\Delta U$, $-\Delta v$, etc. This is done in the rest of this discussion.

Enthalpy, free energy, and unavailable energy

For reactions at constant pressure it is customary to let

$$- \Delta H = - \Delta U - P\Delta v \dots\dots\dots\dots\dots\dots\dots\dots(15)$$

$- \Delta H$ is usually called the decrease in heat content, but, as will be seen, it is generally not that and is preferably called the decrease in enthalpy.[6]

The decrease in enthalpy accompanying an isothermal adsorption represents a decrease in two general classes of energy, namely, *free energy* and *unavailable energy*. That is,

$$- \Delta H = - \Delta G - T \Delta S , \dots\dots\dots\dots\dots\dots (16)$$

where

$- \Delta G$ = decrease in free energy,

$- \Delta S$ = decrease in entropy, and

T = absolute temperature.

The term $- T \Delta S$ represents the decrease in unavailable energy for an isothermal reaction. It is that part of the total energy decrease which, at constant temperature, cannot be converted into external work. If released, it can appear only as heat. Therefore, the unavailable energy can be regarded as stored heat.* In the freezing of water, it is the latent heat of freezing. Without reference to underlying concepts, entropy, S, can be regarded simply as a capacity factor giving the quantity of stored heat in calories per degree of temperature above absolute zero. Hence, TS is the quantity of stored heat, and $T \Delta S$ a change in stored heat, in calories or in whatever energy unit is adopted.

The decrease in free energy, $- \Delta G$, that accompanies an isothermal reaction at constant pressure is that part of the enthalpy-decrease that might be converted into external work. It is that which promotes all spontaneous processes at constant temperature and pressure. In this case it is the energy that promotes hydration, adsorption, swelling, capillary flow, and moisture diffusion. Such processes always take place in such a way as to tend to equalize initial differences in free energy. Thus adsorption occurs when the free energy of the free water or free vapor is greater than the free energy of the adsorbed or capillary condensed water. Moisture diffusion occurs when adsorbed or capillary-condensed water in adjacent regions is at different free-energy levels. The free energy per mole of a given substance is known also as its chemical potential, or thermodynamic potential.

For the conditions of most of these experiments (adsorption in small granules of paste at constant temperature and atmospheric pressure) the decrease in free energy may be assumed to appear entirely as heat. But if work is done by the process, as for example against forces tending to restrain swelling, the free energy expended for such work will not appear as heat.†

---

*This concept is developed at length in an office memorandum by H. H. Steinour. (Special Report No. 1, Series 330, 1945).

†Very recent developments in this subject indicate that adsorption in a comparatively rigid solid such as hardened paste should not be considered to be occurring under a constant external pressure of 1 atmosphere. Since, in a rigid body, swelling or shrinkage may give rise to elastic forces that act on the adsorbed layer, the pressure on the layer is a function of the degree of swelling of the paste, and hence of p/p_s as shown in the section below on Swelling Pressure. Such a variation in external pressure was dealt with by A.B.D. Cassie. See "Adsorption of Water by Wool," *Trans. Faraday Soc.* v. 41, p. 458 (1945) and earlier papers by Barkas in the same journal.

Cassie assumed that the swelling of dry wool fiber produced tension in the filaments of the fiber and compression in the adsorbed water. This assumption may not apply to cement paste. The gel is formed in the fully swollen-state and the elastic bonds that hold the mass together should therefore be considered free of stress in that state, rather than in the dry state as assumed by Cassie. However, since the same reasoning may be applied to the growth of wool fiber, Cassie's results seem to indicate that the reasoning is incorrect. In view of these uncertainties and the recent date of Cassie's paper, the authors have adopted the usual procedures and assumptions for the present paper. A more exact analysis will not be attempted until more experimental data are available.

We may note in passing that Δv of eq. (15) is in the present case the small contraction accompanying adsorption from the liquid state. It amounts, on the average, to about 0.13 cc per cc of water adsorbed. Hence, for an external pressure of 1 atmosphere, 10^6 dynes per sq. cm.,

$$w = 0.13 \times 10^6 \text{ ergs.}$$

or $0.13 \times 10^6 \times 2.39 \times 10^{-8} = .003$ cal. per g. of water adsorbed. Thus it is seen that the work term of eq. (15) is negligible and hence the net heat of adsorption represents the change in internal energy of the system.

Relationship between net heat of adsorption and decreases in internal energy, enthalpy, free energy, and entropy

Since by eq. (13), (14), and (15) $- \Delta H = - Q$, it follows from eq. (16) that:

$$- Q = - (\Delta G + T\Delta S), \quad \dots\dots\dots\dots\dots (17)$$

$$- \Delta G = - (Q - T\Delta S), \dots\dots\dots\dots\dots\dots (18)$$

$$- \Delta S = \frac{- (Q - \Delta G)}{T}, \quad \dots\dots\dots\dots\dots\dots (19)$$

$- \Delta G$ can be computed from the vapor pressure, as will be shown below, and ΔS can be estimated from the measured value of $- Q$ and the corresponding value of $- \Delta G$.

Relationship between change in vapor pressure and change in free energy

As said before, adsorption can occur only when water in the free state has a higher vapor pressure than it has after it is adsorbed. When water in the free state is adsorbed, the change in its free energy is equal to the corresponding change in the free energy of its vapor. Hence, the change in free energy when water changes from one equilibrium condition to another can be calculated from the corresponding change in the free energy of the water vapor.

The relationship between change in free energy and change in vapor pressure may be written

$$dG = v \, dp, \dots\dots\dots\dots\dots\dots\dots\dots\dots\dots\dots\dots (20)$$

where v and p are the volume and pressure, respectively, of 1 mole of vapor at temperature T. Hence, if p_1 is the initial equilibrium vapor pressure of the free water and p_2 the pressure after adsorption, the change in free energy is, for such a finite change,

$$\Delta G = \int_{p_1}^{p_2} v \, dp \; \dots\dots\dots\dots\dots\dots\dots\dots\dots\dots (21)$$

Assuming that the vapor behaves as an ideal gas, we have

$$v = \frac{RT}{p} . \quad \dots\dots\dots\dots\dots\dots\dots\dots\dots\dots\dots\dots (22)$$

Thus,

$$\Delta G = RT \int_{p_1}^{p_2} \frac{dp}{p} ; \qquad \qquad \qquad (23)$$

or,

$$\Delta G = RT \ln p_2/p_1 \text{ (cal per mole of water)}. \qquad \qquad (24)$$

This is the change in free energy when 1 mole of free water, or water vapor, at vapor pressure p_1 is adsorbed by a paste under conditions such that the pressure after adsorption is p_2. The decrease in free energy when the initial vapor pressure is the saturation pressure, p_s, and the final pressure is a smaller pressure, p, is given—in calories per g of water taken up—by the following equation:

$$\Delta G = - \frac{RT}{M} \ln p/p_s ; \qquad \qquad \qquad (25)$$

where M = the molecular weight of the adsorbate.

For our experiments,

$M = 18.02$ (molecular weight of water)

$R = 1.986$ cal per deg. per mole

$T = 298$ K.

Using these values and letting $\ln p/p_s = 2.303 \ log_{10} \ p/p_s$, we obtain

$$- \Delta G = - 75.6 \ log_{10} \ p/p_s \text{ cal per g of water}. \qquad (26)$$

It is to be noted that the solid phase is not directly represented in this equation for reduction in free energy (eq. 26). It is indirectly represented by the difference between p and p_s. Since temperature is constant and since condensed water is present, p can be smaller than p_s only through the action of a solute or some agency external to the water. The nature of this agency is immaterial so far as the thermodynamic relationships are concerned.

Estimation of decrease in entropy from experimental results

From eq. (19) it is seen that the decrease in entropy can be obtained from the difference between $- \Delta G$ and $- Q$. In the present case, $- Q = Q_a$, the net heat of adsorption in cal per g of adsorbent, an integral quantity.* But the decrease in free energy, $- \Delta G$, is given by eq. (26) as the calories lost per gram of water adsorbed when 1 gram of water having vapor pressure p_s is added to a large quantity of paste having vapor pressure p, the quantity of paste being so large that the added gram of water does not change the vapor pressure. In other words, $- \Delta G$ is a differential. It is therefore necessary to obtain the differential net heat of adsorption in cal per g of adsorbed water. This can be done by differentiating the empirical Q_a vs. w relationship.

---

*Note that the tabulated values of Q_a, the heat lost, are given as positive quantities. This is customary in recording adsorption data. Hence, the recorded values must be multiplied by $- 1$ before being used in the thermodynamic equations in place of Q.

The Q_a vs. w relationship found in these experiments is similar to those found by Katz[6] and others for various materials. Katz found that these curves could be represented by empirical equations of the form

$$Q_a = \frac{Aw}{B + w}, \quad \dots\dots\dots\dots\dots\dots\dots\dots\dots\dots\dots\dots (27)$$

where
Q_a = net heat of adsorption, cal per g of solid,
w = vapor adsorbed, g per g of solid, and
A and B = constants for a given system.

Differentiation gives

$$\frac{dQ_a}{dw} = \frac{AB}{(B + w)^2} \quad \dots\dots\dots\dots\dots\dots\dots\dots\dots (28)$$

The constants A and B of eq. (27) and (28) can be obtained by using the following form of eq. (27):

$$\frac{w}{Q_a} = \frac{B}{A} + \frac{w}{A}$$

This shows that if experimental values of w/Q_a are plotted against w, a straight line should result, from which the constants can be evaluated. The data for the two pastes used in this study are given in Table 4-3.

The corresponding values of w/V_m and w/Q_a up to $p = 0.81\ p_s$ are plotted in Fig. 4-8. The points for 16186 lie close to a straight line. Those for 16189 appear more erratic, but between $w/V_m = 1$ and $w/V_m = 2$ they seem to follow the same line as the other points. At any rate,

TABLE 4-3—DATA FOR EVALUATING CONSTANTS OF NET HEAT OF ADSORPTION EQUATION

	Cement 16186			Cement 16189		
p/p_s	$\dfrac{Q_a}{V_m}$ cal/g	$\dfrac{w}{V_m}$	$\dfrac{w}{Q_a}$ g/cal $\times 10^3$	$\dfrac{Q_a}{V_m}$ cal/g	$\dfrac{w}{V_m}$	$\dfrac{w}{Q_a}$ g/cal $\times 10^3$
0.0	0	0		0	0	
0.081	239	0.76	3.18	180	0.72	4.0
0.161	279	0.95	3.40	268	0.98	3.66
0.322	342	1.37	4.00	327	1.34	4.10
0.39	376	1.55	4.12	360	1.54	4.28
0.46	364	1.71	4.70	375	1.72	4.59
0.53	388	1.89	4.88	380	1.86	4.90
0.60	398	2.04	5.13	406	2.08	5.12
0.70	428	2.48	5.80	456	2.60	5.70
0.81	442	3.00	6.79	501	3.40	6.80
0.88	474	3.48	7.34	535	4.15	7.76
0.96	534	4.28	8.02	552	5.50	9.95
1.00	572	5.50	9.6	572	8.65	15.10

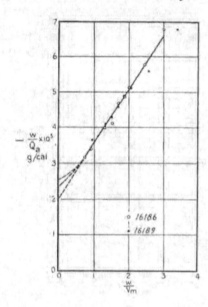

Fig. 4-8—Plot for evaluating constants of net heat of adsorption equation.

Legend in graph: $\circ$ 16186 ; $\bullet$ 16189 ; x-axis $\frac{w}{V_m}$; y-axis $-\frac{w}{Q_a} \times 10^5$ g/cal

no distinction between the two pastes seems justifiable on the basis of these data alone.

The constants for the line as drawn are

$$\frac{B}{A} = 0.0020 \quad ; \quad \frac{A}{B} = 500;$$

$$\frac{V_m}{A} = 0.00152 \quad ; \quad A = 655\, V_m\, ;$$

$$B = 1.31 V_m \quad ; \quad AB = 858 V_m{}^2.$$

Hence, for these experimental data,

$$\frac{Q_a}{V_m} = \frac{655\, w/V_m}{1.31 + w/V_m}, \dots\dots\dots\dots\dots (29)$$

and

$$\frac{dQ_a}{dw} = \frac{858}{(1.31 + w/V_m)^2} \dots\dots\dots\dots (30)$$

Solutions of eq. (26) and (30) are given in Table 4-4 and in Fig. 4-9. These data show, for example, that if 1 g of water were added to a very large quantity of paste having a water content corresponding to $p = 0.2$ p_s, the quantity of paste being so large that the addition of 1 g would not change the vapor pressure, the total heat evolved would be 154 cal per g of water. Of this total, 53 cal per g would be due to the change in free energy. The curves and tabulated data based on the equations represent

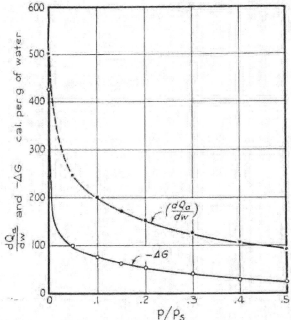

Fig. 4-9—Comparison of differential net heat of adsorption with change in free energy.

—ΔG from eq. (25).

$\frac{dQa}{dw}$ from eq. (29)

the original data rather closely between $p = 0.05\ p_s$ and $p = 0.5\ p_s$ at least for 16186. For lower pressures, the trend of the dQ_a/dw curve is uncertain. This will be discussed more fully below.

Table 4-5 gives solutions of eq. (19) and thus gives the change in unavailable energy and entropy for the same data as Table 4-4. These data show that for the pressure range $p = 0.05\ p_s$ to $p = 0.5\ p_s$, from 60 to 70 percent of the heat-loss represents unavailable energy. For adsorption of water on cellulose over the same pressure range, Babbitt[7] found the change in unavailable energy to be 44 to 60 percent of the total. This may be taken to indicate that when water is adsorbed by cement paste, it undergoes a similar but somewhat greater change than it does when it is adsorbed by cellulose.

Significance of change of entropy

The decrease in entropy is shown in the last column of Table 4-5. That these are relatively large changes in entropy may be judged by comparing them with the change in entropy of water in the various physical and chemical processes given below:

(1) For water at 25 C an increase in pressure from 50 atm. to 400 atm. causes a decrease in entropy of 0.0023 cal per g per deg.[8]

(2) The transition of water to ice at 0 C is accompanied by an entropy decrease of 0.29 cal per g per deg.[9]

TABLE 4-4—COMPUTATION OF DIFFERENTIAL NET HEAT
OF ADSORPTION dQ_a/dw AND FREE ENERGY ΔG

$$\frac{dQ_a}{dw} = \frac{858}{(1.31 + w/V_m)^2} \; ; \; -\Delta G = -75.6 \, log_{10} p/p_s$$

p/p_s	w/V_m*	$1.31 + w/V_m$	$(1.31+ w/V_m)^2$	$\frac{dQ_a}{dw}$	$-\Delta G$
>0	---	---	---	500	---
.05	0.57	1.86	3.46	248	98
.10	0.76	2.07	4.28	200	76
.15	0.92	2.23	4.97	172	62
.20	1.05	2.36	5.57	154	53
.30	1.30	2.61	6.81	126	40
.40	1.52	2.83	8.01	107	30
.50	1.75	3.06	9.36	92	23

*Values taken from curve in Fig. 4-2.

TABLE 4-5—COMPUTATION OF DECREASE IN UNAVAILABLE
ENERGY, $-T\Delta S$ AND DECREASE IN ENTROPY, $-\Delta S$

$$-T\Delta S = \frac{dQ_a}{dw} + \Delta G$$

$$T = 298 \, K$$

p/p_s	w/V_m*	$\frac{dQ_a}{dw}$ cal/g	$-\Delta G$ cal/g	$-T\Delta S$ cal/g	$-\Delta S$ cal/g deg
>0	---	500	---	---	---
.05	0.57	248	98	150	0.50
.10	0.76	200	76	124	0.42
.15	0.92	172	62	110	0.37
.20	1.05	154	53	101	0.34
.30	1.30	126	40	86	0.29
.40	1.52	107	30	77	0.26
.50	1.75	92	23	69	0.23

*Values taken from curve in Fig. 4-2. $T\Delta S$ from eq. (19).

(3) At 25 C, a pressure of about 9000 atm. will change liquid water to a solid of density 1.35 (specific volume 0.74) known as ice VI. This change in phase is accompanied by a decrease in entropy of 0.26 cal per g per deg.[9]

(4) The entropy change of a system comprising $CaSO_4$ and H_2O when the $CaSO_4$ acquires two molecules of water of hydration can be computed as follows:[10]

Compound	Entropy, S, at 25 C
$CaSO_4$....	25.5
$2H_2O$....	33.5
Total....	59.0 cal/deg
$CaSO_4.2H_2O$....	46.4
	$-\Delta S = 12.6$ cal/deg

If this decrease in entropy of the system is ascribed wholly to the water, as is done in the calculations for adsorption, $-\Delta S$ in cal per g of water is

$$\frac{12.6}{2 \times 18} = 0.35 \text{ cal per g per deg}$$

(5) For the system Na_2SO_4 and H_2O reacting to form $Na_2SO_4.10H_2O$, the change in entropy of the system expressed in terms of the water is, when computed as above, also -0.35 cal per g per deg.[10]

(6) For the system CaO and H_2O, reacting to form $Ca(OH)_2$, the change in entropy, computed and expressed as above, is -0.49 cal per g per. deg. [10a] *

A comparison of these figures with those in the last column of Table 4-5 shows that the data have the following indications with respect to the change of state of the water adsorbed in the low-pressure range indicated by the decrease in entropy:

(1) The change in entropy is far greater than could be produced by pressures lower than the pressure required for solidification of water at 25 C.

(2) The change in entropy is fully as great as that corresponding to the transition from normal liquid to ice VI, or to water of crystallization.

(3) The change in entropy for the water taken up at very low pressure, $p = 0.05 \, p_s$, may be as great as the change accompanying the change from normal water to hydroxyl groups chemically combined in $Ca(OH)_2$.

The third conclusion is less valid than the other two. As will be brought out below, there is reason to question whether eq. (27) and (28), on which Table 4-5 is based, are of the correct form for the low pressure range, about $p = 0.05 \, p_s$ and below. If it is not, the estimated $-\Delta S$ may be considerably in error in the direction of being too large. Evidence can be found to show that $-\Delta S$ reaches a maximum in absolute value below $p = 0.05 p_s$. At very low relative vapor pressures, the absolute value of ΔS may be about the same as that estimated for $p/p_s = 0.50$. This would indicate that the estimated decrease in entropy is the resultant of several factors and that the full significance of the entropy decrease cannot be seen until these factors are known in detail.

---

*In Part 2, in connection with Table 5, it was pointed out that the equilibrium relative vapor pressure of water over CaO may be much less than that given in the table. The evidence for this statement is found in the values for change in entropy and enthalpy for the system $CaO-H_2O$. (The enthalpy change is 847 cal/g of water. The equilibrium relative vapor pressure may be calculated by reversing the steps in the procedure for calculating the entropy change of adsorption. The result is $p/p_s = 5.6 \times 10^{-16}$. This is to be compared with 1.3×10^{-4} given in Table 5, Part 2. Although the calculated value may be somewhat in error, the error is not likely to be great enough to account for a million-fold difference. The experimental value is open to more question. It is derived from measurements of the relative efficiency of desiccants. The conditions were such as to warrant the conclusion that the value of p/p_s cannot exceed that given; the true value can be much less.

No evidence has been obtained in this laboratory that any of the desiccants listed in Table 5, Part 2, actually removed water from $Ca(OH)_2$. If the calculated value is accepted as being of the right order of magnitude, then the dehydration of $Ca(OH)_2$ by these desiccants would not be expected.

In general, the data indicate that some of the adsorbed water undergoes a pronounced modification, but the nature of the modification cannot be deduced from the data alone. In Part 3, reasons were given for considering the adsorption process to be a physical one—van der Waal's adsorption. These data are generally compatible with that view, although the estimated $-\Delta S$ values in the low pressure range appear to be rather larger than might be expected. Thus, the possibility of some of the water being taken up by a chemical process is not precluded by these data.

THE ENERGY OF BINDING OF WATER IN HARDENED PASTE

The heat of adsorption is a measure of the energy that must be supplied to enable adsorbed water molecules to break away from the force field of the adsorbent and become vapor. Similarly, the net heat of adsorption (dQ_a/dw) is a measure of the energy required to restore adsorbed water to the normal liquid state. That is, the net heat of adsorption is a measure of the energy of binding between the evaporable water and the solid phase. In the same way, the heat of reaction of the non-evaporable water is a measure of the energy of its binding.

In this connection the value of dQ_a/dw when evaporable water = zero is of special interest. According to eq. (27), this value is equal to A/B. For the data of Fig. 4-9, $A/B = 500$ cal per g. Steinberger[11] remarked that when the vapor pressure is near zero, the surface is so sparsely populated with adsorbed molecules that the molecules can be regarded as having no effect on each other, and therefore the net heat of adsorption at the limit where, in this case, w/V_m approaches zero is a measure of the binding energy of the evaporable water molecules in the gel. In this case it has the further significance that it should also be a measure of the energy of binding of the *least firmly bound part of the non-evaporable water*. This will become evident when it is remembered that in Part 2, Tables 3 and 4, it was shown that the water content of the sample dried over $Mg(ClO_4)_2 \cdot 2H_2O$ is a point on a smooth curve relating water content to vapor pressure. If the chosen drying agent had been P_2O_5, the non-evaporable water contents would have been 80 percent of the present values, and the evaporable water contents would have been correspondingly higher. For example, in Fig. 4-6, the non-evaporable water content would have been 0.163 instead of 0.204. If the heat of reaction of the increment of water $(0.204 - 0.163)$ is the same as the average for all the non-evaporable water, the heat of solution of the dry sample would have been 555 cal per g, represented by the point of intersection of line B and the ordinate at $w = 0.163$. If the heat of reaction of this increment is less than the average, the heat of solution would fall below line B.*

Similarly, had a desiccant of higher vapor pressure been used, the non-evaporable water content would have been higher and the heat of solution of the dried sample lower, the point falling somewhere on the curve now representing evaporable water. The average heat of reaction of the non-evaporable water would have appeared lower.

It is thus clear that the *maximum* net heat of adsorption cannot be greater than the *minimum* heat of reaction of the non-evaporable water. Since the minimum heat of reaction of the non-evaporable water cannot be greater than the average for all the non-evaporable water, the maximum net heat of adsorption cannot exceed the average heat of reaction of the non-evaporable water and is probably less.

This is rather positive evidence that eq. (28) cannot represent the data all the way to $w = 0$. Hence, the value 500 cal per g for $w = 0$ obtained from eq. (30) cannot be accepted; it is too high.† This conclusion is represented by the curved dotted lines in Fig. 4-8. The line terminating at $w/Q_a = 2.40 \times 10^{-3}$ g per cal corresponds to the average heat of reaction of the non-evaporable water in sample 16186, 416 cal per g. It is therefore the *lowest* possible terminus for the line representing that sample. The other point, at 2.55×10^{-3} g per cal, is the lowest possible terminus for sample 16189. It corresponds to the average heat of reaction, 392 cal per g of non-evaporable water.

As discussed in Part 2, one microcrystalline hydrate known to occur in hardened paste is $Ca(OH)_2$. The heat of formation of this compound from CaO and H_2O is about 15,260 cal per mole.[12] Expressed on the basis of the water, as for the net heat of adsorption or the heat of reaction of non-evaporable water, this amounts to about 847 cal per g of water. This figure is to be compared with the 392 and 416 cal per g of water found as the heat of reaction of the non-evaporable water for the two paste samples. It is thus apparent that a considerable portion of the non-evaporable water in hardened paste has much less energy of binding than the part that is in $Ca(OH)_2$. From the relationship pointed out above it follows also that the most firmly bound adsorbed water is loosely bound as compared with that in $Ca(OH)_2$.

The total net heat of adsorption has already been shown to be about $572V_m$ cal per g of sample. The *average* for the gel water alone is therefore about $572V_m \div 4V_m = 143$ cal per g of gel water. We can now observe that the *maximum* net heat of adsorption is of the order of 400 cal per g (392 cal per g of water for one paste and 416 cal per g for the

---

*It could not fall very far below line B, however, since the curve would still have to pass through the point at $w = 0.204$ in line with the smooth curve. It is estimated that the lowest point in Fig. 4-6 that would meet this requirement would be at about 550 cal per g and $w = 0.163$.

†This conclusion may be true also with respect to the use made of eq. (28) by Katz, Steinberger, Babbitt, and others.

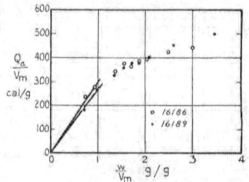

other).   How much of the adsorbed water has this relatively higher energy of binding cannot be told from these data. However, an estimate can be made of the *average* binding energy of the first layer with the aid of Fig. 4-10.   This is a plot of Q_a/V_m vs. w/V_m for both sets of data up to about $w/V_m = 3$. This shows that the average net heat of adsorption of the first layer is about 300 cal per g of water for 16186 and about 270 cal per g for 16189.   This estimate embodies the assumption that all the water taken on in the low-pressure range is held in the first layer, that is, that the layers form consecutively as the pressure is raised. This is probably not true.   According to the B.E.T. theory, when $w/V_m = 1.0$, $p =$ about $0.2\ p_s$ and about 85 percent of the water would be in the first layer at this pressure.   The rest would be in higher layers.   Such a correction, very doubtful as to accuracy, would indicate an average net heat of adsorption of about 320 to 350 cal per g of water in the first layer.

Data published by Harkins and Jura[13] are instructive in this respect. These authors found, by direct calorimetric measurement, the net heat of adsorption of water on anatase (titanium dioxide) to be as follows:

Average for:

1st layer	364 cal per g of water
2nd layer	76
3rd layer	25
4th layer	4.4
5th layer	2.2 (?)
All above 5	1.7 (?)
Total	473 cal per g of water

Since these quantities were computed from experimental data on the assumption that the layers formed consecutively, the average per layer is directly comparable with the figures obtained from Fig. 4-10 without correction for the overlapping of layer-formation. Thus, 364 cal per g for the first layer adsorbed on anatase is comparable with 270 to 300 for the first layer on dried paste. At least a part of the difference is due to the presence of air in our experiments, for the adsorption on anatase occurred in a high-vacuum system. The general indication is that the first layer of water on cement paste is bound with about the same energy as the first layer on anatase.

A comparison of the average heats for successive layers is not feasible because the shapes of our curves are undoubtedly influenced by capillary condensation and the presence of air.

NET HEAT OF ADSORPTION AND C OF THE B.E.T. EQ. (A)

As previously indicated, the constant C of the B.E.T. eq. A is related to the heat of adsorption as follows,

$$C = ke^{\frac{Q_1 - Q_L}{RT}}$$

where

Q_1 = heat of adsorption for the first layer, cal per mole,

Q_L = heat of liquefaction, cal per mole

R = gas constant = 1.986 cal per mole per deg

T = absolute temperature

k = constant

Brunauer et al. assumed that constant k does not differ significantly from unity, and, hence, that

$$Q_1 - Q_L = 2.303 \, RT \, log_{10} C$$

This assumption no longer appears valid in the light of the derivation of the equation by statistical-mechanical methods recently reported by Cassie.[23] On the contrary, it appears that k is of the order 0.02 or less. It follows that $(Q_1 - Q_L)$ calculated on the assumption that k is unity must be too low. However, in some cases, k might approach unity so that $(Q_1 - Q_L)$ calculated on this assumption would approach the experimental values.

The experimental data obtained by the air-stream method show that, for cement pastes, about 90 percent of the values of C lie between 17 and 23. For the particular samples used in the calorimeter tests, $C = 22$. On the assumption that k is unity, $C = 22$ corresponds to 102 cal per g. This is to be compared with 472 cal per g found experimentally. That is, the value of k appears to be far less than unity.

Similar results were obtained in the adsorption of water on non-porous adsorbents by Harkins and Boyd, as shown by the following data:[14]

Kind of solid	Q_a (B.E.T.) cal/g	Q_a (Observed) cal/g
TiO_2 (anatase)	133	445
SiO_2 (quartz)	139	511
$BaSO_4$	178	416

Here also k must be much less than unity to account for the results.

The analysis made by Cassie clarifies somewhat the significance of C, making it appear as a factor which expresses the distribution of molecules between the first and higher layers and placing less emphasis upon its relationship to the heat of adsorption. At the same time, it clarifies the significance of constant V_m. So long as k was assumed to be unity, the discrepancies between calculated and experimental net heat of adsorption raised doubts about the acceptance of V_m on theoretical grounds. Now it appears that this doubt can be dissolved to a considerable extent, though not completely. In any case, it may be noted that the acceptance of V_m as a measure of surface area, discussed in Part 3, rests mainly on the outcome of empirical tests, rather than on literal acceptance of the assumptions used in the derivation of the B.E.T. equation.

SWELLING PRESSURE

Limited-swelling gels

When some kinds of gel are placed in contact with a suitable liquid, they imbibe liquid and swell until they have become molecular or colloidal solutions. This is called *unlimited swelling*. The same gels with another type of liquid may imbibe only a limited amount and show correspondingly *limited swelling*. Such observations suggest that the tendency to swell on contact with a liquid is a manifestation of a tendency of the material to dissolve or at least to peptize to the colloidal-solution state. When swelling is of the limited type, the tendency of the liquid to penetrate and disperse the solid is evidently opposed by cohesive forces that bind the mass together.

Portland cement gel in water belongs to the limited-swelling class. Like other gels of its class, it is not able to swell beyond the dimensions established at the time of its formation. However, it will shrink on loss of evaporable water and swell when evaporable water is regained. As mentioned elsewhere (see Part 2) it undergoes a permanent shrinkage on first drying; that is, only a part of the initial shrinkage is reversible.

When the tendency of a swelling body to expand is resisted, the body may be able to exert great force. For example, dry wooden wedges driven into rock seams will split the rock when the wedges are allowed to take up water, a method of quarrying used by the ancient Egyptians.[15]

It is thus understood that swelling is a movement of the solid units of the gel that can be prevented only by suitable application of force. The magnitude of the force required to prevent swelling, the so-called swelling pressure, can be ascertained from a consideration of the free-energy changes that occur when a swelling body takes up a liquid at a given constant temperature.

Idealized cement gel

In the following derivation it will be assumed, contrary to fact, that the solid particles of the cement gel are not interconnected. Also, the possible effects of any non-gel constituents will be ignored. It will be assumed that these disconnected gel-elements are colloidal particles and that they are packed together in such a way that all interstitial space is filled with adsorbed water. Thus we assume that we are dealing with a highly concentrated colloidal solution. These assumptions make it possible to ascertain the conditions governing the movements of adsorbed water in an actual paste, without the modifying effects of elastic forces in the solid phase. Also, it eliminates the complication introduced by the presence of capillary space. This will be dealt with later.

The thermodynamics of the swelling of such an idealized gel can be treated as if the gel were a true solution. The swelling pressure is related to vapor pressure in the same way that osmotic pressure is related to vapor pressure. The following treatment follows Glasstone's treatment of osmotic pressure.[16] (See also references (7) and (11)).

Derivation of equation for swelling force

Imagine a vessel containing the idealized gel, its water content such as to give a vapor pressure less than that of pure water at the same temperature. If pure water were placed in contact with this gel, the gel would imbibe water and swell until the vapor pressure of the water within the gel became equal to the vapor pressure of pure water. If the external pressure on the gel (which acts alike on both the solid and the liquid phases) were increased sufficiently, the vapor pressure of the water in the gel could thereby be made equal to that of free water at the same temperature. Under this higher external pressure, the gel would be unable to imbibe water and swell. The increase in pressure required to prevent swelling when a dry or partially dry gel has access to free water is, as said above, defined as the swelling pressure.

Let P_s = existing external pressure,

P = external pressure on the gel when it is in equilibrium with free water under external pressure P_s,

$P - P_s = \Delta P$ = swelling pressure,

G_s = free energy of pure water at external pressure P_s, and

G = free energy of adsorbed water at external pressure P_s.

The increase in external pressure required to equalize the free energies of the adsorbed and free water is given by the following expression

$$G_s = G + \int_{P_s}^{P} \left(\frac{\partial G}{\partial P}\right)_T dP \quad \dots\dots\dots\dots\dots (31)$$

For a system such as this the change in free energy with pressure at constant temperature can be shown to be equal to the rate of change in volume of the system with change in water content—on the molar basis, the "partial molal volume" of the adsorbed water, $\overline{V}$. That is,

$$\left(\frac{\Delta G}{\Delta P}\right)_T = \overline{V} \quad \dots\dots\dots\dots\dots\dots\dots\dots (32)$$

Hence,

$$G_s = G + \int_{P_s}^{P} \overline{V}\, dP \quad \dots\dots\dots\dots\dots (33)$$

The increase in free energy of the adsorbed water that takes place when the external pressure is increased can be expressed in terms of the corresponding changes in vapor pressure. If

G = free energy of adsorbed water under initial external pressure, P_s and G_s = free energy of adsorbed water under external pressure P, then $G_s - G = \Delta G$ = increase in free energy when external pressure is raised from P_s to P. The respective free-energies are related to vapor pressures as follows:

$$G = G_r + RT \ln p/p_r \quad \dots\dots\dots\dots\dots (34)$$

and

$$G_s = G_r + RT \ln p_s/p_r \quad \dots\dots\dots\dots\dots (35)$$

where

G_r = free energy of free water in a chosen reference state, and

p_r = vapor pressure of free water in the chosen reference state.

Hence,

$$G_s - G = \Delta G = RT \ln p_s/p \quad \dots\dots\dots\dots\dots (36)$$

and, by eq. (33)

$$\int_{P_s}^{P} \overline{V}\, dP = -RT \ln p/p_s \quad \dots\dots\dots\dots\dots (37)$$

An exact solution of eq. (37) for swelling pressure would require knowledge of the relationship between the specific volume of the adsorbed water and change in external pressure. This relationship is unknown; in a real paste containing capillary water as well as gel water it must be rather complicated. Although the water is densified by adsorption forces in a partially dried sample containing capillary water, it is also subjected to capillary forces that tend to extend it. Without knowledge of the relationship, it is necessary to assume $\overline{V}$ to be independent of pressure and hence a constant. On this assumption, integrating eq. 37 gives

$$P - P_s = \Delta P = -\frac{RT}{\overline{V}} \ln p/p_s \ldots \ldots \ldots \ldots \ldots (38)$$

In terms of ordinary logarithms and specific volume, $\overline{V}$ becomes Mv_f and the swelling pressure becomes

$$\Delta P = -\frac{RT}{Mv_f} 2.303 \, log_{10} p/p_s. \ldots \ldots \ldots \ldots \ldots \ldots (39)$$

Solutions of eq. 39 are given in Table 4-6. The value of specific volume of adsorbed water used in these computations is 0.87, the mean specific volume of the gel water. (See Part 5). This value is no doubt too low for swelling at high vapor pressures and too high at low pressures, but it should be preferable to the specific volume of free water, ordinarily used for this computation.

TABLE 4-6—COMPUTED POTENTIAL SWELLING PRESSURE

$\Delta P = -\frac{RT}{Mv_f} 2.303 \, log_{10} p/p_s$; $T = 298K$; $M = 18.02$; $v_f = 0.87$; $R = 82.07$ cc, atm per deg per mole; $\Delta P = -3593 \, log_{10} p/p_s$ atmospheres or $\Delta P = -52.810 \, log_{10} p/p_s$ psi

p/p_s	Swelling pressure, ΔP	
	atmospheres	psi
1.00	0	0
0.95	80	1178
0.90	165	2419
0.80	348	5118
0.70	557	8181
0.60	797	11710
0.50	1081	15900
0.40	1430	21010
0.30	1879	27620

Computed values such as those given in Table 4-6 have never been satisfactorily tested experimentally, owing to experimental difficulties. For an idealized gel, there is little reason to question the results, except for the error introduced by assuming the specific volume of the adsorbed water to remain constant. At least, they are in line with general observations as to the enormous forces that swelling bodies are able to develop when the tendency to swell is restrained.

It should be understood that the pressures indicated cannot exist unless the movement of swelling is *prevented*; the so-called swelling pressure is really the *potential* pressure. Also, the potential pressures given correspond only to a condition wherein a specimen at initial vapor pressure p is exposed to liquid water or to vapor of pressure p_s. If the specimen is exposed to vapor having a pressure p' such that p' is greater than p but smaller than p_s, the potential swelling pressure may be computed from the pressure ratio p/p'.

Relation of idealized behavior to that of cement paste or concrete

A hardened cement paste or concrete differs from the idealized gel discussed above. The gel in the paste is not composed of discrete particles but is apparently a coherent, porous mass held together by solid-to-solid bonds. Moreover, it contains microcrystals and aggregate particles that resist the shrinkage of the gel. Consequently, swelling (or shrinkage) in concrete is partially opposed by the elastic forces developed throughout the mass according to the relationship

$$\Delta P_e = \alpha\, \Delta V , \quad\dots\dots\dots\dots\dots\dots\dots\dots\dots\dots(40)$$

where

α = the coefficient of compressibility,

ΔP_e = change in elastic force, and

ΔV = change in over-all volume of concrete.

Thus, a change in volume induced by the swelling or shrinking of the gel may be partially opposed by a force that is, presumably, proportional to the change in volume.

However, swelling pressure, as defined above, should be very nearly the same for concrete as for the idealized gel, for if the swelling is *prevented*, ΔV of eq. (40) is zero and the increase in external pressure required to prevent swelling is only that required by eq. (39). However, the required increase in external pressure per unit *gross* area of concrete may be less than ΔP of eq. (39) if the adsorbed water is effective over less than 100 percent of the cross-sectional area of the concrete. In other words, the maximum externally manifested swelling pressure could be less than the theoretical, but not greater.

MECHANISM OF SHRINKING AND SWELLING

Volume change as a liquid-adsorption phenomenon

When volume change is regarded as a swelling phenomenon, as was done in deriving eq. (39), the force is considered to arise from attraction between the liquid and the solid surface. In regions where the solid surfaces are separated slightly, the solid-to-solid attraction tends to draw the solid surfaces together, and at the same time the solid-to-liquid attraction tends to draw the water in between the surfaces. If the water is exposed, its tendency to evaporate or its surface tension, or both, give rise to an opposing force that tends to draw the water out of the adsorbed layer. Thus, the adsorbed water in the gel is the subject of competing forces, and when these opposing forces are in equilibrium the rate of volume change is zero.

From this conception of the mechanism of shrinking and swelling it would appear that the over-all volume change of the paste should be proportional to the change in spacing of the solid bodies that are held apart by adsorbed water. This spacing should decrease as adsorbed water is withdrawn and increase as adsorbed water is added. Since the first layer is much more strongly held than the higher layers, the volume change should be of the order of magnitude that could be accounted for by changing the spacing of the particles by only 2 molecular diameters, about 5 or 6 Ångstrom units, per particle.

To see whether this is within the bounds of possibility, we may consider the data on the particle-size of the solid phase. Imagine the solid matter to be made up of equal spheres having a specific surface equal to that of the hardened paste. The spheres are in some characteristic array that encloses voids equal to the observed pore-volume in the paste. The addition of an adsorbed layer of water will be regarded as equivalent to increasing the sphere radii and hence their center-to-center spacing. The corresponding change in over-all volume is related to the change in radius by the well known relationship for small changes,

$$\frac{\Delta V}{V} = \frac{3\Delta r}{r} , \dots\dots\dots\dots\dots\dots\dots\dots\dots\dots\dots\dots (41)$$

where

V = over-all volume,
ΔV = change in over-all volume,
r = sphere-radius, and
Δr = change in sphere radius.

When hardened paste is dried to equilibrium with a very low vapor pressure, virtually all the adsorbed water is removed. Hence, the possible change in volume may be computed from the thickness of the adsorbed layer and the particle-size of the solid phase. The thickness of the adsorbed layer may be conservatively estimated at one water-molecule diameter, or about 2.7Å. The equivalent sphere radius of the paste particles is estimated at 70Å (see Part 3). Hence,

$$\frac{\Delta V}{V} = \frac{3 \times 2.7}{70} = 0.16 .$$

That is, a change in particle spacing corresponding to the addition or loss of one molecular layer per particle would, under the assumptions given, result in an over-all volume change of 16 percent.

Shrinkage measurements on thin, neat-cement slabs, $w_o/c = 0.5$ by weight, showed a linear shortening of 0.7 percent when all the evaporable water was removed. This corresponds to a volume-shrinkage of about 2 percent, or about one-eighth the amount theoretically possible.

Thus, it appears that the loss or gain of the first adsorbed layer could more than account for the observed amount of volume change. The smallness of the observed volume change, relative to the calculated, could be explained as being due to the restraining effect of non-shrinking bodies embedded in the gel, and elastic forces developed at points where the gel particles are joined by solid-to-solid bonds.

However, the figures should not be taken too literally. If the particles composing the mass are not of equal size and shape, the above computation does not apply exactly. However, unless the simplifying assumption leads to as much as an eight-fold error, which seems unlikely, the conclusion that swelling could be due to changes in adsorbed water content is well within the limit of possibility.

* * * *

It should be observed particularly that by the theory outlined above the change in volume is not considered to be the result of forces acting on the solid phase. Instead, the change is assumed to be the result of an unbalance of the forces acting on the adsorbed water, and the consequent changes toward establishing an equilibrium between those forces.

Volume change as a capillary phenomenon

The shrinkage and swelling of rigid porous bodies that undergo volume changes much smaller than the corresponding changes in water content are regarded by some as capillary phenomena. Plummer and Dore,[17] for example, describe shrinkage of some soils as the result of tension in the capillary water. The reaction of this tension produces compressive stress in the solid phase and thus causes a reduction in volume or length. The force of capillary tension is given by the following equation[18].

$$F = \sigma \left(\frac{1}{r_1} + \frac{1}{r_2} \right) , \quad \dots\dots\dots\dots\dots\dots\dots (42)$$

where F = force of capillary tension,

σ = surface tension of water, and

r_1 and r_2 = principal radii of curvature of the menisci.

The curvature of the water surface is determined by the size and shape of the pores in the solid. Apparently the pores are such that as the water content of the body diminishes, the curvature (concavity) of the water surface increases (the radius decreases) and thus the shrinkage force increases.

Swelling on increase in water content can be accounted for by this theory only by assuming that shrinkage produces elastic strains and thus, when the shrinkage force is released, elastic recovery causes expansion.

When concrete undergoes shrinkage for the first time, it is unable to regain its original dimensions when it becomes resaturated. This can be accounted for in terms of the capillary theory by assuming that the stresses of shrinkage cause plastic flow in the solid phase. Hence, the permanent shrinkage, that is, the irreversible part of the initial shrinkage, can be regarded as permanent set.

According to the capillary-tension theory, any porous body containing small liquid-filled capillaries should contract as the water is removed until the evaporable water content and vapor pressure pass the limit below which a meniscus cannot exist. When this limit is passed, the body should expand. In concrete, this limit might be found at the water content corresponding to $p = 0.45\ p_s$; it certainly would be found at some pressure greater than $p = 0.00$. However, concrete and, as Plummer and Dore[17] point out, fine-grained soils shrink and swell with changes in moisture content even when the moisture content is too low for the existence of a meniscus. In concrete at least, shrinkage is at a maximum when the evaporable water content is zero.* It is thus apparent that the capillary theory alone will not suffice.

The relationship between tension in the capillary water and volume change of cement paste can be clarified with the aid of Fig. 4-11. Here, as in Part 3, the paste is represented by a model composed of spheres. Each sphere represents gel substance together with its associated voids (gel water) and non-gel solids. The interstices between the spheres represent capillary spaces outside the gel.†

Each sphere of Fig. 4-11 is supposed to contain gel water and be in a state of swelling determined by its water content. The water content

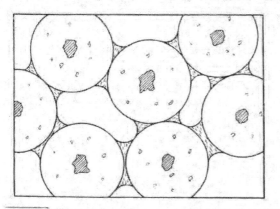

Fig. 4-11.

*Shrinkage probably increases further with loss of some of the non-evaporable water on heating in dry air. No data are available, however.

†It must be emphasized that the authors do not know the shapes of the solid bodies composing hardened paste (except for small amounts of microscopic material) or how they are linked together. The model is offered only because the conditions pictured thereby are such as to give the same adsorption characteristics as hardened cement paste.

in turn is determined by the existing vapor pressure. The capillary water is represented as lenses around points of contact or near-contact between the spheres. The volume of water in each lens is determined by the curvature and position of the spheres and the curvature of the water-surfaces. The latter is determined by the existing vapor pressure according to the relationship

$$\frac{1}{r_1} + \frac{1}{r_2} = -\frac{RT}{Mv_f\sigma} \ln p/p_s, \dots\dots\dots\dots\dots\dots (43)$$

where

r_1 and r_2 = principal radii of water-surface curvature,

σ = surface tension of the water,

and the other symbols have the same significance as before. Eq. (43) is the Kelvin equation discussed in Part 3.

For finite values of $\frac{1}{r_1} + \frac{1}{r_2}$ the capillary water is in tension, the tensile

force F being

$$F = \sigma\left(\frac{1}{r_1} + \frac{1}{r_2}\right) = -\frac{RT}{Mv_f} \ln p/p_s. \dots\dots\dots\dots\dots (44)$$

Comparison of this with the swelling-pressure equation (eq. 39) shows, as must needs be, that for equilibrium with a given vapor pressure p, capillary tension equals potential swelling pressure. That is, potential swelling force is the result of the tendency of water to enter the gel and capillary tension opposes that tendency; at equilibrium the two forces balance.*

Fig. 4-11 is drawn so as to depict a condition in which the gel is only partly covered with capillary-condensed water. In those areas not covered, the tendency of the water molecules to enter the gel is opposed by their tendency to evaporate. This has the same effect as tension arising from a meniscus.

It has been remarked before that the classification of gel water and capillary water adopted in this discussion is somewhat arbitrary. Some of the gel water may occupy space beyond the force-field of the solid material and may therefore be properly classed as capillary water. Nevertheless, even if a less arbitrary definition of capillary water were adopted, the concepts developed above would seem to apply: The spheres in Fig. 4-11 would represent the gel-substance together with whatever part of the total water-fillable space is predominantly in-

---

*Strictly speaking, the *free energies* of the adsorbed water and capillary water are equal at equilibrium, rather than the intensity of forces. That is, at equilibrium,
$$\Delta Pv_f = Fv_f. \quad \text{(Eq. (39) and (44))}$$
Since v_f for the adsorbed water is not the same as that for capillary water, ΔP and F cannot be exactly equal. The discussion in the text, though perhaps not rigorously correct, leads to easily visualized concepts that should not be misleading.

fluenced by van der Waal forces. The interstices would represent the rest of the water-fillable space in the paste.

Relationship between change in volume and change in water content

According to the concepts set forth above, swelling and shrinking should depend on the amount of adsorbed water in the gel. That is, presumably,

$$\Delta V = k \frac{\Delta w_a}{V_m} , \quad \dots \dots \dots \dots \dots \dots \dots \dots (45)$$

where k is a proportionality constant connecting change in over-all volume, ΔV, with change in the amount of adsorbed water, Δw_a, per unit surface of the gel, as represented by V_m. In the range of vapor pressures where capillary condensation takes place ($p > 0.45\ p_s$), any change in adsorbed-water content would be accompanied by a change in capillary water content, Δw_c, so that Δw_t, the change in *total* water content = $\Delta w_a + \Delta w_c$. Hence,

$$\Delta V = \frac{k}{V_m} (\Delta w_t - \Delta w_c) \quad \dots \dots \dots \dots \dots \dots (46)$$

It follows from this that the change in over-all volume will be related to the total change in water content differently in different samples according to the ratios of adsorbed water to capillary water in the respective samples. We should expect, therefore, that the greater the ratio $\Delta w_c/\Delta w_a$, the smaller the average $\Delta V/\Delta w_t$ for a specimen containing a given amount of gel.

A wholly satisfactory experimental check of this deduction cannot be offered at this time because available volume-change data pertain to shrinkage accompanying *desorption* whereas data leading to the evaluation of V_m and w_a are derived from adsorption measurements. However, shrinkage data bear out eq. (46) in a general way. The best available example of this is given in Fig. 4-12, representing a part of a study of shrinkage by Pickett.[19] It was found that the course of shrinkage during the drying of a concrete prism could be represented by an equation analogous to the heat-flow equation. If shrinkage were directly proportional to the concomitant water-loss, the same equation should apply also to water-loss. Pickett found, however, that the water-loss-vs.-time curve could not be represented by a single equation of the heat-flow type. But, by assuming that two classes of water are lost simultaneously during drying, the loss of water in each class following its own law, he could represent the experimental results with two equations of the heat-flow type. This is shown in Fig. 4-12. Pickett called the water that seemed to be unrelated to shrinkage W_a and the rest W_b. The relative proportions W_a and W_b assumed for the computations were arrived at by trial. In the figure the "a" water is represented

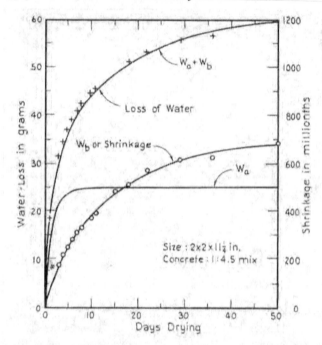

Fig. 4-12—Time rela-
tionships for shrinkage
and water-loss for a con-
crete specimen stored in
air at 50 per cent rela-
tive humidity.

by the computed curve marked W_a. The "b" water is represented by
the computed curve marked W_b, which also represents shrinkage when
appropriate ordinate scales are used. The sum of the ordinates of
these two curves gives the curve marked $W_a + W_b$. The crosses represent the observed total water-losses and the circles the observed shrinkage.

Thus Pickett's experimental data support the deduction expressed
in eq. (45) and (46) that volume change is directly proportional to a *part*
of the total water-loss. It remains for future experiments to prove or
disprove the deduction that the part responsible for volume change is
the adsorbed water. It is of interest in this connection that in Fig.
4-12 the "b" water constitutes 60 percent of the total lost at 50 percent
relative humidity. The highness of this proportion suggests that shrinkage is proportional to the loss of gel water rather than to the loss from
the first adsorbed layer only. This indicates that w_a of eq. (45) includes
about the first four layers of adsorbed water.

CAPILLARY FLOW AND MOISTURE DIFFUSION

In connection with this discussion of the thermodynamics of adsorption, about all that need be said about capillary flow and moisture
diffusion is that these phenomena take place as a result of inequalities
in free energy. Under isothermal conditions, capillary water will move

if the effective radius of curvature (see eq. (42)) is not the same on all exposed surfaces of a continuous body of capillary water. In Fig. 4-11 it is apparent that the addition of water, by condensation or otherwise, to the outer concave water-surfaces, would decrease the curvature of those surfaces. Water would therefore flow inward until the inner water-surfaces would have acquired the same curvature as the outer.

Where capillary water is absent, adsorbed water will move along any continuous surface if a gradient in the free energy of the adsorbed water exists. If an inequality in free energy exists between water on disconnected areas, the transfer of water will occur by distillation through the vapor phase. If surface migration and distillation are both physically possible, both will occur simultaneously. However, in an extremely fine-pored substance such as the gel in hardened paste, most of the transfer is believed to be effected through surface migration.

Inequalities in free energy

Inequalities in free energy under isothermal conditions arise from inequalities in moisture content, as shown indirectly by the water-content-vs.-vapor-pressure isotherms shown in Part 2. Hardened cement paste is of such nature that a change in moisture content of a given region in the paste, however slight the change may be, changes the free energy of the water in that region.*

Inequalities in free energy under isothermal conditions may also arise from deformations of the solid phase. In Fig. 4-11 we can see that if the spacing of any pair of spheres were changed, the surface curvature of the water lens would likewise change. This would require a redistribution of moisture to restore equality in free energy of the capillary water throughout the system. Also, a change in external pressure acting on the adsorbed water would change the free energy of the adsorbed water, as indicated by eq. (32) and (33).

Thus inequalities in stress and strain produce inequalities in the free energies of both the adsorbed water and capillary water and thereby induce redistributions of moisture within the mass. This, as has been pointed out by Lynam,[20] Carlson,[22] and others, is an important factor in the gradual yielding of concrete under sustained stress known as creep or plastic flow. The changes in moisture distribution cause localized shrinkings and swellings with consequent changes in the deformation of the body as a whole.

EFFECT OF TEMPERATURE CHANGES

The experimental part of these studies has not included measurements of the effect of temperature changes. However, some of these

---

*If, however, the external pressure on the adsorbed water changes at the same time, the relationship between water content and vapor pressure will not be the same as when external pressure remains constant. See later discussion.

effects can be deduced qualitatively with the aid of the theories and principles introduced above.

Effect on swelling

It was shown in eq. (44) that at equilibrium the capillary tension equals the potential swelling pressure. That is,

$$\Delta P = F = \sigma \left[\frac{1}{r_1} + \frac{1}{r_2} \right] = -\frac{RT}{Mv_f} \ln p/p_s \dots \dots \dots \dots (47)$$

Since an increase in temperature causes an expansion of the adsorbed water, the surface curvature of the water in the lenses must decrease. Moreover, the surface tension of water decreases with increase in temperature. Hence, the capillary tension must decrease with increase in temperature, provided the water content remains constant. This in turn would mean that an increase in temperature would cause expansion owing to swelling, in addition to the thermal expansion. However, if the specimen is initially saturated, no change in swelling pressure can occur because for this condition capillary tension is zero, or insignificantly small. Obviously, if the specimen contains no evaporable water, no swelling due to moisture can occur when the temperature is increased.

Evidence of this may be found in data published by Meyers.[21] The coefficients of thermal expansion of neat cement and concrete prisms were measured at various degrees of saturation, with results as shown in Table 4-7.

TABLE 4-7—MEYERS' DATA ON THERMAL EXPANSION
FOR SATURATED AND PARTLY SATURATED SPECIMENS

(Temperature range 70 to 120 F)

Type of material	Thermal coefficient in millionths for condition indicated	
	Sealed storage for 9 mo.	After soaking for 1 week
Normal portland cement	10.3	5.7
Concrete (flint aggregate)	8.1	4.9
Cement-sand mortar 1:1	9.2	6.3
High-C_3S cement	11.4	5.6

Note that the sealed specimens* show much greater expansion than the same specimens after soaking. According to the foregoing discussion, the figures in the last column represent the true thermal coefficient of the solid phase, whereas those in the first column represent the combined effect of thermal expansion and swelling caused by the decrease in swelling pressure.

---

*The specimens were stored in copper-foil jackets with soldered seams. Even though sealed they could not remain fully saturated.

It was stated above that if all the evaporable water is removed, a rise in temperature would not cause swelling. This too is confirmed by Meyers' data, as shown in Table 4-8. These data show that driving out all the evaporable water (or most of it) reduced the thermal coefficient of a specimen below that of the same specimen in the partially saturated state. Comparison of Tables 4-7 and 4-8 indicates that the thermal coefficient for the "bone-dry" and saturated states are about equal.

TABLE 4-8—MEYERS' DATA ON THERMAL EXPANSION—
EFFECT OF EXTREME DESICCATION

(Temperature range 70 to 120 F)

Type of material	Thermal coefficient in millionths for condition indicated	
	Before drying	Dried 1 week at 100 C
High early strength cement	9.1	6.0
White cement	10.4	6.5
Normal portland cement	8.0	6.0
Concrete (limestone aggregate)	4.1	2.1

Meyers found that the introduction of a liquid that does not cause swelling, kerosene, did not change the thermal coefficient appreciably.*

Effect on diffusion

If temperature gradients are established in a concrete mass, water must move in the direction of descending temperatures. This follows from rather simple considerations. An increase in temperature in any region of the mass must be accompanied by an increase in the water vapor pressure in that region in accordance with the Clausius-Clapeyron equation. Water then moves toward the regions of lower temperature where the vapor pressure is lower.

The movement of water thus induced is accompanied by shrinkage in the regions where the temperature is increased which tends to offset the expansion due to swelling and thermal expansion. Conversely, in the regions where the temperature is lowered, swelling tends to offset the shrinkage and thermal contraction. However, these effects cannot be evaluated quantitatively at present.

Combined effect of stress, strain, and temperature gradients

It can readily be seen that deformations of the solid phase and temperature changes together or separately cause moisture movements in

*It should be observed that a single thermal coefficient cannot correctly be assigned to a given specimen of concrete. The "coefficient" is a variable that changes with evaporable water content. The function must be such that the coefficient is a minimum for the bone-dry and saturated states and a maximum for some intermediate evaporable water content. Meyers' data indicate that the variation with change in evaporable water content is far from insignificant.

concrete. The separate effects may combine in different ways so that they may offset or augment each other at a given point in the mass. During a period of heating, cooling, or changing external force, the separate effects may combine in different ways at different times at the same point. The over-all result is that in concrete subjected to changing external forces or temperature or both, the evaporable water must be in a continual state of flux. If the ambient humidity also fluctuates, the internal moisture movements are still further complicated. Possibly these effects have an influence on the ability of concrete to withstand weathering.

SUMMARY OF PART 4

(1) This part deals with energy changes of adsorption and with their relationship to shrinking and swelling, capillary flow, and moisture diffusion.

(2) The net heat of adsorption is the heat in excess of the normal heat of condensation that is released when water vapor is adsorbed. The total net heat of adsorption of hardened paste is approximately equal to the heat of immersion of the adsorbent.

(3) The net heat of *surface* adsorption is that part of net heat of adsorption that has its origin in interaction of the adsorbed molecules and the solid surface. It is related to the heat of spreading-wetting and in cement paste is equal to about $472V_m$.*

(4) The net heat of capillary condensation is the total heat of water-surface formation. It is about equal to the difference between the heat of immersion and the heat of spreading-wetting. In cement paste it is equal to about $100V_m$ cal per g.

(5) The net heats of adsorption at 11 different initial water contents were measured, using two different samples of hardened paste.

(6) The total net heat of adsorption was found to be about $572V_m$ cal per g or about 670 ergs per sq cm of solid surface. This is about the same as the heat of immersion of various mineral oxides in water.

(7) Among portland cements of all types the total heat of hydration ranges from about 485 to 550 cal per g of non-evaporable water. Data from two cements indicate that of this amount about three-fourths is due to the heat of reaction of the non-evaporable water and the rest is due to the net heat of adsorption of the evaporable water.

(8) The total internal energy change of adsorption is equal to the change in enthalpy minus a small "$P\Delta v$" work term representing the contraction in volume under constant external pressure that accompanies adsorption. The enthalpy change is thus essentially equal to the net heat

---

*V_m = weight of adsorbed water required to cover the surface of the solid phase with a monomolecular layer.

of adsorption and is the sum of the free energy and unavailable energy changes, i.e.,

$$Q_a = \Delta H = \Delta G + T\Delta S,$$

where

- $-Q_a$ = net heat of adsorption,
- ΔH = change in enthalpy,
- ΔG = change in free energy,
- ΔS = change in entropy,
- T = absolute temperature,
- $T\Delta S$ = change in unavailable energy.

(9) The free energy change of water that occurs when the water becomes adsorbed can be expressed in terms of vapor pressure change alone. When the initial and final vapor pressures are p_s and p, respectively,

$$-\Delta G = -75.6 \, log_{10} p/p_s.$$

where

- p = existing vapor pressure
- p_s = saturation vapor pressure

(10) Unavailable energy is equal to the difference between the net heat of adsorption and the corresponding free-energy term, i.e.,

$$T\Delta S = Q_a - \Delta G.$$

(11) Entropy change, ΔS, is an indication of the extent to which adsorption modifies the adsorbed water. The data show that for water isothermally adsorbed at low vapor pressure the entropy change of adsorption is of the same magnitude as that accompanying solidification, or the combining of water in a salt as water of crystallization.

(12) The differential net heat of adsorption is the differential of the Q_a-vs.-w relationship. It is at a maximum for the first increment adsorbed, and becomes zero with the last increment at $p = p_s$.

(13) The maximum differential net heat of adsorption is about 400 cal per g of water. This is also the *minimum* heat of reaction of the non-evaporable water. Expressed on the same basis, the heat of combination of water in $Ca(OH)_2$ is 847 cal per g of water. This shows that the maximum energy of binding for evaporable water and the minimum for non-evaporable water is much less than that of the bond of water (i.e., hydroxyl groups) to calcium.

(14) The *average* net heat of adsorption of the *gel water* appears to be about 143 cal per g of gel water. The average for the first layer of adsorbed water appears to be about 270 to 300 cal per g. These figures are probably too low owing to the effect of adsorbed air.

(15) The logarithm of the constant C of the B.E.T. equation is theoretically proportional to the net heat of adsorption. Recent work has shown that assumptions concerning the proportionality constant made by

B.E.T. are invalid and that values of net heat of adsorption based on this assumption are too low.

(16) Cement gel belongs to the *limited swelling* class of gels.

(17) Swelling pressure is the increase in external pressure required to prevent swelling. It can be estimated from the following relationship:

$$\Delta P = - \frac{RT}{Mv_f} \, 2.303 \, log_{10}p/p_s \, ,$$

where

ΔP = swelling pressure, excess over normal external pressure,

R = the universal gas constant,

M = molecular weight of adsorbate,

v_f = specific volume of adsorbate.

This gives the pressure required to prevent the isothermal swelling of a gel dried to vapor pressure p when it has access to free water.

(18) The externally manifested swelling pressure of concrete would probably be less than that calculated from the above equation.

(19) The order of magnitude of the total volume change of hardened cement paste can be accounted for on the assumption that the change is due to the removal or addition of the first layer of adsorbed water molecules.

(20) Total volume change cannot be regarded solely as a capillary phenomenon, since expansion does not occur when the evaporable water, and hence meniscuses, disappear. When capillary water is present, capillary tension is equal to swelling pressure when the system is at equilibrium.

(21) Experimental data show that volume change is directly proportional to a *part* of the total change in water content. This agrees with 19, which implies that volume change is independent of the change in capillary-water content. The data suggest that volume change may be proportional to the change in gel-water content, rather than to the change in the first layer only.

(22) Capillary flow or moisture diffusion or both occur under isothermal conditions when there are inequalities in the free energy of the evaporable water in different regions in the specimen. Inequalities in free energy under isothermal conditions arise from inequalities in moisture content, from deformations of the solid phase, and from inequalities in external pressure on the adsorbed water. Resulting moisture movement is an important factor in plastic flow.

(23) An increase in temperature causes a decrease in swelling pressure of partially saturated pastes and thus causes an effect on volume change in addition to the usual thermal expansion. Evidence of this is found in data obtained by Meyers.

(24) Changes in external forces and changes in ambient temperature and humidity keep the evaporable water of a partially saturated specimen in a continual state of flux. This possibly influences durability.

REFERENCES

(1) Wm. D. Harkins and Geo. Jura, *J. Am. Chem. Soc.* v. 66, p. 1362 (1944).
(2) Wm. D. Harkins and Geo. E. Boyd, *J. Am. Chem. Soc.* v. 64, p. 1197 (1942), Table I.
(3) Samuel Glasstone, *Physical Chemistry* (D. Van Nostrand, 1940), p. 175.
(4) A. B. Lamb and A. S. Coolidge, *J. Am. Chem. Soc.* v. 42, p. 1146 (1920).
(5) Luke E. Steiner, *Introduction to Chemical Thermodynamics* (McGraw-Hill, 1941), p. 46.
(6) J. R. Katz, Ergibnisse der Exacten Naturwiss v. 3, p. 316 (1924); v. 4, p. 154 (1925); *Trans. Faraday Soc.* v. 29, p. 279 (1933).
(7) J. D. Babbitt, *Can. J. Res.* v. 20, Sec. A, p. 143 (1942).
(8) E. E. Dorsey, *Properties of Ordinary Water Substance* (Reinhold, 1940), Table 123, p. 267.
(9) Ref. 8, Table 201, p. 467.
(10) R. R. Wenner, *Thermochemical Calculations* (McGraw-Hill, 1941), pp. 177 and 216.
(10a) Ref. 10, p. 178.
(11) R. L. Steinberger, *Textile Research* v. 4, p. 451 (1934).
(12) Ref. 10, p. 44.
(13) Wm. D. Harkins and Geo. Jura, *J. Am. Chem. Soc.* v. 66, p. 919 (1944).
(14) Ref. 2, Table VI.
(15) H. Freundlich, *Colloid and Capillary Chemistry* (E. P. Dutton, 1922), p. 673.
(16) Ref. 3, p. 659.
(17) F. L. Plummer and S. M. Dore, *Soil Mechanics and Foundations* (Pitman, 1940), p. 60.
(18) N. K. Adam, *The Physics and Chemistry of Surfaces* (Oxford University Press, 1930), pp. 8, 9.
(19) Research Reports of the Portland Cement Association Research Laboratory, Appendix 3, July 1942, unpublished.
(20) C. G. Lynam, *Growth and Movement in Portland Cement Concrete* (Oxford University Press, 1934).
(21) S. L. Meyers, *Ind. Eng. Chem.* v. 32, p. 1107 (1940).
(22) R. W. Carlson, *Proc A. S. T. M.*, v. 35, Part II, p. 370 (1935).
(23) A. B. D. Cassie, *Trans. Faraday Soc.* v. 41, p. 450 (1945).

Appendix to Parts 3 and 4

This appendix gives tables of non-evaporable water, w_n, water required for the first monomolecular layer of adsorbed water, V_m, the ratio V_m/w_n, the B.E.T. constant C, and the computed surface of the dry paste for all the series used in this discussion.

In estimating V_m for some of the groups of data from plots of $\dfrac{1}{w}\dfrac{x}{1-x}$ versus w,[*] the same value of C could be used for all items in the group. In other groups the data could be represented best by using different values of C for different items. In some instances the points were too few and too scattered to establish the slope of the line. When this was true, a value of C was estimated and the line was drawn in such a way as to conform to the experimental points and the assumed value of C as closely as possible.

The samples of Series 254-265 were dried over concentrated H_2SO_4 instead of $Mg(ClO_4)_2 \cdot 2H_2O$. This accounts for the relatively low ratio of V_m/w_n and low values of C for this group.

[*]See Part 3.

TABLE 1—V_m, C, COMPUTED SPECIFIC SURFACE
AND OTHER DATA FOR SERIES 254-265[*]

Cement 14502

| Ref. No. | Age at test, days[†] | w_n, g per g of: | | V_m, g per g of: | | $\dfrac{V_m}{w_n}$ | C | Sp. surface of dry paste, cm²/g millions |
		Original cement	Dry paste	Original cement	Dry paste			
323	110	.160	.137	.024	.0210	.152	8.6	0.75
506	110	.179	.158	.030	.0266	.168	11.7	0.95
509	110	.183	.167	.031	.0287	.172	8.5	1.19
512	110	.200	.182	.030	.0272	.150	7.8	0.97
515	110	.232	.208	.037	.0336	.160	5.2	1.20
518	110	.226	.197	.036	.0311	.158	5.7	1.11
521	110	.219	.189	.037	.0324	.170	3.7	1.16

[*]Samples of this group were dried over concentrated H_2SO_4 instead of over $Mg(ClO_4)_2 \cdot 2H_2O$ as in the other tests.   [†]Approximate.

TABLE 2—V_m, C, COMPUTED SPECIFIC SURFACE
AND OTHER DATA FOR SERIES 254-MRB

| Cement No. | Net w/c | Age at test, days | w_n, g/g of: | | V_m, g/g of: | | $\dfrac{V_m}{w_n}$ | C | Sp. surf. of dry paste. cm²/g millions |
			Original cement	Dry paste	Original cement	Dry paste			
14898-1AQ	.382	120	.2171	.1784	.057	.047	.260	18	1.68
14899-1PC	.388	120	.2225	.1820	.056	.046	.253	18	1.64
14900-1SC	.446	126	.2274	.1853	.058	.047	.254	18	1.68
14901-2AQ	.391	126	.2228	.1822	.054	.044	.242	18	1.57
14902-2PC	.393	133	.2273	.1852	.056	.046	.238	18	1.57
14903-2SC	.424	133	.2271	.1851	.056	.046	.248	18	1.64
14904-3AQ	.425	162	.2284	.1859	.061	.050	.268	18	1.79
14905-3PC	.411	162	.2261	.1869	.063	.052	.278	18	1.86
14906-3SC	.476	173	.2344	.1906	.063	.051	.268	18	1.82
14907-4AQ	.406	173	.2185	.1797	.060	.049	.273	18	1.75
14908-4PC	.394	200	.2249	.1836	.060	.049	.267	18	1.75
14909-4SC	.483	200	.2255	.1840	.059	.048	.261	18	1.71
14910-5AQ	.460	204	.2282	.1858	.059	.048	.258	18	1.75
14911-5PC	.464	204	.2294	.1866	.060	.049	.262	18	1.71
14912-5SC	.489	212	.2252	.1838	.062	.051	.276	18	1.82
14913-6AQ	.410	212	.2206	.1807	.062	.051	.282	18	1.82
14914-6PC	.423	222	.2253	.1839	.060	.049	.266	18	1.75
14915-6SC	.437	222	.2240	.1830	.060	.049	.268	18	1.75

TABLE 3—V_m, C, COMPUTED SPECIFIC SURFACE AND OTHER DATA FOR SERIES 254-K4B

Cement No.	Net w/c	Age at test, days	w_n, g/g of: Original cement	w_n, g/g of: Dry paste	V_m, g/g of: Original cement	V_m, g/g of: Dry paste	$\dfrac{V_m}{w_n}$	C	Sp. surf. of dry paste, cm²/g millions
13721-1S	.470	174	.2231	.1824	.0634	.0518	.284	18	1.85
13722-1P	.473	180	.2332	.1891	.0618	.0501	.265	18	1.79
13723-1Q	.425	180	.2290	.1863	.0597	.0486	.261	18	1.74
13730-4S	.463	144	.1786	.1515	.0486	.0412	.272	18	1.47
13731-4P	.460	138	.1772	.1505	.0426	.0362	.240	18	1.29
13732-4Q	.450	138	.1773	.1506	.0447	.0380	.252	18	1.36
13733-5S	.427	150	.1650	.1416					
13734-5P	.453	146	.1589	.1371					
13735-5Q	.456	150	.1650	.1416					
13736-6S	.471	196	.2148	.1768	.0591	.0486	.275	18	1.74
13737-6P	—	191	.2297	.1868	.0637	.0518	.277	18	1.85
13738-6Q	.447	191	.2220	.1817	.0559	.0457	.252	18	1.63
13740-7P	.473	164	.2395	.1932	.0682	.0550	.285	18	1.96
13741-7Q	.480	171	.2390	.1929	.0617	.0498	.258	18	1.78
13752-11P	.445	164	.1864	.1571	.0537	.0453	.288	18	1.62
13753-11Q	.440	172	.1996	.1594	.0530	.0446	.280	18	1.59
13763-15S	.485	202	.2173	.1785	.0597	.0490	.275	18	1.75
13764-15P	—	196	.2109	.1742	.0545	.0450	.258	18	1.61
13765-15Q	.445	202	.2201	.1804	.0553	.0453	.251	18	1.62
13766-16S	—	322	.2096	.1733	.0594	.0491	.283	18	1.75
13767-16P	.464	223	.2256	.1841	.0640	.0522	.284	18	1.86
13768-16Q	.456	223	.2250	.1837	.0623	.0509	.277	18	1.82
13778-20S	.472	170	.2308	.1875	.0611	.0496	.265	18	1.77
13779-20P	.462	167	.2329	.1889	.0565	.0458	.242	18	1.64
13780-20Q	.436	176	.2262	.1845	.0569	.0464	.252	18	1.66

TABLE 4—V_m, C, COMPUTED SPECIFIC SURFACE AND OTHER DATA FOR SERIES 254-8

Ref. No.	Age at test, days	Net w/c	w_n, g/g of: Original cement	w_n, g/g of: Dry paste	V_m, g/g of: Original cement	V_m, g/g of: Dry paste	$\dfrac{V_m}{w_n}$	C	Sp. surf. of dry paste, cm²/g millions
			Cement 14930J						
254-8-1	447	.312	.1808	.1530	.053	.045	.294	21.0	1.61
254-8-2	362	.443	.2006	.1671	.062	.052	.310	21.0	1.83
254-8-3	362	.592	.2101	.1736	.066	.054	.313	21.0	1.94
			Cement 15007J						
254-8-28	479	.351	.1980	.1652	.063	.052	.316	18.0*	1.86*
254-8-29	440	.464	.2169	.1782	.058	.048	.268	17.0	1.70
254-8-30	479	.595	.2323	.1885	.060	.049	.256	20.6	1.73
			Cement 15011J						
254-8-40	478	.319	.1843	.1556	.051	.043	.276	18.0	1.54
254-8-41	368	.442	.2102	.1737	.058	.048	.276	17.3	1.73
254-8-42	368	.596	.2218	.1815	.062	.051	.280	15.0	1.81
			Cement 15013J						
254-8-46	339	.333	.2185	.1793	.052	.043	.239	19.2	1.53
254-8-47	333	.454	.2407	.1940	.058	.047	.242	17.6	1.67
254-8-48	333	.599	.2527	.2017	.057	.045	.224	17.6	1.63

*Estimated; $\dfrac{1}{w}\dfrac{x}{1-x}$ vs. x does not give straight line.

TABLE 5—V_m, C, COMPUTED SPECIFIC SURFACE AND OTHER DATA FOR SERIES 254-9

Ref. No.	Age at test, days	w_n, g/g of: Original cement	Dry paste	V_m, g/g of: Original cement	Dry paste	$\dfrac{V_m{}^*}{w_s}$	C	Sp. surf. of dry paste, cm²/g millions
		Cement 14930J; w/c at 2 hr. 0.300						
254-9-1 Mix A	7	.0804	.0744	.021	.019	.258	18	0.70
	14	.0994	.0904	.027	.024	.274	18	0.88
	28	.1071	.0967	.034	.031	.321	18	1.11
	56	.1292	.1144	.043	.038	.330	18	1.35
	90	.1497	.1302	.046	.040	.304	18	1.41
	180	.1620	.1400	.050	.043	.310	21	1.55
	365	.1704	.1456	.049	.042	.290	21	1.51
		w/c at 2 hr. 0.424						
254-9-2 Mix B	7	.0798	.0739	.021	.020	.268	18	0.71
	14	.1029	.0933	.028	.025	.276	18	0.92
	28	.1165	.1044	.037	.033	.319	18	1.19
	56	.1352	.1191	.049	.043	.303	22	1.54
	95	.1735	.1479	.053	.045	.306	18	1.62
	183	.1853	.1564	.059	.050	.319	21	1.78
	365	.1953	.1634	.059	.049	.302	21	1.76
		w/c at 2 hr. 0.573						
254-9-3 Mix C	7	.0822	.0760	.022	.020	.270	18	0.73
	14	.0896	.0822	.028	.026	.313	18	0.92
	28	.1214	.1083	.043	.038	.351	18	1.36
	56	.1638	.1407	.049	.042	.298	18	1.50
	90	.1850	.1561	.055	.046	.298	18	1.96
	180	.2008	.1672	.056	.047	.279	18	1.66
	365	.2142	.1764	.069	.057	.324	18	2.04
		Cement 15007J; w/c at 2 hr. 0.318						
254-9-4 Mix A	7	.1259	.1118	.036	.032	.284	18	1.17
	14	.1404	.1231	.041	.036	.295	18	1.30
	28	.1538	.1332	.042	.036	.276	16	1.31
	56	.1681	.1439	.047	.040	.281	22	1.44
	90	.1729	.1474	.048	.041	.276	25	1.45
	180	.1835	.1550	.048	.041	.265	16	1.46
		w/c at 2 hr. 0.432						
254-9-5 Mix B	7	.1334	.1177	.036	.032	.270	18	1.14
	14	.1408	.1303	.042	.037	.278	23	1.29
	28	.1714	.1463	.045	.038	.265	18	1.39
	56	.1847	.1559	.049	.041	.266	68	1.48
	90	.1924	.1614	.056	.047	.290	20	1.67
	180	.2018	.1679	.055	.046	.271	16	1.63
		w/c at 2 hr. 0.582						
254-9-6 Mix C	7	.1560	.1350	.037	.032	.235	18	1.13
	14	.1634	.1405	.042	.036	.258	20	1.29
	28	.1839	.1553	.050	.042	.272	18	1.51
	56	.2035	.1690	.053	.044	.259	18	1.57
	90	.2049	.1700	.056	.046	.272	16	1.66
	180	.2132	.1757	.060	.050	.283	20	1.78
		Cement 15011J; w/c at 2 hr. 0.338						
254-9-7 Mix A	7	.1137	.1020	.033	.029	.288	25	1.05
	14	.1333	.1176	.036	.032	.268	16	1.13
	28	.1430	.1251	.045	.040	.317	22	1.42
	56	.1557	.1347	.046	.040	.296	22	1.43
	90	.1643	.1411	.043	.037	.263	22	1.33
	180	.1705	.1457	.045	.038	.264	25	1.37
	365	.1760	.1497	.048	.041	.273	25	1.46
		w/c at 2 hr. 0.433						
254-9-8 Mix B	7	.1228	.1094	.037	.033	.304	22	1.19
	14	.1527	.1325	.038	.033	.247	27	1.17
	28	.1654	.1419	.045	.039	.272	23	1.38
	56	.1781	.1512	.047	.040	.266	23	1.44
	90	.1913	.1606	.051	.043	.267	23	1.53
	180	.1986	.1657	.056	.046	.280	16	1.66

*Calculated before rounding V_m values to 2 significant figures.

(Concluded on p. 599)

TABLE 5—CONCLUDED

Ref. No.	Age at test, days	w_n g/g of: Original cement	w_n g/g of: Dry paste	V_m g/g of: Original cement	V_m g/g of: Dry paste	$\frac{V_m^*}{w_n}$	C	Sp. surf. of dry paste, cm²/g millions
			Cement 15011J; w/c at 2 hr. 0.570					
254-9-9 Mix C	7	.1314	.1161	.034	.030	.261	27	1.08
	14	.1567	.1355	.039	.034	.252	22	1.22
	28	.1756	.1494	.047	.040	.268	18	1.43
	56	.1953	.1634	.054	.045	.274	17	1.60
	90	.2046	.1698	.056	.046	.272	16	1.65
	180	.2136	.1760	.057	.047	.266	16	1.67
			Cement 15013J; w/c at 2 hr. 0.324					
254-9-10 Mix A	7	.1488	.1295	.036	.031	.240	21	1.11
	14	.1639	.1408	.039	.033	.236	20	1.19
	28	.1711	.1461	.043	.036	.250	23	1.30
	56	.1802	.1527	.046	.039	.254	22	1.38
	90	.1913	.1606	.047	.040	.248	22	1.42
	180	.1877	.1580	.051	.043	.272	29	1.54
			w/c at 2 hr. 0.443					
254-9-11 Mix B	7	.1556	.1346	.037	.032	.235	21	1.43
	14	.1828	.1545	.042	.036	.232	21	1.28
	28	.1770	.1504	.048	.041	.271	21	1.46
	56	.2085	.1725	.053	.044	.254	18	1.57
	90	.2152	.1771	.057	.047	.263	15	1.67
	180	.2356	.1907	.058	.047	.248	16	1.69
			w/c at 2 hr. 0.611					
254-9-12 Mix C	7	.1583	.1367	.033	.029	.211	27	1.03
	14	.1828	.1545	.040	.034	.219	21	1.21
	28	.2028	.1686	.046	.038	.226	21	1.36
	56	.2208	.1809	.055	.045	.250	16	1.62
	90	.2357	.1907	.058	.047	.245	19	1.67
	180	.2447	.1966	.059	.047	.239	17	1.68
			Cement 15365; w/c at 2 hr. 0.322					
254-9-13 Mix A	7	.1326	.1171	.034	.030	.254	24	1.06
	14	.1515	.1316	.037	.032	.243	24	1.14
	28	.1488	.1295	.044	.038	.294	20	1.36
	56	.1786	.1515	.047	.040	.264	22	1.43
	90	.1789	.1518	.048	.040	.267	20	1.45
	180	.1815	.1536	.046	.039	.256	25	1.40
			w/c at 2 hr. 0.439					
254-9-14 Mix B	7	.1394	.1223	.034	.030	.244	26	1.06
	14	.1711	.1461	.043	.037	.253	20	1.32
	28	.1841	.1555	.054	.046	.295	19	1.64
	56	.2105	.1739	.055	.045	.261	19	1.62
	90	.2150	.1770	.056	.046	.263	20	1.66
	180	.2224	.1819	.060	.049	.269	19	1.75
			w/c at 2 hr. 0.587					
254-9-15 Mix C	7	.1530	.1327	.037	.032	.242	25	1.15
	14	.1855	.1565	.045	.038	.241	22	1.35
	28	.2102	.1737	.055	.045	.261	19	1.62
	56	.2213	.1812	.057	.047	.259	22	1.68
	90	.2296	.1867	.062	.051	.271	19	1.81
	180	.2546	.2029	.060	.048	.235	19	1.70
			w/c at 2 hr. 0.244					
254-9-15A Neat Cement	7	.1152	.1033	.028	.025	.244	33	0.90
	14	.1259	.1118	.030	.027	.242	33	0.96
	28	.1358	.1196	.032	.028	.232	33	0.99
	56	.1396	.1225	.034	.029	.240	33	1.05
	90	.1452	.1268	.034	.030	.236	33	1.07
	180	.1554	.1345	.035	.031	.230	33	1.09
Isotherm A	270	.1691	.1446	.032	.028	.193	19	0.99
Isotherm B	270	.1722	.1469	.031	.026	.178	16	0.94

*Calculated before rounding V_m values to 2 significant figures.

TABLE 6—V_m, C, COMPUTED SPECIFIC SURFACE AND OTHER DATA FOR SERIES 254-11

Cement No.	Ref. No. 254-	w/c at 2 hr.	w_n, g/g of:		V_m, g/g of:		$\dfrac{V_m{}^*}{w_n}$	C	Sp. surf. of dry paste, cm²/g millions
			Original cement	Dry paste	Original cement	Dry paste			
Age at test 28 days									
15758	11-1	.334	.1707	.1458	.043	.037	.252	18	1.31
"	11-2	.460	.1962	.1640	.050	.042	.254	18	1.49
15756	11-3	.318	.1229	.1094	.034	.031	.281	18	1.10
"	11-4	.446	.1325	.1170	.035	.031	.267	18	1.11
15763	11-5	.324	.0922	.0844	.028	.026	.307	18	0.92
"	11-6	.437	.1013	.0920	.031	.028	.305	18	1.00
15761	11-7	.334	.1621	.1395	.041	.035	.251	18	1.25
"	11-8	.468	.1852	.1563	.049	.042	.266	18	1.48
15754	11-9	.328	.1703	.1455	.044	.037	.256	18	1.33
"	11-10	.449	.1967	.1644	.050	.042	.256	18	1.50
16213	11-11	.443	.1720	.1468	.017	.040	.273	18	1.43
16214	11-12	.448	.1854	.1564	.048	.040	.258	18	1.44
16198	11-13	.444	.1098	.0989	.032	.029	.296	18	1.05
15669	11-14	.452	.1084	.0978	.028	.025	.262	21	0.92
Age at test 90 days									
15758	11-1	.334	.1912	.1605	.047	.039	.245	21	1.41
"	11-2	.460	.2227	.1821	.054	.044	.244	18	1.59
15756	11-3	.318	.1492	.1298	.043	.037	.287	21	1.33
"	11-4	.446	.1684	.1441	.045	.038	.267	18	1.37
15763	11-5	.324	.1335	.1178	.041	.036	.304	18	1.28
"	11-6	.437	.1487	.1295	.045	.039	.303	18	1.40
15761	11-7	.334	.1798	.1524	.048	.040	.264	18	1.44
"	11-8	.468	.2120	.1749	.055	.045	.259	18	1.62
15754	11-9	.328	.1951	.1632	.047	.039	.241	18	1.41
"	11-10	.449	.2301	.1871	.058	.047	.250	18	1.67
Age at test 6 days									
15495A	11-15	.442	.1300	.1150	.032	.029	.249	19	1.02
15497	11-16	.464	.1825	.1543	.044	.037	.240	18	1.32

*Calculated before rounding V_m values to 2 significant figures.

TABLE 7—V_m, C, COMPUTED SPECIFIC SURFACE AND OTHER DATA FOR SERIES 254-13

Ref. No. 254–	w/c at 2 hr.	SO_3 content of cement, percent	w_n, g/g of:		V_m, g/g of:		$\dfrac{V_m*}{w_n}$	C	Sp. surf. of dry paste, cm²/g millions
			Original cement	Dry paste	Original cement	Dry paste			
Cements made from clinker 15367									
13-1	.493	1.5	.2147	.1768	.059	.049	.275	15.4	1.74
13-2	.493	1.9	.2108	.1741	.056	.046	.265	17.7	1.65
13-3	.489	2.4	.2083	.1724	.054	.044	.257	17.7	1.59
13-4	.491	3.5	.1938	.1623	.048	.041	.250	21.0	1.45
13-1B	.486	1.5	.2115	.1746	.058	.048	.276	16.5	1.72
13-2B	.488	1.9	.2158	.1775	.058	.048	.268	18.0	1.70
13-3B	.488	2.4	.2151	.1770	.055	.045	.254	21.0	1.60
13-4B	.492	3.5	.2035	.1691	.050	.041	.245	23.3	1.48
Cements made from clinker 15623									
13-5	.470	1.5	.1518	.1317	.038	.033	.248	17.7	1.17
13-6	.474	2.0	.1509	.1311	.038	.033	.253	15.4	1.19
13-7	.473	2.5	.1515	.1316	.038	.033	.252	13.5	1.19
13-8	.480	3.5	.1444	.1262	.038	.034	.265	13.5	1.20
Cements made from clinker 15699									
13-9	.498	1.5	.1992	.1661	.053	.044	.268	16.5	1.59
13-10	.499	2.0	.1937	.1623	.052	.044	.268	17.7	1.55
13-11	.499	2.5	.1917	.1609	.049	.041	.258	17.7	1.48
13-12	.498	3.5	.1839	.1553	.046	.039	.251	17.7	1.39
Cements made from clinker 15498									
13-13	.488	1.5	.2082	.1723	.053	.044	.256	21.0	1.57
13-14	.487	2.0	.1992	.1661	.050	.042	.252	21.0	1.49
13-15	.493	2.5	.2004	.1669	.049	.041	.244	21.0	1.46
13-16	.491	3.5	.1895	.1593	.047	.040	.250	21.0	1.42
Cements made from clinker 15670									
13-17	.476	1.5	.1108	.0997	.031	.028	.282	18.0	1.01
13-18	.479	2.0	.1182	.1057	.034	.030	.287	18.0	1.08
13-19	.483	2.5	.1842	.1555	.042	.036	.231	18.0	1.28
13-20	.486	3.5	.2087	.1727	.050	.042	.241	18.0	1.49

*Calculated before rounding V_m values to 2 significant figures.

TABLE 8—V_m, C, COMPUTED SPECIFIC SURFACE AND OTHER DATA FOR SERIES 254-16

Ref. No.	Age at test, days	w_n, g/g of: Original cement	Dry paste	V_m, g/g of: Original cement	Dry paste	$\dfrac{V_m*}{w_n}$	C	Sp. surf. of dry paste, cm²/g millions
			Based on maximum weights attained during adsorption test					
16-01A	27	.2031	.1688	.053	.044	.259	22	1.56
16-01B	27	.2051	.1702	.053	.044	.258	22	1.57
16-01C	29	.2042	.1696	.052	.043	.256	22	1.55
Avg.		.2041	.1695	.053	.044	.258	22	1.56
16-02A	42	.1594	.1375	.037	.032	.230	22	1.13
16-02B	44	.1547	.1340	.035	.030	.226	22	1.08
16-02C	44	.1542	.1336	.036	.031	.233	22	1.11
Avg.		.1561	.1350	.036	.031	.230	22	1.11
16-03A	56	.1412	.1237	.036	.032	.255	22	1.12
16-03B	56	.1416	.1240	.037	.032	.258	22	1.15
16-03C	63	.1502	.1306	.039	.034	.260	22	1.21
16-03D	63	.1510	.1312	.039	.034	.258	22	1.21
Avg.		.1460	.1274	.038	.033	.258	22	1.17
			Based on weights at time heat-of-solution measurements were made					
16-01A	27	.2031	.1688	.051	.042	.250	22	1.51
16-01B	27	.2051	.1702	.050	.041	.242	22	1.47
16-01C	29	.2042	.1696	—	—	—	—	—
Avg.		.2041	.1695	.050	.042	.246	22	1.49
16-02A	42	.1594	.1375	.036	.031	.223	22	1.09
16-02B	44	.1547	.1340	.035	.030	.224	22	1.08
16-02C	44	.1542	.1336	.036	.032	.235	22	1.12
Avg.		.1561	.1350	.036	.031	.227	22	1.10

*Calculated before rounding V_m values to 2 significant figures.

Title 43-5e —a part of PROCEEDINGS, AMERICAN CONCRETE INSTITUTE Vol. 43

JOURNAL
of the
AMERICAN CONCRETE INSTITUTE
(copyrighted)

Vol. 18 No. 6   7400 SECOND BOULEVARD, DETROIT 2, MICHIGAN   February 1947

Studies of the Physical Properties of Hardened Portland Cement Paste*

By T. C. POWERS†

Member American Concrete Institute

and T. L. BROWNYARD‡

Part 5.   Studies of the Hardened Paste by Means of Specific-Volume Measurements§

CONTENTS

*Received by the Institute July 8, 1946—scheduled for publication in seven installments; October 1946 to April, 1947. In nine parts:

Part 1. "A Review of Methods That Have Been Used for Studying the Physical Properties of Hardened Portland Cement Paste". ACI JOURNAL, October, 1946.
Part 2. "Studies of Water Fixation"—Appendix to Part 2. ACI JOURNAL, November, 1946.
Part 3. "Theoretical Interpretation of Adsorption Data." ACI JOURNAL, December, 1946.
Part 4. "The Thermodynamics of Adsorption"—Appendix to Parts 3 and 4. ACI JOURNAL, January 1947.
Part 5. "Studies of the Hardened Paste by Means of Specific-Volume Measurements."
Part 6. "Relation of Physical Characteristics of the Paste to Compressive Strength."
Part 7. "Permeability and Absorptivity."
Part 8. "The Freezing of Water in Hardened Portland Cement Paste."
Part 9. "General Summary of Findings on the Properties of Hardened Portland Cement Paste."
†Manager of Basic Research, Portland Cement Assn. Research Laboratory, Chicago 10, Ill.
‡Navy Dept., Washington, D. C., formerly Research Chemist, Portland Cement Assn. Research Laboratory, Chicago 10, Ill.
§The characteristics of the cements mentioned in this section may be found in the Appendix to Part 2.

490　Powers and Brownyard

CLASSIFICATION OF WATER IN SATURATED PASTE ACCORDING TO MEAN SPECIFIC VOLUME

The total water content of a saturated sample of hardened paste has already been classified according to its evaporability, i.e., into evaporable and non-evaporable water. We have seen also that the evaporable water can be subdivided into gel water and capillary water on the basis of vapor pressure data. The following discussion will show that the same conclusion can be reached on the basis of the mean specific volume of the total water.

The non-evaporable water is regarded as an integral part of the solid phase in hardened cement paste. In becoming a part of the solid material some or all of it may have lost its identity as water. Nevertheless, the absolute volume of the solid phase can be considered as being equal to the original volume of the cement plus the volume of the non-evaporable water. If the absolute volume of the original cement, the absolute volume of the whole solid phase, and the weight of the non-evaporable water are known, a hypothetical specific volume can be assigned to the non-evaporable water such as will account for the known volume of the solid phase. This hypothetical specific volume is known to be less than 1.0; that is, the non-evaporable water occupies less space than an equal volume of free water. Moreover, the physically adsorbed part of the evaporable water also has a specific volume less than 1.0. Thus, in any given specimen the mean specific volume of the non-evaporable and adsorbed water is less than 1.0.

On the other hand, any capillary water present will either be in a state of tension or under no stress at all. If the specimen is not saturated, so that the vapor pressure of the contained water is less than p_s but more than about 0.45 p_s, capillary water will be present and under tension. (The magnitude of the tension is theoretically equal to the potential swelling pressure. See eq. (39), Part 4.) If the paste is saturated, so that $p = p_s$, the capillary water will be under no tension. Hence, when capillary water is present, but the paste is not saturated, the specific volume of the capillary water will be greater than 1.0, and if the specimen is saturated, the specific volume will be 1.0, except for a slight effect of the dissolved salts.

Thus, we can divide the total water content of a *saturated* specimen into two categories:

(1) Water that has a specific volume less than 1.0;

(2) Water that has a specific volume equal to 1.0.

The part of the total water in a saturated paste that has a mean specific volume less than 1.0 will be called *compressed water* for want of a better descriptive term. As applied to adsorbed water, the term is appropriate, if used with the reservations discussed in Part 4. Applied to non-evaporable water the term can hardly be taken literally. It does, however, fit the fact that non-evaporable water occupies less space as a part of the solid than it does when free.

The weight-composition of the total water in a sample of saturated paste can be expressed as follows:

$$w_t = w_d + w_c , \dots\dots\dots\dots\dots\dots\dots\dots\dots (1)$$

where

w_d is the weight of the compressed water, g and

w_c is the weight of the capillary water, g.

The *volume* of the total water can be expressed as

$$w_t v_t = w_d v_d + w_c , \dots\dots\dots\dots\dots\dots\dots\dots (2)$$

where v_d is the mean specific volume of the compressed water, and

v_t is the mean specific volume of the total water.

The specific volume of the capillary water is assumed to be 1.0.

Since $w_c = w_t - w_d$, eq. (2) can be rewritten

$$w_d (1 - v_d) = w_t (1 - v_t) \dots\dots\dots\dots\dots\dots\dots (3)$$

Experimental values of the mean specific volume of the total water content, v_t, were obtained by direct measurement. If the weight of the compressed water also could be measured, its mean density could be obtained by means of eq. (3). However, this cannot be done directly. It can be estimated by making certain assumptions, as will be shown below.

Of the water, w_d, that has a specific volume less than 1.0, a part is the non-evaporable water and the rest is adsorbed water, specifically, water within the range of the force-field of the solid phase. That is,

$$w_d = w_n + w_a , \dots\dots\dots\dots\dots\dots\dots\dots\dots\dots (4)$$

where w_n is the weight of non-evaporable water, g and

w_a is the weight of adsorbed water, g.

For samples made with a given cement we may safely assume that

$$w_a = B' w_n , \dots\dots\dots\dots\dots\dots\dots\dots\dots\dots\dots (5)$$

where B' is a constant for the particular cement. That is, it is assumed that the amount of adsorbed water is proportional to the total amount of hydration products* which in turn is in proportion to the amount of non-evaporable water. Hence,

$$w_d = w_n + B' w_n = (1 + B')w_n = B w_n \quad \dots \dots \dots \dots \dots (6)$$

Substitution from eq. (6) into eq. (3) gives

$$v_t = 1 - B(1 - v_d)\frac{w_n}{w_t} \quad \dots \dots \dots \dots \dots \dots (7)$$

Eq. (7) shows that a plot of experimentally determined values of v_t versus the corresponding values for w_n/w_t should give a straight line beginning at $v_t = 1$ when $w_n/w_t = 0$ and having a slope which would equal the product of the decrease in mean specific volume of the *compressed water* and the factor B, which is the ratio of the total amount of compressed water to the non-evaporable water, eq. (6). Experimental data are given in Tables 5-1 to 5-8.

The mean specific volumes of the total water, v_t, were determined as follows: Granular samples were dried to remove all the evaporable water. A portion of each dried sample was analyzed for non-evaporable water, portland cement, and pulverized silica, when present. Another part of the dried sample was brought to the saturated, surface-dry condition by the method described under "Experimental Procedures" (Part 1), and the amount required for saturation was noted. This amount, added to the non-evaporable water, gave the total water content of the sample. The specific volume of the saturated sample was then determined by a conventional pycnometer method, using water as the displacement medium.

Examination of these tables will show how the mean specific volume of the total water was computed. In Table 5-2, for example, columns 5, 6, and 7 give the weight-compositions of the saturated granular samples. Column 8 gives the measured density of the same granules.

Columns 9, 10, 11, and 12 give the weight-composition of 1 cc of each saturated sample. The values were obtained by multiplying the corresponding values in columns 5, 6, and 7 by the density of the saturated sample.

The volumes of cement in 1 cc of each saturated sample appear in column 13. These were obtained by multiplying the values in column 9 by the respective specific volumes of the original cements as measured by displacement of kerosene.

The figures in column 14 are the differences between the total volumes and the volumes of the cements as given in column 13. The difference was taken to be the volume of water. This involved the assumption that the air content was zero. For these particular neat cement specimens the air contents of the original specimens were very low. In the mortar specimens from which the samples represented in other tables were ob-

---

*Because $w_o \sim V_m \sim w_n$ for a given cement.

TABLE 5-1—COMPOSITIONS OF GRANULAR SAMPLES USED IN ADSORPTION AND OTHER TESTS AND COMPUTATION OF MEAN SPECIFIC VOLUME OF TOTAL WATER CONTENT AND OTHER FACTORS

Series 254-MRB

(1)	(2)	(3)	(4)	(5)	(6)	(7)	(8)	(9)	(10)	(11)	(12)	(13)	(14)	(15)	(16)	(17)
				Grams per g of sat'd sample				Grams per cc of saturated sample				Vols. per unit vol. sat'd sample				
Cement No.	Ref. No.	Age, days	v_c*	Cement	Non-evap. water	Evap. water	Density, saturated, g/cc	Cement	Non-evap. water	Evap. water	Total water	Cement	1 − cement	Avg. sp. vol. of water v_t	$\frac{w_n}{w_t}$	$1 - \frac{w_n}{w_t}$
							Clinker No. 1									
14808	1AQ	120	0.3155	0.685	0.149	0.167	2.040	1.397	0.304	0.341	0.645	0.441	0.559	0.867	0.471	0.282
14899	1PC	120	0.3155	0.686	0.153	0.162	2.040	1.399	0.312	0.330	0.642	0.441	0.559	0.871	0.486	0.263
14900	1SC	126	0.3155	0.664	0.131	0.186	1.976	1.312	0.298	0.368	0.666	0.414	0.586	0.880	0.447	0.268
							Clinker No. 2									
14901	2AQ	126	0.3175	0.671	0.149	0.180	2.004	1.345	0.299	0.361	0.660	0.427	0.573	0.868	0.453	0.291
							Clinker No. 3									
14904	3AQ	162	0.3155	0.671	0.153	0.175	2.020	1.355	0.309	0.354	0.663	0.428	0.572	0.863	0.466	0.294
14903	3PC	162	0.3155	0.671	0.154	0.174	2.013	1.351	0.310	0.330	0.660	0.423	0.574	0.870	0.470	0.277
14906	3SC	173	0.3155	0.643	0.152	0.203	1.939	1.251	0.295	0.394	0.689	0.395	0.605	0.878	0.428	0.285
							Clinker No. 4									
14907	4AQ	173	0.3155	0.685	0.150	0.165	2.045	1.401	0.307	0.337	0.644	0.442	0.558	0.866	0.477	0.281
14908	4PC	200	0.3155	0.677	0.152	0.171	2.028	1.373	0.308	0.347	0.655	0.433	0.567	0.866	0.470	0.283
14909	4SC	200	0.3155	0.646	0.146	0.208	1.936	1.251	0.283	0.403	0.686	0.395	0.605	0.882	0.413	0.286
							Clinker No. 5									
14910	5AQ	204	0.3155	0.655	0.150	0.194	1.964	1.286	0.295	0.381	0.676	0.406	0.594	0.879	0.436	0.278
14911	5PC	204	0.3160	0.661	0.151	0.188	1.978	1.307	0.299	0.372	0.671	0.413	0.587	0.873	0.446	0.280
14912	5SC	212	0.3155	0.646	0.146	0.208	1.930	1.247	0.282	0.401	0.683	0.392	0.608	0.890	0.413	0.296
							Clinker No. 6									
14913	6AQ	212	0.3155	0.677	0.149	0.173	2.026	1.372	0.302	0.350	0.652	0.433	0.567	0.870	0.463	0.281
14914	6PC	222	0.3155	0.672	0.151	0.176	2.008	1.349	0.305	0.373	0.658	0.426	0.574	0.872	0.464	0.276
14915	6SC	222	0.3155	0.658	0.147	0.194	1.964	1.292	0.289	0.381	0.670	0.408	0.592	0.884	0.431	0.269

Avg. 0.279

*For most of these cements v_c was not measured. The figure 0.3155 is the average for those that were measured.

TABLE 5-2—COMPOSITION OF GRANULAR SAMPLES USED IN ADSORPTION AND OTHER TESTS AND COMPUTATION OF MEAN SPECIFIC VOLUME OF TOTAL WATER CONTENT AND OTHER FACTORS

Series 254-K4B

(1)	(2)	(3)	(4)	(5)	(6)	(7)	(8)	(9)	(10)	(11)	(12)	(13)	(14)	(15)	(16)	(17)
				Grams per g of sat'd sample			Density, saturated, g/cc	Grams per cc of saturated sample				Vols. per unit vol. sat'd sample		Avz. sp. vol. of water, v_t	$\frac{w_n}{w_t}$	$1 - \frac{w_n}{w_t}$
Cement No.	Ref. No.	Age, days	z_x	Cement	Non-evap. water	Evap. water		Cement	Non-evap. water	Evap. water	Total water	Cement	1 − cement			
								Cements Made from Clinker No. 1								
13721	1-S	174	0.3195	0.648	0.145	0.208	1.925	1.247	0.279	0.400	0.679	0.398	0.602	0.886	0.411	0.277
13722	1-P	180	0.3215	0.641	0.150	0.209	1.910	1.224	0.287	0.399	0.686	0.394	0.606	0.883	0.418	0.280
13723	1-Q	180	0.3216	0.666	0.152	0.182	1.980	1.319	0.301	0.360	0.661	0.424	0.576	0.871	0.455	0.284
								Cements Made from Clinker No. 4								
13730	4-S	144	0.3100*	0.662	0.118	0.222	1.953	1.293	0.230	0.434	0.664	0.401	0.599	0.902	0.345	0.283
13731	4-P	138	0.3100*	0.661	0.117	0.222	1.960	1.296	0.229	0.435	0.664	0.402	0.598	0.901	0.345	0.287
13732	4-Q	138	0.3100*	0.669	0.119	0.212	1.981	1.325	0.236	0.420	0.656	0.411	0.589	0.898	0.360	0.283
								Cements Made from Clinker No. 5								
13733	5-S	150	0.3100*	0.668	0.110	0.222	1.960	1.309	0.216	0.435	0.651	0.406	0.594	0.912	0.332	0.265
13734	5-P	146	0.3100*	0.653	0.105	0.232	1.936	1.284	0.203	0.449	0.652	0.398	0.602	0.923	0.311	0.248
13735	5-Q	150	0.3100*	0.661	0.109	0.230	1.937	1.280	0.211	0.446	0.657	0.397	0.603	0.918	0.321	0.255
								Cements Made from Clinker No. 6								
13736	6-S	196	0.3169	0.663	0.142	0.195	1.966	1.303	0.279	0.383	0.662	0.412	0.588	0.888	0.421	0.265
13737	6-P	191	0.3172	0.658	0.151	0.190	1.956	1.287	0.245	0.372	0.667	0.408	0.592	0.888	0.442	0.253
13738	6-Q	191	0.3186	0.661	0.147	0.192	1.974	1.305	0.290	0.379	0.669	0.416	0.584	0.873	0.433	0.293
								Cements Made from Clinker No. 7								
13740	7-P	164	0.3190†	0.643	0.154	0.204	1.926	1.238	0.297	0.393	0.690	0.395	0.605	0.877	0.430	0.281
13741	7-Q	171	0.3190†	0.646	0.154	0.200	1.934	1.249	0.298	0.387	0.685	0.398	0.602	0.879	0.435	0.278
								Cements Made from Clinker No. 11								
13752	11-P	164	0.3100*	0.660	0.123	0.218	1.951	1.288	0.240	0.425	0.665	0.399	0.601	0.904	0.361	0.266
13753	11-Q	172	0.3100*	0.653	0.126	0.212	1.956	1.297	0.246	0.415	0.661	0.402	0.598	0.905	0.372	0.255
								Cements Made from Clinker No. 15								
13763	15-S	202	0.3160	0.651	0.141	0.208	1.932	1.258	0.272	0.402	0.674	0.398	0.602	0.893	0.404	0.265
13764	15-P	196	0.3182	0.666	0.141	0.193	1.976	1.316	0.279	0.381	0.660	0.419	0.581	0.880	0.423	0.284
13765	15-Q	202	0.3222	0.654	0.144	0.202	1.953	1.277	0.281	0.395	0.676	0.411	0.589	0.871	0.416	0.310

(Concluded opposite page.)

(Table 5-2 concluded)

Cements Made from Clinker No. 16

Ref. No.																
13766 16-S	322	0.319*	0.218	0.647	0.136	1.918	1.241	0.261	0.418	0.679	0.396	0.604	0.890	0.384	0.286
13767 16-P	223	0.319*	0.196	0.656	0.148	1.952	1.281	0.289	0.383	0.672	0.409	0.591	0.879	0.430	0.281
13768 16-Q	223	0.3190*	0.184	0.666	0.150	1.976	1.316	0.296	0.364	0.660	0.420	0.580	0.879	0.448	0.270

Cements Made from Clinker No. 20

Ref. No.																
13778 20-S	170	0.3180	0.202	0.648	0.150	1.942	1.238	0.391	0.392	0.683	0.400	0.600	0.878	0.426	0.286
13770 20-P	167	0.3190	0.201	0.648	0.151	1.954	1.266	0.295	0.303	0.688	0.404	0.596	0.866	0.429	0.312
13780 20-Q	176	0.3197	0.187	0.663	0.150	1.984	1.315	0.298	0.371	0.660	0.420	0.580	0.867	0.445	0.299

Avg. 0.278

*Assumed value for Type IV cements—Density of cement = 3.22; v_c = 0.310.
†Average value for Type I cements.

TABLE 5-3—COMPOSITIONS OF GRANULAR SAMPLES USED IN ADSORPTION AND OTHER TESTS AND COMPUTATION OF MEAN SPECIFIC VOLUME OF TOTAL WATER CONTENT AND OTHER FACTORS

Series 254-7

(1)	(2)	(3)	(4)	(5)	(6)	(7)	(8)	(9)	(10)	(11)	(12)	(13)	(14)	(15)	(16)	(17)	(18)
Ref. No.	Age, mo.	Grams per g of saturated sample				Density, saturated, g/cc	Grams per cc of saturated sample					Vols/unit vol. sat'd sample			Avg. sp. vol. of water, v_s	w_s/w	$1 - v_s / v_s/v_{ci}$
		Cement	Sand	Non-evap. water	Evap. water		Cement	Sand	Non-evap. water	Evap. water	Total water	Cement	Sand	1 − (Cement + sand)			
						Cement 14975; Density of cement = 3.143 g/cc; v_c = 0.3182											
7-1	6	0.772	—	0.126	0.103	2.268	1.751	—	0.286	0.234	0.320	0.558	—	0.442	0.850	0.550	0.273
7-2	6	0.598	0.199	0.105	0.098	2.270	1.358	0.452	0.238	0.222	0.460	0.432	0.170	0.308	0.865	0.517	0.261
7-3	6	0.554	0.249	0.101	0.096	2.278	1.262	0.567	0.230	0.219	0.449	0.402	0.213	0.385	0.858	0.512	0.277
7-4	6	0.467	0.331	0.096	0.106	2.237	1.045	0.740	0.215	0.237	0.452	0.392	0.278	0.390	0.863	0.476	0.288
7-5	6	0.420	0.349	0.099	0.133	2.144	0.900	0.748	0.212	0.285	0.497	0.286	0.281	0.433	0.871	0.427	0.302
7-6	6	0.322	0.452	0.075	0.151	2.008	0.676	0.948	0.157	0.317	0.474	0.215	0.356	0.429	0.903	0.331	0.287
7-7	6	0.284	0.493	0.065	0.158	2.084	0.592	1.027	0.135	0.329	0.464	0.188	0.386	0.426	0.918	0.291	0.281
7-S-1	6	0.709	—	0.154	0.137	2.104	1.492	—	0.324	0.288	0.612	0.475	—	0.525	0.858	0.530	0.268
7-S-2	6	0.574	0.131	0.133	0.162	2.024	1.162	0.265	0.269	0.328	0.597	0.370	0.100	0.530	0.888	0.431	0.248
7-S-3	6	0.471	0.235	0.115	0.179	2.000	0.942	0.470	0.230	0.358	0.588	0.300	0.177	0.523	0.890	0.381	0.281
7-S-4	6	0.397	0.316	0.099	0.188	2.000	0.794	0.632	0.198	0.376	0.574	0.253	0.238	0.500	0.887	0.345	0.328
7-S-5	6	0.377	0.351	0.093	0.179	2.019	0.761	0.709	0.188	0.361	0.549	0.242	0.267	0.491	0.894	0.342	0.310

Avg. 0.284

TABLE 5-4—COMPOSITION OF GRANULAR SAMPLES USED IN ADSORPTION AND OTHER TESTS AND COMPUTATION OF MEAN SPECIFIC VOLUME OF TOTAL WATER CONTENT AND OTHER FACTORS

Series 254-8

(1) Ref. No.	(2) Age, days	(3) Cement	(4) Silica	(5) Non-evap. water	(6) Evap. water	(7) Density, saturated, g/cc	(8) Cement	(9) Silica	(10) Non-evap. water	(11) Evap. water	(12) Total water	(13) Cement	(14) Silica	(15) 1-(Cement+silica)	(16) Avg. sp. vol. of water, v_t	(17) $\frac{w_n}{w_t}$	(18) $1-\frac{w_n}{w_t}$
		Grams per g of saturated sample					*Grams per cc of saturated sample*					*Vols/unit vol. sat'd sample*					
						Cement 14030; Density of cement = 3.218 g/cc; v_t = 0.3108											
8-1	448	0.645	0.102	0.116	0.137	2.157	1.391	0.220	0.250	0.296	0.546	0.432	0.083	0.485	0.888	0.458	0.244
8-2	363	0.498	0.238	0.100	0.165	2.070	1.031	0.493	0.207	0.342	0.549	0.320	0.185	0.495	0.901	0.377	0.262
8-3	363	0.401	0.325	0.084	0.190	2.004	0.804	0.651	0.168	0.381	0.549	0.250	0.245	0.505	0.920	0.306	0.261
						Cement 15007J; Density of cement = 3.189 g/cc; v_t = 0.3136											
8-28	481	0.623	0.112	0.123	0.141	2.115	1.318	0.237	0.260	0.298	0.558	0.413	0.089	0.498	0.892	0.467	0.231
8-29	441	0.474	0.276	0.103	0.147	2.093	0.992	0.578	0.216	0.308	0.524	0.311	0.217	0.472	0.901	0.412	0.240
8-30	441	0.359	0.401	0.083	0.157	2.078	0.746	0.833	0.172	0.326	0.498	0.234	0.313	0.453	0.910	0.345	0.261
						Cement 15008; Density of cement = 3.181 g/cc; v_t = 0.3144											
8-32	464	0.520	0.197	0.110	0.173	2.026	1.054	0.399	0.223	0.350	0.573	0.331	0.150	0.519	0.905	0.390	0.241
8-33	464	0.400	0.329	0.088	0.182	1.994	0.798	0.656	0.175	0.363	0.538	0.251	0.247	0.502	0.933	0.326	0.205
						Cement 15011J; Density of cement = 3.204 g/cc; v_t = 0.3121											
8-40	479	0.647	0.101	0.119	0.133	2.162	1.399	0.218	0.257	0.288	0.545	0.437	0.082	0.481	0.883	0.472	0.248
8-41	368	0.518	0.211	0.169	0.163	2.067	1.071	0.436	0.225	0.337	0.562	0.334	0.164	0.502	0.893	0.400	0.258
8-42	368	0.400	0.343	0.089	0.168	2.056	0.822	0.705	0.183	0.345	0.528	0.256	0.263	0.479	0.907	0.347	0.268
						Cement 15012J; Density of cement = 3.191 g/cc; v_t = 0.3134											
8-44	465	0.493	0.225	0.164	0.179	2.000	0.986	0.450	0.208	0.358	0.566	0.309	0.169	0.522	0.922	0.368	0.212
8-45	465	0.393	0.329	0.088	0.188	1.992	0.787	0.655	0.175	0.374	0.549	0.247	0.246	0.507	0.923	0.320	0.240
						Cement 15013J; Density of cement = 3.163 g/cc; v_t = 0.3162											
8-46	440	0.663	0.049	0.145	0.143	2.089	1.385	0.102	0.303	0.299	0.602	0.438	0.038	0.524	0.870	0.502	0.259
8-47	434	0.510	0.204	0.123	0.162	2.040	1.040	0.416	0.251	0.330	0.581	0.329	0.156	0.515	0.886	0.432	0.265
8-48	434	0.413	0.302	0.104	0.180	2.000	0.826	0.605	0.208	0.360	0.568	0.281	0.228	0.511	0.900	0.367	0.273
						Cement 13014J; Density of cement = 3.175 g/cc; v_t = 0.3150											
8-50	488	0.479	0.217	0.118	0.186	1.957	0.937	0.425	0.231	0.364	0.595	0.295	0.160	0.545	0.916	0.388	0.216
8-51	488	0.380	0.324	0.096	0.193	1.936	0.736	0.627	0.186	0.385	0.571	0.232	0.236	0.532	0.932	0.327	0.214

Avg. 0.245

TABLE 5-5—COMPOSITIONS OF GRANULAR SAMPLES USED IN ADSORPTION AND OTHER TESTS AND COMPUTATION OF MEAN SPECIFIC VOLUME OF TOTAL WATER CONTENT AND OTHER FACTORS

Series 254-9

(1) Ref. No.	(2) w/c	(3) Age, days	(4) Cement	(5) Silica	(6) Non-evap. water	(7) Evap. water	(8) Density, saturated, g/cc	(9) Cement	(10) Silica	(11) Non-evap. water	(12) Evap. water	(13) Total water	(14) Cement	(15) Silica	(16) 1 − (cement + silica)	(17) Avg. sp. vol. of water, v_t	(18) $\dfrac{v_n}{w_t}$	(19) $1 - \dfrac{v_n}{w_t}$
			Grams per g of saturated sample					Grams per cc of saturated sample					Vols/unit vol. sat'd sample					
							Cement 14030J; Density of cement = 3.218 g/cc; v_c = 0.3108											
9–1	.310	7	0.701	0.065	0.062	0.172	2.210	1.649	0.144	0.137	0.380	0.517	0.481	0.054	0.465	0.890	0.265	0.381
		14	0.677	0.099	0.067	0.157	2.222	1.504	0.220	0.149	0.349	0.498	0.467	0.083	0.450	0.901	0.299	0.321
		28	0.603	0.188	0.065	0.146	2.236	1.348	0.420	0.145	0.326	0.471	0.419	0.138	0.423	0.898	0.308	0.331
		56	0.636	0.142	0.083	0.139	2.226	1.416	0.316	0.182	0.309	0.491	0.440	0.119	0.441	0.868	0.371	0.275
		90	0.612	0.172	0.092	0.124	2.236	1.368	0.385	0.206	0.277	0.483	0.425	0.145	0.430	0.880	0.427	0.258
		180	0.608	0.092	0.108	0.131	2.202	1.471	0.203	0.238	0.288	0.526	0.457	0.076	0.467	0.888	0.452	0.248
		365	0.618	0.158	0.105	0.119	2.202	1.361	0.348	0.231	0.262	0.493	0.423	0.131	0.446	0.905	0.469	0.203
9–2	.424	7	0.646	0.230	0.043	0.173	2.166	1.183	0.498	0.093	0.374	0.472	0.365	0.187	0.443	0.943	0.197	0.289
		14	0.516	0.240	0.053	0.173	2.139	1.104	0.533	0.113	0.374	0.487	0.343	0.290	0.457	0.938	0.232	0.217
		28	0.438	0.554	0.051	0.158	2.160	0.946	0.765	0.110	0.341	0.451	0.294	0.288	0.418	0.927	0.244	0.299
		56	0.416	0.386	0.056	0.141	2.190	0.911	0.845	0.123	0.309	0.432	0.283	0.318	0.399	0.924	0.283	0.296
		90	0.470	0.301	0.082	0.148	2.133	1.012	0.648	0.177	0.319	0.496	0.314	0.243	0.442	0.801	0.337	0.305
		183	0.512	0.240	0.093	0.153	2.114	1.082	0.507	0.201	0.323	0.524	0.336	0.191	0.473	0.903	0.384	0.252
		365	0.464	0.299	0.091	0.146	2.117	0.982	0.633	0.193	0.309	0.502	0.305	0.238	0.457	0.910	0.387	0.234
																	Avg.	0.290
						Neat Paste: Cement 14030J; Density of cement = 3.218 g/cc; v_c = 0.3108												
9–3	.573	7	0.302	0.419	0.032	0.157	2.197	0.861	0.921	0.070	0.345	0.415	0.268	0.346	0.386	0.930	0.169	0.414
		14	0.300	0.505	0.027	0.111	2.301	0.690	1.360	0.052	0.255	0.317	0.214	0.480	0.297	0.937	0.196	0.322
		28	0.339	0.554	0.041	0.100	2.144	0.727	0.980	0.088	0.343	0.431	0.226	0.371	0.403	0.935	0.204	0.318
		56	0.378	0.382	0.062	0.178	2.080	0.786	0.795	0.129	0.370	0.499	0.244	0.299	0.457	0.916	0.259	0.323
		90	0.386	0.307	0.072	0.176	2.062	0.796	0.757	0.148	0.363	0.511	0.247	0.283	0.468	0.918	0.290	0.299
		180	0.421	0.341	0.084	0.153	2.100	0.884	0.716	0.176	0.321	0.497	0.273	0.269	0.436	0.918	0.354	0.231
		365	0.379	0.357	0.081	0.183	2.022	0.766	0.722	0.164	0.370	0.534	0.238	0.271	0.491	0.919	0.307	0.234
14030J	.330		0.6431	—	0.1404	0.2157	1.918	1.283	—	0.269	0.414	0.683	0.383	—	0.617	0.908	0.394	0.246
							Cement 15007J (15372); Density of cement = 3.189 g/cc; v_c = 0.313											
9–4	.318	7	0.650	0.120	0.082	0.148	2.198	1.429	0.264	0.180	0.325	0.505	0.448	0.090	0.453	0.897	0.356	0.290
		14	0.637	0.131	0.084	0.143	2.194	1.398	0.287	0.195	0.312	0.507	0.438	0.108	0.454	0.895	0.385	0.273
		28	0.643	0.125	0.096	0.136	2.194	1.406	0.274	0.217	0.298	0.515	0.441	0.103	0.456	0.885	0.421	0.273
		56	0.606	0.081	0.112	0.141	2.168	1.441	0.176	0.243	0.306	0.549	0.453	0.066	0.481	0.876	0.443	0.280
		90	0.673	0.078	0.110	0.133	2.173	1.464	0.170	0.232	0.289	0.541	0.459	0.064	0.477	0.882	0.466	0.240
		180	0.601	0.090	0.121	0.128	2.182	1.442	0.198	0.264	0.279	0.543	0.452	0.074	0.474	0.873	0.486	0.261

(Continued p. 678)

TABLE 5-5—CONTINUED

Series 254-9

(1)	(2)	(3)	(4)	(5)	(6)	(7)	(8)	(9)	(10)	(11)	(12)	(13)	(14)	(15)	(16)	(17)	(18)	(19)
			Grams per g of saturated sample				Density, saturated, g/cc	Grams per cc of saturated sample					Vols./unit vol. sat'd sample					
Ref. No.	w/c	Age, days	Cement	Silica	Non-evap. water	Evap. water		Cement	Silica	Non-evap. water	Evap. water	Total water	Cement	Silica	$1 - \frac{\text{(cement}}{\text{+ silica)}}$	Avg. sp. vol. of water, $\bar{v}$	$\frac{w_c}{w_n}$	$1 - \bar{v}\frac{w_c}{w_n}$
			Cement 15007 J (15372); Density of cement = 3.189 g/cc; z_w = 0.313 (Continued)															
9-5	.432	7	0.503	0.262	0.067	0.168	2.120	1.066	0.555	0.142	0.356	0.498	0.334	0.209	0.457	0.918	0.255	0.288
		14	0.489	0.278	0.073	0.160	2.120	1.037	0.589	0.155	0.339	0.494	0.325	0.221	0.454	0.919	0.314	0.258
		28	0.485	0.277	0.083	0.155	2.114	1.025	0.586	0.175	0.328	0.503	0.321	0.220	0.459	0.912	0.348	0.253
		56	0.510	0.233	0.094	0.161	2.097	1.069	0.491	0.197	0.338	0.535	0.335	0.185	0.480	0.897	0.368	0.280
		90	0.508	0.233	0.098	0.161	2.085	1.059	0.486	0.204	0.336	0.540	0.332	0.183	0.485	0.898	0.378	0.270
		180	0.410	0.364	0.083	0.143	2.132	0.874	0.776	0.177	0.305	0.482	0.274	0.292	0.434	0.900	0.367	0.273
9-6	.582	7	0.411	0.380	0.064	0.144	2.170	0.892	0.825	0.139	0.312	0.451	0.280	0.310	0.410	0.909	0.308	0.295
		14	0.409	0.374	0.067	0.150	2.136	0.874	0.799	0.143	0.320	0.463	0.274	0.300	0.426	0.920	0.309	0.259
		28	0.405	0.358	0.074	0.162	2.094	0.848	0.750	0.155	0.339	0.494	0.266	0.282	0.452	0.915	0.314	0.270
		56	0.404	0.358	0.082	0.156	2.092	0.845	0.749	0.172	0.326	0.498	0.265	0.282	0.453	0.910	0.343	0.261
		90	0.404	0.358	0.082	0.156	2.094	0.845	0.741	0.164	0.313	0.477	0.254	0.270	0.476	(0.998)	0.344	
		180	0.401	0.358	0.086	0.166	2.070	0.830	0.741	0.178	0.344	0.522	0.260	0.279	0.461	0.883	0.341	0.343
		365	0.284	0.527	0.060	0.129	2.171	0.617	1.144	0.130	0.280	0.410	0.193	0.430	0.377	0.920	0.317	0.253
																Avg.	0.273	
			Cement 15013 J; Density of cement = 3.204 g/cc; z_w = 0.3121															
9-7	.338	7	0.666	0.102	0.076	0.156	2.208	1.471	0.225	0.168	0.344	0.512	0.459	0.085	0.456	0.891	0.328	0.332
		14	0.618	0.163	0.082	0.138	2.214	1.368	0.361	0.182	0.306	0.488	0.427	0.136	0.437	0.895	0.373	0.282
		28	0.655	0.119	0.094	0.143	2.058	1.348	0.245	0.193	0.294	0.487	0.421	0.092	0.487	1.000	0.396	0.348
		28	0.655	0.119	0.094	0.143	2.206	1.445	0.263	0.207	0.315	0.522	0.451	0.099	0.450	0.882	0.397	0.277
		56	0.634	0.137	0.099	0.125	2.222	1.409	0.304	0.220	0.287	0.507	0.440	0.114	0.446	0.880	0.434	0.257
		90	0.643	0.124	0.106	0.127	2.206	1.418	0.274	0.234	0.280	0.514	0.443	0.103	0.454	0.883	0.455	0.233
		180	0.683	0.069	0.116	0.132	2.176	1.486	0.150	0.254	0.287	0.539	0.464	0.056	0.480	0.891	0.468	0.233
		365	0.683	0.063	0.120	0.134	2.160	1.475	0.136	0.259	0.289	0.548	0.460	0.051	0.489	0.892	0.473	0.228
9-8	.433	7	0.434	0.364	0.053	0.149	2.182	0.947	0.794	0.116	0.325	0.441	0.296	0.299	0.403	0.918	0.263	0.350
		14	0.490	0.268	0.075	0.167	2.115	1.036	0.567	0.159	0.353	0.512	0.323	0.213	0.464	0.903	0.311	0.302
		28	0.493	0.269	0.082	0.157	2.131	1.051	0.573	0.175	0.335	0.510	0.328	0.215	0.457	0.896	0.343	0.304
		56	0.492	0.266	0.088	0.154	2.123	1.047	0.564	0.187	0.333	0.513	0.327	0.212	0.438	0.903	0.365	0.283
		90	0.515	0.231	0.098	0.156	2.103	1.084	0.486	0.206	0.326	0.513	0.338	0.183	0.462	0.897	0.386	0.271
		180	0.494	0.261	0.098	0.148	2.118	1.046	0.553	0.208	0.313	0.521	0.326	0.208	0.466	0.894	0.389	0.266
9-9	.570	7	0.385	0.384	0.052	0.168	2.116	0.836	0.813	0.110	0.355	0.465	0.261	0.306	0.433	0.931	0.237	0.291
		14	0.403	0.386	0.063	0.149	2.152	0.867	0.831	0.136	0.321	0.457	0.271	0.312	0.417	0.912	0.298	0.295
		28	0.387	0.388	0.068	0.156	2.130	0.824	0.826	0.143	0.332	0.477	0.257	0.311	0.432	0.906	0.304	0.309
		56	0.371	0.389	0.072	0.168	2.080	0.772	0.809	0.150	0.349	0.499	0.241	0.304	0.455	0.912	0.301	0.292
		90	0.400	0.352	0.082	0.167	2.088	0.836	0.735	0.171	0.349	0.520	0.261	0.276	0.463	0.890	0.329	0.335
		180	0.392	0.381	0.084	0.144	2.127	0.834	0.810	0.179	0.306	0.485	0.260	0.305	0.435	0.897	0.369	0.289
																Avg.	0.290	

(Concluded opposite page.)

(Table 5-5 concluded)

Cement 15013J; Density of cement = 3.162 g/cc; v_c = 0.3162

Cement 15365; Density of cement = 3.135 g/cc; v_c = 0.319

Avg. 0.282

Avg. 0.268

TABLE 5-6—COMPOSITIONS OF GRANULAR SAMPLES USED IN ADSORPTION AND OTHER TESTS AND COMPUTATIONS OF MEAN SPECIFIC VOLUME OF TOTAL WATER CONTENT AND OTHER FACTORS—Series 254-11

(1)	(2)	(3)	(4)	(5)	(6)	(7)	(8)	(9)	(10)	(11)	(12)	(13)	(14)	(15)	(16)	(17)	(18)
		Grams per g of saturated sample				Density, satu- rated, g/cc	Grams per cc of saturated sample					Vols/unit vol. sat'd sample			Avg. sp. vol. of water, $\bar{v}$	w_s/w_s	$1-\frac{\bar{v}}{v_s}$
Ref. No.	Age, days	Cement	Silica	Non- evap. water	Evap. water		Cement	Silica	Non- evap. water	Evap. water	Total water	Cement	Silica	$1-$(Cement + silica)			
Clinker No. 2; Cement 15758; Density of cement 3.107; w_n = 0.3219; Sp. surf. 1800 (turb.); 3567 (perm.)																	
11-1	28	0.665	0.071	0.114	0.151	2.110	1.403	0.150	0.240	0.319	0.559	0.452	0.056	0.492	0.880	0.429	0.289
11-2	28	0.500	0.237	0.098	0.164	2.038	1.019	0.483	0.209	0.334	0.534	0.328	0.182	0.490	0.918	0.375	0.219
11-1	90	0.639	0.072	0.126	0.148	2.094	1.380	0.151	0.264	0.310	0.574	0.444	0.057	0.499	0.869	0.460	0.285
11-2	90	0.502	0.213	0.112	0.173	2.014	1.011	0.429	0.226	0.348	0.574	0.325	0.161	0.514	0.895	0.394	0.266
Clinker No. 3; Cement 15756; Density of cement 3.174; w_n = 0.3151; Sp. surf. 1800 (turb.); 3060 (perm.)																	
11-3	28	0.658	0.096	0.081	0.166	2.139	1.407	0.205	0.173	0.355	0.528	0.443	0.077	0.480	0.909	0.328	0.277
11-4	28	0.510	0.250	0.068	0.173	2.094	1.068	0.524	0.142	0.362	0.504	0.337	0.197	0.466	0.925	0.282	0.266
11-3	90	0.660	0.092	0.098	0.130	2.162	1.427	0.199	0.212	0.324	0.536	0.450	0.075	0.475	0.886	0.396	0.288
11-4	90	0.500	0.230	0.086	0.173	2.030	1.033	0.467	0.175	0.355	0.530	0.325	0.176	0.499	0.942	0.330	0.176
Clinker No. 4; Cement 15763; Density of cement 3.215; w_n = 0.3110; Sp. surf. 1800 (turb.); 2760 (perm.)																	
11-5	28	0.684	0.073	0.083	0.180	2.148	1.469	0.177	0.135	0.387	0.522	0.457	0.059	0.484	0.927	0.259	0.282
11-6	28	0.534	0.238	0.054	0.175	2.137	1.141	0.509	0.115	0.374	0.489	0.355	0.191	0.454	0.928	0.235	0.306
11-5	90	0.665	0.091	0.089	0.156	2.169	1.442	0.197	0.193	0.338	0.531	0.448	0.074	0.478	0.900	0.364	0.275
11-6	90	0.508	0.237	0.076	0.180	2.078	1.056	0.492	0.158	0.374	0.532	0.328	0.183	0.487	0.915	0.297	0.286
Clinker No. 5; Cement 15761; Density of cement 3.155; w_n = 0.3170; Sp. surf. 1800 (turb.); 2951 (perm.)																	
11-7	28	0.674	0.057	0.105	0.159	2.114	1.425	0.120	0.230	0.336	0.566	0.452	0.045	0.503	0.889	0.406	0.273
11-8	28	0.516	0.208	0.096	0.181	2.038	1.052	0.424	0.196	0.369	0.565	0.333	0.159	0.508	0.899	0.347	0.291
11-7	90	0.672	0.049	0.121	0.158	2.097	1.409	0.103	0.254	0.331	0.585	0.447	0.039	0.514	0.879	0.434	0.279
11-8	90	0.503	0.214	0.107	0.176	2.038	1.025	0.436	0.218	0.359	0.577	0.325	0.164	0.511	0.886	0.378	0.302
Clinker No. 1; Cement 15754; Density of cement 3.135; w_n = 0.3190; Sp. surf. 1800 (turb.); 3417 (perm.)																	
11-9	28	0.637	0.089	0.112	0.143	2.144	1.409	0.191	0.240	0.307	0.547	0.449	0.072	0.479	0.876	0.439	0.282
11-10	28	0.494	0.245	0.097	0.164	2.069	1.022	0.507	0.201	0.339	0.540	0.325	0.191	0.483	0.894	0.372	0.285
11-9	90	0.638	0.079	0.128	0.134	2.136	1.405	0.169	0.273	0.286	0.559	0.448	0.064	0.488	0.873	0.488	0.260
11-10	90	0.493	0.232	0.114	0.161	2.050	1.011	0.476	0.234	0.330	0.564	0.323	0.179	0.498	0.853	0.415	0.282
Clinker No. 1; Cement 16218; Density of cement 3.135; w_n = 0.3190; Sp. surf. 2426 (perm.)																	
11-11	28	0.494	0.265	0.085	0.156	2.110	1.042	0.559	0.179	0.329	0.508	0.332	0.210	0.458	0.962	0.332	0.278
Clinker No. 1; Cement 16214; Density of cement 3.135; w_n = 0.3190; Sp. surf. 2923 (perm.)																	
11-12	28	0.491	0.259	0.091	0.159	2.086	1.024	0.540	0.190	0.332	0.522	0.327	0.203	0.470	0.980	0.364	0.275

(Concluded opposite page)

(Table 5-6 concluded)

Clinker No. 4; Cement 16198; Density of cement 3.215; t_e = 0.3110; Sp. surf. 3200 (perm.)

| 11-13 | 28 | 0.503 | 0.055 | 0.258 | 0.184 | 2.104 | 1.058 | 0.543 | 0.116 | 0.387 | 0.503 | 0.329 | 0.204 | 0.487 | 0.928 | 0.231 | 0.312 |

Clinker No. 4; Cement 15609; Density of cement 3.215; t_e = 0.3110; Sp. surf. 3810 (perm.)

| 11-14 | 28 | 0.551 | 0.201 | 0.060 | 0.188 | 2.082 | 1.117 | 0.418 | 0.125 | 0.391 | 0.516 | 0.357 | 0.157 | 0.486 | 0.942 | 0.242 | 0.240 |

Avg. 0.274

TABLE 5-7—COMPOSITONS OF GRANULAR SAMPLES USED IN ADSORPTION AND OTHER TESTS AND COMPUTATIONS OF MEAN SPECIFIC VOLUME OF TOTAL WATER CONTENT AND OTHER FACTORS—Series 254-13

(1)	(2)	(3)	(4)	(5)	(6)	(7)	(8)	(9)	(10)	(11)	(12)	(13)	(14)	(15)	(16)	(17)	(18)
		Grams per g of saturated sample					Grams per cc of saturated sample					Vols/unit vol. sat'd sample					
Ref. No.	SO_3 Content of cement, %	Cement	Silica	Non-evap. water	Evap. water	Density, saturated, g/cc	Cement	Silica	Non-evap. water	Evap. water	Total water	Cement	Silica	$1 - \binom{\text{Cement}}{+ \text{silica}}$	Avg. sp. vol. of water, v_1	$\frac{w_n}{v_1}$	$1 - \frac{v}{w_n/w_1}$
Clinker No. 1 (15307); Density of cement* = 3.135; v_e = 0.319																	
13-1	1.5	0.428	0.306	0.092	0.175	2.034	0.871	0.622	0.187	0.356	0.543	0.278	0.234	0.488	0.869	0.344	0.294
13-2	1.9	0.436	0.312	0.092	0.160	2.001	0.901	0.645	0.190	0.331	0.521	0.287	0.243	0.470	0.902	0.365	0.260
13-3	2.4	0.428	0.306	0.089	0.177	2.027	0.868	0.620	0.180	0.359	0.539	0.277	0.233	0.490	0.900	0.353	0.272
13-4	3.5	0.429	0.306	0.083	0.182	2.067	0.887	0.633	0.172	0.376	0.548	0.283	0.238	0.479	0.874	0.314	0.401
Clinker No. 1 (15307); Density of cement* = 3.135; v_e = 0.319																	
13-1B	1.5	0.427	0.305	0.090	0.178	2.026	0.865	0.618	0.182	0.361	0.543	0.276	0.232	0.492	0.906	0.335	0.280
13-2B	1.9	0.428	0.306	0.092	0.173	2.028	0.868	0.621	0.187	0.351	0.538	0.277	0.233	0.490	0.911	0.345	0.296
13-3B	2.4	0.428	0.306	0.092	0.174	2.087	0.893	0.639	0.192	0.363	0.555	0.287	0.240	0.475	0.836	0.346	0.415
14-3B	3.5	0.420	0.305	0.087	0.182	1.969	0.830	0.601	0.171	0.358	0.529	0.268	0.226	0.506	0.957	0.323	0.183
Clinker No. 3 (15623); Density of cement** = 3.175; v_e = 0.315																	
13-5	1.5	0.436	0.312	0.066	0.186	2.040	0.889	0.636	0.135	0.379	0.514	0.280	0.230	0.481	0.936	0.263	0.243
13-6	2.0	0.433	0.308	0.065	0.183	2.028	0.878	0.627	0.132	0.391	0.523	0.277	0.236	0.487	0.931	0.352	0.274
13-7	2.5	0.433	0.301	0.060	0.193	2.016	0.873	0.623	0.133	0.389	0.522	0.275	0.234	0.491	0.953	0.353	0.231
13-8	3.5	0.431	0.308	0.062	0.199	2.022	0.871	0.623	0.125	0.402	0.527	0.274	0.234	0.492	0.934	0.237	0.278
Clinker No. 5 (15670); Density of cement* = 3.155; v_e = 0.317																	
13-9	1.5	0.428	0.306	0.085	0.181	2.031	0.869	0.621	0.173	0.368	0.541	0.280	0.233	0.492	0.909	0.320	0.285
13-10	2.0	0.430	0.307	0.083	0.179	2.033	0.874	0.624	0.169	0.364	0.533	0.277	0.235	0.488	0.916	0.317	0.265
13-11	2.5	0.426	0.304	0.082	0.187	2.018	0.860	0.613	0.165	0.377	0.542	0.273	0.230	0.497	0.917	0.304	0.273
13-12	3.5	0.430	0.307	0.079	0.183	2.027	0.872	0.622	0.160	0.371	0.531	0.276	0.234	0.490	0.923	0.391	0.235
Clinker No. 2 (15408); Density of cement** = 3.108; v_e = 0.322																	
13-13	1.5	0.443	0.315	0.092	0.150	2.010	0.890	0.633	0.185	0.302	0.487	0.286	0.238	0.476	0.977	0.380	0.606
13-14	2.0	0.442	0.316	0.088	0.154	2.052	0.907	0.648	0.181	0.316	0.497	0.292	0.241	0.464	0.934	0.364	0.181

*Effect of varying gypsum neglected.

TABLE 5-8—COMPOSITIONS OF GRANULAR SAMPLES USED IN ADSORPTION AND OTHER TESTS AND COMPUTATIONS OF MEAN SPECIFIC VOLUME OF TOTAL WATER CONTENT AND OTHER FACTORS

Series 254-14.   Age, 28 days

(1)	(2)	(3)	(4)	(5)	(6)	(7)	(8)	(9)	(10)	(11)	(12)	(13)	(14)	(15)	(16)	(17)	(18)	(19)
			Grams per g of saturated sample				Density saturated, g/cc	Grams per cc of saturated sample					Vols./unit vol. sat'd sample			Avg. sp. vol. of water, v_t	w_s/w_t	$1 - \frac{v_s}{w_s/w_t}$
Cement No.	Ref. No.	x_c	Cement	Silica	Non-evap. water	Evap. water		Cement	Silica	Non-evap. water	Evap. water	Total water	Cement	Silica	$1 -$ (cement + silica)			
							Cured 24 hr. at 43 C, 27 days at 23 C											
15954	14-1	0.3176	0.437	0.312	0.083	0.166	2.064	0.902	0.644	0.173	0.343	0.518	0.286	0.212	0.472	0.911	0.338	0.263
15756	14-5	0.3111	0.436	0.311	0.066	0.187	2.040	0.889	0.634	0.135	0.381	0.516	0.277	0.238	0.465	0.940	0.262	0.229
16215	14-11	0.3190	0.430	0.307	0.087	0.176	2.037	0.876	0.625	0.177	0.359	0.536	0.279	0.235	0.486	0.907	0.330	0.282
16195	14-12	0.3216	0.438	0.313	0.080	0.170	2.078	0.910	0.650	0.166	0.353	0.519	0.293	0.244	0.463	0.892	0.329	0.338
							Cured 28 days at 23 C											
15954	14-2	0.3176	0.433	0.309	0.087	0.171	2.051	0.888	0.634	0.178	0.351	0.529	0.283	0.238	0.480	0.907	0.339	0.277
15756	14-4	0.3111	0.434	0.310	0.067	0.189	2.038	0.884	0.632	0.137	0.385	0.522	0.275	0.238	0.487	0.933	0.262	0.236
16186	14-7	0.3190	0.427	0.305	0.091	0.177	2.030	0.867	0.619	0.185	0.359	0.544	0.277	0.233	0.490	0.901	0.340	0.291
16195	14-8	0.3216	0.426	0.305	0.086	0.183	2.024	0.862	0.617	0.174	0.370	0.544	0.277	0.232	0.491	0.903	0.326	0.303
							Cured 24 hr. at 5 C, 27 days at 23 C											
15756	14-3	0.3111	0.436	0.312	0.068	0.184	2.055	0.896	0.641	0.140	0.378	0.518	0.279	0.241	0.480	0.927	0.270	0.270
							Cured 24 hr. at 4 C, 27 days at 23 C											
16186	14-9	0.3190	0.425	0.304	0.090	0.180	2.022	0.859	0.615	0.182	0.364	0.546	0.274	0.231	0.495	0.907	0.333	0.279
16195	14-10	0.3216	0.433	0.310	0.085	0.172	2.050	0.882	0.638	0.175	0.354	0.529	0.287	0.240	0.473	0.894	0.331	0.320
							Autoclaved at 350 F for 6 hr.											
15756	14-6	0.3111	0.459	0.328	0.074	0.138	2.240	1.028	0.735	0.166	0.309	0.475	0.329	0.276	0.404	0.851	0.349	0.427

tained, the air contents were considerable. However, it is believed that the small granules taken for these measurements were smaller than most of the air voids and therefore would contain little air, if any.

Column 15 was obtained by dividing the figures given in column 14 by corresponding figures in column 12.

Plots of v_t vs. w_n/w_t for most of these data are given in Fig. 5-1 to 5-4.

Since v_t depends on the measured volume of the saturated, granular samples, and the computed volume of the original cement and (when present) pulverized silica, small inaccuracies in measurement have rather large effects on v_t. Moreover, any inaccuracies in the corresponding figures for non-evaporable water, due either to errors or to inadvertent departures from the standard drying condition discussed earlier, contribute to random scattering of the plotted points. Nevertheless, when all the plots are considered together, they support the conclusion that the total water content is made up of two components, one being free water and the other being water having a mean specific volume less than 1.0.

This conclusion may not seem wholly convincing in view of the rather wide scatter of points in some cases and the fewness of the points in others. If so, one should consider that the main factor determining the magnitude of w_n is the length of the period of hydration. In the graphs for Series 254-9, Fig. 5-3, the points represent ages ranging from 7 days to 6 months or a year. In every case, the sample at *zero age* would have to be represented by a point at $w_n = 0$, $v_t = 1.0$, for at that time all the water would obviously be free. Consequently, the only uncertainty is whether the real relationship is a straight line beginning at $v_t = 1.0$, or a curve, beginning at that point. If the real relationship were a curve bending upward from the line as now drawn, it would indicate that the specific volume of the compressed water that is combined when w_n is large is greater than when w_n is small. If the curve turned downward, the indication would be the opposite. In either case the indication would be that the products formed at one time would be different from those formed in the same paste at another time.

There is some basis for believing that the products formed at first are different from those formed later. During the first few hours the reactions with gypsum are completed, as mentioned before. Also, the products formed from the finest flour in the cement would differ from those formed later because of the difference between the composition of the flour and that of the coarser particles. However, the effects are apparently not large. This was shown earlier when discussing the relationship between V_m and w_n (Part 3). All things considered, it seems justifiable to assume that one straight line represents the data for any given cement and accordingly that both B eq. (6) and v_d eq. (7) are constant for a given cement.

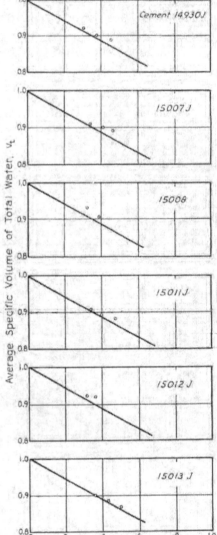

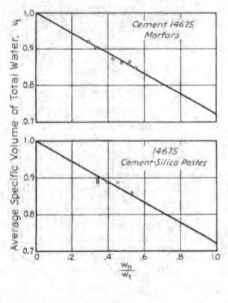 Fig. 5-1 (above)—v_t versus $\dfrac{w_n}{w_t}$
Series 254-7

Fig. 5-2 (right)—v_t versus $\dfrac{w_n}{w_t}$
Series 254-8

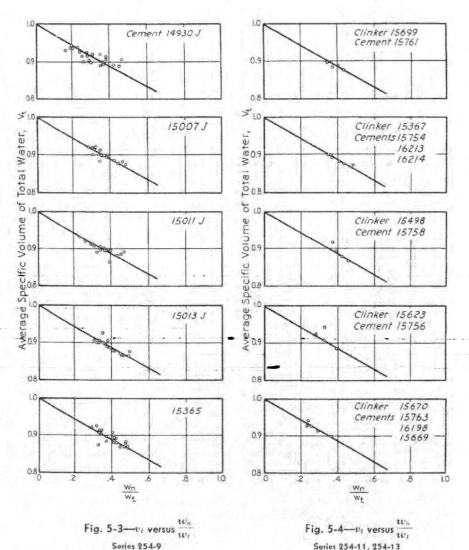

Fig. 5-3—v_t versus $\frac{w_n}{w_t}$

Series 254-9

Fig. 5-4—v_t versus $\frac{w_n}{w_t}$

Series 254-11, 254-13

Mean ratio of $(1 - v_t)$ to w_n/w_t

As stated before, the compressed part of the total water is considered to be the sum of the non-evaporable water and the adsorbed water. The degree of compression of the adsorbed water is probably the same for all cements. This is indicated from data on the heat of adsorption already considered. The degree of "compression" of the non-evaporable water might be different for different cements, however, since there are differences in the proportions of the various reaction products. For example, the proportion of $Ca(OH)_2$ should depend on the C_3S content of the clinker, and the amount of aluminate-hydrates should vary with the C_3A content. With this in mind, the data were classified according to C_3A content, and for each class the values of $\dfrac{(1 - v_t)}{w_n/w_t}$ were averaged separately. The results are shown in Table 5-9.

Application of methods of statistical analysis indicate that the largest difference between the mean ratios of the group are not larger than could be accounted for by chance variation alone. Nevertheless, some of the variation must be due to differences in the chemical compositions of the cements, as mentioned above.

On the whole, the data seem to support the presumption that $(1 - v_t)/(w_n/w_t)$ varies with the composition of the cement but at the same time they show the influence of cement composition to be small. Certainly the random variations are too great to warrant trying to evaluate the effect of cement composition from these data. Accordingly, eq. (8) below, representing the grand average, will be applied to all cements alike in further treatments of the data:

$$v_t = 1 - 0.279 \; w_n/w_t \quad \dots \dots \dots \dots \dots \dots \dots \dots \dots \dots (8)$$

According to Table 5-9, this equation will give v_t for an individual item with a probable error of about 7 percent. The degree of agreement between the data and the equation is shown in Fig. 5-1 to 5-4. In each diagram the line represents eq. (8).

TABLE 5-9—RATIO OF MEAN SPECIFIC VOLUME OF TOTAL WATER TO w_n/w_t

Type of cement	Mean $1 - v_t$ w_n/w_t	Probable error of mean	Probable error of single value	Number of samples
Low C_3A	0.279	± .0028	± .0259	88
Med. C_3A	0.283	± .0024	± .0137	31
High C_3A	0.278	± .0015	± .0129	70
Grand avg.	0.279	± .0015	± .0200	189

Lower limit of mean specific volume of total water

From eq. (8) it is apparent that the greater the weight-fraction of non-evaporable water, w_n/w_t, the smaller will be the mean specific volume, v_t. However, there is an upper limit to w_n/w_t and hence a lower limit to v_t. This conclusion follows from the fact that the evaporable water content of a saturated paste cannot be less than about $4V_m$ (see Part 3). That is, the minimum amount of evaporable water is

$$w_e = w_t - w_n = 4V_m \text{ (min.)} ,$$

or

$$\frac{w_t}{w_n} - 1 = \frac{4V_m}{w_n} \text{ (min.)} .$$

Since $V_m/w_n = k$, for a given cement,

$$\frac{w_t}{w_n} = 1 + 4k \text{ (min.)} ,$$

or

$$\frac{w_n}{w_t} = \frac{1}{1 + 4k} \text{ (max.)} .$$

From the values for k, i.e., V_m/w_n, for different types of cement given in Table 3-6, Part 3, the limits of w_t/w_n and w_n/w_t were computed with the results given in Table 5-10.

TABLE 5-10—LIMITS OF w_n/w_t AND w_t/w_n
FOR DIFFERENT TYPES OF CEMENT

	Type of Cement	$\dfrac{V_n}{w_n}$ $(=k)$	$\dfrac{w_t}{w_n}$	$\dfrac{w_e}{w_t}$
Type I	Normal C_3A	0.255	2.02	0.50
	High C_3A	0.256	2.02	0.50
Type II	High iron	0.259	2.04	0.49
	High silica	0.279	2.12	0.47
Type III	Normal C_3A	0.238	1.99	0.50
	High C_3A	0.240	1.96	0.51
Type IV	High iron	0.282	2.13	0.47
	High silica	0.277	2.11	0.47

From these results we may conclude that *the non-evaporable water cannot become more than about one-half the total water content of a saturated paste.*

From the data given in Table 5-10 and the empirical relationship given in eq. (8), the mean of the specific volumes of the non-evaporable water and gel water can be estimated. That is, when w_n/w_t is a maximum,

w_n/w_t is between 0.47 and 0.51. For most cements w_n/w_t would be about 0.50. Hence, the lower limit of v_t is about

$$(v_t) \text{ min.} = 1 - (0.279 \times 0.50) = 0.860.$$

Since these considerations pertain to pastes in which the total evaporable water $= 4V_m$, hence, to pastes containing no space outside the gel, it follows that *0.860 is the mean specific volume of the total water in a saturated sample that contains no capillary water outside the gel.*

Estimation of the bulk volume of the solid phase and volume of capillary water

With the mean of the specific volumes of the gel water and non-evaporable water established, as given above, it is possible to compute the *bulk volume* of the solid phase and the volume of capillary water at any stage of hydration.

The bulk volume of the solid phase is here defined as the sum of the absolute volumes of the solid material in the hardened paste and the volume of the pores that are characteristic of the gel. In other words, it is the sum of the volumes of the gel-substance, the pores characteristic of the gel, other hydrates, and residues of unhydrated clinker. Or, for a saturated paste, the bulk volume of the solid phase is the sum of the volumes of the solids plus the volume of the gel water. It differs from the over-all volume of the paste by the volume of the capillary water.

The volume-composition of a unit volume of paste can be expressed in terms of its weight-composition as follows:

$$c\,v_c + (w_n + w_g)v_d + w_c = 1 \quad,$$

where

c = weight of cement, g per cc of saturated paste,
w_n = weight of non-evaporable water, g per cc of saturated paste,
w_g = weight of gel water,* g per cc of saturated paste,
w_c = weight or volume of capillary water, g per cc of saturated paste,
v_c = specific volume of original cement, and
v_d = mean specific volume of $(w_n + w_g)$.

Let

$$V_B = 1 - w_c = c\,v_c + (w_n + w_g)v_d$$

where

V_B = bulk volume of solid phase.
Since $w_g = 4V_m$, and $V_m = kw_n$ (see Part 3), $w_g = 4kw_n$.
Hence,

$$V_B = c\,v_c + w_n(1 + 4k)v_d \dots\dots\dots\dots\dots\dots\dots\dots\dots\dots\dots\dots (9)$$

This equation holds for $V_B = 0$ to $V_B = 1.0$.

---

*In this equation w_g, the weight of the gel water, may be identical with w_a, the weight of the adsorbed water appearing in eq. (4). However, until this is proved it is necessary to assume that a saturated gel may contain some water held by capillary condensation, that is, that gel water may comprise both adsorbed water and capillary water. However, the term "capillary water" as used in this discussion includes only the water that is in excess of the gel water.

For an average Type I cement, for which $k = 0.255$ (see Table 5-10) and $v_c = 0.315$, and for $v_d = 0.860$ as given above, this reduces to

$$\frac{V_B}{c\,v_c} = 1 + 5.5\frac{w_n}{c} \quad\dotfill\quad (10)$$

The significance of this equation is illustrated in Fig. 5-5. This diagram gives the bulk volume of the solid phase, or of capillary water, per unit volume of paste at any stage of hydration for any paste. For example, if a paste was originally 0.3 cement and 0.7 water by absolute volume, by the time it had hydrated to an extent such that the non-evaporable water is 0.2 g per g of original cement, the bulk volume of the solid phase will be 0.63 and the volume of the capillary water will be 0.37 cc per cc of paste. The other lines give the compositions at lesser degrees of hydration. At $w_n/c = 0$, a point on the line gives, of course, the original water or cement content of the fresh paste, by absolute volume. The increase in volume due to hydration is also clearly seen in this diagram.

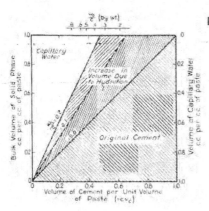

Fig. 5-5—Graphical illustration of eq. (10)

$$V_B = \left[1 + 5.5\frac{w_n}{c} \right] cv_c$$

It should be noted that for any given stage of hydration (given w_n/c) there is a certain cement content above which the paste can contain no capillary water. For example, as shown in Fig. 5-5, when $w_n/c = 0.1$, capillary-water content is zero when the absolute volume of the original cement is 0.65 cc per cc of paste; or, when $w_n/c = 0.2$, $w_c = 0$ when the cement content of the paste is 0.48.

Conversely, for a given cement content there is a degree of hydration at which capillary water disappears. This conclusion is restricted, however, by the fact that for any given cement, w_n/c cannot exceed a certain limit, which is usually about 0.25. This topic will be considered further after the following discussion of the *absolute* volume of the solid phase in hardened paste.

ESTIMATION OF THE ABSOLUTE VOLUME OF THE SOLID PHASE

The absolute volume of the solid phase in hardened paste is defined here as the sum of the volumes of all the hydrated solids and the volume of the unreacted cement. For a saturated paste it differs from the overall volume by the volume of the evaporable water and from the bulk volume of the solid phase by the volume of the gel water. It cannot be determined from the weight of the evaporable water because the mean specific volume of the evaporable water varies with the porosity of the paste and the extent of hydration of the cement. For that reason, attempts to measure the specific volume of the solid phase were made.

Method of measuring volume of solid phase

In preliminary work, the volume of the solid phase was computed from the displacement of the dried granules in water and in other liquids. Owing to the effects of adsorption and to other factors which will be discussed presently, it was necessary to adopt an inert gas as the displacement medium and to develop special apparatus—a volumenometer —for the purpose. This apparatus and its operation are described below.

The apparatus developed for measuring the volume of the solid phase in a hardened paste is illustrated in Fig. 5-6. The volumenometer proper is that part, shown with surrounding water bath, which is located between stopcocks, 1, 2, and 5. This comprises:

(1) A sample bulb, S, which is joined to the rest of the apparatus through a standard-taper, ground-glass joint, and which can be cut off from communication with the rest of the system by means of stopcock 3.

(2) A mercury barometer, B, for measuring the pressure within the volumenometer.

(3) A burette bulb, V, the free volume of which can be altered at will by introducing or withdrawing mercury through stopcock 5, thus altering the gas pressure within the volumenometer.

(4) A stopcock, 4, which enables the sample bulb to be evacuated without evacuating the rest of the volumenometer.

Stopcock 2 connects with a line to the vacuum pump. Beyond stopcock 5 is a mercury reservoir R. The pressure in the volumenometer is maintained at somewhat less than atmospheric so that mercury will siphon into bulb V when R is open to the air and stopcock 5 is open. To withdraw mercury from V, the side-tube on R is connected to the vacuum pump by means of rubber tube T and is evacuated before stopcock 5 is opened.

Stopcock 1 connects the volumenometer to a helium reservoir H in direct communication with a mercury manometer M, which gives the

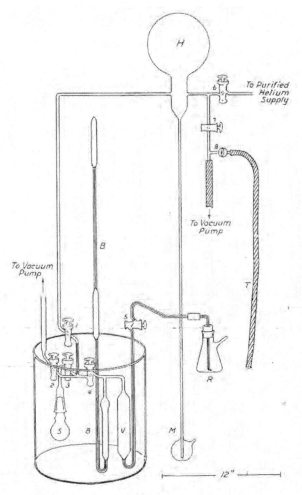

Fig. 5-6

difference between atmospheric and helium pressures. Stopcock 6 connects with the helium supply through two cold traps (not shown) filled with activated charcoal for removing impurities.

Tests are made with the volumenometer to obtain the free volume of the sample bulb S (up to cock 3) with and without a sample in place. The absolute volume of the sample is then found by difference. Volumes are measured by determining the volume of mercury that must be admitted to bulb V in order to restore the helium pressure in the volumenometer after the cock to the evacuated sample bulb is opened.

At the start of a volume measurement the mercury is withdrawn from bulb V until only the capillary remains filled. The flask R with its content of mercury is then removed, weighed, and replaced. Next, the volumenometer inclusive of the sample bulb S is evacuated through cock 2 using a mercury diffusion pump backed by a Cenco-Hyvac pump. If the volumenometer is already filled with pure helium beyond stopcock 4, this cock can be left closed. After evacuation, stopcocks 2 and 3 are closed and 4 is opened. Helium is then admitted through cock 1 until the desired pressure, somewhat less than atmospheric, is obtained. Readings are taken on the lower level of mercury in barometer B until a steady, reliable value is obtained. A micrometer microscope reading to 0.001 mm is used. After the reading has been obtained, a little mercury is withdrawn to flask R to eliminate any air that may have become trapped at the mouth of the siphon-tube when the flask was replaced after the previous weighing. This clears the line for subsequent manipulations.

Next, stopcock 3 is opened, admitting helium to the sample bulb, and the pressure drops. The pressure is then restored by opening stopcock 5, thus allowing mercury to flow into bulb V. The mercury content of V is adjusted until the reading taken on barometer B is the same as before the helium was admitted to the sample bulb. The apparatus is allowed to stand in this condition with further additions of mercury when necessary, until it is obvious that the desired reading is being maintained. Then the weight of flask R and its content of mercury is found and subtracted from the previous weight. When the weight of mercury given by this difference is multiplied by the specific volume of mercury, the volume of the free space in the sample bulb is obtained.

When bulb S contains a paste sample, the times required for evacuation and for helium contact are necessarily much longer than when the volume of the empty bulb is measured. Experience with cement pastes has indicated that overnight pumping out and one or more days of contact with the helium are advisable.

Choice of displacement medium

The displacement medium was chosen on the basis of results of preliminary tests given in Table 5-11. The object in making these measurements was to find a medium that would measure the space occupied by the evaporable water, or its complement, the space occupied by solids. The medium should be able to penetrate any region that can be reached by water, without undergoing the volume change that water does.

The upper half of the table represents data obtained by pycnometer measurements; the lower half represents results obtained with gases as displacement media using an earlier form of the volumenometer described above. These data were obtained when the methods were being

TABLE 5-11

Displacement-fluid	Volume of 1 g of dry sample for samples indicated: (cc)							
	20Q	1S	39	40	41	42	62	N.B.
Liquid displacement fluids								
Water	.395	—	.392	—	.389	.391	—	.450
Acetone	.408	.404	—	—	—	—	.424	—
Carbon tetrachloride	—	—	—	—	—	—	.465	—
Toluene	.429	.444	—	—	—	—	—	—
Gaseous displacement fluids								
Air	—	—	.327	.362	.336	.338	.312	—
Hydrogen	—	—	.392	.422	.392	.396	—	.206
Helium	.424	.433	—	—	—	—	—	.420

N. B.—Silica-gel Lot 15106.

developed and may not be very accurate; however, they serve well enough for the present purpose.

The wide differences among the results shown in Table 5-11 are due, we presume, to such factors as differences in size of molecule and differences in the interaction between the solid and the fluid. The size of the molecules of the various gases is about the same as that of water, or slightly smaller; but the organic liquids have molecules considerably larger than the water molecule, as shown by the following data:

Kind of liquid	Molar volume	Relative volume
Water	18	1.0
Acetone	73	4.0
Carbon tetrachloride	96	5.3
Toluene	106	5.9

Since the sizes of the molecules of the organic liquids ranged from four to six times that of the water molecule, the gases were preferable so far as this factor is concerned.

Among the gases, air and hydrogen proved to be unsatisfactory because they were adsorbed by the solid material. In air, the apparent specific volume of the hydrated cement appeared to be little or no higher than that of the original cement. This obvious absurdity was probably due mainly to the adsorption of oxygen. Hydrogen is adsorbed also; it happened to give apparent displacements virtually the same as those in water. These results with air and hydrogen left only the inert gases as being able to meet the requirements with respect to molecule-size and absence of interaction, for these gases have small molecules and besides are not adsorbed to a measurable degree at ordinary temperature and pressure. Helium was chosen because it was readily available and had been used by others for the purpose.[1]

It cannot be said that the displacement of a sample in helium is an accurate basis for computing the space that had been occupied by evaporable water. An inaccuracy would arise from the salts that appear as solids in the dry paste but which are in solution in the saturated paste. The error from this source is probably small. Another inaccuracy, perhaps more serious, arises from the ability of water to swell the solid and thus possibly to open up and enter regions that are inaccessible to an inert gas. Whether or not helium is excluded from any regions accessible to water is not known. The existence of such regions does not necessarily imply an inaccuracy in the helium determination. That is, if the loss of water from such a region causes a shrinkage equal to the volume of water lost, the helium measurement would correctly indicate the density of the solid phase and the space available to the water even though the helium were not able to penetrate it. However, if the volume change in such a region is not equal to the volume of water lost from that region, the helium displacement will not accurately indicate the space available to water. This is a question which must be left open for the present. However, it might be noted that the possibility of a gel-shrinkage equal to the amount of water removed from the gel is not as remote as might at first be supposed. Although it is true that the over-all volume-change is only about 1/40 of the volume of water removed, there is evidence that the gel itself undergoes much greater shrinkage than the specimen as a whole, the difference being due to mechanical restraints.

Other sources of error are inherent in the apparatus itself. Although the apparatus was constructed and manipulated with care, leakage through the stopcocks seemed to occur occasionally. Also, the readings of the mercury level in the barometer with the micrometer microscope were sometimes affected by changes in the shape of the meniscus in the course of the manipulation of the apparatus.

EXPERIMENTAL RESULTS

Many measurements were made on samples of various descriptions, but the original determinations were later found to be in error because not enough time had been allowed for the helium to penetrate the fine structure of the granules. As was found for carbon black by Rossman and Smith,[2] the first period of rapid penetration is followed by a very long period of slow penetration. Different pastes differed in the time required for the attainment of practical equilibrium. In one case 5 or 6 days of contact seemed to be necessary. The procedure finally adopted was to evacuate the sample for 1 or 2 days and\then to maintain contact with the helium for 1, 2, or as many days as were necessary to establish apparent equilibrium. Even under these circumstances it was difficult to attain as good duplicability in repeat tests as was desired, partly because the long time periods increased the effects of any slight leaks. These sometimes developed at the stopcocks.

Test measurements had to be repeated several times to obtain values for the specific volume of the non-evaporable water with an apparent accuracy of about + 0.01 cc per g. Only four different samples were tested by the final technique, but the cements represented a considerable range of compositions. The specific volumes of the dried pastes (about 6 months old) were all found to be close to 0.41 cc per g (density: 2.44 g per cc). From the individual values the specific volume of the non-evaporable water was computed as explained below.

Specific volume of non-evaporable water

The volume of the solid phase can be considered as being equal to the sum of the volumes of original cement and the volume of the non-evaporable water. That is,

$$V_s = c\,v_a + w_n v_n \,, \dots\dots\dots\dots\dots\dots\dots\dots\dots\dots\dots\dots\dots\dots (11)$$

where

V_s = volume of solid matter,

v_n = hypothetical specific volume of non-evaporable water, and the other symbols have the same significance as before.

The specific volume of the non-evaporable water may have no literal significance, since at least a part of the non-evaporable water probably loses its identity when it enters into chemical combination with the cement constituents. Nonetheless, a figure can be obtained which represents the increase in volume of solid phase per gram of water combined with the cement and which is thus virtually the specific volume of the water. Since this specific volume does not vary widely among cements of various compositions, general use can be made of it for estimating the absolute volume of the solid phase from the non-evaporable water content. This makes available for this study a considerable number of data from samples on which helium-displacement measurements were not made.

The hypothetical specific volume of the non-evaporable water can conveniently be computed from the following form of eq. (11):

$$v_n = \frac{V_s - c\,v_c}{w_n} \quad \dots\dots\dots\dots\dots\dots\dots\dots\dots\dots\dots\dots\dots\dots\dots\dots (12)$$

The values of v_n found from the final, most reliable experiments were as follows:

Cement No.	Computed composition				v_n
	C_3S	C_2S	C_3A	C_4AF	
13721-1P	44.8	26.3	12.7	6.6	0.82
13738-6Q	56.4	17.6	10.5	9.2	0.83
13765-15Q	42.4	28.9	9.9	8.8	0.81
13779-20P	53.0	15.5	13.1	11.5	0.82

In the computations that follow v_n is taken as 0.82 for all cements, on the basis of the results tabulated above.

Specific volume of gel water

With the data now at hand, the approximate specific volume of the gel water can be estimated.

Let v_g = mean specific volume of gel water;

  w_g = weight of gel water;

  $v_n w_n + v_g w_g = v_t w_t$.

In a saturated sample, made of normal Type I cement, containing no capillary space,

$$w_n = 0.50 \ w_t \ ;$$
$$w_g = 0.50 \ w_t \ ;$$
$$v_t = 0.860 \ \ ; \text{and}$$
$$v_n = 0.82 \ .$$

Hence,

$$v_g = \frac{0.860 - 0.50 \times 0.82}{0.50} = 0.90, \text{approximately.}$$

Computation of volume of solid phase from non-evaporable water

Eq. (11) can be written

$$\frac{V_s}{c \ v_c} = 1 + \frac{v_n \ w_n}{v_c \ c} \quad \dots \dots \dots \dots \dots \dots \dots \dots \dots \dots \dots \dots (13)$$

This gives the ratio of the volume of the solid phase to the volume of the original cement in terms of the non-evaporable water (g per g of cement) and the ratio of the specific volume of the non-evaporable water to that of original cement, v_n/v_c. For any given cement v_n/v_c is constant and indeed the same value may be used for various cements without introducing much error. In the following computations v_n is taken as 0.82 for all cements, v_c is the measured value when known and 0.317 when no measured value is available. That is, the value is either $\dfrac{0.82}{v_c}$ or $\dfrac{0.82}{0.317}$

= 2.59.

Computations of solid-phase volumes are recorded in Tables 5-12 to 5-16. These data include results from five different cements and three

TABLE 5-12—COMPUTATION OF VOLUME OF SOLID PHASE

Cement 14930J

$\frac{v_n}{v_c} = \frac{0.82}{0.31} = 2.64$; C_2S 23 percent; C_2S 56 percent; C_3A 6 percent; C_4AF 10 percent;

Specific surface = 2040 sq cm per g; Computations based on eq. (12)

(1)	(2)	(3)	(4)	(5)	(6)	(7)
Ref. No. Series 254-8 & 9	w_a/c	Age, days	$\frac{w_n}{c}$ (g/g)	$\frac{V_s}{c\,v_c}$	$c\,v_c$ cc. per cc. of paste	V_s
Mix A						
9-1	.309	7	.080	1.21	.498	.60
"	"	14	.099	1.26	"	.63
"	"	28	.107	1.28	"	.64
"	"	56	.129	1.34	"	.67
"	"	90	.150	1.40	"	.70
"	"	180	.162	1.43	"	.71
"	"	365	.170	1.45	"	.72
8-1	.311	447	.181	1.48	.494	.73
Mix B						
9-2	.424	7	.080	1.21	.418	.51
"	"	14	.103	1.27	"	.53
"	"	28	.116	1.31	"	.55
"	"	56	.135	1.36	"	.57
"	"	90	.174	1.46	"	.61
"	"	180	.185	1.49	"	.62
"	"	365	.195	1.52	"	.63
8-2	.443	362	.201	1.53	.407	.62
Mix C						
9-3	.573	7	.082	1.22	.347	.42
"	"	14	.090	1.24	"	.43
"	"	28	.121	1.32	"	.46
"	"	56	.164	1.43	"	.50
"	"	90	.185	1.49	"	.52
"	"	180	.201	1.53	"	.53
"	"	365	.214	1.56	"	.54
8-3	.595	362	.210	1.55	.338	.52

different mixes and from six to eight different curing periods for each cement. The increases in solid volume during the course of hydration are shown for each of the cements in Fig. 5-7.*

These curves show that during the first month or so the average rate of hydration of a given cement is greater the greater the original water-cement ratio. After the first 3 months the rate is very low. Because of this the data do not indicate very definitely the trends of the curves at the later ages. Nevertheless, it is clear that even with the slow hardening cements, hydration virtually ceases within a year.

*For description of mixes see S-254-8 & 9, Appendix to Part 2.

TABLE 5-13—COMPUTATION OF VOLUME OF SOLID PHASE
Cement 15007J

$$\frac{v_c}{v_e} = \frac{0.82}{0.314} = 2.61;\ C_3S\ 48\ \text{percent};\ C_2S\ 29\ \text{percent};\ C_3A\ 7\ \text{percent};\ C_4AF\ 10\ \text{percent};$$

Specific surface = 2015 sq cm per g; Computations based on eq. (12).

(1)	(2)	(3)	(4)	(5)	(6)	(7)
Ref. No. Series 254-8 & 9	w_o/c	Age. days	$\dfrac{w_a}{c}$ (g/g)	$\dfrac{V_s}{c\,v_c}$	$\dfrac{c\,v_c}{\text{cc per cc of paste}}$	V_s
			Mix A			
9-4	.316	7	.126	1.33	.493	.66
"	"	14	.140	1.36	"	.67
"	"	28	.154	1.40	"	.69
"	"	56	.168	1.44	"	.71
"	"	90	.173	1.45	"	.72
"	"	180	.184	1.48	"	.73
8-28	.344	480	.198	1.52	.471	.71
			Mix B			
9-5	.433	7	.133	1.35	.416	.56
"	"	14	.150	1.39	"	.58
"	"	28	.171	1.45	"	.60
"	"	56	.185	1.48	"	.62
"	"	90	.192	1.50	"	.62
"	"	180	.202	1.53	"	.64
8-29	.464	440	.217	1.57	.398	.62
			Mix C			
9-6	.570	7	.156	1.41	.347	.49
"	"	14	.163	1.42	"	.49
"	"	28	.184	1.48	"	.51
"	"	56	.204	1.53	"	.53
"	"	90	.205	1.54	"	.53
"	"	180	.213	1.56	"	.54
8-30	.595	440	.232	1.61	.340	.55

Table 5-17 gives the volumes of the solid phase in pastes that had apparently closely approached the maximum possible extent of hydration. The average results from each mix are plotted in Fig. 5-8. This diagram is like Fig. 5-5 except that the solid volume rather than bulk volume is shown. Fig. 5-9 represents a Type I cement cured 6 months. The original specimens were truncated cones of 4-in. base diameter, 1½-in. top diameter, and 6-in. altitude. Some were made of sand-cement mortar; others from cement and pulverized silica.* (See Table 5-18.)

These two diagrams show that as the cement approaches ultimate hydration the volume of the solid phase per unit over-all volume of paste is directly proportional to the original cement content of the paste for

*For complete description see Appendix to Part 2, Series 254-7.

TABLE 5-14—COMPUTATION OF VOLUME OF SOLID PHASE
Cement 15011J

$\frac{v_a}{v_c} = \frac{0.82}{0.312} = 2.63$; C_3S 45 percent; C_2S 29 percent; C_3A 7 percent; C_4AF 10 percent; Specific surface = 1835 sq cm per g; Computations based on eq. (12).

(1) Ref. No. Series 254-8 & 9	(2) w_o/c	(3) Age, days	(4) $\frac{w_n}{c}$ (g/g)	(5) $\frac{V_s}{c\,v_c}$	(6) $c\,v_c$ cc per cc of paste	(7) V_s
		Mix A				
9-7	.316	7	.114	1.30	.492	.64
''	''	14	.133	1.35	''	.66
''	''	28	.143	1.38	''	.68
''	''	56	.156	1.41	''	.69
''	''	90	.164	1.43	''	.70
''	''	180	.170	1.45	''	.71
''	''	365	.176	1.46	''	.72
8-40	.319	478	.184	1.48	.490	.72
		Mix B				
9-8	.432	7	.123	1.32	.413	.54
''	''	14	.153	1.40	''	.58
''	''	28	.165	1.43	''	.59
''	''	56	.187	1.47	''	.61
''	''	90	.191	1.50	''	.62
''	''	180	.199	1.52	''	.63
8-41	.442	368	.210	1.55	.410	.64
		Mix C				
9-9	.582	7	.131	1.34	.350	.47
''	''	14	.157	1.41	''	.49
''	''	28	.176	1.46	''	.51
''	''	56	.195	1.51	''	.53
''	''	90	.205	1.54	''	.54
''	''	180	.214	1.56	''	.55
8-42	.595	368	.222	1.58	.340	.54

those pastes in which the original cement content does not exceed about 45 percent of the over-all paste volume. For this lower range of cement contents the position of the line OB corresponds to $w_n/c = 0.224$; hence, eq. (13) becomes

$$V_s = 1.58\ c\,v_c \Big]_{c\,v_c\ \leq\ 0.45} \cdots\cdots\cdots\cdots\cdots\cdots (14)$$

For pastes having cement contents greater than 45 percent of the over-all volume, the ultimate volume of the solid phase in the hardened paste is not directly proportional to $c\,v_c$. Instead, the relationship, as shown in Fig. 5-8, is

$$V_s = 0.5 + 0.5\ c\,v_c \Big]_{0.45\ \leq\ c v_c\ \leq\ 1.0} \cdots\cdots\cdots\cdots\cdots (15)$$

Eq. (14) is represented in Fig. 5-8 by line OB; eq. (15), by BC.

TABLE 5-15—COMPUTATION OF VOLUME OF SOLID PHASE
Cement 15013J

$\dfrac{v_n}{v_e} = \dfrac{0.82}{0.316} = 2.60$; C_3S 39 percent; C_2S 29 percent; C_3A 14 percent; C_4AF 7 percent;

Specific surface $= 1810$ sq cm per g; Computations based on eq. (12).

(1)	(2)	(3)	(4)	(5)	(6)	(7)
Ref. No. Series 254-8 & 9	w_o/c	Age, days	$\dfrac{w_n}{c}$ (g/g)	$\dfrac{V_s}{c\,v_e}$	$\dfrac{c\,v_e}{}$ cc per cc of paste	V_s
			Mix A			
9–10	.324	7	.149	1.39	.488	.68
,,	,,	14	.164	1.43	,,	.70
,,	,,	28	.171	1.44	,,	.70
,,	,,	56	.180	1.47	,,	.72
,,	,,	90	.191	1.50	,,	.73
,,	,,	180	.188	1.49	,,	.73
8–46	.332	339	.218	1.57	.481	.75
			Mix B			
9–11	.443	7	.156	1.41	.410	.58
,,	,,	14	.183	1.48	,,	.60
,,	,,	28	.177	1.46	,,	.60
,,	,,	56	.208	1.54	,,	.63
,,	,,	90	.215	1.56	,,	.64
,,	,,	180	.236	1.61	,,	.66
8–47	.453	333	.241	1.63	.405	.66
			Mix C			
9–12	.611	7	.158	1.41	.335	.47
,,	,,	14	.183	1.48	,,	.49
,,	,,	28	.203	1.53	,,	.51
,,	,,	56	.221	1.58	,,	.53
,,	,,	90	.236	1.61	,,	.54
,,	,,	180	.245	1.64	,,	.55
8–48	.599	333	.253	1.66	.339	.56

Lines OD and DC in Fig. 5-8 represent the bulk volumes of the solid phase (see Fig. 5-5) corresponding to the solid volumes represented by OB and BC. Line OD corresponds to eq. (10) with $w_n/c = 0.224$. For a saturated paste vertical distances in the area above OD represent capillary water; those in the area between ODC and OBC represent gel water; those in the area $OBCO$ represent non-evaporable water.

In Part 3, data were presented showing that the evaporable water cannot be less than $4V_m$. (V_m = weight of water in first adsorbed layer.) It was shown that as a consequence of this the maximum weight ratio of the non-evaporable to the total water would be between about 0.47 and 0.51, depending on the type of cement. For a Type I cement it would be about 0.50. It is of interest to compare these weight ratios with the volume ratio indicated by BC in Fig. 5-8. (The points along

TABLE 5-16—COMPUTATION OF VOLUME OF SOLID PHASE
Cement 15365

$$\frac{v_n}{v_c} = \frac{0.82}{0.319} = 2.57; \ C_3S \ 45 \text{ percent}; \ C_2S \ 28 \text{ percent}; \ C_3A \ 13 \text{ percent}; \ C_4AF \ 7 \text{ percent};$$

Specific surface $= 1640$ sq cm per g; Computations based on eq. (12).

(1)	(2)	(3)	(4)	(5)	(6)	(7)
Ref. No. Series 254-8 & 9	w_a/c	Age, days	$\dfrac{w_n}{c}$ (g/g)	$\dfrac{V_s}{c\,v_c}$	$c\,v_c$ cc per cc of paste	V_s
			Neat cement			
9-15A	.244	7	.115	1.30	.558	.72
"	"	14	.126	1.32	"	.74
"	"	28	.136	1.35	"	.75
"	"	56	.140	1.36	"	.76
"	"	90	.145	1.37	"	.77
"	"	180	.155	1.40	"	.78
			Mix A			
9-13	.319	7	.133	1.34	.490	.66
"	"	14	.152	1.39	"	.68
"	"	28	.149	1.38	"	.68
"	"	56	.179	1.46	"	.72
"	"	90	.179	1.46	"	.72
"	"	180	.182	1.47	"	.72
			Mix B			
9-14	.439	7	.139	1.36	.412	.56
"	"	14	.171	1.44	"	.59
"	"	28	.184	1.47	"	.61
"	"	56	.210	1.54	"	.63
"	"	90	.215	1.55	"	.64
"	"	180	.222	1.57	"	.65
			Mix C			
9-15	.587	7	.153	1.39	.351	.49
"	"	14	.186	1.48	"	.52
"	"	28	.210	1.54	"	.54
"	"	56	.221	1.57	"	.55
"	"	90	.230	1.59	"	.56
"	"	180	.255	1.66	"	.58

this line represent cements of average Type I composition.) To make this comparison it is necessary to convert the volume ratio represented by BC to the corresponding weight ratio:

$$w_n v_n = 0.5\ w_t v_t \quad \text{(Fig. 5-8)} \dots \dots \dots \dots \dots (16)$$

$$v_t = 1 - 0.279\ \frac{w_n}{w_t} \quad \text{(eq. (8))}.$$

$$v_n = 0.82\ \text{(assumed)} \dots \dots \dots \dots \dots (17)$$

Substitution of eq. (8) and (17) into eq. (16) gives

$$\frac{w_n}{w_t} = 0.52\ .$$

Thus, the maximum weight ratio of w_n to w_t as estimated from the specific-volume measurements is higher than that estimated from the adsorption measurements by 6 percent of the smaller value.   This discrepancy is probably the result of applying eq. (8) for v_t instead of experimental values for the particular cements represented in Fig. 5-8, using the approximate value 0.82 for v_n, and using the estimated weight

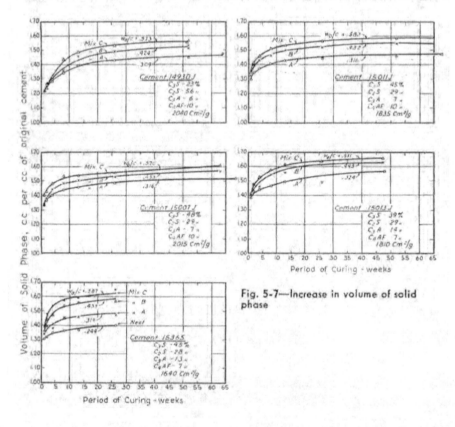

Fig. 5-7—Increase in volume of solid phase

TABLE 5-17—COMPUTATION OF VOLUME OF SOLID PHASE FROM w_n/c FOR PASTES 6 MONTHS OLD OR OLDER

All pastes were from mortar cubes unless otherwise indicated.

(1) Cement No.	(2) Specific surface, cm²/g	(3) Ref. No. Series 254-8 & 9	(4) w_n/c	(5) Age, days	(6) w_n/c	(7) v_c	(8) $\dfrac{0.82}{v_c}\ (=k)$	(9) $\dfrac{V_s}{c\,v_c}$	(10) Cement content of paste ($=c\,v_c$)	(11) V_s
					Neat cement					
14675	—	254-18	.120	4 yr.	.079*	.318	2.58	1.20	.72	.86
15365	1640	9-15A	.244	180	.155	.319	2.57	1.40	.558	.78
					Mix A					
14030J	2040	8-1	.311	447	.181	.311	2.64	1.48	.494	.73
15007J	2015	8-28	.344	480	.198	.314	2.61	1.52	.471	.72
15011J	1835	8-40	.319	478	.184	.312	2.63	1.48	.490	.73
15013J	1810	8-46	.332	339	.218	.316	2.60	1.57	.481	.75
15365	1640	9-13	.319	180	.182	.319	2.57	1.47	.490	.72
Average								1.50	.485	.73
					Mix B					
14030J	2040	8-2	.443	362	.201	.311	2.64	1.53	.407	.62
15007J	2015	8-29	.464	440	.217	.314	2.61	1.57	.398	.62
15011J	1835	8-41	.442	368	.210	.312	2.63	1.55	.410	.64
15013J	1810	8-47	.453	333	.241	.316	2.60	1.63	.405	.66
15365	1640	9-14	.439	180	.222	.319	2.57	1.57	.412	.65
Average								1.57	.406	.64
					Mix C					
14030J	2040	9-3	.573	365	.214	.311	2.64	1.56	.347	.54
15007J	2015	8-30	.595	440	.232	.314	2.61	1.61	.340	.55
15011J	1835	8-42	.505	368	.222	.312	2.63	1.58	.340	.54
15013J	1810	8-48	.599	333	.253	.316	2.60	1.66	.339	.56
15365	1640	9-15	.587	180	.255	.319	2.57	1.66	.351	.58
Average								1.61	.343	.55

*w_n computed from V_m.

524 Powers and Brownyard

ratio based on an average ratio between V_m and w_n that may be in error by as much as 10 percent for a particular cement.

It may be concluded that Table 5-10 and line BC of Fig. 5-8 are substantially in agreement in showing that the maximum possible weight ratio of non-evaporable water to total water is about $\frac{1}{2}$.

Limit of hydration for pastes of high cement content

As already noted, line BC appears to be an upper limit to the amount of hydration (in terms of w_n) that can occur in pastes of high cement content. The data at hand are not sufficient to prove whether this is an absolute limit or whether, given sufficient time, the points will gradually move higher. However, the fact that one of the points represents a water-cured paste 4 years old gives strong support to the supposition that the line as shown marks the upper limit. The significance of the position of line BC and whether or not its slope remains the same may not at first be apparent. Consider the following alternative possibilities.

(1) The process of filling the available space with hydration products could be likened to filling a vessel with like-size spheres; at any given stage in the filling the total void space in the vessel would represent the unfilled space plus the pore space between the spheres; the void space

TABLE 5-18—COMPUTATION OF THE VOLUMES OF THE SOLID
PHASE IN SPECIMENS FROM SERIES 254-7

Cement 14675

$$\frac{V_s}{c\,v_c} = 1 + \frac{v_n}{v_c}\frac{w_n}{c} \quad ; \quad \frac{v_n}{v_c} = \frac{0.82}{0.318} = 2.58$$

Ref. No. 254-7	w_n/c			$1 + 2.58(w_n/c)$			cc_c cc per cc of paste	$(1 + 2.58\,w_n/c)cv_c = V_s$ cc/cc of paste		
	28d	56d	6 mo.	28d	56d	6 mo.		28d	56d	6 mo.
Mortar specimens									
7-1	.1445	.1485	.1626	1.37	1.38	1.42	.554	.76	.77	.79
7-2	.1585	.1605	.1763	1.41	1.41	1.46	.534	.75	.76	.78
7-3	.1665	.1705	.1817	1.43	1.44	1.47	.515	.74	.74	.76
7-4	.1895	.1870	.2046	1.49	1.48	1.53	.477	.71	.71	.73
7-5	.2045	.2115	.2351	1.53	1.55	1.61	.421	.64	.65	.68
7-6	.2115	.2275	.2337	1.55	1.59	1.60	.354	.55	.56	.57
7-7	.2155	.2275	.2303	1.56	1.59	1.59	.306	.48	.49	.49
Cement-silica specimens									
	35d	63d	6 mo.	35d	63d	6 mo.		35d	63d	6 mo.
7-18	.1995	.2007	.2160	1.52	1.52	1.56	.472	.72	.72	.74
7-28	.2133	.2164	.2324	1.55	1.56	1.60	.421	.65	.66	.67
7-38	.2246	.2270	.2433	1.58	1.59	1.63	.373	.59	.59	.61
7-48	.2323	.2303	.2497	1.60	1.59	1.64	.340	.54	.54	.56
7-58	.2351	.2304	.2456	1.61	1.59	1.63	.326	.52	.52	.53

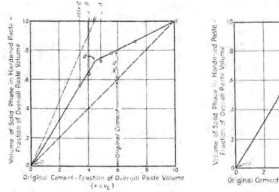 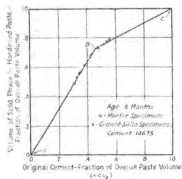

Fig. 5-8 (left) —Relationship between volume of solid phase and original cement content at virtually ultimate hydration
Data from Table 5-17

Fig. 5-9 (right)—Relationship between volume of solid phase and volume of original cement
Data from Table 5-18
See Appendix to Part 2 for description of original specimens

within the vessel could not be reduced below the total volume of the spaces between the spheres when the vessel is full of spheres.

(2) The process could be likened to that of filling a vessel with relatively large spheres and then sifting in smaller spheres that could occupy the spaces between the larger spheres.

If the amount of non-evaporable water reached a point on the line BC and then remained there regardless of the length of the period of curing, thus indicating an unchanging ratio between evaporable and non-evaporable water, the indication would be that the hydration products have a characteristic minimum porosity that cannot be reduced. This would indicate that the space becomes filled by a process analogous to that described in (1). If with continued hydration the slope of BC should become smaller, this would show that the ratio of non-evaporable to evaporable water gradually increases and that the colloidal hydration products become less porous as hydration proceeds. This would indicate that the space becomes filled in the manner pictured in (2); that is, the pores of the gel first formed would become partly filled by hydration products formed at a later time. As pointed out above, the fact that the specimen cured 4 years is represented by a point on BC of Fig. 5-8 is strong evidence that the porosity of the hydration products does not decrease as hydration proceeds. Hence, hydration seems to be a process of forming new products without changing the characteristics of products already formed.

This evidence that the hydration products have a characteristic porosity is compatible with the theory of formation of the gels. When the solid material precipitates from solution, the colloidal particles initially formed by the aggregating molecules are drawn together by interparticle forces having an intensity characteristic of the system. The gel is pictured as a mass of colloidal particles drawn together in random arrangement and held by the forces of flocculation and probably to some extent by rudimentary, submicroscopic crystal growths. If the particles composing the gel (the "micelles") are larger than the normal spaces in the gel, later deposition of new gel in such spaces would seem unlikely. (See Part 3.)

Limit of hydration with capillary water continuously available

For mixes falling to the left of point B, the time required for the solid phase in a given paste to attain a volume represented by a point on the line OB is greater the greater the original cement content of the paste. (It should be noted that time is not represented in Fig. 5-8 or 5-9.) But apparently this line is reached eventually and it marks a limit to the amount of hydration even though capillary water is present in the paste. Such a result would be expected if the position of line OB corresponded to complete hydration of all the cement. However, complete hydration probably does not occur except in cements of unusually high specific surface. Observations by Brownmiller[3] on pastes of $w/c = 0.4$ by weight ($c \; v_e = 0.44$ cc per cc of paste) indicate that all but the coarsest particles of cement, probably those having diameters less than about 40 microns, become completely hydrated if water-cured long enough. According to Brownmiller, a Type III cement of about 2600 specific surface appeared to be about 99 percent hydrated at the seventh day. A Type I cement, specific surface 1800, appeared about 85 percent hydrated at the 28th day. In a section from concrete pavement 6 years old, the cement (specific surface unknown but probably not over 1800) in the part photographed appeared to be completely hydrated except for one 75-micron particle.

Fig. 5-10 gives data obtained in this laboratory on the influence of fineness on the extent of hydration as indicated by the non-evaporable water content. These results indicate that the ultimate increase in solid volume per cc. of original cement is smaller the coarser the cement. These indications that coarse particles of cement remain unhydrated for an indefinite period even when free water is present show that the apparent cessation of hydration is, for cements of ordinary fineness, not due to the attainment of chemical equilibrium. Apparently, the gel around the coarser cement grains becomes so dense that water cannot penetrate it. Absolute stoppage of flow through the gel is hardly conceivable, however.

It is more likely that water continues to penetrate to the cement but does it so slowly that we are unable to detect the effect.

Estimation of volume of unreacted cement

The amount of unreacted cement in hardened paste can be expressed as follows:

$$\frac{V_{uc}}{cv_c} = 1 - n\,\frac{w_n v_n}{c\,v_c} \quad \dots\dots\dots\dots\dots\dots\dots\dots\dots\dots\dots\dots(18)$$

where

$\dfrac{V_{uc}}{cv_c}$ = volume of unreacted cement per unit volume of original cement, and

n = cc. of hydration products per cc. of non-evaporable water.

As said before, we have no data on the amount of unreacted cement in the specimens used in these studies. However, from Brownmiller's observations, mentioned above, it seems reasonable to assume that at ultimate hydration, about 90 percent of a Type I cement becomes hydrated. Making this assumption, assuming that $w_n/c = 0.24$ at ultimate hydration, and letting $v_n/v_c = 2.59$, we obtain

$$0.1 = 1 - n(2.59 \times 0.24).$$

Hence, $\qquad\qquad\qquad n = 1.45.$

With n thus estimated we may write

$$\frac{V_{uc}}{cv_c} = 1 - 3.75\,w_n/c \quad \dots\dots\dots\dots\dots\dots\dots\dots\dots(19)$$

It should be understood that this relationship is only a rough estimate. The value of n will depend on the fineness of the cement, the coarser the cement, the smaller n. For example, if when $w_n/c = 0.24$ the cement is actually completely hydrated, n would equal about 1.6; if 80

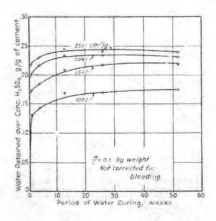

Fig. 5-10—Effect of fineness of grinding on rate and amount of hydration
Cement 14560
C₃S-60%, C₂S-17%, C₃A-7%, C₄AF-13%

percent hydrated, about 1.3. The purpose of the computation is to show the order of magnitude of n and to provide a basis for showing, in the following section, how the correct data would be represented graphically if we had them.

Graphical summary of data on volumes of various phases in hardened cement paste

Fig. 5-11 gives a summary of the relationships brought out in the preceding discussions.

It should be understood that the diagrams represent average values. The slope of BC (eq. (15)) would vary slightly among pastes made with different cements, according to differences in the ratios w_n/w_t for the various cements. Likewise, the relationship between the slope of OB (eq. (13)) and that of OD (eq. (9)) depends on V_m/w_n. The slope of OB at ultimate hydration would be smaller the coarser the cement. Moreover, the slope of OE (eq. (18)) would depend on the fineness and other characteristics of the cement.

With respect to eq. (18), it should be clear that this equation can hold only up to the ordinate of point B. Beyond that point the locus of the point representing unreacted cement must be the straight line EC.

At 0 percent hydration, only the diagonal line would appear, representing unreacted cement and capillary water. At this stage, the capillaries are the spaces between the original cement grains. The manner in which the new phases develop as hydration proceeds may be seen by comparing the four diagrams in consecutive order.

SOME PRACTICAL ASPECTS OF THE RESULTS

No attempt was made in this paper to discuss the implications of the data and the relationships that have been presented. However, the following fairly obvious matters may be pointed out:

(1) Pastes in which the original cement constitutes more than 45 percent of the over-all volume cannot become hydrated to the same extent as pastes containing less cement. In terms of weight ratio, this means that if w_o/c is less than 0.40, ultimate hydration will be restricted. Therefore, conclusions about the extent of hydration of cement in ordinary concrete should not be drawn from data obtained from standard test-pieces—w/c = about 0.25. (The numerical limits mentioned above probably are different for cements of different specific surfaces; the coarser the cement the lower the limiting w_o/c. For specific surfaces between 1600 and 2000, the figures given are satisfactory.)

(2) The average rate of hydration is lower the lower w_o/c. Therefore, the age-strength relationship for ordinary concrete cannot be the same as that for standard test pieces of low w_o/c.

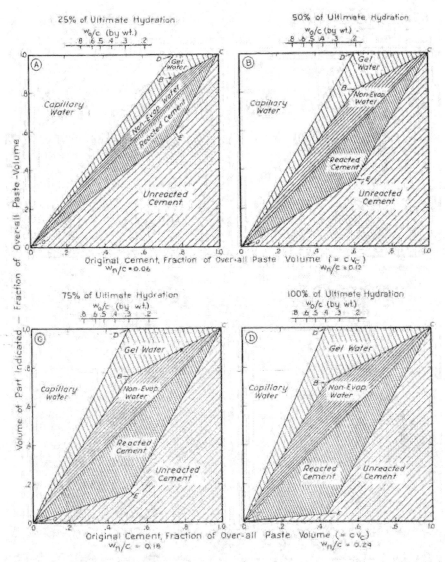

Fig. 5-11—Relationship between volumes of various phases in saturated hardened paste and original cement content at ultimate hydration

(3) The substance that gives concrete its strength and hardness is the solid material formed by the hydration of portland cement. In Fig. 5-11 this cementing substance is represented by the vertical distance from *OEC* to *ODC* at the point on the scale of abscissas representing the original cement content of the paste. The capillary spaces, when present, are distributed through this

substance and weaken it. Therefore, the cementing substance (not the paste as a whole) has its maximum possible strength if the hardened paste can be represented by the ordinate passing through points E, B, and D, or by any ordinate to the right of that one.

(4) It might seem from the foregoing paragraph that a paste represented by the ordinate through EBD has the maximum possible strength and therefore that still richer pastes (necessarily molded under pressure) would be no stronger. However, a limited amount of data obtained from specimens molded under high pressure indicates that the strength of the paste as a whole increases as the composition is made to fall farther to the right of the ordinate passing through EBD. In view of the evidence that the density of the cementing substance is the same in all such pastes, it is concluded that the increase in strength is due to the decrease in the thickness of the layer of cement between the particles of mineral aggregate. In this connection, the unreacted cement may be considered to be a part of the aggregate. The increase may also be due in part to an increase in the degree of "self-desiccation" of the gel, which would be expected to increase with the proportion of unreacted-cement.

(5) The hydraulic radius of the pores in the paste and the porosity are smaller the smaller the proportion of capillary space in the hardened paste. The hydraulic radius is at its lowest possible value when the composition of the hardened paste can be represented on the ordinate passing through points E, B, and D of Fig. 5-11. Porosity of the paste as a whole continues to decrease as the composition is made to fall farther to the right, but the hydraulic radius is not further reduced.

(6) The permeability of hardened pastes to fluids under external pressure probably depends almost entirely on the proportion of capillary water, owing to the extreme smallness of the gel-pores. Hence, permeability is practically zero when the paste can be represented by the ordinate passing through points E, B, and D. This is discussed further in Part 7.

GENERAL SUMMARY OF PART 5

Nomenclature:

c = cement, g per g of saturated paste

w_t = total water, g per g of saturated paste

w_n = non-evaporable water, g per g of saturated paste

w_d = compressed water, g per g of saturated paste

w_c = capillary water, g per g of saturated paste

w_a = adsorbed water, g per g of saturated paste

w_g = gel water, g per g of saturated paste

v_c = specific volume of cement

v_t =   "   "   " total water

v_n =   "   "   . " non-evaporable water

v_d =   "   "   " compressed water

v_g =   "   "   " gel water

B' = ratio of adsorbed water to non-evaporable water

B = $(1 + B')$

k = ratio of V_m to w_n

V_m = constant of B.E.T. equation, proportional to surface area of the gel

V_B = bulk volume of solid phase. It differs from the over-all volume of the paste by the volume of the capillary space outside the gel.

V_s = volume of solid matter in the paste

V_{uc} = volume of unreacted cement in the paste

n = cc of hydration product per cc of non-evaporable water

(1) The total water in a saturated specimen can be divided into two categories: (a) that which has a specific volume less than 1.0; (b) that which has a specific volume equal to 1.0. All the water having a specific volume less than unity is called compressed water. It comprises the non-evaporable water and a part of the evaporable water.

(2) The mean specific volumes of the total water contents were computed from the measured volumes of the saturated granular samples and the volumes and weights of the ingredients, assuming that the cement retained its original volume.

(3) The mean specific volume of the total water in a saturated paste is given by the expression

$$v_t = 1 - 0.279 \frac{w_n}{w_t}.$$

w_n/w_t can vary from zero to about 0.50. Hence, the mean specific volume of the total water varies from 1.0 as a maximum ($w_n = 0$) to about 0.860 as a minimum ($w_n/w_t = 0.50$). Among different types of cement, w_n/w_t (maximum) ranges from 0.47 to 0.51.

(4) When w_n/w_t = about 0.50, the sample contains no capillary water. Hence, 0.860 is the mean of the specific volumes of the non-evaporable water and the gel water.

(5) The mean specific volume of the gel water is estimated to be about 0.90; that of the capillary water is 1.0.

(6) The bulk volume of the solid phase as a fraction of the over-all volume of the paste is given by the expression

$$\frac{V_B}{c\,v_c} = 1 + \frac{w_n}{c}\,(1 + 4k)\,\frac{0.860}{v_c} \quad \text{(for } 0 \gtrsim V_B \gtrsim 1\text{)}$$

For an average Type I cement, $k = 0.255$ and V_B becomes

$$V_B = \left[1 + 5.5\,\frac{w_n}{c}\right] c\,v_c$$

(7) The absolute volume of the solid phase as a fraction of the total paste volume is given as

$$V_s = \left[1 + \frac{v_n}{v_c} \cdot \frac{w_n}{c}\right] c\,v_c$$

(8) The ratio of the solid volume after hydration to the solid volume of the original cement, $V_s/(c\,v_c)$, varies from 1.0 when $w_n/c = 0$ to about 1.63 when w_n/c is maximum. The upper limit is probably lower than 1.63 for cements coarser than those used in this study (1600 to 2000 sq cm per g and may be slightly higher for finer cements.

(9) For pastes having original cement contents greater than about 0.45 of absolute volume, the ultimate solid volume is about

$$V_s = 0.5 + 0.5\ cv_c \Big]_{0.45 \leq cv_c \leq 1.0}$$

(10) The extent of hydration in water-cured pastes having original cement contents below 0.45 by absolute volume is apparently limited by the relative amount of $+40$ micron particles in the original cement. In the richer pastes it is limited by the space available for the hydration products.

* * * * *

For comments on some practical implications of the results, see the section immediately preceding this General Summary.

REFERENCES

(1) A. J. Stamm and L. A. Hansen, *J. Phys. Chem.* v. 41, p. 1007 (1937); G. F. Davidson, *J. Textile Inst.* v. 18, T175 (1927); Stephen Brunauer, *The Adsorption of Gases and Vapors*, v. 1 (Princeton University Press, 1943), Chapter XII.

(2) R. P. Rossman and W. R. Smith, *Ind. Eng. Chem.* v. 35, p. 972 (1943).

(3) L. T. Brownmiller, *Proc. ACI*, v. 39, p. 193 (1943).

Title 43-5f —a part of PROCEEDINGS, AMERICAN CONCRETE INSTITUTE Vol. 43

JOURNAL
of the
AMERICAN CONCRETE INSTITUTE
(copyrighted)

Vol. 18 No. 7   7400 SECOND BOULEVARD, DETROIT 2, MICHIGAN   March 1947

Studies of the Physical Properties of Hardened Portland Cement Paste*

By T. C. POWERS†

Member American Concrete Institute

and T. L. BROWNYARD‡

Part 6. Relation of Physical Characteristics of the Paste to Compressive Strength
Part 7. Permeability and Absorptivity§

CONTENTS PART 6

RELATION OF PASTE STRUCTURE TO COMPRESSIVE STRENGTH

The compressive strengths of mortars and concretes depend on many variable factors. The effects of some of the factors, particularly certain properties of the hardened paste, will be discussed in this section.

*Received by the Institute July 8, 1946—scheduled for publication in seven installments: October 1946 to April, 1947. In nine parts:

Part 1. "A Review of Methods That Have Been Used for Studying the Physical Properties of Hardened Portland Cement Paste". ACI JOURNAL, October, 1946.
Part 2. "Studies of Water Fixation"—Appendix to Part 2. ACI JOURNAL, November, 1946.
Part 3. "Theoretical Interpretation of Adsorption Data." ACI JOURNAL, December, 1946.
Part 4. "The Thermodynamics of Adsorption"—Appendix to Parts 3 and 4. ACI JOURNAL, January 1947.
Part 5. "Studies of the Hardened Paste by Means of Specific-Volume Measurements." ACI JOURNAL February, 1947.
Part 6. "Relation of Physical Characteristics of the Paste to Compressive Strength."
Part 7. "Permeability and Absorptivity."
Part 8. "The Freezing of Water in Hardened Portland Cement Paste."
Part 9. "General Summary of Findings on the Properties of Hardened Portland Cement Paste."

†Manager of Basic Research, Portland Cement Assn. Research Laboratory, Chicago 10, Ill.
‡Navy Dept., Washington, D. C., formerly Research Chemist, Portland Cement Assn. Research Laboratory, Chicago 10, Ill.
§The characteristics of the cements mentioned in this section may be found in the Appendix to Part 2.

The ratio of increase in solid phase to available space

At the time when fresh cement paste of normal properties first congeals, its final volume is established except for a relatively minute expansion in volume that occurs during subsequent hydration and the small volume changes that accompany drying and wetting. Therefore, the space available for the increase in volume of the solid phase is initially equal to the volume occupied by water.

We may tentatively assume that the increase in strength that accompanies an increase in extent of hydration is a function of the increase in the volume of the solid phase per unit of volume of initially water-filled space. In this connection it seems logical (though not essential) to consider the volume of the solid phase to be the sum of the volume of the solid matter and the volume of its associated voids, that is, to consider the bulk volume of the solid phase, rather than its absolute volume. (See Part 5.)

As shown in Part 5, the increase in bulk volume of the solid phase is about

$$0.860 \ (w_n + 4V_m)$$

w_n is the weight of the water that has become a part of the solid phase and therefore represents the increase in absolute volume. $4V_m$ is the weight of the water required to fill the voids of the gel. 0.860 is the mean of the specific volumes of these two classes of water. Hence,

$$\frac{\text{increase in solid phase}}{\text{original space available}} = \frac{0.860(w_n + 4V_m)}{w_o} \quad \dots\dots\dots\dots(1)$$

where w_o is the original water content after bleeding.

For any given cement, V_m/w_n is a constant (see Part 3). Hence, the solid-space ratio is, in general,

$$X' = 0.860 \ \frac{w_n}{w_o} \ (1 + 4k) \dots\dots\dots\dots\dots(2)$$

or

$$X' = 0.860 \ \frac{V_m}{w_o} \left(\frac{1 + 4k}{k} \right) \dots\dots\dots\dots\dots(3)$$

where X' = ratio of increase in solid phase to original water content. It will be shown that compressive strength, f_c, is related to X' by an empirical equation of the form

$$f_c = mX' + B \dots\dots\dots\dots\dots(4)$$

where m is the slope of the empirical line and B, its intercept on the f_c axis.

Substitution for X' from eq. (2) and (3) gives

$$f_c = M' \ \frac{V_m}{w_o} + B \dots\dots\dots\dots\dots(5)$$

and

$$f_c = kM' \frac{w_n}{w_o} + B \ , \dots\dots\dots\dots\dots\dots\dots\dots\dots\dots (6)$$

where

$$M' = 0.860 \left(\frac{1 + 4k}{k} \right) m \ .$$

The constants M' and B can be evaluated by plotting observed values of f_c versus V_m/w_o or w_n/w_o. Such data for four different cements are given in Tables 6-1, 6-2, and 6-4* and are plotted in Fig. 6-1 and 6-2. The points represent mixes A, B, and C of Series 254-9 and the mixes used in Series 254-11, where they were the same as A and B of 254-9. The curing periods ranged from 7 days to about 1 year.

The straight line drawn in Fig. 6-1 represents the relationship

$$f_c = 120{,}000 \frac{V_m}{w_o} - 3600 \ \dots\dots\dots\dots\dots\dots\dots\dots\dots (7)$$

It will be noted that the deviations of the individual points from this line seem to be random. That is, there is no indication that the points for any particular age or cement or mix can be distinguished by their positions with respect to the line. In view of the fact that V_m/w_n (i.e., k) differs considerably among the four cements, it seems that strength is not much influenced by this ratio. If w_n represents all the hydration products and V_m only the gel (material of high specific surface—see Part 3), this in-

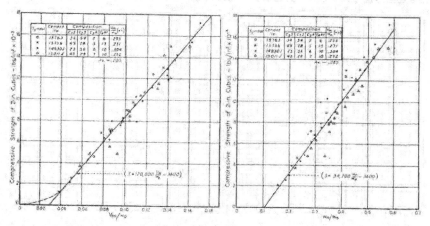

Fig. 6-1 (left)—Relationship between compressive strength and V_m/w_o for cements low in C_3A

Data from Tables 6-1, 6-2, & 6-4, Series 254-8-9 & 11

Fig. 6-2 (right)—Strength versus w_n/w_o for the same materials represented in Fig. 6-1

Series 254-8-9 & 11

*All Part 6 tables follow text pp. 858 to 864.

dicates that strength depends primarily on the gel and is therefore little influenced by differences in w_n when V_m is fixed.

This point is illustrated further by Fig. 6-2, where f_c is plotted against w_n/w_o. The straight line has the slope Mk where $M = 120{,}000$ and $k = 0.285$, the mean value of k for the four cements. That is, the equation for the line is $f_c = 34{,}200 \dfrac{w_n}{w_o} - 3600$. Although the points scatter to a similar degree, the scattering in Fig. 6-2 differs from that in Fig. 6-1 in that there is clear evidence of segregation of the triangles (representing cement 15011J) whereas in Fig. 6-1 the points are rather well mixed.

The gel-space ratio

It thus appears that the increase in strength is directly proportional to the increase in V_m/w_o regardless of age, original water-cement ratio, or identity of cement. Accordingly, it appears advisable to discard the assumption that strength is a function of the ratio of the total increase in solid phase to available space, in favor of the assumption that it is a function of the ratio of the volume of the gel to the original space available. We may call this the gel-space ratio. Thus, we may assume that

$$X = \beta \frac{V_m}{w_o} \dotfill (8)$$

where $X =$ gel-space ratio
$\beta =$ proportionality between V_m and the total volume of the gel.

Substitution of eq. (8) into eq. (4) gives

$$f_c = M \frac{V_m}{w_o} + B \dotfill (9)$$

where $M = m\beta$. Comparison of eq. (9), (6), and (4) shows that the above is merely a redefinition of the meaning of the slope of the line represented by eq. (4), the new definition taking into account the observation that k need not be included. Eq. (7) is thus now defined as the relationship between strength and the gel-space ratio.

Limitations of f_c vs. V_m/w_o relationship

Although the four cements represented in Fig. 6-1 differ considerably in C_3S and C_2S content, they are all similarly low in C_3A. When cements of various C_3A contents are included, the f_c vs. V_m/w_o relationship is found to be influenced by the C_3A content of the cement. This is illustrated in Fig. 6-3 and 6-4 (plotted from data of Tables 6-1 through 6-7), in which cements of various C_3A contents, including the cements of Fig. 6-1, are represented. Fig. 6-3 represents cements of low C_3A content;

Fig. 6-4, those of medium or high C_3A content. In each diagram, the diagonal line represents eq. (7).

In Fig. 6-4 it will be seen that the strengths developed by cements of medium or high C_3A content were in general lower than would be computed from eq. (7). (Certain exceptions will be discussed below.) The conclusion follows that cements of different C_3A contents develop different strengths at the same value of V_m/w_o, at least among those cements containing more than about 7 percent C_3A (computed).

Before further discussion of the relation between cement composition and strength, it is necessary to consider some other factors.

Effect of sand particles

In Fig. 6-3 and 6-4 three different series of tests are represented. Series 254-9 comprised three mixes, A, B, and C, as described previously (see Appendix to Part 2). Mix A contained sand and cement only. Mixes B and C contained sand and pulverized silica of cement fineness, the amount of the silica being 33 percent and 73 percent of the weight of the cement, respectively. Series 254-11 comprised mortar mixes of the same proportions as mixes A and B of Series 254-9. The data from these two series are, therefore, directly comparable. On the other hand, the data from Series 254-13 (appearing in Fig. 6-3A, B and Fig. 6-4A, B, and D) represent specimens containing only cement and pulverized silica, the amount of silica being 71 percent of the weight of the cement. The question, therefore, arises as to whether the results from Series 254-13 are comparable with those from the other two series.

In this connection it is of interest to examine Fig. 6-4C, which represents data obtained from mixes A, B, and C, and from neat cement. This is the only case where neat cement and mortar can be compared. Note that the strength of the neat cement at a given V_m/w_o exceeds by a considerable margin that of the specimens containing sand (No. 4 maximum size). The points appearing immediately below those representing neat cement are the ones representing mix A, which contained no pulverized silica, and mix B, which did contain silica. The results indicate, therefore, that the introduction of sand lowered the strength. It is presumed that the decrease in strength resulting from the introduction of sand is due to the decrease in homogeneity with respect to elastic properties, and possibly to a modification of the mode of failure as described by Terzaghi.[1]* On this basis one would not expect the introduction of pulverized silica to affect the strength adversely, owing to the smallness of the silica grains. Therefore, it would seem that neat cement specimens or specimens containing only pulverized silica as aggregate would not be directly comparable with specimens containing relatively coarse sand particles.

*See references at end of text, Part 6.

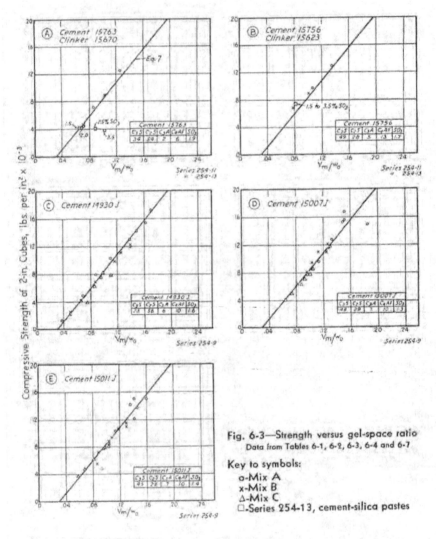

Fig. 6-3—Strength versus gel-space ratio
Data from Tables 6-1, 6-2, 6-3, 6-4 and 6-7

Key to symbols:
o-Mix A
x-Mix B
△-Mix C
□-Series 254-13, cement-silica pastes

However, the trend of the neat-cement points is such as to suggest that the strength of the neat cement and mortar would be equal at about $V_m/w_o = 0.10$. It happens that most of the points representing the cement-silica specimens of Series 254-13 fall near this point or lower on the V_m/w_o scale. Also, it may be observed that the strengths of these cement-silica specimens were about the same as or lower than the strengths obtained from the mortar specimens having equal values of V_m/w_o. It thus appears that, at least within the range of gel-space ratios that embraces the results from Series 254-13, the introduction of sand had little or no effect on strength and therefore that the mortars and cement-

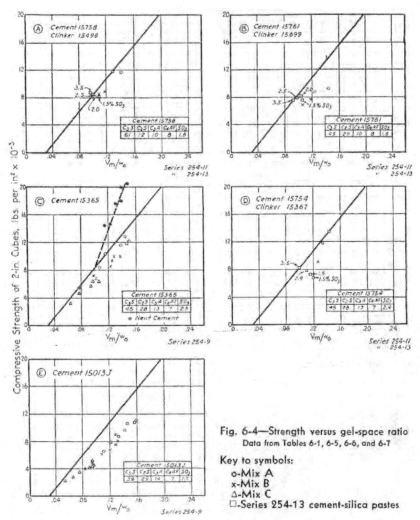

Fig. 6-4—Strength versus gel-space ratio
Data from Tables 6-1, 6-5, 6-6, and 6-7

Key to symbols:
o-Mix A
x-Mix B
△-Mix C
□-Series 254-13 cement-silica pastes

silica pastes can be compared directly in this instance. As brought out before, this indication is supported by the trend of the neat cement points appearing in Fig. 6-4C.

Influence of gypsum content of cement

The data from Series 254-13 offer a clue as to the cause of the relatively low strengths at a given V_m/w_o produced by the high C_3A cements. These data are given in Table 6-7 and are plotted in Fig. 6-3 and 6-4, as mentioned above. In this series, four cements were prepared from each of five different clinkers. The SO_3 content in each group of four cements ranged from 1.5 to 3.5 percent. Cement-silica cubes were made and tested after 28 days of water curing.

Note first the diagrams for the cements prepared from clinkers 15498, 15699, and 15367 in Fig. 6-4—medium or medium-high C_3A cements. In each case, increasing the gypsum content *increased* the strength to a value equal to or slightly greater than the mean of the low C_3A cements as represented by eq. (7) (that is, by the diagonal line).

As remarked above, it is somewhat questionable whether the data of Series 254-13 are comparable with eq. (7). Hence, the indications of the data must be taken with some reservation. However, it may tentatively be concluded that the relatively low strengths, at a given V_m/w_o, of cements of the type noted above can be increased and brought into line with the strengths of low C_3A cements by appropriate increases in gypsum content.

This conclusion was reached first by Lerch[2] in an investigation carried on parallel with this one. By means of calorimeter measurements of the rates of reaction and of strength and shrinkage tests, he found that the relatively low strength of high C_3A cements was associated with a premature depletion of gypsum during the early stages of hardening. Maximum strengths were produced when the gypsum content was so adjusted that the dissolved gypsum did not become depleted during the first 24 hours. Marked reductions in drying shrinkage also resulted from such an adjustment in gypsum content. Lerch's results have been confirmed in some respects by Whittaker and Wessels.[3]

It should be noted particularly that increasing the gypsum content of cements prepared from clinkers 15498 and 15367 increased the strength and at the same time *reduced* the ratio V_m/w_o. Since w_o was substantially the same for the different cements of a given group, this indicates that the reduction in the gel-space ratio was due to a reduction in the amount of gel. Thus we have a *reduction* in gel associated with an increase in strength whereas the normal effect would appear to be a reduction in strength. This apparent anomaly cannot yet be explained with assurance. However, it appears that the observed increase accompanying the decrease in gel content could be the result either of a change in the composition of the gel or of a reduction of the proportion of a gel having little intrinsic strength. Lerch[2] has pointed out that gypsum combines with C_3A to form calcium sulfoaluminate, most of the reaction taking place during the first few hours. Therefore, if the hydrate of C_3A is colloidal, as other evidence indicates, and if calcium sulfoaluminate is microcrystalline, the greater the amount of sulfoaluminate produced, the smaller V_m should be. With the type of cement considered here, the C_3A content is in excess of the gypsum on a combining-weight basis, and therefore the amount of calcium sulfoaluminate depends on the proportion of gypsum.

Hence, it appears that with medium- and high-C_3A cements, an increase in gypsum content reduces the ultimate amount of colloidal hydration product of C_3A. If this product is a hydrous calcium aluminate gel, it might have a weakening effect on the paste through an intrinsic weakness of such a gel. Another possibility is that the C_3A that does not react with gypsum becomes a constituent of a complex aluminosilicate gel. Presumably, it has a weakening effect on the gel.

The explanation given above is compatible with the results obtained from one of the low-C_3A cements but is possibly not in accord with the results from the other. As shown in Fig. 6-3, increasing the gypsum content of the low-C_3A cements prepared from clinker 15623 had little effect on either strength or gel-space ratio. This result is in accord with the above explanation. But with the cements prepared from clinker 15670, very low in C_3A, increasing the gypsum content greatly increased the gel content and slightly reduced the strength. This result is definitely not explained above. It might be that in this high-silica, low-R_2O_3 type of cement, the gypsum produces a colloidal hydrate, or causes some normally non-colloidal product to appear in the colloidal state. In either event the new colloidal product would have to be such as to have little effect on strength; that is, it would have no strength of its own and have no effect on the strength of the gel formed from other compounds. This matter will probably not be satisfactorily explained until new information on the constitution of hydration products is available.

Whatever the correct explanation may be, it is apparent that the strength of hardened paste depends on its chemical constitution as well as its gel-space ratio. This is substantially the same conclusion reached earlier by Bogue and Lerch.[4]

Effect of steam curing

The experiment with a steam-cured paste made of cement and pulverized silica was described in Part 2 and Part 3. No strength tests were made on this material, but the effects of the steam treatment can be estimated from the data published by Menzel.[5] These data show that steam-cured mixtures of cement and pulverized silica were as strong as or stronger than companion specimens cured normally. The adsorption data mentioned above indicate that the gel content of steam-cured material is not over 5 percent of that of the specimen normally cured for 28 days. This seems to be a clear demonstration that the gel-space ratio is not the controlling factor when curing temperature and pressure are variable. At least, it proves that the relation of f_c to V_m/w_0 found for specimens cured at one temperature and pressure will not hold at another widely different temperature and pressure.

Menzel's data indicate that among specimens cured at different temperatures ranging from 70 to 350 F, the properties of the specimens show no differences that are disproportionate to the difference in curing temperature. This is particularly well illustrated by the data on shrinkage. The plot of total shrinkage at 35 percent relative humidity vs. temperature of curing, results in a smooth curve having a negative slope that diminishes slowly and rather steadily with increase in temperature. (See Menzel's Fig. 8.) Likewise, the initial rate of water-loss increases progressively as the curing temperature increases. From this we conclude that the f_c-vs.-V_m/w_o relationship must change progressively as the temperature of curing is increased above normal. Presumably, it would change also if the temperature were lowered.

DISCUSSION AND SUMMARY

Werner and Giertz-Hedström[6] found that strength could be expressed as a function of the volume of solid phase *per unit volume of hardened paste*. The solid phase was defined as the volume of the original cement plus the water that is not evaporable in the presence of concentrated H_2SO_4. The plotted data of Werner and Giertz-Hedström (see their Fig. 9) showed that the increase in strength was approximately proportional to the increase in the volume of the solid phase over the initial volume in the fresh paste. Thus, the relationship found was virtually the same as that shown in Fig. 6-2 of this paper.

Lea and Jones[7] found a fairly good relationship between fixed water *per unit of original cement* and strength. The fixed water was determined on neat pastes, $w/c = 0.25$, and the strengths on 1:2:4 concrete cubes. Since w_o/c of the concrete was a constant, a measure of the extent of hydration would also be virtually equivalent to our w_n/w_o. However, since the extent of hydration was estimated from companion specimens of much lower w_o/c, the shape of the curve obtained was no doubt influenced by the difference between the rate of hydration of the neat cement and that of the same cement in concrete.

Giertz-Hedström[8] concluded from these experiments and those of several other investigators that "it is thus possible as a first approximation to regard strength as a function of the degree of hydration and independent of the kind of cement." However, he goes on to say, ". . . . this can obviously not be the whole truth, as emerges for instance from the spreading of test values." He points out also that tests by Bogue and Lerch on pastes made of pure C_3S and C_2S "indicate that the silicate gel, which is the sole cause of the hardening of dicalcium silicate, is also chiefly responsible for the hardening of tricalcium silicate, but is to a certain extent helped here by calcium hydroxide." However, the data of Bogue and Lerch are of doubtful significance with respect to this particular question. The original water-cement ratios of the pastes were not equal and therefore a measure of the extent of hydration alone was not an adequate description of the concentration of the hydration products in the space available to them.

Freyssinet[9] introduced two factors that he regarded as measures of important physical properties of hardened paste. These are:

(1) The "concentration of the cement," defined as:

$$\frac{\text{volume of hydrated cement}}{\text{volume of hydrated cement} + \text{volume of non-combined water}};$$

(2) The total area of the interstitial surfaces per unit volume of paste.

It will be seen that (1) represents the concept on which Giertz-Hedström based his analysis and that (2) is similar to the gel-space ratio as used by the authors.

Any attempt to express the strength of concrete or mortar as a function of only one independent variable is certain to meet with but limited success, at best, for the reason that more than one independent variable is involved. We have seen that in some combinations of paste and sand, the sand lowers the strength below that of the strength of pure paste of the same composition. Another factor influencing the strength of mortars and concretes is the existence of minute fissures under the aggregate particles, especially the larger particles. These fissures are the result of unequal settlement of paste and aggregate during the plastic state.[10,11,12] They occur to different degrees with different materials and proportions.

Another factor influencing strength is the air content, the higher the air content the lower the strength, other factors being equal. Weymouth[13] found that among plastic mixes the air content of fresh concrete depends on the water content and sand-cement ratio. He found also that the air content is approximately constant in different mixes of the same materials if the slump is constant. Therefore, variations in consistency of the fresh concrete will result in variations in strength of the hardened concrete (when other factors are equal) because of the corresponding variations in air content. The effect of air introduced by air-entraining agents is now well known.[14]

Also, although pertinent data are lacking, we may surmise that the strengths of adhesion between the hardened paste and the aggregate differ among concretes made with aggregates of different mineral composition. This will account for differences in strength, especially tensile strength.

All these independent factors influencing strength are secondary to the strength of the paste. Nevertheless, they cannot be ignored either in theoretical studies or construction practice. In the tests described in the foregoing pages most of these factors were absent, or were kept as near constant as possible. Consequently, the results depended mainly on the properties of the hardened paste. However, the problem of evaluating the factors influencing the strength of the paste is not much less complicated than that of the concrete as a whole. The degree of success achieved in this direction is indicated by the following summary of the results described in the foregoing pages.

(1) The strength of 2-in. mortar cubes made with cements of normal gypsum content and low C_3A content (less than about 7 or 8 percent) cured continuously wet at about 73 F conformed (within $\pm$ 10 percent) to the following relationship, regardless of differences in age or original water-cement ratio:

Compressive strength of 2-in. cubes, psi $= 120,000 \, \dfrac{V_m}{w_o} - 3600.$

(2) Under the same curing conditions, mortar cubes made with cement of medium or high C_3A contents, containing the normal amount of gypsum, produced strengths that are too low to conform with the above equation.

(3) Some cements of medium or high C_3A content could be brought into conformity with the above equation by increasing the gypsum content, the required increase differing among different cements. Increasing the gypsum content of such cements reduced the gel content of the hardened paste.

(4) The tests indicated that with cements low in C_3A both the gel-space ratio and the strength may be unaffected by an increase in gypsum content, or the strength may remain unaffected while the gel-space ratio is increased. In the last-mentioned case, the results were not in conformity with the equation.

(5) The relationship between strength and V_m/w_o given in the above equation did not apply to specimens cured at temperatures other than about 73 F.

(6) In general, strength could be expressed as a function of the volume of the hydration products and the space originally available for them, only when factors such as cement composition and curing conditions were not available.

When cements of ordinary C_3A content are compared, the findings given above show that the strength at a given V_m/w_o is highest for the low-C_3A cements. It should be noted that this observation does not pertain to the rate of hydration or the rate of strength development. Cements high in C_3A usually hydrate more rapidly and develop higher early strengths than those low in C_3A. The conclusion mentioned means that when two pastes of the same original water-cement ratio reach the same degree of hydration, as indicated by their gel-space ratios, the cement having the lower C_3A content will probably have the higher strength.

REFERENCES

(1) K. Terzaghi, *Proc. A.S.T.M.*, v. 45, p. 777.

(2) Wm. Lerch, A.S.T.M. Preprint A-4, 1946. See *A.S.T.M. Bulletin*, Jan. 1946.

(3) A. G. Whittaker and V. E. Wessels, *Rock Products*, v. 48, p. 95 (Aug. 1945).

(4) R. H. Bogue and Wm. Lerch, *Ind. Eng. Chem.* v. 26, p. 837 (1934) or Paper No. 27, Portland Cement Association Fellowship (Aug. 1934).

(5) Carl A. Menzel, *Proceedings*, ACI v. 31, p. 125 (1934).

(6) D. Werner and S. Giertz-Hedström, *Zement*, v. 20, pp. 984, 1000 (1931).

(7) F. M. Lea and F. E. Jones, *J. Soc. Chem. Ind.* v. 54, p. 63T (1935).

(8) S. Giertz-Hedström, "The Physical Structure of Hydrated Cements," Symposium on the Chemistry of Cements, Stockholm, 1938.

(9) E. Freyssinet, *Science et Industrie* (Jan. 1933).

(10) H. J. Gilkey, *Eng. News-Record*, v. 98, p. 242 (1927).

(11) T. C. Powers, *Proceedings*, ACI v. 25, p. 388 (1929); Bulletin 2, P.C.A. Research Laboratory (1939).

(12) I. L. Collier, *Proc. A.S.T.M.*, v. 30, Part II, p. 731 (1930).

(13) C. A. G. Weymouth, *Proc. A.S.T.M.*, v. 38, Part II, p. 354 (1938).

(14) C. E. Wuerpel, *Proceedings* ACI v. 42, p. 305 (1946); (See particularly bibliography in this paper).

TABLE 6-1—STRENGTHS AND GEL-SPACE RATIOS FOR SERIES 254-11

Ref. No. (S-254)	Mix	w_o/c	Age, days	Strength 2-in. cubes, psi	w_n/c	V_m/c	w_n/w_o	V_m/w_o
Cement 15758; clinker 15498; $V_m/w_n = 0.248$									
11–1	A	.334	28	11760	.171	.043	.512	.129
			90	11660	.191	.047	.572	.141
11–2	B	.460	28	8320	.196	.050	.426	.109
			90	8810	.223	.054	.485	.117
Cement 15756; clinker 15623; $V_m/w_n = 0.271$									
11–3	A	.318	28	9750	.123	.034	.387	.107
			90	13010	.149	.043	.468	.135
11–4	B	.446	28	6830	.132	.035	.296	.078
			90	9010	.168	.045	.377	.101
Cement 15763; clinker 15670; $V_m/w_n = 0.295$									
11–5	A	.324	28	7170	.092	.028	.284	.086
			90	12420	.134	.041	.414	.126
11–6	B	.437	28	4610	.101	.031	.231	.071
			90	8990	.149	.045	.341	.103
Cement 15761; clinker 15699; $V_m/w_n = 0.262$									
11–7	A	.334	28	8660	.162	.041	.485	.123
			90	9200	.180	.048	.539	.144
11–8	B	.468	28	6850	.185	.049	.395	.105
			90	7620	.212	.055	.453	.118
Cement 15754; clinker 15367; $V_m/w_n = 0.258$									
11–9	A	.328	28	11820	.170	.044	.518	.134
			90	13460	.195	.047	.594	.143
11–10	B	.449	28	7970	.197	.050	.439	.111
			90	9110	.230	.057	.512	.127

TABLE 6-2—STRENGTHS AND GEL-SPACE RATIOS FOR CEMENT 14930J—
SERIES 254-9
$V_m/w_n = 0.304$

Ref. No. (S-254)	w_o/c	Age, days	Strength 2-in. cubes, psi	w_n/c	V_m/c	w_n/w_o	V_m/w_o
			Mix A				
9-1	.309	7	4950	.080	.021	.259	.068
		14	7960	.099	.027	.320	.088
		28	10280	.107	.034	.346	.110
		56	12970	.129	.043	.417	.139
		90	14210	.150	.046	.485	.149
		180	15410	.162	.050	.524	.162
8-1	.311	447	17260	.181	.053	.582	.170
			Mix B				
9-2	.424	7	2580	.080	.021	.189	.050
		14	4320	.103	.028	.243	.066
		28	6930	.116	.037	.274	.087
		56	9860	.135	.049	.318	.116
		90	11180	.174	.053	.410	.125
		180	12310	.185	.059	.436	.139
8-2	.443	362	11910	.201	.062	.452	.140
			Mix C				
9-3	.573	7	1230	.082	.022	.143	.038
		14	2140	.090	.028	.157	.049
		28	3940	.121	.043	.211	.075
		56	6200	.164	.049	.286	.086
		90	7580	.185	.055	.322	.096
		180	8280	.201	.056	.350	.098
8-3	.595	362	7940	.210	.066	.353	.111

TABLE 6-3—STRENGTHS AND GEL-SPACE RATIOS FOR CEMENT 15007J—
SERIES 254-9

$V_m/w_n = 0.272$

Ref. No. (S-254)	w_o/c	Age, days	Strength 2-in. cubes, psi	w_n/c	V_m/c	w_n/w_o	V_m/w_o
			Mix A				
9-4	.316	7	9660	.126	.036	.399	.114
		14	11830	.140	.041	.443	.130
		28	12810	.154	.042	.488	.133
		56	15310	.168	.047	.532	.149
		90	15600	.173	.048	.548	.152
		180	16780	.184	.048	.583	.152
8-28	.344	479	14970	.198	.064	.576	.186
			Mix B				
9-5	.433	7	6380	.133	.036	.307	.083
		14	8080	.150	.042	.346	.097
		28	9400	.171	.045	.395	.104
		56	11080	.185	.049	.427	.113
		90	11600	.192	.056	.443	.129
		180	12150	.202	.055	.467	.127
8-29	.464	440	11120	.217	.058	.468	.125
			Mix C				
9-6	.570	7	4060	.156	.037	.274	.065
		14	5000	.163	.042	.286	.074
		28	6280	.184	.050	.323	.088
		56	7070	.204	.053	.358	.093
		90	7840	.205	.056	.360	.098
		180	8540	.213	.060	.374	.105
8-30	.595	479	7780	.232	.060	.390	.101

TABLE 6-4—STRENGTHS AND GEL-SPACE RATIOS FOR CEMENT 15011J—
SERIES 254-9

$$V_m/w_n = 0.272$$

Ref. No. (S-254)	w_o/c	Age, days	Strength 2-in. cubes, psi	w_n/c	V_m/c	w_n/w_o	V_m/w_o
			Mix A				
9-7	.316	7	8050	.114	.033	.361	.104
		14	10400	.133	.036	.421	.114
		28	12100	.143	.045	.453	.142
		56	13750	.156	.046	.494	.146
		90	14180	.164	.043	.519	.136
		180	15020	.170	.045	.538	.142
8-40	.319	478	15020	.184	.051	.576	.160
			Mix B				
9-8	.432	7	5550	.123	.037	.285	.086
		14	7140	.153	.038	.354	.088
		28	8900	.165	.045	.382	.104
		56	9500	.178	.047	.412	.109
		90	10720	.191	.051	.442	.118
		180	11020	.199	.056	.461	.130
8-41	.442	368	11500	.210	.058	.475	.131
			Mix C				
9-9	.582	7	3720	.131	.034	.225	.058
		14	4820	.157	.039	.270	.067
		28	6320	.176	.047	.302	.081
		56	4880	.195	.054	.335	.093
		90	7850	.205	.056	.352	.096
		180	7970	.214	.057	.368	.098
8-42	.595	368	8440	.222	.062	.373	.104

TABLE 6-5—STRENGTHS AND GEL-SPACE RATIOS FOR CEMENT 15013J—
SERIES 254-9

$$V_m/w_n = 0.244$$

Ref. No. (S-254)	w_o/c	Age, days	Strength 2-in. cubes, psi	w_n/c	V_m/c	w_n/w_o	V_m/w_o
			Mix A				
9-10	.324	7	6620	.149	.036	.460	.111
		14	7960	.164	.039	.506	.121
		28	8780	.171	.043	.528	.133
		56	9680	.180	.046	.555	.142
		90	10610	.191	.047	.590	.145
		180	11020	.188	.051	.580	.158
8-46	.332	339	10820	.218	.052	.656	.157
			Mix B				
9-11	.443	7	4010	.156	.037	.352	.084
		14	4940	.183	.042	.413	.095
		28	6120	.177	.048	.400	.108
		56	6740	.208	.053	.470	.120
		90	7600	.215	.057	.485	.129
		180	8060	.236	.058	.533	.131
8-47	.453	333	9040	.241	.058	.532	.128
			Mix C				
9-12	.611	7	2250	.158	.033	.259	.054
		14	2750	.183	.040	.299	.065
		28	3480	.203	.046	.332	.075
		56	4180	.221	.055	.362	.090
		90	4280	.236	.058	.386	.095
		180	4520	.245	.059	.401	.096
8-48	.599	333	5210	.253	.057	.422	.095

TABLE 6-6—STRENGTHS AND GEL-SPACE RATIOS FOR CEMENT 15365—
SERIES 254-9

$$V_m/w_n = 0.254$$

Ref. No. (S-254)	w_o/c	Age, days	Strength 2-in. cubes, psi	w_n/c	V_m/c	w_n/w_o	V_m/w_o
			Neat cement				
9–15A	.244	7	14440	.115	.028	.471	.115
		14	14640	.126	.030	.515	.123
		28	17600	.136	.032	.556	.131
		56	17960	.140	.034	.573	.139
		90	20000	.145	.034	.594	.139
		180	20500	.155	.036	.635	.148
			Mix A				
9–13	.319	7	8380	.133	.034	.417	.107
		14	10380	.152	.037	.476	.116
		28	11550	.149	.044	.467	.138
		56	11800	.179	.047	.561	.147
		90	12170	.179	.048	.561	.150
		180	12760	.182	.046	.571	.144
			Mix B				
9–14	.439	7	5340	.139	.034	.316	.078
		14	7170	.171	.043	.390	.098
		28	8480	.184	.054	.419	.123
		56	9400	.210	.055	.478	.125
		90	9870	.215	.056	.490	.128
		180	9940	.222	.060	.505	.137
			Mix C				
9–15	.587	7	3220	.153	.037	.260	.063
		14	4670	.186	.045	.317	.077
		28	5680	.210	.055	.358	.094
		56	6280	.221	.057	.376	.097
		90	6320	.230	.062	.392	.106
		180	6720	.255	.060	.435	.102

TABLE 6-7—STRENGTHS AND GEL-SPACE RATIOS WITH THE AMOUNT OF GYPSUM IN THE CEMENT AS A VARIABLE—SERIES 254-13

Cement-silica pastes

Ref. No. (S-254)	w_o/c	SO_3 cont. of cement, percent	28-day strength 2-in. cubes, psi	w_n/c	V_m/c	w_n/w_o	V_m/w_o
			Cements made from clinker 15367				
13–1	.493	1.5	6970	.215	.059	.435	.120
13–1B	.486	1.5	6640	.212	.058	.436	.119
13–2	.493	1.9	7630	.211	.056	.428	.113
13–2B	.488	1.9	6870	.216	.058	.442	.119
13–3	.489	2.4	8090	.208	.054	.425	.110
13–3B	.488	2.4	7610	.215	.055	.441	.113
13–4	.491	3.5	8240	.194	.048	.395	.098
13–4B	.492	3.5	8250	.204	.050	.414	.102
			Cements made from clinker 15623				
13–5	.470	1.5	7530	.152	.038	.323	.081
13–6	.474	2.0	7440	.151	.038	.319	.080
13–7	.473	2.5	7440	.152	.038	.321	.080
13–8	.480	3.5	7000	.144	.038	.300	.079
			Cements made from clinker 15699				
13–9	.498	1.5	7510	.199	.053	.400	.106
13–10	.499	2.0	8160	.194	.052	.389	.104
13–11	.499	2.5	7860	.192	.049	.385	.098
13–12	.498	3.5	7530	.184	.046	.369	.092
			Cements made from clinker 15498				
13–13	.488	1.5	8120	.208	.053	.426	.109
13–14	.487	2.0	8120	.199	.050	.409	.102
13–15	.493	2.5	8550	.200	.049	.405	.099
13–16	.491	3.5	8710	.190	.047	.387	.096
			Cements made from clinker 15670				
13–17	.476	1.5	4240	.111	.031	.233	.065
13–18	.479	2.0	4440	.118	.034	.246	.071
13–19	.483	2.5	4070	.184	.043	.380	.089
13–20	.486	3.5	3800	.209	.050	.431	.103

Part 7. Permeability and Absorptivity

CONTENTS PART 7

PERMEABILITY OF HARDENED PORTLAND CEMENT PASTE

The following discussion deals with the relationship between the physical properties of hardened paste and the rate at which water may flow through a saturated specimen of paste under a given pressure gradient. In view of the results published by Ruettgers, Vidal, and Wing,[1] we may assume that such flow takes place in accord with Darcy's law.

Darcy's law

Darcy's law for low-velocity flow, first found empirically from experiments with flow through beds of sand, may be written

$$\frac{dq}{dt}\frac{1}{A} = K_1\frac{\Delta h}{L} , \dots\dots\dots\dots\dots\dots\dots\dots (1)$$

where

$\dfrac{dq}{dt}$ = rate of volume efflux, cc per sec,

A = area of the porous medium, sq cm,

Δh = drop in hydraulic head across the thickness of the medium, cm,

L = thickness of the medium, cm, and

K_1 = a constant depending on the properties of the porous medium and the kinematic viscosity of the fluid, cm per sec.

K_1 of eq. (1) depends on both the properties of the medium and of the fluid. Thus, K_1 represents the permeability of a porous medium to a specified fluid at a specified temperature. The following, more general expression is preferred:[2]

$$\frac{dq}{dt}\frac{1}{A} = \frac{K_2}{\eta}\frac{\Delta P'}{L} \dots \dots (2)$$

in which

η = viscosity of fluid, poises, dyne-sec per sq cm,

$\Delta P'$ = pressure drop across the medium, dynes per sq cm, and

K_2 = coefficient of permeability, sq cm.

In terms of hydraulic gradient rather than pressure differential

$$\frac{dq}{dt}\frac{1}{A} = \frac{K_2 g\, d_f\, \Delta h}{\eta\, L} \dots \dots (3)$$

where d_f = density of the fluid, g per cc, and

g = acceleration due to gravity, cm per sec per sec.

As Muskat[2] has pointed out, the coefficient of permeability, K_2, is a constant determined by the characteristics of the medium in question and is entirely independent of the nature of the fluid.

Permeability equation for hardened paste

In the following discussion, the theoretical coefficient of permeability of hardened paste will be evaluated analytically from the original cement content, the non-evaporable water content, and V_m (see Part 3). This is accomplished by means of the following relationship found theoretically by Kozeny[3] and verified experimentally on beds of granules by Carman:[4d]

$$K_2 = k\epsilon\, m^2 \dots \dots (4)$$

where k = a dimensionless constant,

ϵ = ratio of pore volume to total volume, and

m = hydraulic radius.

For the derivation of this equation reference should be made to the original articles by Kozeny and especially those by Carman. The equation rests on the assumption that the particles composing the bed have a completely random packing, and on the use of hydraulic radius in Poiseuille's equation for capillary flow. The hydraulic radius is

$$m = \frac{\text{void-volume}}{\text{surface area of void-boundaries}} = \frac{\epsilon}{S} \dots \dots (5)$$

Hence

$$K_2 = k\frac{\epsilon^3}{S^2} \dots \dots (6)$$

Various experiments of Carman and those of Fowler and Hertel[5] show that $k = 0.2$ can be assumed for a wide variety of media.

Applied to beds of relatively large particles, eq. (6), with $k = 0.2$, was found by Carman to be a satisfactory basis for predicting permeability from the *total* porosity of the bed and the specific surface of the particles. Applied to certain fine-textured media, the equation was found to give permeability coefficients that were much too high if the total porosity was used for ϵ. Carman found such to be the case for beds of clay.[4b] By assuming that a certain amount of the interparticle space was not effective in transmitting water, Carman was able to obtain agreement between the theoretical and experimental results. Powers[6] and Steinour[7] adapted the Kozeny equation (eq. (4)) to the rate of bleeding of portland cement paste and found that a similar modification was necessary. These different experiments show that for certain fine-textured media,

$$\epsilon_e = \epsilon - \alpha(1 - \epsilon) , \dots\dots\dots\dots\dots\dots\dots (7)$$

where ϵ = total porosity,

    ϵ_e = effective porosity, and

    α = amount of immobile fluid per unit volume of solids in the medium.

Steinour[7] found that for fluid flow through concentrated suspensions of particles, α depended on

(1) the amount of fluid chemically or physically combined with the particle surfaces,

(2) the angularity of the particles, and

(3) the presence or absence of flocculation of the particles.

In a solid porous medium such as hardened paste, item (1) would be the amount of fluid attached to the pore walls, item (2), the irregularity of the wall surfaces, and item (3), the variations in cross-sectional area along the conduits through the medium.

For cement pastes, the total porosity, ϵ, may be taken as being equal to the volume of the total evaporable water. According to eq. (7), the effective porosity, ϵ_e, should be smaller than the total by some quantity proportional to $(1 - \epsilon)$, the volume of the solid phase. However, the effect of the three items mentioned above can be taken care of adequately enough for the present purpose by assuming that the amount of water in a saturated paste that remains immobile is proportional to the total surface area, regardless of the cause of its immobility. Thus, since the total surface area is proportional to V_m,

$$\epsilon_e = w_e - k_1 V_m \dots\dots\dots\dots\dots\dots\dots\dots\dots (8)$$

where w_e = total evaporable water in cc per cc of hardened paste.
Let $w_e/V_m = N$. Then

$$\epsilon_e = V_m(N - k_1) \dots\dots\dots\dots\dots\dots\dots\dots\dots (9)$$

The total surface area in the paste is

$$S = (35.7 \times 10^6)V_m \dots\dots\dots\dots\dots\dots\dots(10)$$

(See Part 3.)

Using ϵ_e for ϵ and substituting from eq. (9) and (10) into eq. (6) gives

$$K_2 = \frac{k}{(35.7 \times 10^6)^2} V_m(N - k_1)^3 \dots\dots\dots\dots(11)*$$

(In the above equations V_m is in g per cc of paste.) Since,

$$k = 0.2 \text{ (Carman)},$$

eq. (11) may be written

$$K_2 = 15.7 \times 10^{-17} V_m(N - k_1)^3 \dots\dots\dots\dots(12)$$

Eq. (12) gives the coefficient of permeability in terms of three factors that are constant for a given sample. V_m and N are measurable. However, k_1 is unknown and cannot be evaluated without further permeability tests.

Comparison with data of Ruettgers, Vidal, and Wing

No experimental data are available for checking eq. (12) quantitatively. However, Ruettgers, Vidal, and Wing[8] published the results of permeability tests on neat cement made with a special cement resembling the present A.S.T.M. Type II, except that it was considerably coarser than present-day cements (15 percent retained on No. 200). From their plotted results, the coefficients of permeability for neat cement cured 60 days were estimated to be as shown in the last column of Table 7-1.

Before comparing the results of the tests and the computations the basis of the computations must be explained. To compute the permeability of the specimens tested by Ruettgers, Vidal, and Wing, V_m and the total evaporable water for the saturated state must be known and a value for k_1 must be assumed. However, only the nominal water-cement ratio, the composition of the cement, and the heat of hydration of the cement were available. The cement content was estimated from the nominal water-cement ratio. w_n/c was computed from the relationship

$$\text{heat of hydration} = 525 \ w_n/c \ \text{(see Part 4)}$$

and found to be about 0.15. From the composition of the cement and eq. (4) of Part 3, V_m was estimated at $0.256 \ w_n$.

Ruettgers, Vidal, and Wing gave their results in terms of K_1 of eq. (1), in ft. per sec, whereas eq. (12) is in terms of K_2 of eq. (3). A comparison of eq. (1) and (3) shows that

$$K_1 = \frac{K_2 d_f g}{\eta}.$$

---

*It may be noted that, in deriving eq. (11) from eq. (6), the total surface in contact with the flowing water is presumed to be equal to the surface area of the solid phase as measured by water-vapor adsorption. This is exactly correct if the only immobile water is the first adsorbed layer and if the surface area of the first adsorbed layer is equal to the surface area of the solid phase. At present there is no way to check the validity of the final equation, except crudely by the reasonableness of the results obtained.

TABLE 7-1—COMPUTATION OF COEFFICIENT OF PERMEABILITY FROM EQ. (13)

$$K_1 = 0.5 \times 10^{-12} V_m (N - k_1)^3$$

w/c (nom)	c g per cc of paste	$\dfrac{w_n}{c}$	$\dfrac{0.256 \times w_n/c}{= V_m/c}$	$\dfrac{V_m}{c} \cdot c$	$\dfrac{w_o - w_n}{c} = w_e/c$	$\dfrac{w_e/c}{V_m/c} = N$	K_1 computed (ft per sec) $\times 10^{12}$				$K_1 \times 10^{12}$ Ruettgers, Vidal, and Wing
							$k_1 = 1$	$k_1 = 2$	$k_1 = 3$	$k_1 = 4$	
0.5	1.22	0.15	0.038	0.047	0.35	9.2	13	9	6	3	15*
0.6	1.09	0.15	0.038	0.043	0.45	11.8	27	20	15	10	100
0.7	0.98	0.15	0.038	0.037	0.55	14.5	45	36	28	22	550†
0.8	0.90	0.15	0.038	0.034	0.65	17.1	70	59	48	38	1830
1.0	0.76	0.15	0.038	0.029	0.85	22.3	—	—	—	—	3730
1.2	0.66	0.15	0.038	0.025	1.05	27.6	—	—	—	—	8530

*Estimated by extrapolation.
†Estimated by interpolation.

For water, $d_f = 1$, $\eta = 0.01$, and $g = 980$ may be assumed. Hence,
$$K_1, \text{ in cm per sec} = 98000\ K_2,$$
or
$$K_1, \text{ in ft. per sec} = 3220\ K_2.$$
Therefore, from eq. (12)
$$K_1 = 50 \times 10^{-14}\ V_m\ (N - k_1)^3 \text{ ft. per sec.} \dots\dots\dots\dots (13)$$
To be strictly consistent, we would have converted the weights of the total evaporable water to volumes. However, such a refinement seemed unnecessary in view of other uncertainties. Therefore, the estimated weights in grams per unit volume of paste were used.

To k_1, the immobile-water factor, no value could be assigned from known or estimated values of physical composition. Four values were tried, as shown in Table 7-1. The assumption $k_1 = 1.0$ amounts to assuming that only the first adsorbed layer is immobile. The assumption that k_1 is greater than 1 is, of course, that the immobile liquid is more than the amount in the first adsorbed layer.

In Table 7-1 the first indication to be noted is that the computed values are less than the experimental values in all cases. Only for the paste of lowest water-cement ratio do the two values approach equality and then only when k_1 is given its minimum value. Even here, the apparent agreement may be fortuitous because the experimental value given was obtained by an uncertain extrapolation. The second point is that the observed permeabilities increase with increase in w/c much faster than the computed values. Had the computation been based on net rather than nominal w/c, the divergence at high w/c would have been even greater. Possibly the lack of agreement and the divergence just noted are the result of some fault in the theory on which the computations are based, but it cannot be accepted as proof of such faults. There is good reason to believe, as shown in the following paragraph, that the discrepancies between observed and computed values can be accounted for on the basis of decreases in the degree of homogeneity of test specimens accompanying increases in w/c.

Both Powers[6] and Steinour[7c] found from studies of fresh paste made of water and normal portland cement that for w/c's up to about 0.5 by weight, the flocculated cement particles formed a continuous structure having a permeability that could be computed from a modification of the basic Kozeny equation (eq. (4)). At such water ratios, the mass of paste constitutes one continuous floc, and the permeability of the mass as a whole depends on the floc texture. At very high dilution the particles form flocs that are more or less independent of each other. The permeability of such a mass is not determined by the floc texture, but largely by the size of the individual flocs and their concentration.

In an intermediate range of w/c's, the fresh paste exhibits some of the qualities of both extremes. The permeability is determined in part by floc texture and in part by channels that develop in the flocculated mass. This condition is denoted by the appearance of localized channels during the bleeding period. In either the intermediate or the high range of w/c's, the effective size and number of the conduits through the mass of particles cannot be computed from the composition of the mass as a whole, because such masses do not have the homogeneity assumed in the computation.

The homogeneity of a fresh paste, or the lack of it, probably persists in some degree after the paste hardens. Hence, it is probable that for hardened pastes having w/c's greater than 0.6, or thereabouts,* the permeability of a test disk is determined not only by the permeability of the hardened paste, but also by vertical channels that represent discontinuities in the paste—the discontinuities that developed during the bleeding period. In the neat cement disks in question, such channels would extend from the top surface well into the interior and thus greatly increase the permeability of the disk as a whole. The higher the original w/c above the minimum at which channels develop, the greater the number and size of such by-passes around the relatively dense, homogeneous material composing the bulk of the hardened paste.

It is probable that even if channeling did not occur, eq. (13) would not correctly represent the permeability of hardened pastes of all degrees of porosity. This may be inferred from Fig. 5-11 of Part 5. From this figure we may recall the earlier conclusion that saturated, hardened cement pastes may contain only the gel water, or they may contain both gel water and capillary water, depending on the original water-cement ratio and the extent of hydration. Capillary water is absent when the total evaporable water is equal to $4V_m$. It is possible that the permeability of a given paste depends on the permeability of the gel itself and on the size and number of the capillaries outside the gel. The hydraulic radius of these capillaries would be

$$\frac{w_e - 4V_m}{S_c} = \frac{V_m(N - 4)}{S_c} ,$$

where

S_c = superficial area of the gel, and

$N = w_o/V_m$.

S_c is not known. It is probably much smaller than the total surface area of the solid phase as indicated by V_m. If so, the permeability of the capillary space would be of a higher order than that of the gel itself when w_e is greater than $4V_m$.

---

*The limiting water ratio depends on the characteristics of the cement, particularly its specific surface, and on the character and amount of subsieve aggregate. Air-entraining agents tend to raise the limit.

The discrepancies between computed and observed values of K_1 seen in Table 7-1 are in accord with the considerations expressed above. That is, it appears that the permeability of pastes of relatively high w/c is probably determined in major degree by the by-passes around the hydration products, or in other words, by residues of the original water-filled space not filled by gel or other hydration products; but in pastes of low w/c, well cured, the permeability of the paste as a whole is fixed mainly by the permeability of the gel and the amount of gel per unit volume of paste.

Theoretical minimum permeability

For rich pastes the minimum permeability attainable can be estimated from eq. (13) on the assumption that the equation is valid at least for pastes in which $w_e = 4V_m$. The composition of such pastes may be expressed as follows:

$$cv_c + w_nv_n + w_gv_g = 1 \, ,$$

where

c = original cement, g per cc of paste,
w_n = non-evaporable water, g per cc of paste,
w_g = gel water, g per cc of paste, and
$v_c, v_n,$ and v_g = the respective specific volumes.

On the basis of data given in Part 5, let

$w_n = 3.9V_m$
$w_g = 4V_m$
$v_n = 0.82,$ and
$v_g = 0.90.$

Then

$$V_m = 0.147(1 - cv_c) \dots\dots\dots\dots\dots(14)$$

Hence, noting that $N = 4$, we obtain from eq. (13),

$$K_1 = 50 \times 10^{-14} \times 0.147(1 - cv_c)(4 - k_1)$$
$$= 7.4 \times 10^{-14}(1 - cv_c)(4 - k_1) \dots\dots\dots\dots(15)$$

Eq. (15) shows that K_1 can be zero when $cv_c = 1$ or when $k_1 = 4$. The condition that $cv_c = 1$ means that the paste is a voidless mass of un-hydrated cement. (As shown in Part 5, cv_c as high as 0.72 can be produced by molding the paste under high pressure. Normally, it is near 0.50.) Hence, the cv_c term cannot make K_1 zero. Constant k_1 has a minimum value of 1. Its maximum value is not known but it is not likely that it can be as great as 4 since this would mean that all the water in such pastes is held immobile by the solid surface. It seems more likely that only the first layer could be wholly immobile and hence that hardened paste cannot be absolutely impermeable. If this is assumed, the minimum permeability would be of the order of 10^{-12} to 10^{-13} ft. per sec.

These estimates indicate that well cured, neat paste of low w/c is practically impermeable. (Ruettgers, Vidal, and Wing[1] give the permeability of granite as ranging from 2 to 10×10^{-12} ft. per sec.).

Relationship between permeability of paste and permeability of concrete

This subject was discussed fully by Ruettgers, Vidal, and Wing and therefore requires only brief mention here. Introduction of aggregate particles into paste tends to reduce the permeability by reducing the number of channels per unit gross cross-section and by lengthening the path of flow per unit linear distance in the general direction of flow. However, during the plastic period, the paste settles more than the aggregate and thus fissures under the aggregate particles develop. In saturated concrete these fissures are paths of low resistance to hydraulic flow and thus increase the permeability of the concrete. In general, with paste of a given composition and with graded aggregate the permeability is greater the larger the maximum size of the aggregate. Obviously, the permeability of concrete as a whole is much higher than the theoretical permeability as developed above for a homogeneous medium.

The above discussions indicate that for well cured concretes having water-cement ratios above about 0.5, the permeability is determined largely by the by-passes around the gel and the by-passes around the paste in the concrete structure as a whole.

THE ABSORPTIVITY OF HARDENED PASTE

The term "absorptivity" pertains to the characteristic rate at which dry or partially dry paste absorbs water without the aid of external hydraulic pressure.

For pastes containing capillary space outside the gel, it is believed that the water is taken in by two different processes. The water enters the capillary system under the influence of capillary force, i.e., surface tension. Probably most of the water entering the gel, if not all, is drawn by adsorption forces. The resistance to the inward flow into the capillary system should be indicated by the coefficient of permeability of the saturated paste. The resistance to the flow into the gel, where initial flow presumably takes place along surfaces of unfilled channels, would probably not be determined by the permeability, but by a coefficient of diffusivity.

These suppositions are supported by several considerations already discussed. Perhaps the most pertinent consideration is that illustrated by Fig. 4-12, Part 4. This shows that the evaporable water lost when a saturated specimen is exposed to a relative vapor pressure of 0.5 could be divided into two classes—one that was lost rapidly without apparent relation to shrinkage, and one that was lost more gradually and was directly related to shrinkage.

No attempt will be made here to derive a theoretical relationship for absorptivity. However, an empirical relationship between absorptivity and capillary porosity will be shown.

Relationship between absorptivity and the capillary porosity

It can be shown (see later) that for either capillary penetration or diffusion, the adsorption of water during a short initial period, under proper experimental conditions, follows the relationship

$$\frac{q}{A} = (K_a t)^{1/2} , \dots\dots\dots\dots\dots\dots\dots\dots\dots\dots\dots\dots\dots(16)$$

where q/A = amount of water per unit area absorbed in elapsed time t, and

K_a = a constant characteristic of the absorbent, in its initial state of dryness, called the coefficient of absorptivity. It has the dimensions sq cm per sec.

K_a was evaluated for several mortar prisms, $2 \times 2 \times 9\frac{1}{2}$ in., that had been water-cured and then dried in air of 50 percent relative humidity for 6 or 7 months. They were broken into halves transversely and then coated with paraffin so that only the broken end was exposed. Each specimen was then suspended under water at 73 F from one end of a beam-balance and its change in weight with time was recorded. Plotting q/A vs. the square root of time for these specimens produced straight lines for about the first 60 minutes.

Two different kinds of cement were used, with the following two mixes for each cement:

Ref. No.	Type of cement (A.S.T.M.)	Parts by weight		
		Cement	Standard sand	Pulverized silica
290–41 & –43	III	1	1.63	—
290–42 & –44	IV	1	2.30	0.33

The pulverized silica was of about the same specific surface (sq cm per cc) as the cement. The mortars were plastic when fresh and relatively homogeneous after hardening, since the paste had relatively low bleeding capacity and the paste content was relatively high. (The above mixes are the same as mixes A and B described in Appendix to Part 2.) The compositions of the specimens were the same as those given in Table A-30, first four lines, Appendix to Part 2. The results of absorptivity tests, together with data derived from Tables A-30 and A-33 are given in Table 7-2.

We may surmise that the coefficient of absorptivity depends on the porosity and on the size of the pores of the specimen. As remarked

TABLE 7-2—ABSORPTIVITY DATA

Ref. No.	W_o g per cc of spec.	C, g per cc of spec.	W_n g per cc of spec.	$0.86 \times (1 + 4k)$	$0.86 \times (1 + 4k) \times W_n$	$W_o - 0.86 \times (1 + 4k) \times W_n$	K_a (observed), sq cm per sec $\times 10^7$ Spec. A	Spec. B
				Cement 15758 A.S.T.M. Type III, $k = 0.248$*				
290–41	.252	.755	.129	1.71	.220	.032	13.5†	8.3
290–42	.250	.542	.106	1.71	.181	.069	23.5	23.0
				Cement 15756 A.S.T.M. Type IV, $k = 0.271$*				
290–43	.255	.769	.095	1.79	.170	.085	27.4	28.0
290–44	.252	.560	.074	1.79	.132	.120	73.5	76.1

*See Part 3, Fig. 3-7A and B.
†Doubtful result based on first 15 minutes only. Others are based on about first hour.

above, it is probable that the initial, comparatively rapid adsorption takes place almost exclusively in the capillary system. That is, although the gel is not saturated, the gel pores are so small that very little water can enter them, as compared with the amount that enters the capillary system during a limited time. On this basis, we may write

$$K_a = f(p_c, r_c) \quad , \dots\dots\dots\dots\dots\dots\dots\dots\dots\dots\dots\dots\dots\dots (17)$$

where p_c = volume of capillary pores per cc of mortar—the *capillary porosity*, and r_c = effective radius of the capillaries.

The capillary-porosity can be estimated conveniently in terms of the water content of the fresh mortar (after bleeding) and the increase in the volume of the solid phase due to hydration. That is, the capillary porosity is the difference between the increase in volume of the solid phase (due to hydration) and the original volume of pores:

$$p_c = W_o - V_B - Cv_c , \dots\dots\dots\dots\dots\dots\dots\dots\dots\dots\dots\dots (18)$$

where V_B = bulk volume of the solid phase, including gel pores and unhydrated cement, in cc per cc of specimen,

and C = cement content of specimen, grams per cc of specimen.
From Part 5, eq. (9),

$$V_B = Cv_c - 0.86(1 + 4k)W_n , \dots\dots\dots\dots\dots\dots\dots\dots\dots\dots (19)$$

where 0.86 = v_d = mean of the specific volumes of gel water and non-evaporable water, and

W_n = non-evaporable water, grams per cc of specimen.
Hence, from eq. (18) and (19),

$$p_c = W_o - 0.86(1 + 4k)W_n \dots\dots\dots\dots\dots\dots\dots\dots\dots\dots (20)$$

As shown previously, there is no satisfactory way of evaluating the size of the capillaries. However, capillary radius is at a maximum before hydration begins and becomes zero when all original capillary space ($= W_o$) becomes filled with hydration products. At intermediate stages the relationship may be such that capillary radii are about the same among different pastes when the original capillary space in each paste is filled to the same degree. To the extent that this is true,

$$r_c = f[W_o - 0.86(1 + 4k)W_n] \qquad \ldots\ldots\ldots\ldots\ldots\ldots\ldots(21)$$

A comparison of eq. (17), (20), and (21) indicates that K_a should be some function of $W_o - 0.86(1 + 4k)W_n$ only. The nature of the function is indicated by the plotted experimental data given in Fig. 7-1.

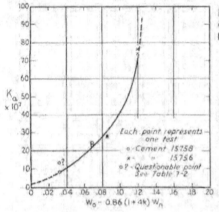

Fig. 7-1—Empirical relationship between coefficient of absorptivity and capillary porosity

Series 254 and 290

It should be noted that according to eq. (21), capillary radius becomes zero when $0.86(1 + 4k)W_n = W_o$, that is, when capillary porosity is zero. Hence, if the assumptions made in arriving at the basis of plotting used in Fig. 7-1 are valid, or approximately so, the curve should appear to go through the origin. Fig. 7-1 shows that a reasonable curve through the points could pass through or very near the origin. This only illustrates, however, the relative smallness of the gel pores, for it is certain that K_a is not zero when capillary porosity is zero. The curve probably should intercept the K_a-axis slightly above zero, possibly about as indicated in Fig. 7-1.

The empirical curve probably does not indicate the relationship between K_a and capillary porosity correctly, for no account is taken of the fact that the capillary pores were not entirely empty at the start of the absorption test. However, at $p = 0.5\ p_s$, reached by desorption, the capillaries are probably not far from empty. The presence of capillary water in the specimen at the start probably reduces K_a below what it would be if the capillaries were entirely empty, but it probably does not influence the indications as to the trend of the curve as capillary porosity approaches zero, the matter of interest here.

On the whole, these absorptivity data support other indications that the capillary pores are much larger than those in the gel, and that relationships given in Part 5 distinguish between water held in capillary spaces and that held in the pores of the gel with satisfactory accuracy.

It should be remembered that when $W_o = 0.86(1 + 4k)W_n$, that is, when capillary porosity is zero, the specimen must be such that, when saturated, the total evaporable water $= 4V_m$. (See Part 3.) These absorptivity data thus constitute a significant independent check of the conclusion reached from other considerations, that the weight of the water required to saturate the gel is equal to $4V_m$.

Dependence of K_a on initial water content of the specimen

It must be remembered that the value of K_a for a given specimen will depend on the initial water content of the specimen, at least for water contents high enough to partly fill the capillaries. If the specimens were first dried completely and then allowed to *adsorb* vapor before the adsorption test, K_a would probably be about the same for all initial water contents up to that corresponding to about $p = 0.45 \, p_s$. This follows from the evidence presented earlier indicating that the capillaries do not begin to fill by capillary condensation below about $p = 0.45 \, p_s$, and that the initial rapid *absorption* takes place almost exclusively in the capillaries, when capillaries are present. For specimens dried only by *desorption*, data now available do not indicate clearly how low the final vapor pressure must be to empty the capillaries completely. Such data as there are indicate that the required pressure might be as low as $p = 0.1 \, p_s$, though theory indicates that it might be about $p = 0.3 \, p_s$.[9]

Relationship between absorptivity and permeability

In view of the evidence given above, we may conclude that the initial rapid absorption of water by paste containing capillaries outside the gel is predominantly capillary absorption. Consequently, the rate of absorption should be, according to Darcy's law,

$$\frac{dq}{dt}\frac{1}{A} = \frac{(K_2)_c}{\eta} d_f \frac{\Delta h}{L} g , \dots\dots\dots\dots\dots\dots(22)$$

in which $(K_2)_c$ is the coefficient of permeability for flow through the capillary system alone, $d_f \Delta h$ is the hydraulic head in g per sq cm causing the flow, and L is the depth of the saturated layer in which the flow is taking place.

For horizontal capillary penetration

$$g \, d_f \Delta h = \sigma\left(\frac{1}{r_1} + \frac{1}{r_2}\right) , \dots\dots\dots\dots\dots\dots(23)*$$

---

*Eq. (23) is based on the assumption that the angle of contact between the meniscus and the solid boundary is zero. This assumption seems permissible in this case because of the strong attraction between the solid and the liquid and because of the extreme slowness of the movement of the meniscus. It would not be permissible, however, for specimens that contain stearates or other "water-repellent" substances or for coarsely porous materials in which the capillary penetration is rapid.

where

σ = surface tension of water, dynes per cm,

g = acceleration due to gravity,

r_1 and r_2 = principal radii of curvature of the menisci.

Carman [14d] has shown that $\left(\dfrac{1}{r_1} + \dfrac{1}{r_2}\right)$ can be replaced by the reciprocal of the hydraulic radius. That is,

$$\frac{1}{r_1} + \frac{1}{r_2} = \frac{S}{\epsilon_c} , \dots\dots\dots\dots\dots\dots\dots(24)$$

where

ϵ_c = volume of the capillaries per unit volume of the specimen,

and S = surface area of capillary boundaries.

For our data,

$$\frac{S}{\epsilon_c} = \frac{S_c}{w_e - 4V_m} = \frac{S_c}{V_m(N - 4)} , \dots\dots\dots\dots\dots(25)$$

in which

S_c = superficial surface area of the gel, and

w_e = total evaporable water.

We may note also that

$$L = \frac{q}{\epsilon_c A} = \frac{q}{V_m(N - 4)A} , \dots\dots\dots\dots\dots(26)$$

where A = exposed area of the specimen.

Substitution from eq. (23), (24), (25), and (26) into eq. (22) gives

$$\frac{dq}{dt}\frac{1}{A} = \frac{(K_2)_c}{\eta}\sigma \frac{S_c}{V_m(N - 4)} \frac{V_m(N - 4)A}{q}$$

$$= \left[\frac{(K_2)_c A}{\eta}\sigma S_c\right]\frac{1}{q} . \dots\dots\dots\dots(27)$$

All the quantities within the brackets are constant for a given specimen. Hence, we may write

$$\int q\, dq = \left[\frac{(K_2)_c A^2}{\eta}\sigma S_c\right]\int dt$$

which, when integrated, gives

$$\frac{q}{A} = \left[\frac{2(K_2)_c}{\eta}\sigma S_c\right]^{\frac{1}{2}} t^{\frac{1}{2}} \dots\dots\dots\dots\dots(28)$$

From eq. (16) and (28) it follows that

$$K_a = \frac{2(K_2)_c}{\eta}\sigma S_c \dots\dots\dots\dots\dots\dots(29)$$

It thus appears that if the superficial surface area of the gel were known, the coefficient of permeability for flow through the capillary system (which is virtually the total flow) could be computed from the coefficient of absorptivity as determined from the initial rate of absorption. However, S_c cannot be measured by any method now available. We may surmise that in a fresh paste, where the hydration products exist mainly as a thin coating on the cement grains, the superficial area of the hydration products, S_c, must be virtually the same as that of the original cement grains. While hydration proceeds, either an increase or a decrease in S_c is conceivable. If the cement grains were sufficiently separated, and if hydration merely enlarged the grains, S_c would increase until the boundaries of the grains began to merge. After a certain extent of this merging, S_c would begin to decrease and would wither eventually reach zero—if the paste were sufficiently dense—or some finite minimum value. (See Fig. 5-11, Part 5.)

SUMMARY OF PART 7
Permeability

(1) The permeability of well cured neat cement paste of low w/c is, theoretically,

$$K_1 = 50 \times 10^{-14} V_m (N - k_1)^3$$

in which K_1 = coefficient of permeability to water in ft. per sec.;

$\qquad V_m$ = amount of water required to form the first adsorbed layer, g per cc of paste;

$\qquad N$ = ratio of total evaporable water to V_m; and

$\qquad k_1$ is a constant depending on the amount of immobile water per unit of solid surface—k_1 is probably near 1.

(2) For pastes in which N is considerably greater than 4, the permeability is much higher than the theoretical value computed from the above equation. This is believed to indicate that the flow in such pastes is predominantly in the capillary spaces outside the gel and, in tests on neat-cement disks of high w/c, through vertical channels formed during the period of bleeding.

(3) The theoretical permeability of pastes containing no capillary space outside the gel is

$$K_1 = 0.7 \times 10^{-12} (1 - cv_c) \Big]_{0.45 \leq cv_c \leq 1.0}$$

where c = cement content, g per cc of paste and v_c = specific volume of the cement. K_1 cannot be zero in practice because cv_c must be less than 1. At $cv_c = 0.45$, approximately the minimum cement content of pastes containing no capillary space outside the gel, $K_1 = 1 \times 10^{-12}$. According to Ruettgers, Vidal, and Wing, this is of the same order as the permeability of granite.

(4) The permeability of concrete is generally much higher than the theoretical permeability owing to fissures under the aggregate that

permit the flow partially to by-pass the paste and owing to the capillaries in the paste that permit the flow in the paste to by-pass the gel.

Absorptivity

(1) The absorption of water by a dry specimen during the first 30 to 60 minutes follows the relationship

$$\frac{q}{A} = (K_a t)^{\frac{1}{2}},$$

in which q/A = the amount absorbed per unit of exposed area and K_a = the coefficient of absorptivity at t = time.

(2) The empirical relationship between K_a and capillary porosity indicates that K_a is near zero when capillary porosity is zero. Hence, the empirical relationship indicates that the initial absorption takes place almost exclusively in the capillaries outside the gel, when such capillaries are present.

(3) The theoretical relationship between absorptivity and permeability is

$$K_a = \frac{(K_2)_c}{\eta} \sigma S_c,$$

in which $(K_2)_c$ = the coefficient of permeability for flow through the capillary system of the paste; σ and η = surface tension and viscosity of water, respectively; g = gravitational constant; S_c = superficial surface area of the gel. This pertains to specimens in which the capillaries are initially empty, or nearly so. S_c has not been measured. It probably diminishes as $(K_2)_c$ diminishes. If so, K_a is a relative measure of $(K_2)_c$.

REFERENCES

(1) A. Ruettgers, E. N. Vidal, and S. P. Wing, *Proceedings* ACI v. 31, p. 382 (1935).

(2) M. Muskat, *The Flow of Homogeneous Fluids through Porous Media* (McGraw-Hill, 1937), p. 71.

(3) J. Kozeny, *S. B. Akad. Wiss. Wien*, v. 136, Part IIa, p. 271 (1927).

(4) P. C. Carman (a) *Symposium on New Methods of Particle Size Distribution in the Subsieve Range*, A.S.T.M. Publication (1941), p. 24.

    (b) *J. Agr. Sci.* v. 29, p. 262 (1939).

    (c) *J. Soc. Chem. Ind.*, v. 57, p. 225 (1938).

    (d) *Soil Science* v. 52, p. 1 (1941).

(5) J. L. Fowler and K. L. Hertel, *J. Applied Phys.* v. 11, p. 496 (1940).

(6) T. C. Powers, "The Bleeding of Portland Cement Paste, Mortar and Concrete," Bulletin 2 of the Research Laboratory, Portland Cement Association, 1939.

(7) H. H. Steinour (a) P.C.A. Research Laboratory Bulletin 3, 1944; or *Ind. Eng. Chem.* (b) v. 36, p. 618 (1944); (c) v. 36, p. 840 (1944); (d) v. 36, p. 901 (1944).

(8) Discussion of paper by A. Ruettgers, E. N. Vidal, and S. P. Wing, *Proceedings* ACI v. 32, p. 378 (1936).

(9) L. H. Cohan, *J. Am. Chem. Soc.* v. 66, p. 98 (1944).

Title 43-5g —a part of PROCEEDINGS, AMERICAN CONCRETE INSTITUTE Vol. 43

JOURNAL
of the
AMERICAN CONCRETE INSTITUTE
(copyrighted)

Vol. 18 No. 8   7400 SECOND BOULEVARD, DETROIT 2, MICHIGAN   April 1947

Studies of the Physical Properties of Hardened Portland Cement Paste*

By T. C. POWERS†

Member American Concrete Institute

and T. L. BROWNYARD‡

Part 8.   The Freezing of Water in Hardened Portland Cement Paste§

Part 9.   General Summary of Findings on the Properties of Hardened Portland Cement Paste

CONTENTS PART 8

---

*Received by the Institute July 8, 1946—scheduled for publication in seven installments; October 1946 to April, 1947. In nine parts:

Part 1.   "A Review of Methods That Have Been Used for Studying the Physical Properties of Hardened Portland Cement Paste". ACI JOURNAL, October, 1946.
Part 2.   "Studies of Water Fixation"—Appendix to Part 2. ACI JOURNAL, November, 1946.
Part 3.   "Theoretical Interpretation of Adsorption Data." ACI JOURNAL, December, 1946.
Part 4.   "The Thermodynamics of Adsorption"—Appendix to Parts 3 and 4. ACI JOURNAL, January, 1947.
Part 5.   "Studies of the Hardened Paste by Means of Specific-Volume Measurements." ACI JOURNAL February, 1947.
Part 6.   "Relation of Physical Characteristics of the Paste to Compressive Strength." ACI JOURNAL, March, 1947.
Part 7.   "Permeability and Absorptivity." ACI JOURNAL, March, 1947.
Part 8.   "The Freezing of Water in Hardened Portland Cement Paste." ACI JOURNAL, April 1947.
Part 9.   "General Summary of Findings on the Properties of Hardened Portland Cement Paste." ACI JOURNAL, April, 1947.

†Manager of Basic Research, Portland Cement Assn. Research Laboratory, Chicago 10, Ill.
‡Navy Dept., Washington, D. C., formerly Research Chemist, Portland Cement Assn. Research Laboratory, Chicago 10, Ill.
§The characteristics of the cements mentioned in this section may be found in the Appendix to Part 2.

570   Powers and Brownyard

This part of the paper contains data on the amount of ice that can exist in hardened portland cement paste under given conditions. Also some theoretical aspects of the data are considered.

THEORETICAL FREEZING POINTS

From the fact that the evaporable water in hardened paste exhibits different vapor pressures when the sample is at different degrees of saturation, we could anticipate the now known fact that not all the evaporable water in a saturated paste can freeze or melt at a fixed temperature. This can readily be deduced from Fig. 8-1, which is a diagram illustrating (on a distorted scale) the relationship between the vapor pressure and temperature for water and ice. The upper curve represents the relationship for pure water under the pressure of its own vapor, p_s. Similarly, the curve marked "ice" represents the relationship for ice under the pressure of its vapor, p_i. The vapor pressures of the two phases are equal only at point A. This is the only point where the free energies of the ice and pure water are equal and hence the only point where ice and pure water can coexist. If a salt is added to the water, the vapor pressure of the solution bears a nearly fixed ratio to the vapor pressure of pure water at all temperatures, as indicated by the line marked "solution." (The position of this line depends on the salt concentration.) Pure ice can coexist with the solution only at point B, which is at a temperature below 0 C.

It is clear, therefore, that the evaporable water in a saturated hardened paste will not begin to freeze at 0 C because of its content of dis-

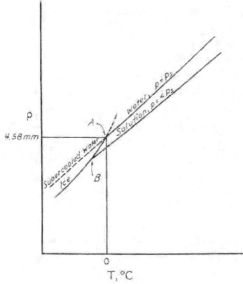

Fig. 8-1—Phase equilibrium diagram for water and ice (distorted)

solved hydroxides. Moreover, when freezing begins, and pure ice separates from the solution, the solution becomes more concentrated and thus the freezing point is lowered further. It follows that the evaporable water will freeze progressively as the temperature is lowered.

At this point we recall the discussion in Part 3 showing that the reduction in the vapor pressure of evaporable water is caused not only by the dissolved salts but also by capillary tension and adsorption. At saturation the effect is due entirely to dissolved material, but as the evaporable water is removed the effect of capillary tension and adsorption increases, and it exceeds that of the dissolved material after only a little of the evaporable water has been removed. A given reduction in vapor pressure signifies the same reduction in freezing point, regardless of the mechanism by which the reduction is effected. Hence, we may conclude that if the ice separates from capillary water or adsorbed water in the same way that it does from a solution, the freezing point will be the same as for a solution of the same vapor pressure.

Application of Washburn's equation

The reduction in freezing point for such a system can be ascertained from the following semi-empirical relationship given by Washburn[1]*

$$log_{10} \frac{p_i}{p_s} = \frac{1.1489t}{273.1 + t} + 1.33 \times 10^{-5}t^2 - 9.084 \times 10^{-8}t^3, \quad .(1)$$

in which

*See references end of Part 8.

p_i = vapor pressure of ice at temperature t,

p_s = vapor pressure of pure water at temperature t, and

t = temperature, deg. C.

Let p = vapor pressure of evaporable water in cement paste.

Then, where the ice and the evaporable water are in equilibrium, that is, at the freezing point, $p = p_i$, and

$$log_{10} p/p_s = \text{eq. (1)} \quad \dots \dots \dots \dots \dots \dots \dots \dots \dots \dots (2)$$

Thus, eq. (1) gives the relative vapor pressure of water (or solution) that will be in equilibrium with ice at any given temperature. In other words, it gives the freezing temperature corresponding to any given value of p/p_s for the system. A plot of this equation appears in Fig. 8-2.

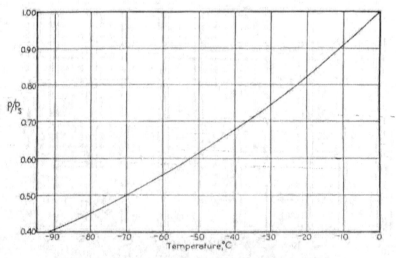

Fig. 8-2—Relationship between p/p_s and freezing point

Eq. (1) gives substantially the same result as the following equation given by Kubelka[2]:

$$\frac{T_o - T}{T_o} = \frac{2v_f\sigma_f}{rq}, \quad \dots \dots \dots \dots \dots \dots \dots \dots \dots \dots \dots \dots \dots \dots \dots (3)$$

where T_o = normal freezing point, deg. K,

T = freezing point in capillary system, deg. K,

v_f = molar volume of fluid,

σ_f = surface tension of fluid,

r = radius of curvature of fluid surface, and

q = latent heat of fusion of fluid.

This equation was derived from thermodynamic considerations, taking into account the influence of capillary tension. It involves the assumption that the liquid phase is in tension while the ice is under normal pressure.

One of the objects of this investigation was to verify eq. (1) as applied to cement paste, or to find an empirical substitute for it. It is apparent that from the correct relationship the amount of water in a saturated paste that is freezable at any given temperature could be obtained from the adsorption curves, after applying temperature corrections. That is, the amount of freezable water could be obtained from the sorption characteristics measured at 25 C, for example, after correcting the value of p/p_s at 25 C to what it would be at the freezing point.

To apply eq. (1) to the freezing of water in cement paste is tantamount to assuming that the ice forms as a separate microcrystalline phase, the crystals being so large that they exhibit the normal properties of ice, and that the ice is under normal external pressure. As will be seen, the experimental data do not definitely confirm these assumptions, but they indicate that the assumptions are substantially correct, at least for the freezing of saturated pastes. The causes of uncertainty will be discussed later.

APPARATUS AND METHODS

Test samples

The test samples were granules of cement paste or cement-silica paste. They were obtained by the method described in Part 2. The original specimens (cylinders or cubes) were crushed and sieved, the particles caught between the No. 14 and No. 28 sieves being taken for the freezing experiments. Each sample was treated as follows:

The evaporable water was removed from the granulated sample by drying in vacuo over $Mg(ClO_4)_2.2H_2O + Mg(ClO_4)_2.4H_2O$. Then water was added to the dry granules in such quantity as to saturate them. This procedure is described in Part 2.

Most of the sample prepared in this way was then transferred to a dilatometer, without packing the granules in the bulb. All operations involved in the transfer were carried out in a water-saturated atmosphere to minimize losses of moisture from the sample.

Dilatometers

A drawing of a typical dilatometer is shown in Fig. 8-3. This is essentially the same instrument used by Elsner von Gronow[3] in his experiments with hardened paste and by Foote and Saxton,[4] Jones and Gortner,[5] and Bouyoucos,[6] who studied various materials.

Freezing and thawing procedure

The sealed dilatometer was placed in a cryostat (initially at room temperature) with the stem vertical. During the ensuing night, the

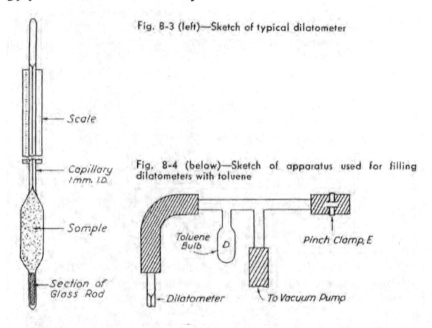

Fig. 8-3 (left)—Sketch of typical dilatometer

Scale

Capillary
1mm. I.D.

Sample

Section of
Glass Rod

Fig. 8-4 (below)—Sketch of apparatus used for filling
dilatometers with toluene

Toluene
Bulb   D

Pinch Clamp, E

Dilatometer

To Vacuum Pump

temperature of the cryostat was allowed to drop gradually to about
−20 C. The bulb of the dilatometer was then cooled quickly to about
−78 C by placing it in a mixture of solid carbon dioxide and alcohol. The
stem was connected to a vacuum pump through the apparatus shown in
Fig. 8-4. After the air was removed, toluene in bulb D was caused to flow
into the dilatometer by manipulating flexible connections and pinch
clamp E which admitted atmospheric pressure. By repeating such
manipulations, all the space surrounding the frozen grains, as well as the
bore of the capillary stem, was filled with toluene.

After the level of the toluene in the stem had been adjusted to a point
near the bottom of the scale, the top of the calibrated stem was sealed
to prevent loss of toluene by evaporation. Then the loaded dilatometer
was transferred back to the cryostat, still at about −20 C, without
allowing the sample to thaw during the transfer. The final dilatometer
reading at −20 C was taken the following morning.

After the initial −20 C reading was obtained, the temperature was
raised stepwise, allowing time for the level of the toluene in the stem to
come to rest after each change in temperature. A constant level was
usually established in about one-half hour, but each temperature was
maintained for at least 1 hour.

The procedure described above was used for most of the data discussed herein. Other data were obtained earlier when the methods were
less well developed. In some cases, the saturated sample was sealed in

Fig. 8-5—Cryostat used for freezing studies

Left—Over-all view
Above—Top of cryostat proper

the dilatometer and the toluene was introduced with the aid of a vacuum pump without first freezing the sample. Although the granules were wetted with toluene before they were subjected to low pressure, this procedure probably resulted in a small loss of evaporable water. Also, the top of the dilatometer stem was sealed only with a rubber cap. This permitted a small loss of toluene during the course of the experiments. The samples prepared in this manner were usually started above the freezing point and the freezing curves as well as thawing curves were obtained.

Description of cryostat

The cryostat used in these experiments is shown in Fig. 8-5 and diagrammatically in Fig. 8-6. It consists of an alcohol container G, equipped with cooling coils. Within this container is a double-walled glass vessel also containing alcohol. This is the cryostat proper. It contains an electrical heating coil, not shown, a motor-driven stirrer, C, and a mercury-toluene type thermoregulator, B. The temperature of the alcohol

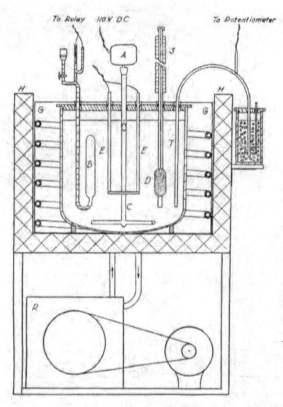

Fig. 8-6—Freezing study apparatus

is indicated by the 8-junction copper-constantan thermopile, T, having its cold junction in melting ice outside the cryostat, as indicated. The e.m.f. of the thermopile is measured by means of a Type K potentiometer and suitable galvanometer. A single dilatometer, D, is shown. Actually, four dilatometers could be accommodated simultaneously.

GENERAL ASPECTS OF EXPERIMENTAL RESULTS

Dilatometer curves

Results of a typical experiment on a saturated sample are given in Fig. 8-7. Beginning at point A, the temperature was lowered stepwise and the corresponding changes in dilatometer readings were observed. These changes were converted into volume change, the volume at −0.2 C being taken as the reference point. As shown, the points describe the straight line AB. This represents the thermal contraction of the whole system, pyrex-glass bulb, toluene, and water-saturated sample. At about −7.5 C, point B, a sudden expansion occurred, giving the rise BC. Further cooling produced the curve CD. Since CD does not fall as steeply as AB, we may conclude that further expansion accompanied the change from −7.5 to −25 C.

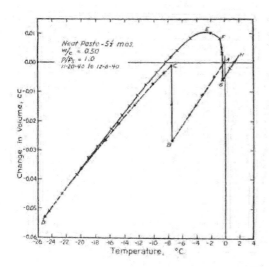

Fig. 8-7—Typical results of dilatometric study of saturated sample

Beginning at −25 C (point D) the temperature was raised stepwise and the curve D to H was obtained. A comparison of the slope of AB with the various slopes of DH shows that each increment of temperature caused expansion up to point E. But the expansion accompanying each increment of temperature was less than the normal thermal expansion. This indicates a progressive melting of ice. Along EF, contraction occurs, showing that the contraction due to melting exceeded the thermal expansion. At temperatures above G, the volume increase is due to thermal expansion only, as shown by the parallelism of GH and AB.

The results described above are typical of all such tests made on saturated granules of paste. During the time when the points fell along AB, below −0.2 C, the water remained in a supercooled state. All the water that might have frozen between −7.5 and −0.2 C changed to ice at −7.5 C. In various experiments the extent of supercooling ranged from about −5 C to −12 C. Sometimes freezing was started by tapping the stem of the dilatometer. It seems likely that at other times chance vibrations determined the extent of supercooling.

The fact that DE and DC do not coincide is probably another manifestation of hysteresis. We have already seen that the progressive drop in freezing point indicates a corresponding progressive drop in relative vapor pressure of the unfrozen evaporable water. The freezing of a part of the evaporable water has an effect on the unfrozen evaporable water similar to the loss of evaporable water by drying. Likewise, the melting of ice has an effect like that of increasing the evaporable water content of a partially dry specimen. Hence, by analogy we can see that the freezing curve is a desorption curve, with temperature representing vapor pressure. The melting curve is conversely an adsorption curve.

Fig. 8-8—Freezing and thawing of silica gel

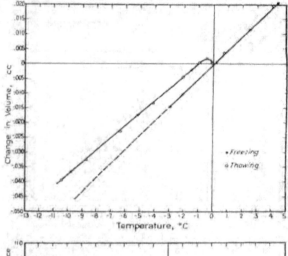

Fig. 8-9—Results of experiment for measuring freezing and thawing of ice in hardened cement paste by the dielectric method

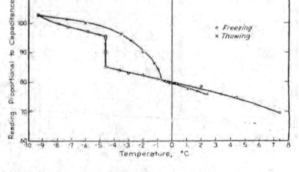

The curves DE and DC in Fig. 8-7 show, by comparison with AB that the contraction per degree on melting is less than the expansion per degree on freezing. This result is as would be anticipated from the fact that the decrease in evaporable water content per unit decrease in p/p_s is, in the upper range of pressures, less than the increase in evaporable water content per unit increase in p/p_s.

Effect of hydration during the experiment

A significant feature of Fig. 8-7 is the position of point G with respect to A. Point G is that at which all ice disappears—the final melting point. The fact that it is below A shows that the volume of the system decreased permanently during the freezing and thawing cycle.* Repeated cycles on one sample showed that shrinkage increases with each cycle. It was suspected that the shrinkage was due at least in part to hydration of cement in the sample during the test. To check this possi-

*This particular example showed a considerably greater permanent change than did others. It represents a test made before the practice of sealing the dilatometer stem was adopted. Consequently, most of the change may be due to loss of toluene.

bility, some special tests were made on silica gel. Fig. 8-8 gives the result.

The amount of evaporable water that was in this sample of silica gel is not known exactly, owing to losses of moisture during the preparation of the dilatometer. However, it is believed to have been slightly more than the amount required to saturate the granules of silica gel. The feature to be noted especially is that the volume after the cycle was completed was almost exactly the same as the original volume at the same temperature. The same degree of reversibility was found in three other tests on silica gel.

In view of the results obtained from silica gel, it was concluded that the permanent contraction in volume such as is shown in Fig. 8-7 is due, at least in part, to continued hydration of the cement during the course of the experiment. Such an explanation is plausible, even though the original material had been cured under water for several months, because the granulation of the original specimen exposed fresh clinker surfaces and admitted water into fine gel structure that had become partially desiccated in the whole specimen (see Part 2).

Effect of dissolved material

One other feature of Fig. 8-7 should now be noted. Point G, the final melting point, is slightly below 0 C. This is the effect of dissolved materials, chiefly alkalies. It will be seen later that the final melting point of one of the samples was −1.6 C, owing to its unusually high alkali content.

Detection of freezing by means of the change in dielectric constant

Alexander, Shaw, and Muckenhirn studied the freezing of water in soils and other porous media by means of the accompanying change in dielectric constant.[7] The dielectric constant of water is about 80 and that of ice about 4. By using the material to be tested as the dielectric medium between the plates of a fixed condenser, these authors were able to follow the course of ice-formation by measuring the change in capacitance of the condenser.

Through the courtesy of Horace G. Byers, Chief, Soil Chemistry and Physics Research, U. S. Dept. of Agriculture, Washington, D. C., Mr. Alexander very kindly tested a saturated, granular sample of hardened paste for us. The results are shown in Fig. 8-9. Since this represents but a single run, we cannot assume that all the features shown are significant. Nevertheless, they are of considerable interest in connection with the interpretation of the results obtained by the dilatometer method.

In Fig. 8-9 the scale of ordinates gives the dial readings of the apparatus. An increase in reading denotes an equal decrease in the capacitance of the fixed condenser and hence a decrease in the dielectric constant of the sample. The curves show that in the range above 0 C, lowering the temperature decreased the dielectric constant of the sample. As the temperature fell below zero, the water in the sample remained in a supercooled state. At −4.5 C, freezing was started by tapping the condenser, producing the change in dielectric constant indicated. Lowering the temperature further caused a further decrease in dielectric constant, the decrease being greater than could be accounted for by a linear extrapolation of the curve for the supercooled system. After the temperature reached −9.3 C, the temperature was raised stepwise and the melting curve was obtained. The final melting point was at −0.7 C. This depression below 0 C may be due entirely to the alkali content, but it is probably due in part to a slight loss of moisture from the sample that occurred while it was being transferred to the fixed condenser.

The final melting point appears to be exactly on the cooling curve, indicating that the sample returned to its initial state at the end of the cycle. However, the slope of the thawing curve above 0 C is not the same as that of the corresponding part of the freezing curve. This might indicate a permanent change in the dielectric constant of the sample. Such a change would take place if some of the originally evaporable water would become non-evaporable through reaction with unhydrated cement. Since the sample was in the fixed condenser for four days, some additional hydration is not unlikely.

On comparing these results with those given in Fig. 8-7, we find that the major features of the results obtained from the dilatometer method were found also with the electrical method. (A possible exception is the evidence concerning the permanent change in the sample during the cycle.) It seems, therefore, that supercooling and hysteresis are not peculiarities of the dilatometric method but are characteristic of the paste.

METHOD OF ESTIMATING THE AMOUNT OF ICE FROM THE MELTING CURVE

Curves such as that shown in Fig. 8-7 show the algebraic sums of simultaneous expansions and contractions that accompany changes in temperature. To estimate the amount of ice that exists at any given temperature it is necessary to ascertain the net expansion, that is, the difference between the existing volume at the given temperature and the volume that the system would have had, had no freezing occurred. This difference was not determined with exactness for several reasons discussed below.

In those tests where the specimens were cooled stepwise, as in the case represented in Fig. 8-7, the volume change that would have occurred

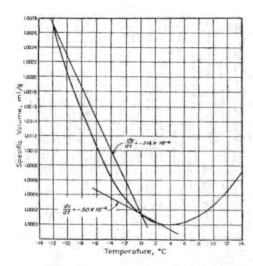

Fig. 8-10—Specific volume of water at a pressure of 1 atmosphere

N. E. Dorsey, *Properties of Ordinary Water Substance* (New York, Reinhold Publishing Corp., 1940) Table 94

had no ice formed could be estimated with satisfactory accuracy from the slope of the line established while the freezable water remained in a supercooled state. However, in the majority of tests only the melting curve was obtained and the volume change in the system when it was free from ice could be observed only in the range from 0 to +2 C. An extrapolation of the line so established into the range below 0 C involves an assumption that the coefficients of expansion of all parts of the system are, in the absence of ice formation, constant throughout the temperature range involved, usually −20 to +2 C. So far as the solid phase of the paste and the pyrex bulb are concerned, this is probably not far from true. With respect to the water and toluene, however, such an assumption is at variance with fact.

As may be seen in Fig. 8-10, water expands as the temperature is changed in either direction from +4 C. Hence, the volume change of the water is in the same direction as that of the rest of the system only when the temperature is above +4 C. Therefore, it follows that at readings taken between 0 and +2 C, the volume change of the water is opposite to that of the rest of the system over all parts of the curve. However, Fig. 8-10 shows that the mean coefficient for the water in the 0 to +2 C range is much different from what it is over a 15-deg. range below 0 C. Hence, a mean slope established by data in the 0 to +2 C range cannot be the same as the mean slope in the lower range. It is necessary, therefore, to find a means of determining the mean slope over the lower range from the empirically established mean slope in the 0 to +2 C range. This may be done as follows:

Let V_o = volume of contents of bulb at 0 C, or volume of pyrex bulb at 0 C,

V_t = volume of contents of bulb at temperature t,

V_{dt} = volume of pyrex bulb at temperature t,

v_{ao} and v_{at} = volume of solids in bulb at 0 and t, respectively,

v_{bo} and v_{bt} = volume of evaporable water in bulb at 0 and t, respectively, and

v_{co} and v_{ct} = volume of toluene in bulb at 0 and t, respectively.

The apparent change in volume for a specified temperature change will be

$$(V_t - V_o) - (V_{dt} - V_o) = V_t - V_{dt} = \Delta V.$$

From the above definitions it follows that

$$\Delta V = (v_{at} - v_{ao}) + (v_{bt} - v_{bo}) + (v_{ct} - v_{co}) - (V_{dt} - V_o)$$

$$v_{at} = v_{ao} + \frac{\Delta v_a}{\Delta t} \Delta t, \text{ etc., for each term of the above equation.}$$

Hence,

$$\frac{\Delta V}{\Delta t} = \frac{\Delta v_a}{\Delta t} + \frac{\Delta v_b}{\Delta t} + \frac{\Delta v_c}{\Delta t} - \frac{\Delta V_d}{\Delta t} \quad \dots \dots \dots \dots (4)$$

The mean coefficients for each part are as follows:

For the solid phase of the paste:

$$\frac{\Delta v_a}{\Delta t} = 32 \times 10^{-6} v_{ao} \text{ (Ref. 8)}$$

For water:

$$\frac{\Delta v_b}{\Delta t} = -50 \times 10^{-6} v_{bo}, \text{ for 0 to 2 C (See Ref. 10 and Fig. 8-10)}$$

$$\frac{\Delta v_b}{\Delta t} = -216 \times 10^{-6} v_{bo}, \text{ for 0 to } -12 \text{ C (See Ref. 10 and Fig. 8-10)}$$

For toluene:

$$\frac{\Delta v_c}{\Delta t} = 1051 \times 10^{-6} v_c, \text{ for 0 to 2 C}$$

$$\frac{\Delta v_c}{\Delta t} = 1038 \times 10^{-6} v_c, \text{ for 0 to } -12 \text{ C (Ref. 9)}$$

For the bulb (Pyrex-brand glass):

$$\frac{\Delta V_d}{\Delta t} = 10 \times 10^{-6} V_o$$

These figures substituted into eq. (4) give

$$10^6 \frac{\Delta V}{\Delta t} = 32 v_{ao} - 50 v_{bo} + 1051 v_{co} - 10 V_o, \text{ for 0 to 2 C} \dots \dots \dots \dots (5)$$

and

$$10^6 \frac{\Delta V}{\Delta t} = 32v_{ao} - 216v_{bo} + 1038v_{co} - 10V_{o}, \text{ for } 0 \text{ to } -12 \text{ C}. \quad \ldots\ldots(6)$$

Let m = mean slope of dilatometer curve, $\Delta V/\Delta t$, from 0 to 2 C, and m' = mean slope from 0 to -12 C.

Then, from eq. (5) and (6)

$$10^6(m' - m) = -166v_{bo} + 13v_{co}$$

and

$$\frac{m'}{m} = 1 - \frac{166v_{bo} + 13v_{co}}{10^6 m} \quad \ldots\ldots\ldots\ldots\ldots\ldots\ldots\ldots\ldots\ldots(7)$$

Thus the ratio of the mean slope from 0 to -12 C to that from 0 to 2 C is found in terms of the amounts of water, v_{bo}, and toluene, v_{co}, and the experimentally established slope above 0 C. As applied to any specific case the line represented by eq. (4) was extended to -15 C and in some cases to -20 C. This was necessary because data on supercooled water below -12 C were not available.

With the mean slope of the line representing the supercooled system thus established for each test, the amount of ice at any given temperature was estimated from the difference between the observed volume and the corresponding computed volume of the supercooled system, this difference being the observed net expansion. Let

Δv = net expansion,

B_t = expansion resulting from freezing 1 gram of water at the existing temperature, and

w_f = amount of ice (freezable water).

Then

$$w_f = \frac{\Delta v}{B_t} \quad \ldots\ldots\ldots\ldots\ldots\ldots\ldots\ldots\ldots\ldots\ldots\ldots\ldots\ldots(8)$$

B_t is itself a function of temperature, since the coefficients of expansion of water and ice differ both in magnitude and sign. Table 8-1 gives values of B_t at various temperatures calculated from values of the specific volume of ice and water assembled by Dorsey.[10]

The method of obtaining the amount of ice in the dilatometer described above obviously decreases in accuracy as the temperature becomes lower. This is due not only to the inaccuracy of the experimental value for m but also to limitations on the use of Table 8-1. As will be seen later, the water that freezes above a dilatometer temperature of about -6 C is almost entirely capillary water. But below -6 C, some of the gel water is extracted and freezes with the capillary water. Since the mean specific volume of the gel water is about 0.90 (Part 5), Table 8-1 does not correctly represent the volume change of gel water on freezing.

TABLE 8-1—VOLUME CHANGE OF 1 GRAM OF WATER WHEN
FREEZING OCCURS AT GIVEN TEMPERATURES

Temp., deg. C	Volume change, ml ($= B_t$)
0	0.0907
− 1.0	0.0904
− 1.5	0.0903
− 2.0	0.0902
− 2.5	0.0900
− 3.0	0.0898
− 3.5	0.0897
− 4.0	0.0896
− 5.0	0.0892
− 6.0	0.0889
− 8.0	0.0881
−10.0	0.0872
−12.0	0.0863
−15.0	0.0849
−20.0	0.0812

Because of these considerations, the method of obtaining w_f described above cannot be considered reliable below about − 15 C. A preferable procedure would be to establish the slope by supercooling the sample as far as possible, after the final melting curve has been obtained.

EFFECT OF TOLUENE ON THE MELTING CURVE

Owing to the fact that the paste granules were surrounded with toluene, it is necessary to consider the effect of the toluene on the position of the melting curve. This will be done indirectly by considering its effect on water vapor pressure.

At any given temperature below 0 C, equilibrium between ice and capillary water can be maintained because of the effect of capillary tension on the free energy of the water. The fact that with ice present the capillary tension is maintained indicates that the unfrozen capillary water either becomes separated from the ice so as to maintain its meniscus, or else it retains its continuity and remains in contact not only with the ice but also with the external phase. Such contact might be maintained through channels too small to be frozen at the existing temperature. If the external phase is air, as in the electrical method described earlier, the capillary tension will depend on surface curvature and the interfacial tension at the air-water interface (i.e., the surface tension), according to Kelvin's equation. (See Part 3.) If the external phase is toluene, the capillary tension will depend on surface curvature as before, but now it will depend on the interfacial tension at the toluene-water interface rather than the tension at the air-water interface. Therefore, the melting curves of the granules submerged in toluene should not be the same as when the granules are exposed to air.

We can estimate the effect of substituting a toluene-water interface for an air-water interface by making use of eq. (3).   Let

σ_w = surface tension of water against air,

σ_{wt} = interfacial tension, water against toluene,

T_o = normal freezing point of water, deg. K,

ΔT_1 = depression of freezing point with sample in contact with air,

ΔT_2 = depression of freezing point with sample in contact with toluene, and

let the other symbols have the same meaning as before.   Then,

$$\frac{\Delta T_1}{T_o} = \frac{2v_f}{rq}\sigma_w$$

and

$$\frac{\Delta T_2}{T_o} = \frac{2v_f}{rq}\sigma_{wt} .$$

We may assume that v_f and q are the same in both cases.   Hence,

$$\frac{\Delta T_1}{\Delta T_2} = \frac{\sigma_w}{\sigma_{wt}} .$$

Interfacial tension and surface tension are functions of temperature. For the air-water interface, we may obtain satisfactory figures for given temperatures from published data.   For the toluene-air interface no data are available except for 25 C.   For the similar liquid, benzene, the temperature coefficient is given as -0.058 for the temperature range 10 to 40 C.   We will assume that this holds for toluene and for the lower temperature range.

On the basis just described, the following results were obtained:

t, deg. C	σ_w	σ_{wt}	$\dfrac{\sigma_w}{\sigma_{wt}}$
0	75.64	37.6	2.01
− 5	76.33	37.8	2.02
−10	77.00	38.1	2.02

Hence, it may be concluded that

$\Delta T_1 = 2\Delta T_2$, approximately.

That is, the depression of the freezing point with the sample in contact with air would be about twice the amount observed in these experiments. Or, the amount of water freezable in these experiments at −15 C, for example, is about the same as would be freezable at −30 C if the samples were exposed to air.

QUANTITIES OF ICE FORMED IN VARIOUS SAMPLES

The amounts of ice formed in various samples are given in Tables 8-2 to 8-6 and compositions of the samples in Table 8-7. The relationships between ice-content and temperature are given graphically in Fig. 8-11 and 8-12. The results are analyzed further in succeeding sections.

Influence of soluble alkalies

The curves shown in Fig. 8-11 and 8-12 show that the final melting point differed among the various specimens. These differences are believed to be due to differences in the amount of soluble salts, particularly the alkalies, in the evaporable water. The basis for this conclusion is more clearly indicated by the data as arranged in Table 8-8.

It will be noted that with three of the five cements, the final melting point is higher the higher the original water-cement ratio. This is undoubtedly the result of the leaching out of alkalies during the 28-day period of water storage; the higher w_s/c the higher the rate of leaching.

The dissolved alkali not only lowers the final melting point but also the amounts of ice that can exist at lower temperatures. The effect is probably proportional to the concentration in the part that remains unfrozen. What this concentration is, or how it changes with temperature, cannot be told from information now available, mainly because the effects of adsorption by the solid phase on both the solvent and the solute cannot be evaluated.

THEORETICAL AMOUNT OF FREEZABLE WATER AT A GIVEN TEMPERATURE

Locus of ice in the paste

In the majority of the tests considered here, the samples were first cooled to −78 C. This is the temperature at which ice has about the same vapor pressure as the non-evaporable water. (See Part 2.) Hence, if equilibrium is reached, all the evaporable water should be frozen. However, it should be observed that the *freezing in place* of adsorbed water is very unlikely. As shown in Part 4, when water is adsorbed it undergoes a change, as indicated by its decrease in entropy. The indications are that the entropy change of adsorption is greater than that accompanying the transition from water to ice. It hardly seems possible that water that has already been changed to such an extent could be caused to crystallize only by lowering the temperature. To be considered also are the relative sizes of the gel pores and the capillaries. As shown in Part 3, the hydraulic radius of the gel pores is estimated to be about 10Å. The average width of the pores is probably between 2 and

TABLE 8-2—MELTING-CURVE DATA FOR SAMPLES MADE WITH CEMENT 15754
(For compositions of samples, see Table 8-7.)

Temp., deg. C $\times(-1)$	Ref. 10-4; $w_o/c = 0.32$ 28 days w_f/c	28 days w_f/V_m	90 days w_f/c	90 days w_f/V_m	Ref. 10-1; $w_o/c = 0.45$ 28 days w_f/c	28 days w_f/V_m	90 days w_f/c	90 days w_f/V_m	Ref. 10-3; $w_o/c = 0.62$ 28 days w_f/c	28 days w_f/V_m	90 days w_f/c	90 days w_f/V_m
0.1	—	—	—	—	—	—	—	—	—	—	—	—
0.15	—	—	—	—	—	—	—	—	.0165	0.29	—	—
0.25	—	—	—	—	—	—	—	—	.0557	0.99	.0350	0.57
0.50	.0157	0.35	.0149	0.30	.0455	0.86	.0424	0.70	.1160	2.07	.1275	2.09
0.75	.0293	0.65	.0287	0.59	.0744	1.40	.0663	1.09	.1627	3.39	.1562	2.56
1.0	.0384	0.85	.0376	0.77	.0909	1.72	.0762	1.25	.1897	4.01	.1751	2.87
1.5	.0415	0.92	.0417	0.85	.1075	2.03	.0898	1.47	.2243	4.38	.2061	3.38
2.0	.0449	1.00	.0432	0.88	.1207	2.28	.0996	1.63	.2452	4.65	.2259	3.70
2.5	.0473	1.05	.0452	0.92	.1294	2.44	.1045	1.71	.2602	4.86	.2387	3.91
3.0	.0496	1.10	.0467	0.95	.1350	2.55	.1093	1.79	.2724	5.05	.2482	4.07
3.5	.0520	1.16	.0485	0.99	.1404	2.65	.1142	1.87	.2829	5.21	.2547	4.18
4.0	.0560	1.24	.0507	1.03	.1445	2.73	.1177	1.93	.2916	5.46	.2636	4.32
5.0	.0600	1.33	.0539	1.10	.1556	2.94	.1250	2.05	.3055	5.66	.2773	4.55
6.0	.0663	1.47	.0583	1.19	.1655	3.12	.1316	2.16	.3172	6.06	.2885	4.73
8.0	.0704	1.56	.0622	1.27	.1779	3.36	.1449	2.38	.3396	6.46	.3096	5.08
10.0	.0744	1.65	.0648	1.32	.1893	3.57	.1542	2.53	.3616	6.69	.3267	5.36
12.0	.0823	1.83	.0672	1.37	.1993	3.76	.1622	2.66	.3749	7.00	.3397	5.57
15.0	.0930	2.07	.0734	1.50	.2093	3.95	.1738	2.85	.3919	7.57	.3559	5.83
20.0					.2270	4.28	.1965	3.22	.4240			
Final Melting Point		— 0.5°		— 0.5°		— 0.25°		— 0.20°		— 0.05°		— 0.05°

TABLE 8-3—MELTING-CURVE DATA FOR SAMPLES MADE WITH CEMENT 15756
(For compositions of samples, see Table 8-7.)

Temp., deg. C × (−1)	Ref. 10-C; $w_0/c = 0.34$ 29 days		Ref. 10-B; $w_0/c = 0.48$ 29 days		Ref. 10-A; $w_0/c = 0.67$ 29 days		Ref. 10-14; $w_0/c = 0.45$ 90 days		Ref. 10-13; $w_0/c = 0.63$ 90 days	
	w_f/c	w_f/V_m	w_f/c	w_f/V_m	w_f/c	w_f/V_m	w_f/c	w_f/V_m	w_f/c	w_f/V_m
0.1	—	—	—	—	.0252	0.60	—	—	—	—
0.25	.0101	0.28	.0470	1.21	.0994	2.37	.0273	0.58	.0448	0.91
0.50	.0242	0.67	.0916	2.35	.1755	4.18	.0558	1.19	.1289	2.63
0.75	.0391	1.09	.1156	2.96	.2260	5.38	.0816	1.74	.2056	4.20
1.0	.0469	1.30	.1345	3.45	.2624	6.25	.0957	2.04	.2168	4.42
1.5	.0600	1.67	.1637	4.20	.3128	7.45	.1161	2.47	.2638	5.38
2.0	.0717	1.99	.1864	4.78	.3489	8.31	.1311	2.79	.2910	5.94
2.5	.0802	2.23	.2068	5.30	.3727	8.87	.1443	3.07	.3138	6.40
3.0	.0889	2.47	.2196	5.63	.3910	9.31	.1549	3.30	.3322	6.78
3.5	.0951	2.64	.2311	5.93	.4071	9.69	.1636	3.48	.3476	7.09
4.0	.1013	2.81	.2410	6.18	.4198	10.00	.1724	3.67	.3608	7.36
5.0	.1139	3.16	.2578	6.61	.4459	10.62	.1863	3.96	.3817	7.79
6.0	.1218	3.38	.2732	7.01	.4624	11.01	.1972	4.20	.3965	8.09
8.0	.1354	3.76	.2934	7.52	.4859	11.57	.2024	4.31	.4175	8.52
10.0	.1413	3.92	.2988	7.66	.4942	11.77	.2251	4.79	.4305	8.79
12.0	.1468	4.08	.3079	7.89	.5030	11.98	.2343	4.99	.4401	8.98
15.0	.1563	4.34	.3184	8.16	.5157	12.28	.2477	5.27	.4557	9.30
20.0	.1721	4.78	.3431	8.80	.5417	12.90	.2691	5.73	.4851	9.90
Final Melting Point	− 0.1°		− 0.1°		− 0.05°		0°		0°	

TABLE 8-4—MELTING-CURVE DATA FOR SAMPLES MADE WITH CEMENT 15758
(For compositions of samples, see Table 8-7.)

Temp., deg. C × (−1)	Ref. 10-12; $w_o/c = 0.32$				Ref. 10-11; $w_o/c = 0.45$				Ref. 10-10; $w_o/c = 0.62$			
	28 days		91 days		28 days		91 days		28 days		91 days	
	w_f/c	w_f/V_m	w_f/c	w_f/V_m	w_f/c	w_f/V_m	w_f/c	w_f/V_m	w_f/c	w_f/V_m	w_f/c	w_f/V_m
0.25	—	—	—	—							.0529	0.96
0.50	—	—	—	—	.0280	0.55	.0177	0.34	.1040	1.93	.1042	1.89
0.75	—	—	—	—	.0510	1.00	.0358	0.69	.1723	3.19	.1474	2.68
1.0	.0019	0.04	.0199	0.45	.0714	1.40	.0538	1.03	.2048	3.79	.1766	3.21
1.5	.0197	0.47	.0335	0.76	.0919	1.80	.0724	1.39	.2386	4.18	.2027	3.68
2.0	.0276	0.66	.0406	0.92	.1045	2.05	.0844	1.62	.2636	4.88	.2272	4.13
2.5	.0324	0.77	.0462	1.05	.1146	2.25	.0933	1.79	.2799	5.18	.2415	4.39
3.0	.0379	0.90	.0493	1.12	.1222	2.40	.1031	1.98	.2925	5.61	.2540	4.62
3.5	.0418	0.99	.0510	1.16	.1272	2.49	.1039	2.00	.3031	5.80	.2586	4.70
4.0	.0449	1.07	.0529	1.20	.1321	2.59	.1082	2.08	.3131	5.98	.2657	4.83
5.0	.0520	1.24	.0583	1.32	.1384	2.71	.1169	2.25	.3229	6.21	.2820	5.13
6.0	.0582	1.38	.0613	1.39	.1445	2.83	.1256	2.42	.3356	6.62	.2909	5.29
8.0	.0694	1.65	.0674	1.53	.1546	3.03	.1397	2.69	.3575	6.93	.3118	5.67
10.0	.0783	1.86	.0727	1.65	.1624	3.18	.1473	2.83	.3741	7.12	.3257	5.92
12.0	.0857	2.04	.0765	1.74	.1678	3.29	.1566	3.01	.3848	7.45	.3376	6.14
15.0	.0924	2.20	.0793	1.80	.1763	3.46	.1673	3.22	.4024	8.08	.3529	6.42
20.0	*		*		*		*		.4363		*	
Final Melting Point	− 0.9°		− 0.85°		− 0.25°		− 0.25°		− 0.15°		− 0.10°	

* Not available.

TABLE 8-5—MELTING-CURVE DATA FOR SAMPLES MADE WITH CEMENT 15761
(For compositions of samples, see Table 8-7.)

Temp. deg. C × (−1)	Ref. 10-6; $w_0/c = 0.32$ 28 days		Ref. 10-2; $w_0/c = 0.45$ 28 days		90 days		Ref. 10-5; $w_0/c = 0.63$ 28 days	
	w_f/c	w_f/V_m	w_f/c	w_f/V_m	w_f/c	w_f/V_m	w_f/c	w_f/V_m
0.75	—	—	—	—	—	—	.1063	1.93
1.0	—	—	.0854	—	.0191	0.34	.1894	3.44
1.5	—	—	.1199	1.71	.0892	1.59	.2548	4.63
2.0	.0316	0.77	.1357	2.40	.1083	1.93	.2858	5.20
2.5	.0455	1.11	.1459	2.71	.1201	2.14	.3100	5.64
3.0	.0515	1.26	.1547	2.92	.1296	2.31	.3240	5.89
3.5	.0568	1.38	.1630	3.09	.1371	2.45	.3376	6.14
4.0	.0615	1.50	.1779	3.26	.1431	2.56	.3478	6.32
5.0	.0697	1.70	.1918	3.56	.1550	2.77	.3655	6.64
6.0	.0747	1.82	.2130	3.84	.1664	2.97	.3793	6.90
8.0	.0830	2.02	.2289	4.26	.1837	3.28	.4012	7.29
10.0	.0888	2.16	.2410	4.58	.1949	3.48	.4145	7.54
12.0	.0928	2.26	.2542	4.82	.2046	3.65	.4235	7.70
15.0	.0942	2.30	.2780	5.08	.2152	3.84	.4373	7.95
20.0	.0964	2.35		5.56	.2310	4.12	.4425	8.04
Final Melting Point	−1.6°		−0.9°		−0.85°		−0.5°	

TABLE 8-6—MELTING-CURVE DATA FOR SAMPLES MADE WITH CEMENT 15763

(For compositions of samples, see Table 8-7.)

Temp., deg. C × (−1)	Ref. 10-9; $w_f/c = 0.31$				Ref. 10-8; $w_0/c = 0.44$				Ref. 10-7; $w_f/c = 0.62$	
	28 days		91 days		Dil. No. 5 28 days		Dil. No. 6 28 days		28 days	
	w_f/c *	w_f/V_m	w_f/c	w_f/V_m	w_f/c	w_f/V_m	w_f/c	w_f/V_m	w_f/c	w_f/V_m
0.10	—				.0112	0.34	.0092	0.28	.0392	1.12
0.15	.0126	0.42	.0058	0.15						
0.25	.0228	0.76	.0244	0.64	.0586	1.78	.0478	1.45	.1110	3.17
0.50	.0459	1.53	.0358	0.94	.1003	3.04	.0908	2.75	.1963	5.61
0.75	—		.0430	1.13	.1352	4.10	.1269	3.85	.2648	7.57
1.0	.0772	2.57	.0538	1.42	.1600	4.85	.1525	4.62	.3041	8.69
1.5	.0932	3.11	.0603	1.59	.1914	5.80	.1827	5.54	.3580	10.23
2.0	.1046	3.49	.0652	1.72	.2128	6.45	.2036	6.17	.3890	11.11
2.5	.1128	3.76	.0698	1.84	.2276	6.90	.2177	6.60	.4123	11.78
3.0	.1185	3.95	.0727	1.91	.2391	7.24	.2294	6.95	.4306	12.30
3.5	.1231	4.10	.0768	2.02	.2456	7.44	.2386	7.23	.4452	12.72
4.0	.1273	4.24	.0822	2.16	.2523	7.64	.2467	7.48	.4566	13.04
5.0	.1347	4.49	.0875	2.30	.2639	8.00	.2563	7.77	.4705	13.44
6.0	.1378	4.59	.0939	2.47	.2731	8.28	.2658	8.05	.4889	13.97
8.0	.1437	4.79	.0983	2.59	.2828	8.57	.2757	8.35	.4973	14.21
10.0	.1481	4.94	.1014	2.67	.2913	8.83	.2814	8.62	.5061	14.46
12.0	.1509	5.03	.1037	2.73	.2937	8.90	.2846	8.76	.5153	14.72
15.0	.1545	5.15	.1045	2.75	.2962	8.98	.2892	8.90	.5272	15.06
20.0					.3028	9.18	.2963	8.98	.5500	15.71
Final Melting Point	− 0.05°		− 0.05°		− 0.05°		− 0.05°		− 0.05°	

* Not available.

TABLE 8-7—COMPOSITION OF SAMPLES USED IN DILATOMETERS

(For cement characteristics, see Appendix to Part 2.)

Ref. No.	Age, days	$\dfrac{w_o}{c}$	Composition, g/g of cement					$\dfrac{w_e}{V_m}$
			$\dfrac{w_n}{c}$	$\dfrac{w_e}{c}$	$\dfrac{w_t}{c}$	$\dfrac{(w_n)_{.33}}{c}$	$\dfrac{V_m}{c}$	
			Cement 15754; $V_m/w_n = 0.258$					
10–4	28	0.32	0.176	0.213	0.389	0.064	0.045	4.73
10–4	90	0.32	0.189	0.220	0.409	0.065	0.049	4.49
10–1	28	0.45	0.207	0.351	0.558	0.076	0.053	6.63
10–1	90	0.45	0.237	0.335	0.572	0.081	0.061	5.50
10–3	28	0.62	0.217	0.536	0.753	0.081	0.056	9.57
10–3	90	0.62	0.235	0.538	0.773	0.088	0.061	8.82
			Cement 15756; $V_m/w_n = 0.271$					
10–C	28	0.34	0.134	0.272	0.406	0.051	0.036	7.56
10–B	28	0.48	0.145	0.443	0.589	0.052	0.039	11.36
10–A	28	0.67	0.154	0.648	0.802	0.057	0.042	15.43
10–14	90	0.45	0.172	0.391	0.563	0.063	0.047	8.32
10–13	90	0.63	0.182	0.611	0.793	0.066	0.049	12.47
			Cement 15758; $V_m/w_n = 0.248$					
10–12	28	0.32	0.168	0.224	0.392	0.058	0.042	5.33
10–12	91	0.32	0.179	0.227	0.406	0.061	0.044	5.16
10–11	28	0.45	0.204	0.353	0.557	0.074	0.051	6.92
10–11	91	0.45	0.211	0.365	0.576	0.076	0.052	7.02
10–10	28	0.62	0.218	0.555	0.773	0.078	0.054	10.28
10–10	91	0.62	0.222	0.535	0.757	0.083	0.055	9.73
			Cement 15761; $V_m/w_n = 0.262$					
10–6	28	0.32	0.158	0.248	0.406	0.057	0.041	6.05
10–2	28	0.45	0.190	0.390	0.580	0.069	0.050	7.80
10–2	90	0.45	0.215	0.381	0.596	0.078	0.056	6.80
10–5	28	0.63	0.209	0.613	0.822	0.083	0.055	11.15
			Cement 15763; $V_m/w_n = 0.295$					
10–9	28	0.31	0.101	0.278	0.379	0.045	0.030	9.27
10–9	91	0.31	0.130	0.237	0.367	0.056	0.038	6.24
10–8	28	0.44	0.113	0.424	0.537	0.048	0.033	12.85
10–7	28	0.62	0.119	0.624	0.743	0.050	0.035	17.83

4 times the hydraulic radius. Thus the average gel pore is estimated to be between 20 and 40Å wide. The width of the average capillary cannot be estimated very accurately, but it is at least 10 or 20 times the width of the gel pore. Owing to the fact that the melting point of a crystal is higher the smaller the crystal—for crystals in the colloidal size-range—any ice that might form in the gel pores would have a higher melting point than that of the ice in the capillaries. It seems, therefore, that if the gel water freezes, it first moves out of the gel and then joins the ice already

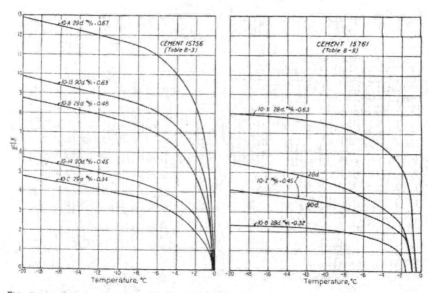

Fig. 8-11—Relationship between ice content and temperature for samples made with cements indicated

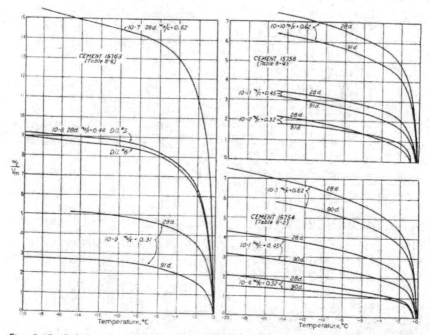

Fig. 8-12—Relationship between ice content and temperature for samples made with cements indicated

formed in the capillaries. The movement of the water could be either by surface migration or by distillation.

Relation of freezing to drying

As mentioned before, the process of freezing out gel water would be fundamentally the same as removing it by evaporation. In either case, the equilibrium vapor pressure of the gel water at any time is determined by the degree of saturation of the gel. Consequently, the amounts of freezable and unfreezable water should be determinable in terms of the vapor pressure isotherm. For the conditions of these experiments, the adsorption isotherm may be used.

TABLE 8-8—INFLUENCE OF ALKALIES ON FINAL MELTING POINT

Cement No.	Alkali content of cement, percent			w_o/c	Final melting point, deg. C	
	Na_2O	K_2O	Total		28 days	90 days
15754	0.17	0.16	0.33	0.32	−0.50	−0.50
				0.45	−0.25	−0.20
				0.62	−0.05	−0.05
15756	0.05	0.17	0.22	0.34	−0.10*	—
				0.45	—	0
				0.48	−0.10*	—
				0.63	—	0
				0.67	−0.05	—
15758	0.30	0.40	0.70	0.32	−0.90	−0.85†
				0.45	−0.25	−0.25†
				0.62	−0.15	−0.10†
15761	1.13	0.44	1.57	0.32	−1.60	—
				0.45	−0.90	−0.85
				0.63	−0.50	—
15763	0.05	0.22	0.27	0.31	−0.05	−0.05†
				0.44	−0.05	—
				0.62	−0.05	—

*29 days.
†91 days.

Relation of freezable water to total evaporable water

We have already seen (Part 3) that the water content that produces a given vapor pressure *in the lower range of pressures* is the same per unit V_m* for all samples. Therefore, for the lower range of vapor pressures, and hence for the lower range of freezing temperatures, the amount of *unfreezable* water at a given temperature per unit V_m should be the same for all samples. Thus if we let

---

*V_m is the constant in the B.E.T. equation that represents the quantity of water required to cover the surface with a single layer of molecules. It is considered to be proportional to the surface area of the solid phase and a measure of the gel content of well-hydrated samples.

w_e = total evaporable water,
w_u = unfreezable water, and
w_f = freezable water,

then

$$\frac{w_f}{V_m} = \frac{w_e}{V_m} - u, \dots\dots\dots\dots\dots\dots\dots\dots\dots\dots\dots\dots\dots(9)$$

where $u = w_u/V_m$ and is a constant for a given temperature.

From eq. (9) it can be seen that plotting w_f/V_m vs. w_e/V_m should produce a straight line having a slope of unity for whatever range of temperatures w_u/V_m is actually constant. Such plots are shown in Fig. 8-13 for six different temperatures. In each diagram the solid straight line has a slope of 1.0 as required by eq. (9). With the exception of those obtained above -6 C, the experimental points conform fairly well to this slope. Hence, we may conclude that for temperatures of about -6 C or lower, the following empirical relationships may be used for estimating the amount of freezable water:

$$\left(\frac{w_f}{V_m}\right)_{-6°} = \frac{w_e}{V_m} - 4.0 \dots\dots\dots\dots\dots\dots\dots\dots\dots\dots\dots(10)$$

$$\left(\frac{w_f}{V_m}\right)_{-10°} = \frac{w_e}{V_m} - 3.7 \dots\dots\dots\dots\dots\dots\dots\dots\dots\dots\dots(11)$$

$$\left(\frac{w_f}{V_m}\right)_{-15°} = \frac{w_e}{V_m} - 3.2 \dots\dots\dots\dots\dots\dots\dots\dots\dots\dots\dots(12)$$

The temperatures indicated are for freezing in toluene. For freezing in air, the temperatures should be multiplied by 2, as shown in a preceding section. That is,

$$(w_f)_{-6°} \text{ in toluene} = (w_f)_{-12°} \text{ in air, etc.}$$

Reference to Fig. 8-13 shows that at a dilatometer temperature of -6 C or higher, the amount of freezable water is roughly proportional to the amount of capillary water, $w_e - 4V_m$, the proportionality constants being about 1.0 at -6 C, 0.86 at -4 C, 0.7 at -2 C, and 0.6 at -1 C. This indicates that in this upper temperature range, the amount of water extracted from the gel by freezing is negligible. Below -6 C, the contribution from the gel water is appreciable. As already mentioned it could contribute a maximum of $4V_m$ at about -78 C.

It should be noted that eqs. (10), (11), and (12) can be used only for estimating the *maximum* amount of freezable water. If a specimen were cooled only a few degrees below its final melting point, as is frequently the case for concrete exposed to the weather, the amount of freezable water would probably be smaller than would be indicated by these equations because of the hysteresis in the vapor-pressure-vs.-water-content relationship. Very little specific information on this point can be given until more experimental work is done.

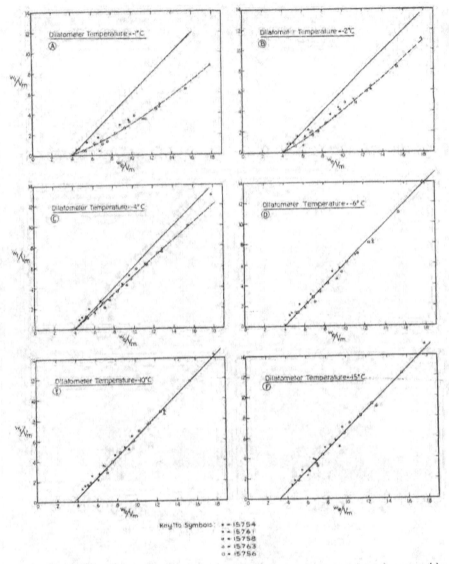

Fig. 8-13—Relationship between maximum freezable water content and total evaporable water in saturated pastes

RELATIONSHIP BETWEEN THE AMOUNT OF WATER UNFREEZABLE AT A GIVEN TEMPERATURE AND THE 25C VAPOR PRESSURE ISOTHERM

Theoretical relationship

As mentioned before, one of the objects of this investigation was to establish the relationship between melting point and vapor pressure so that the amount of water freezable at a given temperature could be estimated from sorption data alone. As pointed out in connection with Fig. 8-1, at any given temperature below 0 C, the vapor pressure of the unfrozen evaporable water must be the same as that of ice at the existing temperature. On the assumption that the ice exists as a pure, microcrystalline phase under atmospheric pressure only, we can ascertain its relative vapor pressure at given temperatures from eq. (1) or (2). The results of such computations are plotted in Fig. 8-2. That curve shows that at -30 C, for example, the vapor pressure of ice is about $0.75\ p_s$, where p_s is the saturation pressure at -30 C. As shown above, the amount of water freezable at -30 C is about the same as the amount freezable in the toluene-filled dilatometer at -15 C.

To estimate the point on the 25 C adsorption isotherm corresponding to a given relative vapor pressure at a lower temperature, we may use the Kelvin equation (see Part 3):

$$ln\ p/p_s = -\frac{Mv_f\sigma_f}{RT}\left(\frac{1}{r_1}+\frac{1}{r_2}\right),\ \dots\dots\dots\dots\dots\dots\dots \text{(13)}$$

where

$$p/p_s = \text{relative vapor pressure,}$$
$$M = \text{molecular weight of the fluid,}$$
$$v_f = \text{molar volume of the fluid,}$$
$$\sigma_f = \text{surface tension of the fluid,}$$
$$r_1 \text{ and } r_2 = \text{principal radii of surface curvature of the fluid,}$$
$$R = \text{gas constant, and}$$
$$T = \text{absolute temperature.}$$

Let

$$h_{25} = p/p_s \text{ at 298 K (25 C),}$$
$$h_t = p/p_s \text{ at temperature } T,$$
$$\sigma_{25} = \text{surface tension at 25 C, and}$$
$$\sigma_t = \text{surface tension at temperature } T.$$

Then

$$ln\ h_{25} = -\frac{\sigma_{25}\,M(v_f)_{25}}{R298}\left(\frac{1}{r_1}+\frac{1}{r_2}\right)$$

and

$$ln\ h_t = -\frac{\sigma_t\,M(v_f)_t}{RT}\left(\frac{1}{r_1}+\frac{1}{r_2}\right),$$

where

T = the lower temperature, in deg. K, and the other symbols have the same significance as before. Hence,

$$\frac{\ln h_{25}}{\ln h_t} = \frac{\sigma_{25}}{\sigma_t} \frac{T}{298} \frac{(v_f)_{25}}{(v_f)_t} \quad \ldots \ldots \ldots \ldots \ldots (14)$$

The ratio $(v_f)_{25}$ to $(v_f)_t$ varies so little from 1.0000 over the temperature range involved here that it can be taken as unity at all temperatures.

The ratio of σ_{25}/σ_t can be evaluated from the relationship

$$\sigma_t = 75.64 - 0.1391t - 0.00003t^2 \text{ (Ref. 12)} \ldots \ldots \ldots (15)$$

Solutions of this equation are given below in Table 8-9:

TABLE 8-9—SOLUTIONS OF EQ. (15)

t, deg. C	σ_t	$\dfrac{\sigma_{25}}{\sigma_t}$
25	71.97	1.0000
0	75.64	0.9515
−4	76.19	0.9446
−6	76.46	0.9413
−8	76.75	0.9377
−10	77.06	0.9339
−12	77.47	0.9290
−15	77.79	0.9251
−20	78.30	0.9192
−30	79.54	0.9048

The above data, substituted into eq. (14), give the results shown in Table 8-10.

TABLE 8-10—SOLUTIONS OF EQ. (14)

t, deg. C	T, deg. K	h_t from Fig. 8-2	h_{25}
0	273.1	1.000	1.000
−4	269.1	0.958	0.965
−6	267.1	0.945	0.953
−8	265.1	0.927	0.939
−10	263.1	0.908	0.924
−12	261.1	0.893	0.911
−15	258.1	0.865	0.890
−20	253.1	0.823	0.859
−30	243.1	0.746	0.806

According to the foregoing discussion, the amount of ice formed in the dilatometer at -15 C, for example, is about the same as that which would form in the same sample exposed to air at -30 C. Table 8-10 shows that the water remaining unfrozen at this temperature would have a relative vapor pressure of 0.806 at 25 C. Thus, if all the assumptions made above are valid, the amount of unfrozen water in a sample at -15 C in the dilatometer should be approximately the same as the evaporable water content of the same sample having a relative vapor pressure of 0.806 at 25 C. The extent to which the data bear out this assumption will be shown after the empirical relationship has been examined.

Comparison of theoretical and empirical relationships

Consider a given sample in a dilatometer at -15 C. It will contain a certain quantity of unfrozen evaporable water in equilibrium with ice. We have already seen that to maintain equilibrium between the same amount of unfrozen water and ice in the absence of toluene, the temperature would have to be -30 C. At this temperature the ice, and hence the unfrozen water, would have a vapor pressure of 0.746 p_s (see Fig. 8-2). According to Table 8-10, the corresponding vapor pressure at 25 C would be 0.806 p_s. Similarly, for dilatometer temperatures of -10 C and -6 C, the corresponding vapor pressures at 25 C would be 0.859 and 0.911, respectively.

Table 8-11 gives the ratio of evaporable water, w, to V_m in samples at equilibrium with these pressures at 25 C. These data were obtained from smooth isotherms, representing samples almost identical with those used in the freezing experiments. They represent the theoretical amounts of unfrozen water at dilatometer temperatures of -6 C, -10 C, and -15 C.

The experimentally observed amounts of unfreezable water are indicated by the intercepts of the straight lines in Fig. 8-13 D, E, and F. These intercepts represent experimental averages, comparable with the grand averages given in Table 8-11.

The two sets of figures may be compared in the following table:

Dilatometer temperature, deg. C	Unfreezable water, w_u/V_m		
	Observed	Theoretical	Ratio
-6	4.00	3.72	1.08
-10	3.70	3.25	1.13
-15	3.20	2.93	1.09

600 Powers and Brownyard

TABLE 8-11—RATIO OF EVAPORABLE WATER TO V_m IN HARDENED PASTES
REPRESENTATIVE OF THOSE USED IN FREEZING STUDIES

w_o/c	Age, days	$w/V_m{}^*$ at p/p_s (25 C) indicated		
		0.911	0.859	0.806
Cement 15754				
0.33	28	3.35	3.05	2.85
0.33	90	3.10	2.90	2.75
0.45	28	3.60	3.30	3.00
0.45	90	3.45	3.10	2.90
		Avg. 3.38	3.09	2.88
Cement 15756				
0.32	28	4.10	3.45	3.05
0.32	90	3.45	3.05	2.85
0.45	28	4.40	3.70	3.20
0.45	90	3.90	3.30	2.95
		Avg. 3.96	3.38	3.01
Cement 15758				
0.33	28	3.70	3.20	2.80
0.33	90	3.35	2.95	2.70
0.46	28	3.80	3.35	3.05
0.46	90	3.70	3.25	2.90
		Avg. 3.64	3.19	2.86
Cement 15761				
0.33	28	3.80	3.30	2.95
0.33	90	3.50	3.05	2.80
0.47	28	3.80	3.30	2.95
0.47	90	3.55	3.20	2.90
		Avg. 3.66	3.21	2.90
Cement 15763				
0.32	28	4.25	3.65	3.25
0.32	90	3.45	3.05	2.75
0.44	28	4.35	3.65	3.25
0.44	90	3.85	3.25	2.85
		Avg. 3.98	3.40	3.02
		Grand Avg. 3.72	3.25	2.93

*w = evaporable water, g/g cement; V_m = constant from B.E.T. eq. A, g/g cement.

This indicates that the observed amount of unfreezable water averages about 10 percent greater than the theoretical amount. Such a difference could be due to the smallness of the ice crystals, which would tend to raise their melting point. Or it might be due to an error in the theoretical figure arising from the assumption that the effects of temperature changes on the solutions in the paste are the same as for pure water.

The degree of agreement between the observed and theoretical values is such as to warrant estimating the amount of water freezable at a given temperature from the 25 C isotherm.

EQUATIONS FOR ESTIMATING MAXIMUM FREEZABLE WATER FROM THE NON-EVAPORABLE WATER CONTENT

The maximum amount of water in a saturated paste that may be frozen at a given temperature may be estimated from the non-evaporable and total water contents. The bases for such estimates are developed below:

Eq. (9) may be written
$$w_f = w_s - uV_m .$$
Since, for an average cement,
$$V_m = 0.26 \, w_n \quad \text{(Part 3, eq. (4))},$$
and
$$w_s = w_t - w_n ,$$
then
$$w_f = w_t - w_n(1 + 0.26u) \dots \dots \dots (16)$$
Using the values of u given in eqs. (10), (11), and (12), we obtain
$$(w_f)_{-6°} = w_t - 2.04 \, w_n \dots \dots \dots (17)$$
$$(w_f)_{-10°} = w_t - 1.96 \, w_n \dots \dots \dots (18)$$
$$(w_f)_{-15°} = w_t - 1.83 \, w_n \dots \dots \dots (19)$$

The above equations may be used when the *total water content* of the saturated paste is known. When only the *original water-cement ratio* is known (corrected for bleeding), the relationships developed below may be used.

On the assumption that the volume of the hardened paste is the same as that of the fresh paste after bleeding, we may write
$$w_o = w_i v_t \dots \dots \dots (20)$$
Since
$$v_t = 1 - 0.279 \frac{w_n}{w_t} \quad \text{(Part 5, eq. (8))},$$
$$w_o = w_t - 0.279 \, w_n \dots \dots \dots (21)$$
Substitution into eq. (16) gives
$$w_f = w_o + 0.279 w_n - w_n(1 + 0.26u)$$
$$= w_o - (0.721 + 0.26u)w_n \dots \dots \dots (22)$$

Again using values of u from eqs. (10), (11), and (12) we obtain

$$(w_f)_{-6^\circ} = w_o - 1.76\,w_n; \dots\dots\dots\dots\dots\dots\dots\dots (23)$$
$$(w_f)_{-10^\circ} = w_o - 1.68\,w_n; \dots\dots\dots\dots\dots\dots\dots\dots (24)$$
$$(w_f)_{-15^\circ} = w_o - 1.55\,w_n \dots\dots\dots\dots\dots\dots\dots\dots (25)*$$

It should be noted that all these empirical equations give the amounts of water freezable in the dilatometers, with the saturated paste in contact with toluene. As mentioned before, the temperature drop required to freeze equal amounts of water in the absence of toluene is, theoretically, two times the temperature in degrees C indicated, i.e., -12 C, -20 C, and -30 C, respectively.

SATURATED PASTES CONTAINING NO FREEZABLE WATER

For the range of temperatures over which the equations derived from eq. (9) were found to apply, it seems that the freezable water contents of some saturated hardened pastes should be zero. For example, eq. (25) indicates that $w_f = 0$ when $w_o = 1.55\,w_n$. Thus, when hydration has proceeded to the point where $w_n/c = 0.2$, $w_f/c = 0$ when $w_o/c = 0.2 \times 1.55 = 0.31$. In other words, according to eq. (25), a saturated paste having an original water-cement ratio of 0.31 would contain no water freezable in the dilatometer at -15 C after w_n/c has increased to 0.2. This may not be literally true since all saturated pastes contain a quantity of evaporable water equal to at least $4V_m$, all of which is theoretically freezable at about -78 C, and parts are freezable at higher temperatures, as indicated by the vapor pressure isotherm for gel water. However, in pastes in which the gel fills all available space ($w_e = 4V_m$) freezing may not occur because of the difficulty of starting crystallization in such extremely small spaces. If ice did form in the dilatometer experiment with such a paste, it probably would form as a separate phase on the surface of each granule. This remains a matter for speculation, since no tests were made on pastes containing no capillary space.

Whether or not freezing can occur within such pastes, the quantity that could form at ordinary freezing temperatures is so small that it can be regarded as zero from the practical point of view.

FINAL MELTING POINTS FOR SPECIMENS NOT FULLY SATURATED

As would be expected, the final melting point, that is, the highest temperature at which ice can exist in a specimen of hardened paste, is lower the lower the degree of saturation of the specimen. This is shown

---

*Note: An equation similar to eq. (25) was given in an earlier publication, *Proc. ACI* v. 41, p. 245, or P.C.A. Research Laboratory Bulletin 5, eq. (3). That equation was based on a preliminary analysis of the data presented in this paper. The difference between the two equations is due mainly to a difference in the assumed relationship between w_o and w_n. In the earlier equation, the relationship for the particular samples used in the freezing studies was used. In this paper, eq. (23) was used instead. For some unknown reason the difference between the w_o and w_f values for the samples used in the freezing study were abnormally high.

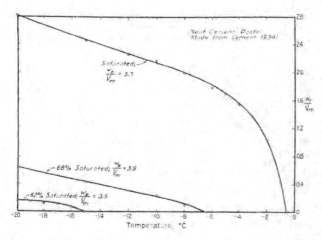

Fig. 8-14—Melting curves for saturated and partially saturated pastes

by the data plotted in Fig. 8-14. The upper curve represents a fully saturated specimen, and the other two lesser degrees of saturation, as indicated. The results agree approximately with eqs. (10), (11), and (12), which were derived empirically from tests on saturated samples.

For the sample represented by the middle curve, the amount of evaporable water was $3.9V_m$. By eq. (10), the amount of water freezable at -6 C should be

$$\left(\frac{w_f}{V_m}\right)_{-6^\circ} = 3.9 - 4.0 .$$

This indicates that none of the water present was freezable at -6 C, which agrees roughly with the observed fact that the final melting point was -6.5 C.

Similarly for the lowest curve, the amount of water freezable at -15 C is indicated by eq. (14) to be $0.3V_m$. The experimental data show the final melting point to be -15.5 C. This result may be considered as indicating substantial agreement between the equation and the observation.

SUMMARY OF PART 8

(1) Dilatometer studies were made on neat cement and cement-silica pastes to determine the amounts of ice that can exist in hardened paste under given conditions.

(2) Under the conditions of these tests, freezing did not occur on cooling until after the saturated samples had been supercooled 5 to 12 C.

(3) When freezing occurred, further cooling caused more ice to form.

(4) Raising the temperature stepwise from -20 to $+2$ C or higher showed that the melting was progressive. This result is as would be

predicted from the known effects of dissolved salts, adsorption, and capillary tension on the vapor pressure of the evaporable water.

(5) The final melting point in a saturated paste (temperature at which the last increment of ice disappears) ranged from -0.05 to -1.6 C. The temperature seemed to depend on the alkali content of the cement, the higher the alkali content, the lower the final melting point.

(6) The ice is believed to form in the capillary space outside the gel. It is unlikely that the gel water freezes in place, although, at low temperatures, it contributes to the ice.

(7) The maximum amount of water, w_f, that can freeze at a given temperature, can be estimated from the total evaporable water content, w_e, and V_m by use of the following empirical equations:

$$(w_f)_{-6°} = w_e - 4.0V_m$$
$$(w_f)_{-10°} = w_e - 3.7V_m$$
$$(w_f)_{-15°} = w_e - 3.2V_m$$

(8) The maximum freezable water content may be estimated in terms of the total water content, w_t, and the non-evaporable water content, w_n, as follows:

$$(w_f)_{-6°} = w_t - 2.04w_n$$
$$(w_f)_{-10°} = w_t - 1.96w_n$$
$$(w_f)_{-15°} = w_t - 1.83w_n$$

(9) The maximum freezable water content can be estimated from the original water content, w_o, and w_n, as follows:

$$(w_f)_{-6°} = w_o - 1.76w_n$$
$$(w_f)_{-10°} = w_o - 1.68w_n$$
$$(w_f)_{-15°} = w_o - 1.55w_n$$

(10) The temperatures given in the above equations are for freezing in a toluene-filled dilatometer. For freezing in air, the same equations apply (theoretically) if the temperatures (deg. C below zero) are multiplied by 2.

(11) Under freezing conditions differing from those used in these experiments, the amount of freezable water may be less than the amount indicated in the above equations, owing to the hysteresis in the sorption isotherms.

(12) The compositions of pastes that can contain practically no freezable water can be estimated from the above equations.

(13) The maximum amount of water freezable at a given temperature can be estimated from the 25 C isotherm with the aid of Fig. 8-1 and Table 8-10.

(14) When a paste is not fully saturated, the final melting point is lower than that for the same paste when saturated. The maximum

amount of freezable water in a paste at a given degree of saturation can be estimated approximately from the 25 C sorption isotherm and Fig. 8-1.

REFERENCES

(1)   E. W. Washburn, *Monthly Weather Review* v. 52, p. 488 (1924); *International Critical Tables* v. 3, 210 (1928).

(2)   P. Kubelka, *Z. Electrochem.* v. 38, p. 611 (1932).

(3)   E. von Gronow, *Zement*, v. 25, pp. 485-90 (1936).

(4)   H. W. Foote, B. Saxton, *J. Am. Chem. Soc.* v. 39, pp. 627-30 (1917).

(5)   I. D. Jones, R. A. Gortner, *J. Phys. Chem.* v. 36, pp. 387-436 (1932).

(6)   G. J. Bouyoucos, Mich. Agr. College Exp. Station Tech. Bull. No. 36 (1917); also, *J. Agr. Research* v. 8 ,pp. 195, 217 (1917).

(7)   L. T. Alexander, T. M. Shaw, and R. J. Muckenhirn, *Proc. Soil Sci. Soc. Am.* v. 1, p. 113 (1937). Also, L. T. Alexander and T. M. Shaw, *J. Phys. Chem.* v. 41, p. 955 (1937).

(8)   S. L. Meyers, *Ind. Eng. Chem.* v. 32, p. 1107 (1940).

(9)   J. S. Burlew, *J. Am. Chem. Soc.* v. 62, p. 690 (1940).

(10)   N. E. Dorsey, *Properties of Ordinary Water Substance* (New York: Reinhold Publishing Corp., 1940), Table 100.

(11)   G. Jones and F. C. Jelen, *J. Am. Chem. Soc.* v. 57, p. 2532 (1935).

(12)   Ref. 10, p. 514.

606   Powers and Brownyard

Part 9.   General Summary of Findings on the Properties of Hardened
Portland Cement Paste

CONTENTS PART 9

INTRODUCTION

In this, the final part of the paper, the concepts concerning the characteristics of hardened paste that have emerged from this study are set down in brief. It is not implied that the concepts are new and unique. On the contrary, they agree in general with previously expressed views of those who have believed the colloidal state of the hydration products to be a dominant characteristic of the hardened paste. However, it is now possible to consider these characteristics in more detail and on a quantitative or semi-quantitative basis.

This summary includes only the facts and relationships that can be set down with a minimum of discussion. The reader should not depend on this part alone for an understanding of the subject, since the finer points of interpretation and many significant details and illustrative graphs are omitted.

Some of the relationships given below do not appear in the preceding parts of the paper, but they are derived from relationships already given.

In the preceding parts of this paper the sequence of topics was determined according to the requirements for an orderly development of concepts and interrelationships between variables. In this summary it is assumed that the reader is familiar with the background material and the subject is presented, as far as possible, in the form of an analysis of the properties of hardened paste.

The following should be noted carefully before proceeding with the summary: All the data and relationships discussed below pertain only to specimens cured continuously at about 70 F. Without modification, they do not apply to other curing conditions.

GENERAL

Many of the technically important properties of concrete can be attributed to the peculiar nature of the hydration products of portland cement. The hardened paste is considered to be not a continuous, homogeneous solid, but rather to be composed of a large number of primary units bound together to form a porous structure. The chemical constitution of the units of this structure is not definitely known. However, it appears that many significant characteristics are dependent not primarily on chemical constitution but rather on the physical state of the solid phase of the paste and its inherent attraction for water.

The extreme smallness of the structural units of the paste, the smallness of the interstitial spaces, and the strong attraction of the solid units for water account for the fact that changes in ambient conditions are always accompanied by changes in the moisture content of the hardened paste; moreover, these factors account for the changes in volume, strength, and hardness that accompany changes in moisture content. They also account for the peculiarities of the relationship between ice-content and temperature when saturated or partially saturated paste is cooled below the normal freezing point of water.

Various findings concerning the properties of the solid phase in hardened paste, and the interaction between the solid phase and evaporable water, are summarized in the following sections.

PASTE POROSITY

The pores in hardened portland cement paste are here considered to be the space in the paste that may be occupied by evaporable water. Evaporable water is defined as that which exhibits a vapor pressure greater than about 6×10^{-4} mm Hg at 23 C. It is roughly equivalent to the amount lost when a saturated paste is oven-dried at about 105 C.

The pores in a paste (exclusive of entrained air) are of two kinds: capillary pores and gel pores. The relative proportion of each kind can be determined from suitable data and the relationships given below.

Capillary pores

Before hydration begins, and during the time when the paste remains plastic, a cement paste is a very weak solid held together by forces of interparticle attraction. These forces probably act across thin films of water at points of near-contact between the particles. The water-filled spaces between the particles constitute an interconnected capillary system. After the plastic stage, when the final reactions of hardening begin, the capillary channels of the fresh paste tend to become filled with solids produced by the reaction between water and the constituents of cement. This process rapidly reduces the volume and size of the capillaries, but apparently does not destroy their continuity. The volume of the capillaries at various stages of hydration can be estimated with satisfactory accuracy from the relationships given below.

Before hydration starts,

$$p_c = w ,\dotfill (1)$$

where p_c = volume of capillary pores, and

w = volume of water.*

Eq. (1) is correct only for an instant after the cement and water are mixed. Solution and reaction begin at once, the average rate during the first 5 minutes being higher than during any subsequent 5-min. period. Within the initial 5-min. period, the rate of reaction decreases

---

*In this and the following equations, cgs units are intended and the same symbol is used for either weight (grams) or volume (cc) of free water. That is, w (general term for free water), w_o (not free water after bleeding), and w_o (capillary water) all are assumed to have a specific volume of 1.0 and thus may represent either grams or cc. The assumption that specific volume is unity introduces no error of practical importance.

abruptly and becomes very low. This low rate persists, under normal, controlled laboratory conditions, for a considerable period, usually about an hour. If the paste has been stirred continuously during the period of rapid initial reaction, or if it is restirred at the end of that period, it will remain plastic during the ensuing, relatively dormant period. If left undisturbed, the paste will "bleed" and its volume will thereby be diminished. After bleeding, its porosity (now equivalent to the remaining water-filled space, entrained air neglected) will be approximately

$$p_c = w_o - (V_B - cv_c) , \dots\dots\dots\dots\dots\dots\dots\dots\dots\dots (2)$$

where w_o = original water content after bleeding, grams (or cc),

$\quad V_B$ = total volume of solid phase including increase due to hydration and pores in the gel,

$\quad c$ = weight of cement,

$\quad v_c$ = specific volume of the cement, i.e., the volume of a unit weight,

$\quad (V_B - cv_c)$ = increase in volume of the solid phase due to hydration.

The volume of the solid phase at any stage of hydration can be evaluated as follows:

$$V_B = cv_c + 0.86(1 + 4k)w_n , \dots\dots\dots\dots\dots\dots\dots\dots\dots (3)$$

where 0.86 = mean specific volume of the non-evaporable water and gel water,

$\quad k$ = a constant characteristic of the cement, and

$\quad w_n$ = weight of non-evaporable water.*

Eliminating V_B and cv_c between eqs. (2) and (3) gives

$$p_c = w_o - 0.86(1 + 4k)w_n . \dots\dots\dots\dots\dots\dots\dots\dots (4)$$

k will range from 0.24 to 0.28 among different cements, but for an average Type I cement, $k = 0.255$ (see Part 5) and eq. (4) becomes

$$p_c = w_o - 1.74w_n . \dots\dots\dots\dots\dots\dots\dots\dots\dots\dots\dots (5)$$

At early stages of hydration, that is, during the first few hours, when w_n is very small, eqs. (4) and (5) probably do not represent the facts very accurately because the numerical constants were evaluated from data obtained over a range of ages during which reactions involving gypsum could not occur. Therefore, the constants are probably not quite correct for periods during which gypsum-reactions are taking place to an appreciable extent.

From eq. (4) it follows that capillary porosity is zero when

$$0.86(1 + 4k)w_n = w_o,$$

or for an average cement, when $1.74w_n = w_o$ (see eq. (5)). For example, when $w_n/c = 0.2$, $p_c = 0$ if w_o/c is equal to or less than $0.2 \times 1.74 = 0.35$.

---

*Non-evaporable water is that having a vapor pressure equal to or less than about 6×10^{-4} mm Hg at 23C. It includes chemically combined water.

The highest possible water-cement ratio at which p_c can be made zero by prolonged curing depends on the magnitude of the highest possible value of w_n and on k. Both $(w_n)_{max}$ and k depend on the characteristics of the cement. $(w_n)_{max}$ depends principally on the degree to which the cement approaches complete hydration, which, in turn, depends principally on the proportion of the cement that is made up of particles finer than about 50 microns. (The coarsest particles fail to hydrate completely even though the wet-curing period is long.) It is related also to the computed chemical composition, as shown by the following relationship for w_n after six months of water-curing at 70 F.*

$$w_n/c = 0.187(C_3S) + 0.158(C_2S) + 0.665(C_3A) + 0.213(C_4AF),\ldots (6)$$

where the symbols in parentheses represent the computed weight-proportion of the compound indicated. This relationship may be considered to represent the average value of w_n/c when the cement is not far from its ultimate degree of hydration, provided that w_n/c is not less than about 0.44 and that the specific surface of the cement is between 1700 and 2000, by the Wagner turbidimeter. For finer cements $(w_n/c)_{max}$ will be higher, but not much higher. For coarser cements, it will be lower to a degree about proportional to the residue on the 325-mesh sieve. For cements having a specific surface of about 1800 (Wagner), $(w_n/c)_{max}$ ranges from about 0.20 to 0.25, the higher value corresponding to cements relatively high in C_3S and C_3A.

Likewise, k is related to computed compound composition as follows:

$$k = 0.230(C_3S) + 0.320(C_2S) + 0.317(C_3A) + 0.368(C_4AF) \ldots (7)$$

This relationship holds for any age with accuracy sufficient for most purposes.

With an average Type I cement, capillary pores will be present, even at ultimate hydration in any paste having an original water-cement ratio greater than about 0.44 by weight.

Gel pores

The quantity $(V_B - cv_c)$ appearing in eq. (2) and implicitly in eq. (4) is the increase in volume of the solid phase including the pores that are characteristic of the hydration products, presumably the pores in the gel. Consequently, the *total* porosity of the paste is greater than that given by the above equations. That is,

$$p_t = p_c + p_g,\ldots (8)$$

where p_t = volume of total pores,
p_g = volume of gel pores, and
p_c = volume of capillary pores.

---

*This empirical relationship was not given in preceding parts of this paper. It was established by the method of least squares using about 100 items of data.

The volume of gel pores is given approximately by the following relationship:

$$p_g = 0.9 \times 4V_m = 3.6V_m , \dots\dots\dots\dots\dots\dots\dots\dots\dots\dots (9)$$

where $4V_m$ is the weight of water that would saturate the gel, V_m is a factor proportional to the surface area of the gel (see eq. (12)), and 0.9 is the mean specific volume of the water in saturated gel.

For any given cement,

$$V_m = kw_n , \dots\dots\dots\dots\dots\dots\dots\dots\dots\dots\dots\dots\dots\dots (10)$$

where k is the same constant that appears in eqs. (4) and (7). Hence, for an average cement, for which $k = 0.255$,

$$p_g = 0.92w_n . \dots\dots\dots\dots\dots\dots\dots\dots\dots\dots\dots\dots\dots (11)$$

SURFACE AREA OF THE SOLID PHASE IN HARDENED PASTE

The surface area of the solid phase in hardened paste is computed by the following relationship

$$S = (35.7 \times 10^6)V_m , \dots\dots\dots\dots\dots\dots\dots\dots\dots\dots (12)$$

where S = surface area of solid phase, sq cm, and

   V_m = grams of water required to form a complete monomolecular adsorbed layer of water on the solid surface.

Since $V_m = kw_n$, and since $k = 0.255$ for an average cement, the surface area of a hardened paste made from an average cement can be obtained from w_n by using the following relationship:

$$S = (35.7 \times 10^6)0.255w_n$$
$$= (9.1 \times 10^6)w_n . \dots\dots\dots\dots\dots\dots\dots\dots\dots\dots\dots (13)$$

In a typical paste, $w_c/c = 0.6$, the surface area per unit volume of paste reaches about 2.4×10^8 sq cm at ultimate hydration.

Since the internal surface area of the paste is predominantly that of the gel, V_m is here usually considered to be proportional to the surface area of the gel, S_g.

MEAN SIZE OF GEL PORES

The mean diameter of the gel pores is probably between 2 and 4 times the hydraulic radius. The hydraulic radius is evaluated as follows:

$$m_g = p_g/S_g , \dots\dots\dots\dots\dots\dots\dots\dots\dots\dots\dots\dots\dots (14)$$

where m_g = hydraulic radius of gel pores, cm,

   p_g = volume of gel pores, cu cm, and

   S_g = surface area in the gel, sq cm.

Thus, from eqs. (9) and (12),

$$m_g = \frac{3.6V_m}{(35.7 \times 10^6)V_m} = 10 \times 10^{-8} \text{ cm} . \dots\dots\dots\dots (15)$$

Hence, the mean diameter of the gel pores is from 20 to 40 Ångstrom units.

SIZE OF CAPILLARY PORES

The mean diameter of the capillary pores cannot be determined from data now available. However, results of absorptivity tests indicate that the capillary pores are very much larger than the gel pores, except perhaps in pastes in which the gel nearly fills the available space.

PERMEABILITY

A saturated, hardened paste is permeable to water. Under a given pressure gradient and at a given temperature, the rate of flow is a function of the effective hydraulic radius of the pores and the effective porosity. The general theoretical equation for this function, called the coefficient of permeability, is

$$K_1 = 50 \times 10^{-14} V_m (N - k_1)^3 , \dots \dots \dots (16)$$

in which K_1 = coefficient of permeability to water, in ft. per sec,
$\quad\quad V_m$ = weight of water required for the first adsorbed layer, g per cc of paste,
$\quad\quad N$ = ratio of total evaporable water to V_m, and
$\quad\quad k_1$ = a constant interpreted as the number of layers of immobile water per unit of solid surface, or the difference between total and effective porosity.

Indications of a limited amount of data are that eq. (16) would give results in reasonable agreement with experiment (Ruettgers, Vidal, and Wing) only for pastes in which N is not greater than about 4, that is, for pastes containing no capillary space. For such pastes, the theoretical permeability is given by

$$K_1 = 2.0 \times 10^{-12}(1 - cv_c) \Big|_{0.45 \,\leqq\, cv_c \,\leqq\, 1.0}$$

where $\quad c$ = cement content, g per cc of paste, and
$\quad\quad v_c$ = specific volume of cement.

This result indicates that cement gel has about the same degree of permeability as granite (Ruettgers, Vidal, and Wing).

For pastes containing much capillary space outside the gel, actual permeability exceeds the theoretical by a wide margin. This is believed to indicate that in such pastes the flow is predominantly in the relatively large capillary pores outside the gel.

The permeability of concrete is generally greater than can be accounted for from the actual permeability of the paste (Ruettgers, Vidal, and Wing). This indicates that the water is able to flow through the fissures that develop under the aggregate during the bleeding period and thus to partially by-pass the paste.

ABSORPTIVITY

The characteristic rate at which a dry specimen absorbs water is here called the absorptivity of the specimen. The adsorption during the first 30 to 60 minutes follows the relationship

$$q/A = (K_a t)^{1/2} \dots \dots (17)$$

in which

q/A = the amount of water absorbed per unit area in time t, and

K_a = coefficient of absorptivity.

An empirical relationship was found between K_a and capillary porosity. That is,

$$K_a = f\left[W_o - 0.86(1 + 4k)W_n \right], \dots \dots (18)$$

where the quantity in brackets is the capillary porosity,

W_o = water content of original mix, after bleeding, g (or cc) per cc of specimen,

W_n = non-evaporable water, g per cc of specimen, and

k = a constant characteristic of the cement. (See eq. (3), (7), and (10).)

The quantity $0.86(1 + 4k)W_n$ is the increase in volume of the solid phase due to hydration. When it equals W_o, capillary porosity is zero. The experimental curve showed that K_a was also zero, or nearly so, at this point. Thus the data show that the initial absorption of water by a dried specimen takes place almost exclusively in the capillary spaces outside the gel.

PROPERTIES OF WATER IN HARDENED PASTE

In a saturated, hardened cement paste, three classes of water are here recognized:

(1) non-evaporable water,
(2) gel water, and
(3) capillary water.

Non-evaporable water

Non-evaporable water is defined as that part of the total that has a vapor pressure of not over about 6×10^{-4} mm Hg at 23 C. It is a constituent of the solid material in the paste. Some of it exists as OH groups in $Ca(OH)_2$; some, probably as water of crystallization in calcium sulfoaluminate. The rest is combined in the solid phase in ways not yet known. Of this part, some may be combined chemically with the hydrous silicates and hydrous alumina-bearing compounds; some may be held by van der Waal forces, that is, physical forces.

For purposes of volume-analysis, the non-evaporable water may be treated as an entity. Its volume added to that of the original cement gives the absolute volume of the solid phase in the paste. Thus,

$$V_S = cv_c + w_n v_n , \ldots \ldots \ldots \ldots \ldots \ldots \ldots \ldots \ldots \ldots \ldots \ldots \ldots \ldots \ldots (19)$$

where V_S = absolute volume of solid phase in the paste,

c = cement content of the paste,

w_n = non-evaporable water content of the paste,

v_c = specific volume of the cement, and

v_n = mean specific volume of the non-evaporable water.

The specific volume of the non-evaporable water is an empirical factor that will account for the observed increase in the absolute volume of the solid phase per gram increase in amount of non-evaporable water. Its value is about 0.82.

Gel water

The gel water is that contained in the pores of the gel. The pores in the gel are so small that most if not all the gel water is within the range of the van der Waal surface forces of the solid phase. This is indicated by the fact that the mean specific volume of the gel water is about 0.90.

The vapor pressure of the gel water at a fixed temperature is a function of the degree of saturation of the gel. The lowest pressure just exceeds 6×10^{-4} mm at 23 C, which is the highest pressure of the non-evaporable water. The highest pressure is nearly, but not quite, equal to that of pure water in bulk at the same temperature; the difference is due principally to the alkali hydroxides in solution. The vapor pressure at a given intermediate degree of saturation may be any value between limits fixed by the manner in which the existing water content was reached. It will be a maximum if the existing water content was reached by continuous adsorption, beginning with a dry sample. It will be a minimum if the water content was reached by continuous desorption, starting with a saturated sample. Intermediate pressures will be found if the given water content was reached by adsorption after partial desorption, or if it was reached by desorption after partial saturation by adsorption. These peculiar relationships are due to hysteresis in the sorption isotherm. They are found only for water contents that fall within the hysteresis loop. The limits of the loop are not now definitely known.

The weight of gel water in a saturated paste is equal to $4V_m$, where V_m is the weight required to form a complete monomolecular adsorbed layer on the solid phase. For volume analysis of the paste, the weight of the gel water may be used to determine the total volume (rather than absolute volume) of the solid phase in the paste. Thus,

$$V_B = V_S + 0.9w_g = V_S + 3.6V_m, \dots \dots \dots \dots \dots \dots (20)$$

where V_B = total volume (or bulk volume) of the solid phase,
V_S = absolute volume of solid phase, and
w_g = grams of gel water per cc of saturated paste = $4V_m$.

Capillary water

Like the gel water, the capillary water is really a solution of alkalies and other salts. The capillary water is that which occupies space in the paste other than the space occupied by the solid phase together with characteristic pores of the gel. That is,

$$w_c = V_t - V_B, \dots \dots \dots \dots \dots \dots \dots \dots \dots \dots \dots \dots (21)$$

where w_c = volume of capillary water,
V_t = over-all (total) volume of saturated paste, exclusive of cavities,
V_B = bulk volume of solid phase in the paste.

Practically all the capillary water lies beyond the range of the surface forces of the solid phase. Hence, in a saturated paste, the capillary water is under no stress and its specific volume is the same as the normal specific volume of a solution having the same composition as the capillary water.

In a partially saturated paste, the capillary water is subjected to tensile stress. This stress is due to curvature of the air-water interface and the surface tension of the water. The magnitude of the stress is given by the following equation:

$$F = -\frac{RT}{Mv_f} \ln p/p_s, \dots \dots \dots \dots \dots \dots \dots \dots \dots (22)$$

where F = force of capillary tension,
R = gas constant,
M = molecular weight of water,
v_f = specific volume of water,
p = vapor pressure of capillary water at the existing temperature,
p_s = saturation pressure of water at the existing temperature, and
$\ln$ = natural logarithm.

The vapor pressure of the capillary water depends on the degree of saturation of the paste and on the factors arising from hysteresis discussed in the preceding section. However, if the existing vapor pressure is reached by continuous adsorption from the dry state, capillary water does not exist in the paste at pressures below about 0.45 p_s.

Since at vapor pressures greater than $0.45 p_s$ and less than p_s, the capillary water is present and under tension, its specific volume must be greater than 1.0 and a function of F of eq. (22). No attempt has been made to verify this experimentally.

Some of the gel water may be fundamentally the same as capillary water. The distinction used here is made on the basis of relationship to the solid phase. The quantity of gel water always bears a fixed ratio to the quantity of hydration products, whereas the quantity of capillary water is determined by the porosity of the paste.

PHYSICAL STATE OF THE HYDRATION PRODUCTS

Microscopic observation of hardened paste indicates that only $Ca(OH)_2$ crystals and unhydrated residues of the original cement grains can readily be identified. Other microcrystalline constituents, particularly calcium sulfoaluminate, may be present in small amount but are generally obscured by the abundant "amorphous" constituents.

The size and volume of the pores in hardened paste indicate that the solid material is finely subdivided, though the solid units are obviously bonded to each other. If the units were equal spheres, the sphere diameter would be about 140Å. Since the computations leading to this figure included the volume of microcrystalline constituents, the units of "amorphous" material must be somewhat smaller than just indicated. The size indicated is definitely in the colloidal size-range. Since a gel is defined as a coherent mass of colloidal material, it follows that the principal constituent of hardened paste is a gel, here called cement gel.

The cement gel is composed of hydration products that contain all the principal oxides: CaO, SiO_2, Al_2O_3, and Fe_2O_3. This is shown by the fact that the total surface area of the solid phase is related to the computed cement composition in the following way:

$$\frac{V_m}{w_n} = 0.230(C_3S) + 0.320(C_2S) + 0.317(C_3A) + 0.368(C_4AF) , \ldots (23)$$

where the symbols in parentheses represent the computed weight-fraction of the compounds indicated. The similarity of the numerical coefficients and the magnitude of particle size given above show that all constituents either may be present in a single complex hydrate of high specific surface or they may be constituents of two or more different hydrates having similar specific surfaces. The relative smallness of the coefficient of C_3S is in line with the fact that this compound hydrolyzes to give microcrystalline (low specific surface) $Ca(OH)_2$ as one of its reaction products.

ENERGY CHANGES OF HYDRATION, ADSORPTION, AND CAPILLARY CONDENSATION

Heat of hydration

When cement and water react, the total amount of heat evolved is directly proportional to the total amount of non-evaporable water in the paste. Thus,

$$\text{total heat of hydration} = \text{constant} \times w_n .$$

The proportionality constant varies with cement composition. For all types of portland cement, it ranges from 485 to 550 calories per gram of non-evaporable water.

The total heat of hydration is the sum of the heat of combination of the non-evaporable water, the net heat of adsorption of water on the surface of the solid phase, and the net heat of capillary condensation.

Total net heat of surface adsorption

The net heat of surface adsorption is the amount of heat in excess of the normal heat of liquefaction that is evolved when water vapor interacts with the solid phase. For all cement pastes,

$$Q_{sl} = 472 V_m \text{ calories (approx.)} \dots\dots\dots\dots\dots\dots\dots (24)$$

where Q_{sl} = total net heat of surface adsorption when the paste is changed from the dry to the saturated state.

Net heat of capillary condensation

Adsorption at low vapor pressures causes the solid phase to become covered with a film of water having a surface area presumably equal to the covered area of the solid phase. At pressures above $0.45 p_s$ adsorption is accompanied by capillary condensation which progressively diminishes the exposed water-surface as the pressure is raised. The heat evolved from the destruction of water-surface is the net heat of capillary condensation. When a paste is changed from the dry to the saturated state,

$$Q_{cl} = 100 V_m \text{ calories (approx.)}, \dots\dots\dots\dots\dots\dots\dots (25)$$

where Q_{cl} = total net heat of capillary condensation.

Total net heat of adsorption

The total net heat of adsorption is the sum of the total net heat of surface adsorption and the total net heat of capillary condensation. That is,

$$Q_{al} = 472 V_m + 100 V_m = 572 V_m \text{ calories (approx.)}, \dots (26)$$

where Q_{al} = total net heat of adsorption. This amounts to about 670 ergs per sq cm of solid surface and is about the same as the heat of immersion of various minerals, particularly the mineral oxides, in water.

Enthalpy change of adsorption

The total net heat of adsorption (eq. (26)) is practically equal to the decrease in enthalpy of the system. The decrease in enthalpy represents the sum of the decrease in free energy and the decrease in unavailable energy. Thus,

$$- \Delta H = - \Delta G - T \Delta S , \dots\dots\dots\dots\dots\dots\dots\dots\dots\dots (27)$$

where $- \Delta H$ = decrease in enthalpy,
       $- \Delta G$ = decrease in free energy,
       $- \Delta S$ = decrease in entropy,
         T = absolute temperature, and
    $- T\Delta S$ = decrease in unavailable energy.

Decrease in free energy

Shrinking and swelling, moisture diffusion, capillary flow, and all other effects involving changes in moisture content of the paste at constant temperature are due to the free surface energy of the solid phase, or to the free surface energy of the water, or to both surface energies. All such effects are accompanied by a decrease in free energy and, in this case, a decrease in entropy, but the forces producing these effects are derived solely from the free energy.

The decrease in free energy can be expressed as a function of the ratio of the vapor pressure of the adsorbed water to that of free water at the same temperature without regard to the nature of the underlying solid phase.

$$- \Delta G = - 75.6 \, log_{10}p/p_s, \text{ cal per g of water} \dots\dots\dots (28)$$

It thus varies from zero when $p = p_s$ to a very large value when p is very much smaller than p_s.

Decrease in entropy

A change in entropy denotes some sort of internal change in the substance or substances involved in a reaction. In this case, the change is assumed to take place solely in the water as it changes from the free to the adsorbed state.

The decrease in entropy was estimated for adsorption over the pressure range $p = 0.05p_s$ to $p = 0.5p_s$. The decrease ranged progressively from $- \Delta S = 0.22$ cal/g/deg at $p = 0.5p_s$ to 0.50 cal/g/deg at $p = 0.05p_s$.

The magnitude of $- \Delta S$ indicates that some of the water is changed by adsorption in this range of pressures more than free water is changed by freezing under ordinary conditions and as much as or more than free water is changed by becoming water of crystallization. Water adsorbed at $p = 0.05p_s$ undergoes a change as great as the change from normal water to hydroxyl groups chemically combined in $Ca(OH)_2$.

Energy of binding of water in hardened paste

The net heat of adsorption (decrease in enthalpy) is a measure of the energy that must be supplied to restore adsorbed water to the normal liquid state.

The maximum energy of binding of the adsorbed water is estimated at about 400 cal/g of water. The average energy of binding of the first complete adsorbed layer is estimated at about 300 cal/g of water. The average energy of binding of the gel water is about 143 cal/g of gel water. These figures are probably somewhat too low inasmuch as the effect of adsorbed air was neglected.

These values indicate that most of the non-evaporable water is less firmly bound than the water in $Ca(OH)_2$ for which the energy of binding is 847 cal/g of water.

The capillary water cannot be considered "bound" in the same sense as the non-evaporable water and gel water. The energy required to remove all the capillary water from a saturated paste, if that could be done separately, would be $100V_m$ calories, regardless of the amount of capillary water in the paste.

VOLUME CHANGE

Mechanism of shrinkage and swelling

Cement paste shrinks and swells as the cement gel loses or gains water. Swelling results when the surface forces of the solid phase are able to draw water into the narrow spaces between the solid surfaces. The magnitude of the swelling can be accounted for by assuming that the total volume change that occurs when a dry specimen is saturated is due to the increase in spacing of the solid surfaces required to accommodate a monomolecular layer on each opposing solid surface.

Shrinking results when water is withdrawn from the gel. It is probably due to the solid-to-solid attraction that tends to draw the solid surfaces together, though capillary tension and elastic behavior may also be involved.

By this theory, volume change is regarded as being the result of an unbalance in the forces acting on the adsorbed water. These forces are the solid-to-liquid attraction and capillary tension. When the solid-to-liquid attraction and capillary tension are equal, the volume of the gel remains constant.

Swelling pressure

Swelling pressure is the force that would be just able to prevent water from entering the gel. For isothermal swelling it is related to the magnitude of the free-energy change that would occur if the water entered the gel. Thus,

$$\Delta P = \Delta G / v_f , \quad \dots\dots\dots\dots\dots\dots\dots\dots\dots\dots\dots\dots\dots (29)$$

where ΔP = increase over existing external pressure required to prevent swelling,

ΔG = increase in free energy of adsorbed water when swelling occurs, and

v_f = specific volume of adsorbed water, assumed to be independent of pressure.

Or, in terms of the change in vapor pressure of the adsorbed water that
accompanies swelling,

$$\Delta P = -\frac{RT}{Mv_f} \ln p/p_s \qquad \qquad (30)$$

This equation is probably reasonably accurate (except for low values of
p/p_s) for a hypothetical gel composed of discrete colloidal particles.
When the gel is composed of interconnected particles and encloses stable
microcrystals and aggregate particles, as in concrete, shrinking or
swelling is partially opposed by elastic forces. Hence, some difference
between the theoretical and actual swelling pressure should be expected.

Capillary tension

In a partially saturated paste the tendency of the water to enter the
gel is opposed by tension in the capillary water. The force of capillary
tension,

$$F = \sigma \left[\frac{1}{r_1} + \frac{1}{r_2} \right] = -\frac{RT}{Mv_f} \ln p/p_s , \qquad \qquad (31)$$

where σ = surface tension of water,

r_1 and r_2 = principal radii of curvature of the menisci, and

v_f = specific volume of capillary water.

Thus, capillary tension and potential swelling pressure have the same
relationship to relative vapor pressure except for a difference in v_f.* When
the vapor pressure of the gel water and the capillary water are equal,
volume remains constant.

In saturated paste that contains no capillary water ($w_s = 4V_m$) it
would appear that there could be no capillary tension. However, some
of the gel water may actually be capillary water; that is, menisci may
develop as the gel is dried. Whether or not capillary tension can develop
in the gel, the tendency of the water to evaporate from the gel would
have an effect on adsorbed water equivalent to capillary tension.

Relationship between change in volume and change in water content

When drying occurs, capillary water and gel water are lost simultaneously. Since the resulting change in volume is due only to the
change in gel-water content, it follows, theoretically, that

$$\Delta V = (\text{constant}) \frac{\Delta w_t - \Delta w_c}{V_m} , \qquad \qquad (32)$$

where ΔV = change in volume of specimen,

Δw_t = change in total water content, grams,

Δw_c = change in capillary-water content, grams,

---

*See footnote, page 586, Part 4.

$\Delta w_t - \Delta w_c$ = change in gel-water content, grams, and
(constant) = a value characteristic of the concrete in question.
(It probably changes slightly as curing proceeds.)

V_m is here considered to be a factor proportional to the amount of gel. Hence,

$$\frac{\Delta V}{\Delta w_t} = (\text{constant}) \frac{1 - \dfrac{\Delta w_c}{\Delta w_t}}{V_m} . \quad \dots\dots\dots\dots\dots\dots(33)$$

Thus, the change in volume per unit change in total water content will depend on the ratio of capillary water to total water.

Contraction in volume of the system cement + water

When cement and water react, there is a diminution in the sum of their absolute volumes. On the assumption that the contraction is confined entirely to the water and that the over-all apparent volume of the hardened paste does not change after bleeding is over,

$$w_t v_t = w_o , \dots\dots\dots\dots\dots\dots\dots\dots\dots\dots\dots\dots\dots(34)$$

where w_t = weight of total water in the saturated hardened paste,
v_t = specific volume (mean) of the total water, and
w_o = volume of original water in the paste.

The difference between w_o and w_t is the amount of water that must be absorbed by the specimen during the course of hydration for the specimen to remain saturated.

At any stage of hydration,

$$v_t = 1 - 0.279 \frac{w_n}{w_t} , \dots\dots\dots\dots\dots\dots\dots\dots\dots\dots(35)$$

where

v_t = mean specific volume of the total water (both evaporable and non-evaporable) in saturated paste, and
w_n = non-evaporable water, grams.

Hence,

$$\Delta v_w = w_t - w_o = 0.279 w_n , \dots\dots\dots\dots\dots\dots\dots(36)$$

where Δv_w = contraction of the water, cc.

Self-desiccation

If a specimen is kept sealed after its bleeding period, so that no extra water is available to it during the course of hydration, the pores in the paste will become partially emptied. This is here called self-desiccation.

The degree to which the pores become emptied can be estimated as follows:

Let w_e = evaporable water content of the saturated paste
$= w_t - w_n .$

Then

$$\frac{\Delta v_{w}}{w_{e}} = \text{ratio of empty-pore volume to total-pore volume (ignoring differences in specific volume),}$$

and

$$\frac{\Delta v_{w}}{w_{e}} = \frac{0.279w_{n}}{w_{t} - w_{n}}.$$

Since $w_{t} = w_{o} + 0.279w_{n}$,

$$\frac{\Delta v_{w}}{w_{e}} = \frac{0.279w_{n}}{w_{o} - 0.721w_{n}} \quad \ldots\ldots\ldots\ldots\ldots\ldots\ldots\ldots\ldots (37)$$

This gives the deficiency in evaporable water on a weight-ratio basis, which is close enough to the volume ratio for practical purposes.

For an illustrative example, let $w_{o}/c = 0.5$ and $w_{n}/c = 0.2$. Then,

$$\frac{\Delta v_{w}}{w_{e}} = \frac{0.279 \times 0.2}{0.5 - (0.721 \times 0.2)} = 0.16 \quad \ldots\ldots\ldots\ldots\ldots\ldots (38)$$

That is, in such a specimen and under conditions that prevent loss or gain of water, the deficiency in evaporable water would be 0.16 g/g of total evaporable water, when hydration had proceeded to the point where $w_{n}/c = 0.2$.

Such self-desiccation is believed to be an important factor contributing to the frost resistance of concrete. Experimental evidence indicates that when specimens of good quality are stored in moist air, or even under water, they are unable to absorb enough water to compensate completely for self-desiccation. Consequently, cement paste is seldom found in a completely saturated state, and hence is seldom in a condition immediately vulnerable to frost action.

CAPILLARY FLOW AND MOISTURE DIFFUSION

From the standpoint of thermodynamics, capillary flow and moisture diffusion are considered to be the results of inequalities in free energy. Inequalities in free energy under *isothermal* conditions arise from

(1) inequalities in moisture content,

(2) inequalities in deformations of the solid phase, and

(3) inequalities in the external pressure acting on the adsorbed water.

When such inequalities arise, the evaporable water will always tend to redistribute itself in such a way as to equalize its free energy. This has an important influence on plastic flow under sustained stress.

EFFECT OF TEMPERATURE CHANGES AT CONSTANT MOISTURE CONTENT

Effect on swelling

As mentioned above, potential swelling pressure and capillary tension have the following relationships at equilibrium:

$$\Delta P = F = \sigma \left[\frac{1}{r_1} + \frac{1}{r_2} \right] \dots\dots\dots\dots\dots\dots\dots\dots\dots (39)$$

At constant water content, a rise in temperature would expand the capillary water and thus decrease its surface curvature. Also, it would decrease the surface tension, σ. Consequently, a rise in temperature causes capillary tension to decrease and thus causes water to enter the gel and restore equilibrium between ΔP and F. Thus, a rise in temperature at constant water content causes swelling in addition to the normal thermal expansion. The swelling of the solid phase would be absent in a dry specimen or in a saturated specimen where $p = p_s$.

From the above it follows that the "thermal coefficient" of a given sample of concrete is not a constant, unless the sample is completely dry or saturated.

Effect on diffusion

When counteracting effects are absent, evaporable water moves in the direction of descending temperature.

Combined effect of stress, strain, changes in humidity, and temperature gradients

In concrete subjected to changing external forces, changing temperatures, and fluctuating ambient humidity, the evaporable water must be in a continual state of flux. As a consequence, the concrete swells, shrinks, expands, and contracts under the changing conditions in a highly complicated way. The separate effects may combine in different ways at a given point in the mass so that they offset or augment each other. Possibly these effects have an influence on the ability of concrete to withstand weathering.

FACTORS GOVERNING THE EXTENT AND RATE OF HYDRATION OF PORTLAND CEMENT

Extent of hydration

The principal factors governing the ultimate degree of hydration, regardless of the time required, are the relative proportion of particles having mean diameters greater than about 50 microns, and the original water-cement ratio. Incomplete data indicate that cements containing no particles larger than 50-micron diameter (or thereabouts), become completely hydrated if w_a/c is not too low. The ultimate extent of hydration appears to be about inversely proportional to the 325-mesh residue.

With any given cement the ultimate degree of hydration is proportional to the water content of the paste in all pastes in which w_o/c is less than a definite limiting value. With an average cement the limiting value is about 0.44 by weight. That is, this is the lowest w_o/c that will permit the ultimate degree of hydration with an average cement. Presumably, the greater the 325-mesh residue, the lower this limiting value of w_o/c.

Rate of hydration

With other factors equal, the average rate of hydration is lower the smaller w_o/c, except during a short initial period. Consequently, the time required to reach ultimate hydration becomes longer as w_o/c is made smaller.

During the early stages of hydration, say during the first week or two, the rate of hydration is higher by a large factor, the higher the specific surface. But during the later stages, the rates of hydration for cements of widely different specific surface differ comparatively little.

Self-desiccation influences the rate of hydration. As the pores become partly emptied, the vapor pressure of the remaining evaporable water is correspondingly reduced. Experiments indicate that even though the remaining water is chemically free, its rate of reaction with cement is a function of its relative vapor pressure. If the relative vapor pressure in the paste drops below about 0.85, hydration virtually ceases. Consequently, sealed specimens hydrate more slowly than those having access to water, and they may never reach the ultimate degree of hydration possible when extra water is available. This has a bearing on the efficiency of membrane or seal-coat curing.

The foregoing discussion indicates that conclusions concerning the rate and amount of hydration of portland cement *in concrete* ($w/c = 0.45$ to 0.70) should not be drawn from data on standard test pieces ($w/c = 0.25 \pm$). Moreover, specimens cured in sealed vials should not be expected to hydrate at the same rate and to the same extent as similar specimens cured in water or fog. Also, it should be noted that for samples in sealed vials, water separated from the paste by bleeding must be considered as extra water.

RELATION OF PASTE POROSITY TO COMPRESSIVE STRENGTH

The compressive strength of 2-in. mortar cubes is, with certain restrictions, given by the relationship

$$f_c = 120{,}000 \frac{V_m}{w_o} - 3600, \dots\dots\dots\dots\dots\dots\dots\dots\dots (40)$$

where f_c is compressive strength, psi, and V_m/w_o is considered to be a factor proportional to the degree to which the gel fills the originally water-filled space, here called the gel-space ratio. The relationship holds for all ages and apparently for all cements low in C_3A (less than about 7 percent computed).

For cement of average or high C_3A content, and especially for those high in both alkali and C_3A the strengths obtained at a given V_m/w_o are lower than those indicated by the equation. The results obtained with some such cements can be brought into compliance with the equation by increasing the gypsum content of the cement.

The relationship given by eq. (40) is considered to be empirical— neither fundamental nor general. Independent variables that are not adequately taken into account are as follows:

(1) some features of cement composition,

(2) effect of aggregate particles,

(3) entrained air,

(4) fissures under the aggregate particles that form during the bleeding period, and

(5) variations in curing temperature.

FREEZING OF WATER IN HARDENED PASTE

Owing to the nature of the relationship between water content and free energy, as shown by sorption isotherms, the water in a saturated paste freezes or melts progressively as the temperature is varied below the normal melting point. An example of the progressive melting of ice in a particular frozen, saturated paste follows:

Temperature*	Amount of ice, g/g of cement	Amount of ice, as percent of amount at −30 C
0	0	0
− 0.5	0.045	21
− 1.5	0.075	36
− 2.0	0.093	44
− 3.0	0.109	52
− 4.0	0.122	59
− 5.0	0.131	62
− 6.0	0.137	65
− 8.0	0.147	70
−12.0	0.168	80
−16.0	0.181	86
−30.0	0.210	100

*The temperatures indicated are for samples exposed to air or water. For exposure to toluene, as in the experiments, the figures for temperature should be divided by 2.

The capillary water is believed to freeze in place, at least under the conditions of the experiments. However, the gel water probably flows or distills from the gel to the capillaries before it freezes.

The temperature at which the last increment of ice disappears on progressive melting is here called the final melting point. It would be the same as the initial freezing point, were it not for the occurrence of supercooling.

The final melting point in saturated pastes ranges from about -1.6 C to about -0.05 C. The depression of the final melting point is due to dissolved material in the mixing water, principally alkalies.

The final melting point in a paste that is not fully saturated depends not only on the dissolved material but also on the degree of saturation; the lower the degree of saturation the lower the final melting point.

All the evaporable water is freezable, but a minimum temperature of about -78 C is required to freeze all of it.

At any given temperature between -78 and -12 C*, the maximum amount of freezable water in saturated paste is

$$w_f = w_e - u V_m \; ; \quad \dots \dots \dots \dots \dots (41)$$

or, approximately,

$$w_f = w_t - w_n (1 + 0.26u) \; ; \quad \dots \dots \dots \dots (42)$$

or

$$w_f = w_o - (0.721 + 0.26u)w_n , \quad \dots \dots \dots (43)$$

in which w_f = freezable water,

$\quad w_e$ = total evaporable water,

$\quad V_m$ = factor here considered to be proportional to the gel content of the paste,

$\quad w_n$ = non-evaporable water, and

$\quad u$ = a constant equal to w_u/V_m, where w_u is the amount of water unfreezable at a given temperature.

The following are empirical relationships for the maximum amounts of water freezable in saturated pastes at given temperatures, in terms of w_n and w_o:

$$(w_f)_{-12°} = w_o - 1.76w_n$$
$$(w_f)_{-20°} = w_o - 1.68w_n$$
$$(w_f)_{-30°} = w_o - 1.55w_n$$

At -12 C†, the amount of freezable water is equal to the volume of the capillary water outside the gel. At lower temperatures gel water is frozen, but the gel water probably leaves the gel and becomes a part of the ice already formed in the capillaries.

---

*See footnote below table on previous page.
†The temperatures indicated are the theoretical values for freezing in air or water. They correspond to -6 C, -10 C, and -15 C, respectively, for freezing in contact with toluene. (See Part 8.)

At temperatures above -12 C, the maximum amount of freezable water is roughly proportional to the amount of capillary water, $w_a - 4V_m$, or (approximately) $W_o - 1.76w_n$. The proportionality constants are about 1.0 at -12 C, 0.86 at -8 C, 0.7 at -4 C, and 0.6 at -2 C.

The maximum amount of ice will not be present unless the temperature has previously dropped to a low value, -50 C or perhaps lower. If the maximum cooling is only a few degrees below the final melting point, the amount of ice formed would probably be less than the amount indicated by the relationship given above. This is a result of the hysteresis in the water content vs. free-energy relationship as indicated by the sorption isotherms.

For practical purposes, the freezable water can be considered to be identical with the capillary water. Hence, pastes that contain no capillary space outside the gel are considered to be without freezable water.

CONVERSION FACTORS—INCH-POUND TO SI (METRIC)*

To convert from	to	multiply by
Length		
inch	millimeter (mm)	25.4E‡
foot	meter (m)	0.3048E
yard	meter (m)	0.9144E
mile (statute)	kilometer (km)	1.609
Area		
square inch	square centimeter (cm^2)	6.451
square foot	square meter (m^2)	0.0929
square yard	square meter (m^2)	0.8361
Volume (capacity)		
ounce	cubic centimeter (cm^3)	29.57
gallon	cubic meter (m^3)‡	0.003785
cubic inch	cubic centimeter (cm^3)	16.4
cubic foot	cubic meter (m^3)	0.02832
cubic yard	cubic meter (m^3)‡	0.7646
Force		
kilogram-force	newton (N)	9.807
kip-force	newton (N)	4448
pound-force	newton (N)	4.448
Pressure or stress (force per area)		
kilogram-force/square meter	pascal (Pa)	9.807
kip-force/square inch (ksi)	megapascal (MPa)	6.895
newton/square meter (N/m^2)	pascal (Pa)	1.000E
pound-force/square foot	pascal (Pa)	47.88
pound-force/square inch (psi)	kilopascal (kPa)	6.895
Bending moment or torque		
inch-pound-force	newton-meter (Nm)	0.1130
foot-pound-force	newton-meter (Nm)	1.356
meter-kilogram-force	newton-meter (Nm)	9.807

Conversion Factors—Inch-Pound to SI (Metric)

To convert from	to	multiply by
Mass		
ounce-mass (avoirdupois)	gram (g)	28.34
pound-mass (avoirdupois)	kilogram (kg)	0.4536
ton (metric)	megagram (Mg)	1.000E
ton (short, 2000 lbm)	megagram (Mg)	0.9072
Mass per volume		
pound-mass/cubic foot	kilogram/cubic meter (kg/m^3)	16.02
pound-mass/cubic yard	kilogram/cubic meter (kg/m^3)	0.5933
pound-mass/gallon	kilogram/cubic meter (kg/m^3)	119.8
Temperatures§		
deg Fahrenheit (F)	deg Celsius (C)	$t_C = (t_F - 32)/1.8$
deg Celsius (C)	deg Fahrenheit (F)	$t_F = 1.8t_C + 32$

* This selected list gives practical conversion factors of units found in concrete technology. The reference source for information on SI units and more exact conversion factors is "Standard for Metric Practice" ASTM E 380. Symbols of metric units are given in parentheses.

† E indicates that the factor given is exact.

‡ One liter (cubic decimeter) equals 0.001 m^3 or 1000 cm^3.

§ These equations convert one temperature reading to another and include the necessary scale corrections. To convert a difference in temperature from Fahrenheit to Celsius degrees, divide by 1.8 only, i.e., a change from 70 to 88 F represents a change of 18 F or 18/1.8 = 10 C.

Index